Mathematics
A World of Ideas

BEVAN K YOUSE

Emory University

MATHEMATICS

A World of Ideas

ALLYN AND BACON, INC.

Boston

Photograph Credits

1. CARL FRIEDRICH GAUSS: David Eugene Smith Collection, Columbia University Libraries.
2. DAVID HILBERT: David Eugene Smith Collection, Columbia University Libraries.
3. GEORG CANTOR: David Eugene Smith Collection, Columbia University Libraries.
4. KARL WEIERSTRASS: David Eugene Smith Collection, Columbia University Libraries.
5. PIERRE FERMAT: David Eugene Smith Collection, Columbia University Libraries.
6. HENRI POINCARÉ: The Bettmann Archive, Inc.
7. BLAISE PASCAL: Library of Congress.
8. GEORGE BOOLE: The Bettmann Archive, Inc.
9. JOHN VON NEUMANN: The Bettmann Archive, Inc.
10. LEONHARD EULER: David Eugene Smith Collection, Columbia University Libraries.
11. RENÉ DESCARTES: Library of Congress.
12. ISAAC NEWTON: Crown Copyright.
13. GOTTFRIED WILHELM LEIBNIZ: Library of Congress.
14. RICHARD DEDEKIND: From Richard Dedekind, *Gesammelte mathematische Werke*, Vol. 1, Braunschweig: Vieweg, 1930.
15. EVARISTE GALOIS: The Bettmann Archive, Inc.

Contents

Preface   *ix*

1 **The Nature of Mathematics**   1
   1. What is Mathematics?   2

2 **Numbers and Numerals**   7
   1. Sets and Cardinal Numbers   8
   2. Rational Operations and Basic Properties   12
   3. Algorithms for a Positional Notation   18
   4. Other Notational Systems   27
   5. Computing in Other Bases (Optional)   35

3 **Checks and Pseudo-checks**   41
   1. The Missing Digit   42
   2. Divisibility Tests   45
   3. Halve-double-sum Technique   54
   4. Casting Out Nines   56

4 **The Expanding World of Numbers**   63
   1. Rational Numbers   64
   2. Negative Numbers   70
   3. Real Numbers   76
   4. Decimal Notation   80
   5. Complex Numbers (Optional)   86

5 **Number Patterns**   93
   1. *Arithmetic Sequences*   94
   2. *Geometric Sequences*   100
   3. *A Look at the Primes*   107
   4. *Making Conjectures*   111
   5. *Perfect Numbers*   115
   6. *Other Types of Sequences*   122

6 **A Look at Topology**   129
   1. *Houses, Maps, and Vests*   130
   2. *Networks*   134
   3. *The Regular Polyhedra*   145

7 **Probability and Statistics**   157
   1. *Introduction*   158
   2. *Counting Collections*   159
   3. *Basic Ideas of Probability*   168
   4. *Introduction to Statistics*   178
   5. *Measures of Central Tendency and Dispersion*   183

8 **Logic and the Axiomatic Approach**   189
   1. *Introduction to Logic*   190
   2. *Testing the Validity of Arguments*   200
   3. *Introduction to Axiomatics*   209
   4. *Venn Diagrams and Lewis Carroll Puzzles*   217

9 **The Principles of Computer Programming**   227
   1. *Simple Computer Programs*   228
   2. *Programming Repetitive Procedures*   235
   3. *Applications*   241

10 **Number Theory**   247
   1. *Number Congruence*   248
   2. *Pythagorean Numbers*   253
   3. *Mathematical Induction*   259
   4. *Fundamental Theorem of Arithmetic*   264
   5. *Euclidean Algorithm*   269

11 Analytic Geometry 277

1. *Introduction*   *278*
2. *The Coordinate Plane*   *279*
3. *Lines and Circles*   *284*
4. *Relations and Functions*   *291*
5. *Linear Programming (Optional)*   *297*

12 Differential Calculus 307

1. *Introduction*   *308*
2. *The Derivative*   *316*
3. *Maxima and Minima*   *322*
4. *Antiderivatives*   *332*

13 Integral Calculus 337

1. *Introduction*   *338*
2. *The Riemann Integral*   *345*
3. *Volume (Optional)*   *353*

14 Number Fields 360

1. *Field Properties*   *362*
2. *Order Properties*   *365*
3. *Completeness Property (Optional)*   *370*

15 A Look at Modern Algebra 375

1. *Examples of Groups*   *376*
2. *Elementary Theory of Groups*   *387*

Appendix A: Suggested Reading   **A-1**
Appendix B: Lame's Theorem   **A-3**
Appendix C: Tables   **A-7**
Appendix D: Answers to Odd-numbered Exercises   **A-20**

Index   *A-73*

Preface

It is mathematics that offers the exact natural sciences a certain measure of security which, without mathematics, they could not obtain.

ALBERT EINSTEIN

The main purpose of this book is to provide an introduction to the nature and scope of mathematics. The text was developed from notes used in a course at Emory University. A broad range of topics is presented to provide an introduction to mathematics that will appeal to students with varying degrees of preparation and interests. Many topics should be of particular interest to prospective teachers of elementary or secondary mathematics.

The level of difficulty of the material determined the present arrangement of chapters. The potential motivational quality of the topics also influenced this arrangement; a few sacrifices were made in the logical order for pedagogical reasons. Most chapters were written so that preceding chapters are not prerequisites. The presentation should make it easy for the teacher to tailor a course to fit both the interests of the students and the personality of the class. Some topics in the last few chapters are rather sophisticated, but it is not expected that every chapter will be studied in each course where the text is used.

It is my belief that in a course of this nature one of the least concerns should be "covering" topics. With this in mind, the chapter exercises were designed to promote lively discussions. In class-testing this material, discussion of the exercises often led to related questions that furthered class discussion.

To encourage students to discover solutions on their own, answers to the even-numbered problems are not included in the text. I hope the student will realize that for a given problem the first goal is to obtain a correct solution; obtaining an elegant solution may be a second goal. Since it is also worthwhile to discuss and evaluate different solutions to a problem, the lack of some answers should not only help promote such discussions but also avert intimidating or prejudicing them.

Much of mathematics can be, and occasionally is, obscured from the view of the nonmathematician by a superabundance of unfamiliar terminology and notation. Although the terminology and notation are important to the professional mathematician, only that which seems essential or advantageous to our study is introduced. Furthermore, no apology is made if occasionally some mathematical elegance is sacrificed for the sake of simplicity or for clarity of presentation.

In the first few chapters, we discuss many problems associated with the counting numbers 1, 2, 3, 4, 5, 6, 7, 8, 9, 10, 11, ... Thereafter, we turn our attention to many topics from such diversified fields of mathematics as arithmetic, number theory, analysis, logic, probability, statistics, algebra, geometry, and topology. Except for Chapters 11, 12, and 13, the presentation of the material in each chapter is reasonably independent from that in the other chapters; therefore, a chapter of special interest might be read without reading each of the preceding chapters.

When you read the text, you should keep in mind two major points. (1) Do not try to read this book, or almost any mathematics book, as you would read a novel; take your time and try to comprehend each new idea as it is presented. Of course, if you find some point particularly difficult to understand, read on and return to it later. (2) Always have a pencil and paper at hand and participate in the "action." (You cannot learn mathematics or enjoy it as a game without active participation any more than you can learn to play tennis without a racket.)

At the end of the text is a list of books for reference and suggested reading. It is hoped that the student will make use of the list and pursue in depth some of the topics discussed in the following chapters. The books written by Bell, Boyer, and Eves concerning the history of mathematics should be of general interest and deserve particular attention.

Chapters 1 to 10 have been published separately under the title AN INTRODUCTION TO MATHEMATICS, 2nd edition. It was suggested that these first 10 chapters would be suitable for use in a one-semester or a one-quarter course.

I am particularly indebted to James A. Yorke, Research Professor at the University of Maryland, for contributing Chapter 9, *The Principles of Computer Programming.* I am sure that the student will also appreciate his excellent presentation of this important topic.

I would also like to express my deep appreciation to the mathematicians who read the manuscript at various stages and made many valuable suggestions.

Especially helpful was the advice of the following reviewers:

Charles W. Austin, California State University at Long Beach
Carl B. Boyer, Brooklyn College
Joseph Dorsett, St. Petersburg Junior College
Michael Greeley, Boston State College
Roy Mazzagatti, Miami Dade Junior College, South Campus
Edward J. Ordman, University of Kentucky
Anne D. Pauley, St. Andrews Presbyterian College
Joseph A. Raab, Metropolitan State College
Howard L. Rolf, Baylor University

Marcia C. Saile, Palm Beach Junior College
Aloysius A. Sieracki, Marquette University
Richard and Susan Tennant, Bronx Community College
Arthur D. Wirshup, California Polytechnic State University

I also acknowledge with gratitude the assistance of Mrs. Lorraine Ruff whose expertise in typing and preparing the manuscript was exceptional.

Due to the varied interests and mathematical backgrounds of students who might read this book, a conscious effort has been made to provide the student with a readable book and the teacher with a teachable text. I would appreciate any suggestions for improvement.

BEVAN K YOUSE

Carl Friedrich Gauss (1777–1855)

Carl Friedrich Gauss was born in Brunswick, Germany, on April 30, 1777. His father was a hardworking, poorly educated man who had little money or personal enthusiasm to contribute to his son's academic pursuits. However, Gauss did receive encouragement from his mother and from Johann Martin Bartels, a friend who helped Gauss in his early study of mathematics and who later helped him to obtain entrance into Caroline College in Brunswick. Even more important for Gauss' career, Bartels helped him obtain from the Duke of Brunswick the financial assistance needed for college, assistance that was to continue during the Duke's lifetime. By the time Gauss was 30 years old, he was known throughout Europe; it was at that time he became Director of the Göttingen Observatory, a position he held until his death. Gauss made extensive contributions to nearly every branch of mathematics. He gave the first satisfactory proof of what is called the Fundamental Theorem of Algebra; along with Bolyai and Lobachevsky, he was among the first mathematicians to be interested in the noneuclidean geometries; and he made extensive contributions to analysis, probability, and number theory. His penchant for number theory is clearly indicated by his statement that "mathematics is the queen of the sciences and the theory of numbers is the queen of mathematics." He has been called the "prince of mathematicians," and he ranks with Archimedes and Newton as one of the greatest mathematicians of all time.

1

The Nature of Mathematics

1. What is Mathematics?

Mathematics has a light and wisdom of its own, above any
possible application to science, and it will richly reward
any intelligent human being to catch a glimpse of what
mathematics means to itself. This is not the old doctrine
of art for art's sake; it is art for humanity's sake.

ERIC TEMPLE BELL

1. WHAT IS MATHEMATICS?

What is mathematics? That is a good question, and one for which we
do not have an immediate or satisfactory answer. We could say
that "mathematics is what mathematicians do." This definition is
"operational," but it is hardly satisfactory since it poses the question—"What is a mathematician?". Of course, an obvious answer to
the latter question is that a mathematician is one who does mathematics, but the answer resembles a dog chasing its tail. Such circular definitions are hardly satisfactory.

A precise definition of mathematics and one that would be acceptable to all mathematicians would be extremely difficult, if not impossible, to devise. A concise and precise definition that would explain
the whole of mathematics to a nonmathematician is surely unat-
tainable. Of course, definitions of mathematics do exist. At the
beginning of each chapter, we present either a definition of mathematics or a statement about mathematics. Although the student could
profit by reading each of them now, the statements about mathematics (such as the one at the beginning of this chapter) are likely to be
more revealing at the present than the definitions. By the time the
student has read the text, it is hoped and expected that each definition will be understood and each will contribute to a better understanding of the subject.

arithmetic   At present, "mathematics" will be an undefined term, as are
"point" and "line" in geometry. However, do not despair, for we can
still hope to discover what mathematics is by inquiring into its nature, surveying its scope, and considering several of its many facets.

Mathematics has its origins in a number concept possessed by
early man. If we designate as *arithmetic* that part of mathematics

which deals with the computational aspects associated with numbers, then we see that this branch of mathematics has ancient origins. After man began to become skilled in the computational aspects of numbers, he developed an interest in the abstract ideas concerned with numbers and then he studied the intrinsic relationships existing between numbers. We designate as *number theory* the branch of mathematics devoted to the abstract study of number. Our definition makes arithmetic an older branch of mathematics than number theory. However, number theory is still not such a new field since the Pythagoreans of 2,000 years ago would be classified as number theorists, as well as arithmeticians.

number theory

Early man was also concerned with form and, in turn, made critical observations of the objects with which he had contact. A study of plane and solid figures coupled with observations of the relationships that exist between them led man to develop the field of mathematics called *geometry*. In geometry, the number concept is expanded and becomes useful as a measure of angle, measure of length, measure of area, etc.

geometry

Later, we shall discuss several other fields, or branches, of mathematics, but we now put to rest the sometimes held belief that mathematics consists only of arithmetic, number theory, geometry, and the other branch of mathematics we all learn something about in high school, *algebra*. One of the other large branches of mathematics is *analysis*. Although some of the basic ideas of analysis were considered as far back as Archimedes (287–212 B.C.), mathematical analysis essentially became a distinguishable part of mathematics with the development of calculus. The creation of calculus in the mid-seventeenth century by Newton and Leibniz marked the beginning of modern mathematics. We should realize that calculus is only a very small part of the vast field of analysis. Some people also have the mistaken impression that calculus is the culmination of mathematics; actually, it is only the beginning of modern mathematics.

algebra

analysis

To emphasize the quantity of mathematics that has been developed, it is worth noting that the body of mathematical literature probably doubled in the eighteenth century, and at least five times more mathematics was created in the nineteenth century than was created in the previous history of man. Twentieth century mathematicians will surely more than double the body of mathematical literature.

A genius such as Newton opens new vistas to be explored and pursued. A century later his ideas may be assimilated into the general body of mathematics and what may have been the ideas of a genius become, for many, common knowledge. This in no way detracts from the feats of earlier mathematicians; the importance of the foundation is enhanced, not decreased, as the superstructure is erected. Newton clearly exhibited his respect for the contributions of his predecessors when he said, "If I have seen farther than other men it is because I have stood on the shoulders of giants." Because other mathematical giants have emerged since the time of Newton, our horizons have been expanded considerably in the last three hundred years.

We have identified a few of the subdivisions of mathematics. To give an even better idea of what mathematics is, let us discuss some specific aspects of the subject. First, mathematics is a tool. Nearly everyone recognizes the practicality of the subject through its uses for such things as balancing a check book or determining the trajectory of a rocket to the moon. As "Queen of the Sciences," mathematics has had a prominent role in the development of science and technology over the past three centuries.

Nevertheless, the practical side of mathematics is often overemphasized as a motivating factor in the development of mathematics. Man's love of wisdom has probably been the single most important contributing factor to its development. The practical aspect of mathematics, though vitally important, seems to have played "second fiddle" in the development of the subject since the time of Pythagoras (540 B.C.). We should not overlook the fact that man's abstractions from his perceptions of physical surroundings have been the fountainhead of much of mathematics so, in the words of Lobachevsky, "there is no branch of mathematics which may not some day be applied to phenomena of the real world." In fact, mathematical structures have been created which had no practical applications until many years after their development. Not only have inventions and innovations in science resulted from a fertile mathematical mind but, of course, new branches of mathematics developed as a result of practical problems in science.

In addition to man creating mathematics in the pursuit of wisdom or in the quest to solve practical problems, many of the early investigations in geometry and number theory had their origins in primitive rituals. For example, one of the most famous unsolved (later proved unsolvable) problems of Greek geometry is said to have originated with an attempt to construct by euclidean methods a cubical altar to a Greek god; the goal was to construct an altar whose volume would be exactly twice that of a given altar. More certainly, the mysticism of the Pythagoreans contributed greatly to their interest in the study of numbers.

Mathematics also qualifies as a science according to any acceptable definition of science. The fact that mathematics is also an art is less evident to the uninitiated. It will become clear that mathematics is not discovered; rather, it is composed, created, or invented.

Mathematics is also a game; it can be fun. Fortunately, we need not be mathematicians to be amused or amazed by many of the problems and ideas of mathematics. The text should provide ample evidence of this delightful bonus that awaits the student of mathematics.

The world of mathematics is in a way like the physical universe that surrounds us. We can admire its majesty, view its vastness, solve some of its mysteries, and even appreciate some of its gems without a deep or extensive study of each of its many facets. A person with a moderate background in mathematics and with some degree of intellectual curiosity should find that the following chapters contribute further to answering the question—"What is mathematics?". Many problems from various fields of mathematics are presented in order to give the student a better idea of the nature and scope of the subject. Hopefully, the book will reveal many realms worthy of further investigation.

EXERCISES

1. List several reasons why mathematics has commanded the attention of man.
2. Give your interpretation of the meaning of Bell's statement about mathematics given at the beginning of the chapter.
3. Give a dictionary definition of the word *mathematics*.
4. Determine, if possible, the origin of the word *mathematics*.
5. Give a dictionary definition of the word *arithmetic*.
6. Determine, if possible, the origin of the word *arithmetic*.
7. Give a dictionary definition of the word *algebra*.
8. Determine, if possible, the origin of the word *algebra*.
9. Give a dictionary definition of the word *geometry*.
10. Determine, if possible, the origin of the word *geometry*.
11. Give a dictionary definition of the word *calculate*.
12. Determine, if possible, the origin of the word *calculate*.
13. Give a dictionary definition of the word *tally*.
14. Determine, if possible, the origin of the word *tally*.
15. Give a dictionary definition of the word *cipher*.
16. Determine, if possible, the origin of the word *cipher*.

David Hilbert (1862–1943)

David Hilbert was born at Königsberg in East Prussia on January 23, 1862. He received his Ph.D. degree in 1885 and taught in Königsberg before he became a professor at Göttingen in 1893. A renowned Professor of Mathematics at Gottingen, he had as students such men as John von Newmann, Enrico Fermi, and J. Robert Oppenheimer.

Hilbert is famous for many mathematical accomplishments. His *Foundations of Geometry,* published in 1899, revised the classical presentation of Euclid's *Elements,* eliminated basic flaws and omissions, and attempted to put it on a sound foundation. At the International Mathematical Congress in Paris in 1900, he presented twenty-three unsolved problems that he felt should occupy the interest of twentieth century mathematicians. Not only did the problems prove significant in opening new avenues of research, but they also provided an avenue to fame for the mathematicians who first solved them. Besides the foundations of geometry, Hilbert worked in other fields such as theory of algebraic numbers, mathematical logic, differential equations, and the calculus of variations. He is considered the founder of the formalist school of mathematics. The controversy in this century between the formalists led by Hilbert and the intuitionists led by Brouwer is essentially the modern version of the controversy between two earlier mathematicians, Cantor and Kronecker.

2

Numbers and Numerals

1. Sets and Cardinal Numbers
2. Rational Operations and Basic Properties
3. Algorithms for a Positional Notation
4. Other Notational Systems
5. Computing in Other Bases (Optional)

1. SETS AND CARDINAL NUMBERS

Through the clouds of prerecorded history, it is difficult to obtain an accurate account of the early development of mathematics. When man developed his first languages, it was likely that different words were used for "three" when discussing three birds, three trees, three rocks, etc. It must have required hundreds of years to recognize the characteristic common to such sets. The development of an abstract number concept of *threeness* that was independent of physical objects signaled a great step in the advancement of the human intellect.

It should be clear that the existence of a *number sense* must precede both counting and the creation of a number system. What is by no means clear is whether the basic number concept is primarily a product of man's experience or is an intrinsic attribute of the mind possessed by primitive man. Without question, however, the creation of a number system from a rudimentary number concept is perhaps man's most important and distinctive creation.

cardinal number

For a set S, *cardinal number* indicates the *size* of the set. We use *three* as the name for the cardinal number that denotes the size of the set $\{a, b, c\}$, and we use the numeral (symbol) "3" to denote the number. To better understand the distinction between numbers, names for numbers, and numerals for numbers, notice that the German word for the cardinal number of the set $\{a, b, c\}$ is *drei* and the Roman numeral notation for the number is III. Although a failure to maintain a careful distinction between numbers, number notations, and the number words does not always lead to major difficulties, it does remain a major source of confusion in elementary mathematics. However, maintaining a fastidious distinction can also impede reasonable progress.

Basically, cardinal numbers have to do with size only. We can determine if two sets have the same size by pairing the elements in the two sets; it is not necessary to count the elements in each set.

8

Historically, however, the use of numbers in the cardinal sense has been inseparable from their use in the ordinal sense. *Ordinal numbers* indicate a particular (linear) order. When persons are ordered according to height, age, weight, grades, etc., numbers are used in the ordinal sense to rank the individuals in the set.

ordinal numbers

The *counting numbers* are called the *natural numbers;* today, we write them 1, 2, 3, 4, 5, 6, 7, 8, 9, 10, 11, 12, 13, ... The natural numbers were the first numbers developed by man. After many centuries, the number concept was expanded to include the number zero. "Zero" answers the question "How many?" after all elements in a set have been removed. The creation of zero required a much higher degree of sophistication than was needed to develop the natural numbers.

natural numbers

The numbers $\{0, 1, 2, 3, 4, 5, 6, 7, . . .\}$ consisting of the natural numbers and zero are called *whole numbers*. Because of the special treatment required for zero in performing the arithmetic operations, it is important to recognize and keep in mind the distinction between the set of natural and the set of whole numbers.

whole numbers

In Section 3, we shall discuss some of the notations developed to denote the natural numbers. The student would find it both instructive and interesting to read a more detailed account of the various numeration systems developed by man. Such information is available in several excellent books devoted to the history of arithmetic and the history of mathematics. (See Appendix A.)

Since the idea of set is important to the development of every branch of mathematics, let us review briefly the fundamental set concepts. Our discussion is not an in-depth study of set theory; rather, it is an introduction to the language and notation of modern mathematics.

If S represents the set $\{a, b, c\}$, then we write $S = \{a, b, c\}$. The cardinal number of S is denoted by $n(S)$; thus, $n(S) = 3$. If $T = \{u, v, w, x, y, z\}$, then $n(T) = 6$.

$n(S)$

In addition to listing elements to define a set, we often define a set by stating characterizing properties of the elements. For example, the set $S = \{1, 2, 3, 6\}$ is also defined by $S = \{x \mid x$ is a natural number and a factor of 6$\}$ (read, "S is the set of all x such that x is a natural number and a factor of 6"). For sets with many elements, the second method is obviously more efficient. If two sets S and T contain exactly the same elements they are said to be *equal;* equality of sets is denoted by $S = T$.

equal

Example 1. Let $R = \{1, 2, 4, 8, 16\}$, let $S = \{x \mid x$ is a natural number and a factor of 16$\}$, and let $T = \{x \mid x = 2^{n-1}$ where $n = 1, 2, 3, 4, 5\}$. Then $R = S = T$.

9

If we let P denote the set of prime numbers, then 2 is an element in P. We write $2 \in P$ (read, "2 is in P") to indicate the given membership. To express that 6 is not an element in P, we write $6 \notin P$ (read, "6 is not in P"). Often we use a symbol (letter) to denote an element in a set. For example, we might write, "let x be an element in P," or "let $x \in P$." A symbol used in this manner is called a *variable* on the set.

variable

Example 2. Let $S = \{p \mid p$ is a natural number and $2^p - 1$ is a prime$\}$. Thus, S is the set of natural numbers such that p is in S if and only if $2^p - 1$ is a prime. Since $2^2 - 1 = 3$ is a prime, $2 \in S$. Since $2^4 - 1 = 15$ is not a prime, $4 \notin S$.

union, $\cup$

If S and T are sets then the *union* of the two sets, denoted by $S \cup T$, is the set consisting of the elements in S, in T, or in both S and T. For example, if $S = \{a, b, c\}$ and $T = \{b, c, d, e\}$ then

$$S \cup T = \{a, b, c, d, e\}$$

intersection, $\cap$

If S and T are sets then the *intersection* of the two sets, denoted by $S \cap T$, is the set consisting of the elements that both S and T have in common. For example, if $S = \{a, b, c\}$ and $T = \{b, c, d, e\}$, then

$$S \cap T = \{b, c\}$$

empty, or null, set

We admit the existence of a set with no elements; it is called the *empty set,* or *null set,* and is denoted by $\varnothing$. The cardinal number of the empty set is zero; thus, $n(\varnothing) = 0$. Since two given sets might not have any elements in common, the existence of the empty set makes it possible to state that not only is the union of two sets a set but the inter-

disjoint

section of any two sets is also a set. Two sets, such as $A = \{a, b\}$ and $B = \{d, e, f\}$, that have no elements in common are said to be disjoint; more specifically, two sets S and T are *disjoint* if and only if $S \cap T = \varnothing$.

commutative property

For two sets A and B, it is obvious that both $A \cup B$ and $B \cup A$ contain the same elements. The fact that $A \cup B = B \cup A$ is called the *commutative property* of set union. It is also true that $(A \cup B) \cup C = A \cup (B \cup C)$; this is called the *associative property* of set union.

associative property

Furthermore, for sets A, B, and C, $A \cap B = B \cap A$ and $(A \cap B) \cap C = A \cap (B \cap C)$; these are called the commutative property and associative property of set intersection, respectively.

Let $S = \{a, b, c, d, e\}$ and let $A = \{a, b\}$. Not only do S and A have elements in common but every element in A is in S. A set A is

subset, $\subseteq$

said to be a *subset* of a set S, denoted by $A \subseteq S$, if and only if each element in A is in S. Since each element in any set S is in S, it follows from the definition of subset that $S \subseteq S$. Also, for any set S

the empty set is a subset of S; symbolically, $\emptyset \subseteq S$. If A is a subset of S and if $A \neq S$ (that is, A is not equal to S), then A is called a *proper subset* of S; symbolically, $A \subset S$.

Example 3. Let $S = \{a, b, c\}$. The subsets of S are $\emptyset$, $\{a\}$, $\{b\}$, $\{c\}$, $\{a, c\}$, $\{a, b\}$, $\{b, c\}$, $\{a, b, c\}$.

If $A \subseteq S$ then the set consisting of the elements in S and not in A is called the *complement of A relative to S;* it is denoted by A'_S. If $S = \{a, b, c, d, e\}$ and $A = \{a, b\}$, then $A \subseteq S$ and $A'_S = \{c, d, e\}$.

Example 4. Let S be the set of students in a given class, let B be the set of boys in S and let G be the set of girls in S.
(a) $G \cup B = S$
(b) $G \cap B = \emptyset$
(c) $G'_S = B$
(d) $B'_S = G$

Example 5. Let $S = \{1, 2, 3, 4, 5\}$, $A = \{3, 4, 5\}$, and $B = \{2, 4, 6, 8\}$
(a) $A \subseteq S$ and $A'_S = \{1, 2\}$
(b) $A \cap B = \{4\}$
(c) $B \cap S = \{2, 4\}$

EXERCISES

In Exercises 1 through 6, let $A = \{a, b, c\}$, $B = \{b, c, d, e, f\}$, $C = \{d, e, f, g, h, k\}$, and $S = \{a, b, c, d, e, f, g, h, i, j, k\}$.

1. List the elements in each of the following sets.
   (a) $A \cup B$ (b) $A \cup C$ (c) $B \cup C$
2. List the elements in each of the following sets.
   (a) $(A \cup B) \cup C$ (b) $A \cap (B \cup C)$ (c) $A \cap B$
3. Describe each of the following sets.
   (a) $A \cap C$ (b) $A \cap \emptyset$ (c) $A \cup \emptyset$
4. Determine each of the following:
   (a) $n(A)$ (b) $n(B)$ (c) $n(C)$
5. List the elements in each of the following sets.
   (a) A'_S (b) B'_S (c) C'_S
6. List the elements in each of the following sets.
   (a) $A'_S \cap B'_S$ (b) $(A \cup B)'_S$ (c) $(A \cap B)'_S$

In Exercises 7 through 12, let $A = \{a, b, c, d\}$, $B = \{c, d, e, f, g\}$, $C = \{x, y, z\}$, and $S = \{a, b, c, d, e, f, g, x, y, z\}$.

7. List the elements in each of the following sets.
   (a) $A \cup B$ (b) $A \cup C$ (c) $B \cup C$

8. List the elements in each of the following sets.
   (a) $(A \cup B) \cup C$ (b) $A \cap (B \cup C)$ (c) $A \cap B$

9. Describe each of the following sets.
   (a) $A \cap C$ (b) $A \cap \varnothing$ (c) $A \cup \varnothing$

10. Determine each of the following:
    (a) $n(A)$ (b) $n(B)$ (c) $n(C)$

11. List the elements in each of the following sets.
    (a) A'_S (b) B'_S (c) C'_S

12. List the elements in each of the following sets.
    (a) $A'_S \cap B'_S$ (b) $(A \cup B)'_S$ (c) $(A \cap B)'_S$

13. List all the subsets of $\{a, b, c, d\}$.

14. (a) If $A \subseteq S$, what is $A \cap S$? (b) If $A \subseteq S$, what is $A \cup S$?

2. RATIONAL OPERATIONS AND BASIC PROPERTIES

rational operations

The basic operations of arithmetic are addition, multiplication, subtraction, and division. They are called the *rational operations*. In this section, we define each of the rational operations on the set of whole numbers and discuss the basic properties of addition and multiplication. The properties of addition and multiplication will prove indispensable when we discuss the positional notation for numbers and verify the techniques for performing the rational operations on the set of whole numbers.

sum

Let A and B be two *disjoint* sets with a and b elements in each, respectively; that is $A \cap B = \varnothing$, $n(A) = a$ and $n(B) = b$. The *sum* of the two whole numbers a and b, denoted by $a + b$, is the number of elements in $A \cup B$; thus, if $A \cap B = \varnothing$, then

$$a + b = n(A \cup B)$$

For example, if $A = \{x, y, z\}$ and $B = \{e, f, g, h\}$, then $A \cap B = \varnothing$, $A \cup B = \{x, y, z, e, f, g, h\}$, $n(A) = 3$, $n(B) = 4$, $n(A \cup B) = 7$, and $3 + 4 = 7$.

binary operation

Any *method* which assigns one and only one number to any *two* given numbers is called a *binary operation*. The binary operation which assigns the number called the sum of a and b is called *addition*. A set is said to be *closed* with respect to a binary operation if and only if the operation assigns an element *in the set* to each pair of numbers in the set. Since the sum $a + b$ of any two whole numbers is a whole number, the set of whole numbers is closed with respect to addition.

addition

If A is a set with a elements, then since $A \cap \varnothing = \varnothing$ it follows from the definition of addition that $n(A) + n(\varnothing) = n(A \cup \varnothing)$. Since $n(\varnothing) = 0$ and $A \cup \varnothing = A$,

$$a + 0 = a$$

for any whole number a. We call zero the *additive identity;* its sum with any number is the number itself.

Let a and b be whole numbers and let A and B be disjoint sets such that $n(A) = a$ and $n(B) = b$. Since $A \cup B = B \cup A$, it follows that $n(A \cup B) = n(B \cup A)$ and

$$a + b = b + a$$

The fact that $a + b = b + a$ for any two whole numbers is called the *commutative property of addition.* The commutative property of addition for whole numbers is an immediate consequence of the commutative property of set union.

Let a, b, and c be whole numbers and let A, B, and C be pairwise disjoint sets such that $n(A) = a$, $n(B) = b$, and $n(C) = c$. When we say that the sets are pairwise disjoint, we mean that $A \cap B = \emptyset$, $B \cap C = \emptyset$, and $A \cap C = \emptyset$. From the definition of addition for whole numbers,

$$a + b = n(A \cup B)$$
$$b + c = n(B \cup C)$$
$$a + (b + c) = n[A \cup (B \cup C)]$$
$$(a + b) + c = n[(A \cup B) \cup C]$$

Since $A \cup (B \cup C) = (A \cup B) \cup C$, we conclude that

$$a + (b + c) = (a + b) + c$$

This is called the *associative property of addition.* The associative property of addition for whole numbers is an immediate consequence of the associative property of set union.

The operation of subtraction is defined in terms of addition. For any numbers a and b, if there exists one and only one number c such that $a + c = b$ then c is called the *difference* of b subtract a. In other words,

$$b - a = c \quad \text{if and only if} \quad a + c = b$$

where c is unique.

Since $4 + 5 = 9$, $9 - 4 = 5$. Of course, since $5 + 4 = 9$, we also have that $9 - 5 = 4$. Furthermore, since there is no *whole* number x such that $15 + x = 8$, for example, the set of whole numbers is not closed with respect to subtraction.

In the definition of addition for whole numbers, recall that we insisted the sets be disjoint. If we let $A = \{a, b, c, d\}$ and $B = \{c, d, e, f, g\}$, then $n(A) = 4$ and $n(B) = 5$. Since $A \cup B = \{a, b, c, d, e, f, g\}$, $n(A \cup B) = 7$, and $n(A) + n(B) \neq n(A \cup B)$. The equality fails to hold since the two given sets are not disjoint; the two elements c and

13

d, the elements in the intersection of the given sets, are "counted twice" in the sum $n(A) + n(B)$. Thus, the number in the union of the two sets is 2 less than $n(A) + n(B)$. In general, for any two sets A and B,

$$n(A \cup B) = n(A) + n(B) - n(A \cap B)$$

The last equality is obviously true for disjoint sets A and B since zero is the cardinal number of the empty set.

Example 1. Suppose that in a class of 25 students 19 passed the first test, 22 passed the second test, and no one failed both tests. How many passed both tests?

Solution: If we let A be the set of students who passed the first test and B be the set of students who passed the second test, then $A \cap B$ is the set of students who passed both tests. Since no one failed both tests, we know that $A \cup B$ is the entire class and $n(A \cup B) = 25$. Since $n(A) = 19$ and $n(B) = 22$,

$$25 = 19 + 22 - n(A \cap B)$$
and $$n(A \cap B) = 41 - 25 = 16$$

Therefore, 16 students passed both tests.

Grouping objects into sets such that each set has the same number of objects has served as a method of counting since the time of early man. This counting process leads naturally to the definition (creation) of the operation of multiplication. If we have six different sets each containing four objects, then the total number of objects is

$$4 + 4 + 4 + 4 + 4 + 4$$

The sum 24 is called the product of 6 times 4. In general, if a is any natural number greater than 1 and if b is any whole number, then we define the *product* of a times b, denoted by $a \times b$, or ab, to be the *sum* of a numbers each of which is b. Since the set of whole numbers is closed with respect to addition, any such product is always a whole number.

product

Since $4 + 4 + 4 + 4 + 4 + 4 = 6 + 6 + 6 + 6$, it follows that $6 \times 4 = 4 \times 6$. Another way to show this fact is to consider the following rectangular arrangement of dots.

We can see that four rows with six dots each has the same total number of dots as six columns with four dots each. The technique generalizes to show that $a \times b = b \times a$ where a and b are natural numbers different from 1.

From the definition of multiplication, 0×6 has not been defined since we cannot talk about adding 0 sixes. (Addition is a binary operation.) From the definition of multiplication we do have $6 \times 0 = 0$; in order to preserve closure and the commutative property of multiplication we *define* 0×6 to be zero. In general, for any whole number a, we define $0 \times a$ to be zero; thus,

$$a \times 0 = 0 \times a = 0$$

Similarly, since addition is a binary operation, we cannot talk about the sum, say, of one 7. However, since $7 \times 1 = 7$, we *define* 1×7 to be 7. In general, for any whole number a, we define $1 \times a$ to be a; thus,

$$a \times 1 = 1 \times a = a$$

multiplicative identity

We call 1 the *multiplicative identity*.

Observe that the set of whole numbers is *closed* with respect to the binary operation of multiplication. Also, the set has the *commutative property of multiplication*.

commutative property of multiplication

Now, let us turn our attention to the associative property of multiplication. Notice that

$$3 \times (4 \times 6) = 3 \times 24 = 72 \quad \text{and} \quad (3 \times 4) \times 6 = 12 \times 6 = 72$$

Of course, one example does not prove that multiplication is an associative operation. Without finding the products, let us show that $3 \times (4 \times 6) = (3 \times 4) \times 6$. We see in Figure 2.1 that there is the same number of dots in both configurations. On the left, each plane (collection) consists of 4×6 dots. Since there are three planes, the total number of dots is

$$3 \times (4 \times 6)$$

On the right, the front plane contains 3×4 dots. Since there are 6 such planes, the total number of dots is $6 \times (3 \times 4)$, or

$$(3 \times 4) \times 6$$

by the commutative property of multiplication. The procedure generalizes to show that if a, b, and c are whole numbers then

$$a \times (b \times c) = (a \times b) \times c$$

associative property of multiplication

This is called the *associative property of multiplication*.

Let us discuss one more property that is important enough to deserve a distinguishing name. Consider the product $4 \times (5 + 7)$.

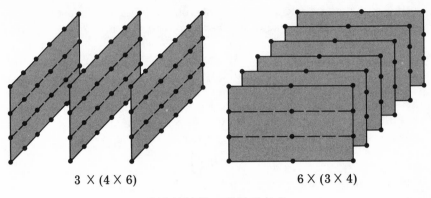

3 × (4 × 6)   6 × (3 × 4)

3 × (4 × 6) = (3 × 4) × 6
Associative Property

FIGURE 2.1

From the definition of multiplication for whole numbers,

$$4 \times (5 + 7) = (5 + 7) + (5 + 7) + (5 + 7) + (5 + 7)$$

Using the associative and commutative properties of addition, we obtain

$$4 \times (5 + 7) = (5 + 5 + 5 + 5) + (7 + 7 + 7 + 7)$$

Again, by definition of multiplication,

$$4 \times (5 + 7) = (4 \times 5) + (4 \times 7)$$

In general, if a, b, and c are whole numbers, then

$$a(b + c) = ab + ac$$

distributive property   This is called the *distributive property*. From the symmetric property of equality, we have that $ab + ac = a(b + c)$. Thus, the distributive property also verifies factorization of a factor common to the terms of a sum.

Division is defined in terms of multiplication in a manner quite similar to the way subtraction is defined in terms of addition. Let a and b be any numbers. If *there exists one and only one number c* such *quotient*   that $ac = b$, then c is called the *quotient* of b divided by a. In other words,

$$b \div a = c \quad \text{if and only if} \quad ac = b$$

where c is unique.

Since $2 \times 3 = 3 \times 2 = 6$, we conclude that $6 \div 3 = 2$ and $6 \div 2 = 3$.

Obviously, there is no whole number c such that $2c = 7$; thus, the set of whole numbers is not closed with respect to division.

EXERCISES

1. If $a \neq 0$, using the definition of division explain why $a \div 0$ is meaningless.
2. Using the definition of division explain why $0 \div 0$ is meaningless.
3. Use set, subset, and complement of a set to give an interpretation of subtraction.
4. Use set, subset, and complement of a set to give an interpretation of division.
5. In a group of 512 persons it is found that each one drinks tea or coffee (or both). If 278 drink tea and 334 drink coffee, how many drink both tea and coffee?
6. In a group of 1,000 car owners who own only Makes A or B, it was found that 627 owned Make A and 831 owned Make B. How many of the group owned both Makes A and B?

Consider the following mathematical system. Two operations (which we shall call addition and multiplication) are defined on the set $\{e, p, q, r\}$ by the following (addition and multiplication) tables. *Note:* In the tables, the element in the ith row, not counting the headline, and the jth column, not counting the sideline, is the sum, or product, of the element in the ith row of the sideline plus, or times, the element in the jth column of the headline. For example, $p + r = e$ and $r \times q = e$. Use the tables to work Exercises 7 through 16.

+	e	p	q	r
e	e	p	q	r
p	p	q	r	e
q	q	r	e	p
r	r	e	p	q

×	p	q	r	e
p	p	q	r	e
q	q	p	e	r
r	r	e	p	q
e	e	r	q	p

7. (a) Does the system have the closure property with respect to addition?
   (b) Does the system have the closure property with respect to multiplication?
8. Determine the following sums:
   (a) $r + q$ (b) $r + r$ (c) $q + e$
   (d) $p + q$ (e) $e + e$ (f) $r + e$

9. Determine the following products:
   (a) $r \times q$ (b) $r \times r$ (c) $q \times e$
   (d) $p \times q$ (e) $e \times e$ (f) $r \times e$

10. Using the obvious definition for subtraction, find the following differences:
    (a) $r - q$ (b) $r - r$ (c) $q - e$
    (d) $p - q$ (e) $e - e$ (f) $r - e$

11. Using the obvious definition for division, find the following quotients:
    (a) $r \div q$ (b) $r \div r$ (c) $q \div e$
    (d) $p \div q$ (e) $e \div e$ (f) $r \div e$

12. (a) Is the system closed with respect to addition? (b) Subtraction? (c) Multiplication? (d) Division?

13. (a) What element would be called the multiplicative identity?
    (b) What element would be called the additive identity?

14. (a) Does the system have the commutative property of addition?
    (b) Does the system have the commutative property of multiplication?

15. (a) Does the system have the associative property of addition?
    (b) Does the system have the associative property of multiplication?

16. (a) Determine if $p(q + r) = pq + pr$.
    (b) For any elements a, b, and c in the system, is it true that $a(b + c) = ab + ac$?

3. ALGORITHMS FOR A POSITIONAL NOTATION

After early man developed a number concept and words for numbers, the next step was to create (shorthand) symbols for numbers. At the outset, numbers probably were represented by sticks in much the same way we sometimes use |, ||, |||, ||||, |||| , |||||, etc. to represent one, two, three, four, five, six, etc. It is rather obvious that such a notation is less than desirable if we need to write numbers such as ninety-eight, one hundred fifty, or two thousand.

The Egyptian hieroglyphic symbol for ten was ∩; the notation for twenty was ∩ ∩. Although the Egyptian heelbone symbol for ten may be unfamiliar, the use of two such symbols for twenty should not seem unnatural when we recall that "X" is the Roman notation for ten and "XX" is the Roman notation for twenty. (It is worth noting that the Greeks, Babylonians, and Mayan Indians all had their own unique symbols for ten.)

numerals   The basic *symbols* used to denote numbers are called *numerals*. The numerals 0, 1, 2, 3, 4, 5, 6, 7, 8, and 9 were developed from those of the Hindus. Later, they were adopted by the Arabs who also contributed to the further development of the number system. Our system of notation, which was probably introduced into Europe around 711 A.D. with the Moors' invasion into Spain, is called the *Hindu-Arabic number system.*

Hindu-Arabic number system

We mentioned the fact that the Romans used a different set of numerals for numbers. The *Roman numerals* are I, V, X, L, C, D, and M where "I" denotes one, "V" denotes five, "X" denotes ten, "L" denotes fifty, "C" denotes one hundred, "D" denotes five hundred, and "M" denotes one thousand. As late as the seventeenth century, these numerals were still in prominent use in Europe for the purpose of keeping records.

Roman numerals

The Hindu-Arabic notation is a positional system for writing numbers. For example, "3,425" represents three thousands (ten hundreds), four hundreds (ten tens), two tens, and five ones. The system is said to have ten as its base number. Essentially, the *base number* indicates the number of objects selected for the basic grouping of elements for purposes of counting. It should be clear that the base number for a positional notation is arbitrary. If man had developed eight fingers instead of ten, we would surely have selected eight as the grouping number and would use eight as our base number. In base eight, "23" (read, "two-three") would represent two eights and three ones; that is, "23" with eight as base number denotes the number nineteen. (We shall have more to say about other number bases in Section 5.)

base number

Our words for the natural numbers clearly indicate the use of ten for grouping. For example, sixteen is six and ten, twenty-seven is two tens and seven, sixty is six tens, etc. The only words which appear to be exceptions are "eleven" and "twelve"; "eleven" and "twelve" are traceable to *ein-lif* and *zwo-lif* where *lif* is old German for ten, *ein* is the word for one, and *zwo* is the word for two. However, with the exception of "five," which can be traced back to a word for hand, the original meanings of most number words in the European langages have been lost.

Since the base number selected for a positional notation is arbitrary, it should not be too surprising that some civilizations developed numeration systems using a base number other than ten. The Babylonians used sixty as base number. There is residual evidence of this system in some of the basic groupings we use today. For example, there are sixty seconds in a minute and sixty minutes in an hour.

In a positional notation, we use "0" as a *place-holder,* or *spacer.* The numeral is used in order for us to be able to distinguish between such numbers as 68 (sixty-eight) and 6,008 (six thousand and eight). Of course, if we consider the numeral "0" as representing the cardinal

place-holder

number of the empty set, then "6,008" represents 6 thousands, 0 hundreds, 0 tens, and 8 ones. Because of our familiarity with the number zero, it would be both cumbersome and pointless to consider "0" as only a place-holder when discussing a positional notation for natural numbers.

We should realize that the number zero had to travel an arduous route to become an accepted and well-integrated idea in man's number concept. The name for the number has experienced some changes worth noting. The Hindu word for empty was *sunya*. In the tenth century, when the Arabs adopted the Hindu notation the word used was *sifr* which meant empty in Arabic. When the Hindu-Arabic notation was introduced into Europe, *sifr* was latinized as *zephirum* from which we obtain *zero*. In Germany, *sifr* was changed to *cifra* which, in turn, was to become the English word *cipher*.

It is obvious that Roman numerals differ considerably (as symbols) from Hindu-Arabic numerals. Another obvious difference is the number of numerals in each system. A more important difference in the two numeration systems is the fact that the Roman notation is not a positional system; the positions do not specify groupings. In Roman numerals, "VI" denotes six (five plus one), "VIII" denotes eight (five plus three), and "IV" denotes four (five less one). We should observe that for a nonpositional system, such as the Roman system, a spacer such as "0" is unessential.

Obviously, a notational system for numbers is not selected only for its facility in writing numbers. Since the notation for numbers is an integral part of how we perform the rational operations, our acceptance of a notational system will depend heavily on its contribution in making it relatively easy to add, subtract, multiply, and divide.

In the Middle Ages, most persons could not perform more than the simplest arithmetic calculations. For the ill-informed, it might appear that man's intellect has improved greatly since the twelfth century, because today's elementary school child can perform arithmetic computations relegated to the few of that era. However, the change in the numeration system has been primarily responsible for the change in the facility for doing arithmetic computations. The fact that the Hindu-Arabic system replaced the well-entrenched Roman system should be ample evidence of the merits of our present system.

Let us review the basic techniques of arithmetic and show why they accomplish what they are intended to do. It should be clear that the techniques to add, subtract, multiply, and divide depend on the basic number properties, the positional aspects of the notation system, but *not* on the base number.

To find the sum $35 + 58$, we proceed as follows:

METHOD 1.
$$\begin{array}{r} 58 \\ \underline{35} \\ 13 \\ \underline{80} \end{array}$$
Sum   93

METHOD 2.
$$\begin{array}{r} ①58 \\ \underline{35} \end{array}$$
Sum   93

Notice that

$$35 + 58 = (3 \text{ tens} + 5 \text{ ones}) + (5 \text{ tens} + 8 \text{ ones})$$

By associative and commutative properties of addition,

$$\begin{aligned} 35 + 58 &= (3 \text{ tens} + 5 \text{ tens}) + (5 \text{ ones} + 8 \text{ ones}) \\ &= 8 \text{ tens} + (1 \text{ ten} + 3 \text{ ones}) \\ &= (8 \text{ tens} + 1 \text{ ten}) + 3 \text{ ones} \\ &= 9 \text{ tens} + 3 \text{ ones} \\ &= 93 \end{aligned}$$

Since $8 + 5 = 13 = 1$ ten $+ 3$ ones, in Method 2 we "carried" 1 to be added in the tens' column.

To find the difference $85 - 28$, we proceed as follows:

$$\begin{array}{r} 7 \\ 8^15 \\ \underline{2 \ 8} \\ 5 \ 7 \end{array}$$

Since 5 is less than 8, we "regroup" 8 tens $+$ 5 ones into 7 tens $+$ 15 ones. Often it is said that we "borrow one" from the tens' column. Obviously, the technique of subtracting by columns presents no difficulty in finding the difference $78 - 23$.

Let us exhibit several techniques to find the product 7×46. The first method is quite detailed and demonstrates the underlying features; each successive technique is a variation or shortened version of the preceding one.

METHOD 1.
$$\begin{aligned} 7 \times 46 &= 7 \times (4 \text{ tens} + 6) \\ &= 28 \text{ tens} + 42 \\ &= 28 \text{ tens} + 4 \text{ tens} + 2 \\ &= 32 \text{ tens} + 2 \\ &= 320 + 2 \\ &= 322 \end{aligned}$$

METHOD 2. $\quad$ 46
$\quad\quad\quad\quad$ 7
$\quad\quad\quad\quad\overline{\quad 42}$
$\quad\quad\quad\quad 280$
$\quad\quad\quad\quad\overline{322}$

METHOD 3. $\quad$ 46
$\quad\quad\quad\quad$ 7
$\quad\quad\quad\quad\overline{\quad 42}$
$\quad\quad\quad\quad 28$
$\quad\quad\quad\quad\overline{322}$

METHOD 4. $\quad$ 446
$\quad\quad\quad\quad\quad$ 7
$\quad\quad\quad\quad\overline{\quad 322}$

To multiply 57 times 46, we notice that $57 = 5$ tens $+ 7$. Then, we find the products 7×46 and 5×46 as above and use the fact that 5×46 tens $= 230$ tens $= 2,300$. The standard algorithm is as follows:

$$\begin{array}{r} 46 \\ 57 \\ \hline 322 \\ 230 \\ \hline 2,622 \end{array}$$

Finding the quotient $18 \div 3$ is equivalent to finding how many groups containing 3 objects are in a set containing 18 objects; of course, the number is 6. Since a set with 22 objects cannot be "split" into disjoint subsets such that each subset will contain exactly 3 elements, $22 \div 3$ is not a whole number. It is natural to ask two questions: (1) What is the maximum number of groups containing 3 elements each that can be removed from a set with 22 elements? (2) After all such groups have been removed, how many elements are left over in the set? (Obviously, the answer to the second question must be a whole number less than 3.*) In the slightly more abstract setting of basic number concepts, we seek the whole number q such that $3q$ is the greatest multiple of 3 less than or equal to 22 and the whole number r where $r = 22 - 3q$. One method to answer Question 1 would be as follows. Find the difference $22 - 3$ (take away three objects); then subtract 3 from the difference 19 (take away three additional objects); and continue the process of repeated subtraction until the difference is a whole number less than 3. The number of subtractions will be q and the final difference will be r.

Number of Subtractions	1	2	3	4	5	6	$7 = q$
	22	19	16	13	10	7	4
	3	3	3	3	3	3	3
Differences	19	16	13	10	7	4	$1 = r$

---

* Here we assume a basic knowledge of the meaning of *less-than* and *greater-than*. For an extensive discussion, see Chapter 4.

Assume a and b are natural numbers such that a is greater than or equal to b. The set of natural numbers that are multiples of b and less than or equal to a is not empty since b is a multiple of b and b is less than or equal to a. If qb is the greatest multiple of b less than or equal to a, then the number q is called the *incomplete quotient* and $a - qb$ is called the *remainder* in the *incomplete division* of a by b. We call a the *dividend* and b the *divisor*. If $a - qb = 0$, then $a = qb$ and $a \div b = q$. Hence, if the remainder is zero, the incomplete quotient is the quotient $a \div b$. (We should carefully maintain the distinction between the rational operation of division, defined in terms of multiplication, and the operation of incomplete division defined on the set of natural numbers.)

incomplete quotient

remainder

Our immediate task is to discover an efficient algorithm to find the incomplete quotient and remainder in the incomplete division of any pair of natural numbers. For two given numbers such as $a = 678$ and $b = 23$, we could find the numbers q and r by repeated subtractions, but the process would hardly be efficient.

To find the number q such that $23q$ is the greatest multiple of 23 less than or equal to 678, we could proceed by listing the successive multiples of 23 until we found one which exceeded 678. That is, we could proceed as follows:

$$1 \times 23 = 23$$
$$2 \times 23 = 46$$
$$3 \times 23 = 69$$
$$4 \times 23 = 92$$
$$5 \times 23 = 115$$
$$6 \times 23 = 138$$
$$\cdots \cdots \cdots$$
$$25 \times 23 = 575$$
$$26 \times 23 = 598$$
$$27 \times 23 = 621$$
$$28 \times 23 = 644$$
$$29 \times 23 = 667$$
$$30 \times 23 = 690$$

Thus, 29×23 is the greatest multiple of 23 less than or equal to 678; hence, $q = 29$. Since $678 - (29 \times 23) = 678 - 667 = 11$, we conclude that $r = 11$. Notice that r is a whole number less than the divisor.

Performing repeated subtractions and listing successive multiples are generally quite inefficient methods to find q and r. Another and more efficient method would be as follows.

23

Our experience with multiplication tells us that

$$20 \times 23 < 678$$
and
$$30 \times 23 > 678$$

The first inequality shows that the greatest multiple of 23 less than or equal to 678 is at least as large as 20×23. The second inequality shows that the greatest multiple of 23 less than or equal to 678 is less than 30×23. Since $20 \times 23 = 460$,

Subtract: 678
            $\underline{460} = 20 \times 23$
Difference   218

If we do not recognize that 9×23 is less than 218, we might proceed as follows:

$$
\left.
\begin{array}{rl}
678 & \\
\underline{460} = & 20 \times 23 \\
\textit{Difference} \quad 218 & \\
\underline{69} = & 3 \times 23 \\
\textit{Difference} \quad 149 & \\
\underline{69} = & 3 \times 23 \\
\textit{Difference} \quad 80 & \\
\underline{69} = & 3 \times 23 \\
\textit{Difference} \quad 11 \ \textit{Remainder} &
\end{array}
\right\} = 29 \times 23
$$

Thus, $678 - (29)(23) = 11$, $q = 29$, and $r = 11$. Although this technique is not the standard algorithm to find q and r, it is quite correct.

Let us now present other methods to find the numbers q and r. For example, let $a = 7,846$, $b = 231$ and determine q and r such that $7,846 = 231q + r$ where $r \geq 0$ and $r < 231$. The first method we use is the one just described and the second method is a variation of the first.

METHOD I.   7,846
              $\underline{6,930} = 30 \times 231$
Difference   916
              $\underline{693} = 3 \times 231$
Difference   223

METHOD II. $231\overline{)7,846}$
              $\underline{6,930} \ | \ 30$
              916
              $\underline{693} \ | \ 3$
$r = \quad 223 \ | \ 33 = q$

Thus, $q = 33$ and $r = 223$.

Let a and b be natural numbers such that $a \geq b$. We can prove that there exist unique whole numbers q and r such that $a = qb + r$

and $r < b$. Although it is a misnomer, this *fact* is generally called   *division*
the *division algorithm*. The technique to find q and r is often called   *algorithm*
long division. We give several variations of long division to find q
and r in the incomplete division of 80,336 by 378; the student should
study each carefully.   *long division*

METHOD I. $378\overline{)80,336}$
                  $\underline{75,600}$ 200
                    $4,736$
                    $\underline{3,780}$ 10
                       956
                       $\underline{756}$ $\underline{2}$
                  $r = 200$ $212 = q$

                         2
                        10
                    $\underline{200}$
METHOD II. $378\overline{)80,336}$ $q = 212$
                  $\underline{75,600}$
                    $4,736$
                    $\underline{3,780}$
                       956
                       $\underline{756}$
                  $r = 200$

                      $212 = q$
METHOD III. $378\overline{)80,336}$
                  $\underline{75,600}$
                    $4,736$
                    $\underline{3,780}$
                       956
                       $\underline{756}$
                       $200 = r$

                      $212 = q$
METHOD IV. $378\overline{)80,336}$
                    $\underline{756}$
                     473
                     $\underline{378}$
                       956
                       $\underline{756}$
                       $200 = r$

25

An incomplete division problem can be checked by finding the product of the divisor and the incomplete quotient and then adding the remainder to the product; the sum should be equal to the dividend. From the last example, we find that

$$(378 \times 212) + 200 = 80,336$$

Hence, 212 is the incomplete quotient and 200 is the remainder.

EXERCISES

1. Let a and b be natural numbers where a is less than b. Prove that there are whole numbers q and r such that $a = qb + r$ where r is less than b.

2. Use reference material to find the different symbols used by the Greeks, Babylonians, and Mayan Indians to denote ten.

3. Find the incomplete quotient and remainder in the incomplete division of 612 by 38 by each of the following methods. (a) Repeated subtractions. (b) Listing successive multiples of 38. (c) Long division algorithm.

4. Find the incomplete quotient and remainder in the incomplete division of 681 by 52 by each of the following methods. (a) Repeated subtractions. (b) Listing successive multiples of 52. (c) Long division algorithm.

5. Find the incomplete quotient and remainder in the incomplete division of 497 by 29 by each of the following methods. (a) Repeated subtractions. (b) Listing successive multiples of 29. (c) Long division algorithm.

6. Find the incomplete quotient and remainder in the incomplete division of 756 by 63 by each of the following methods. (a) Repeated subtractions. (b) Listing successive multiples of 29. (c) Long division algorithm.

7. Suppose that *un, do, to, fo,* and *dot* are the words used for the first five counting numbers and suppose five is the base number of the number system. If *un, do, to, fo, dot, undot, dodot, todot, fodot, dodoty, dodoty-un* are the names of the first eleven natural numbers, list reasonable names for the next thirteen counting numbers.

8. If *dooty* were the name given to five groups of five in the base five system described in Exercise 7, state the standard name in English for each of the following numbers. (a) Un dooty and un. (b) Un dooty and dot. (c) Un dooty and fo. (d) Do dooty and dodoty-do. (e) Fo dooty and fodoty-fo.

9. For the number system with five as base number discussed in Exercises

7 and 8, use "0" as a spacer and let ١, ٢, ٤, ٦ be the numerals for *un, do, to, fo,* respectively. If a positional notation is constructed using these numerals and five as base number, the first eleven numbers would be written as follows:

١, ٢, ٤, ٦, 10, 11, 12, 14, 16, 20, 21

Use the notation to write the next fifteen numbers.

10. Use the notation in the preceding exercise to write each of the numbers in Exercise 8.

*11. If each *x* represents one of the digits 0 through 9, except no first digit in any number is zero, determine the divisor, dividend, and quotient in the following. (No guessing is necessary.)

$$
\begin{array}{r}
x\ x,\ 8\ x\ x \\
x\ x\ x\overline{)x\ x,\ x\ x\ x,\ x\ x\ x} \\
\underline{x\ \ x\ x} \\
x\ x\ x\ x \\
\underline{x\ x\ \ x} \\
x\ \ x\ x\ x \\
\underline{x\ \ x\ x\ x} \\
0
\end{array}
$$

12. Find the digits represented by the letters in the following addition if no two different letters represent the same digit.

$$
\begin{array}{r}
F\ O\ R\ T\ Y \\
T\ E\ N \\
T\ E\ N \\
\hline
S\ I\ X\ T\ Y
\end{array}
$$

*13. The multiplication of a three-digit number times a two-digit number has the form

$$
\begin{array}{r}
p\ p\ p \\
p\ p \\
\hline
p\ p\ p\ p \\
p\ p\ p\ p \\
\hline
p\ p\ p\ p\ p
\end{array}
$$

where each "p" can be any one of the digits 2, 3, 5, or 7. Determine the two given numbers.

4. OTHER NOTATIONAL SYSTEMS

As we stated earlier, the base number for a positional notation is arbitrary. The naturalist Buffon seriously suggested in the last century that we should change to a base twelve (duodecimal) notation.

In the eighteenth century, the mathematician Lagrange pointed out that a prime number base has distinct advantages. The followers of Buffon would see advantages if the base number had a large number of factors; twelve has six factors. A follower of Lagrange would probably be a mathematician whose primary concern was structure and not applications; to him a base number with the least number of factors, a prime, would be appealing. It might appear that ten is a good compromise as base number; actually, it is not. However, base ten is so entrenched in the human experience that a change to a different base is highly unlikely, if not foolish to suggest.

It is worthwhile, however, to study positional notations with other base numbers since it provides a better insight into the base ten system. If we were going to use a positional notation with eight as base number, then we would first need to "invent" eight numerals. (In the exercise set of the last section, we did invent numerals for a base five notational system.) Generally, we take the easy way out and use the familiar eight numerals 0, 1, 2, 3, 4, 5, 6, and 7. Observe that "8" and "9" are "marks" which have no place in the base eight system. An advantage of using these familiar symbols is that "3", for example, denotes three, and we do not have to learn a new symbol for the number. However, there is a distinct disadvantage; the symbol "10" in base eight represents *eight and not ten*. In order to avoid the obvious difficulty, we usually write "10_{eight}" (read, "one-zero, base eight") to emphasize that we are using base eight notation. In base eight, "236_{eight}" represents two sixty-fours (eight eights), three eights, and six units; that is,

$$236_{eight} = 2(10_{eight})^2 + 3(10_{eight}) + 6$$

To convert 236_{eight} to base ten notation, we use the fact that

$$236_{eight} = 2(8)^2 + 3(8) + 6$$

where the expression on the right-hand side of the equality is in base ten notation. Thus,

$$236_{eight} = 128 + 24 + 6$$

and $\qquad\qquad 236_{eight} = 158_{ten}$

Let us list the first seventy-two natural numbers in base eight notation. By observing the pattern it is easy to see how to write the first, say, one thousand natural numbers in base eight. (See page 29.)

Starting from 6 in column one, if we "count" five more numbers, we arrive at 13_{eight}. Thus, $6 + 5 = 13_{eight}$. Since "13_{eight}" represents one eight plus three, this, of course, is 11 in base ten. To find the product 6×5 in base eight notation, we could start in the first column and mark off consecutively six groups each containing five numbers and

1	11_{eight}	21_{eight}	31_{eight}	41_{eight}	51_{eight}	61_{eight}	71_{eight}	101_{eight}
2	12_{eight}	22_{eight}	32_{eight}	42_{eight}	52_{eight}	62_{eight}	72_{eight}	102_{eight}
3	13_{eight}	23_{eight}	33_{eight}	43_{eight}	53_{eight}	63_{eight}	73_{eight}	103_{eight}
4	14_{eight}	24_{eight}	34_{eight}	44_{eight}	54_{eight}	64_{eight}	74_{eight}	104_{eight}
5	15_{eight}	25_{eight}	35_{eight}	45_{eight}	55_{eight}	65_{eight}	75_{eight}	105_{eight}
6	16_{eight}	26_{eight}	36_{eight}	46_{eight}	56_{eight}	66_{eight}	76_{eight}	106_{eight}
7	17_{eight}	27_{eight}	37_{eight}	47_{eight}	57_{eight}	67_{eight}	77_{eight}	107_{eight}
10_{eight}	20_{eight}	30_{eight}	40_{eight}	50_{eight}	60_{eight}	70_{eight}	100_{eight}	110_{eight}

then look at the last number in the final group; it is 36_{eight}. Another way to determine the product in base eight is to use our knowledge that 6×5 is thirty (three eights and six units). Before continuing, an instructive and worthwhile task is to complete the following addition and multiplication tables for base eight notation. We shall make considerable use of them in the next section.

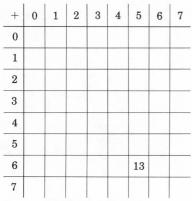

Addition Table

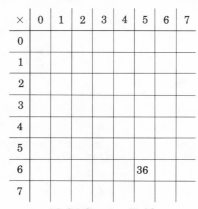

Multiplication Table

Base Eight

Example 1. (a) Since $8 + 6 = 14$, $14_{ten} = 16_{eight}$.
　　　　　 (b) Since $6(8) + 1 = 49$, $49_{ten} = 61_{eight}$.

Example 2. (a) $7 + 7 = 16_{eight}$.
　　　　　 (b) $7 \times 7 = 61_{eight}$.

We see that the addition and multiplication tables for base eight each contain sixty-four entries. Similar tables for base ten each contain one hundred entries. One obvious advantage of a smaller base number is that there are fewer addition and multiplication number facts to be memorized.

With a little reflection, it should be clear that the algorithms (techniques) for performing arithmetic calculations depend on the positional notation and not on the base number. Thus, the techniques for doing calculations in any base are essentially the same as for base ten. Of course, the addition and multiplication tables and the notations are different. In the next section, we shall exhibit the techniques for doing computations in other number bases.

Most of the modern electronic computers use a positional notation with two as base number. The base two system is called the *binary system*. In the binary system, we need only a spacer (zero) and a unit (one). In the binary notation, "1011_{two}" represents one eight (four twos), zero fours (two twos), one two, and one unit. In what is called *expanded notation,*

$$1011_{two} = 1(10_{two})^3 + 0(10_{two})^2 + 1(10_{two}) + 1$$

binary system (margin note)

Since $10_{two} = 2$, $(10_{two})^2 = 4$, and $(10_{two})^3 = 8$, it follows that

$$\begin{aligned}1011_{two} &= 1(8) + 0(4) + 1(2) + 1 \\ &= 8 + 2 + 1 \\ &= 11_{ten}\end{aligned}$$

Example 3. (a) $110_{two} = 6_{ten}$ (b) $1101_{two} = 13_{ten}$
(c) $11111_{two} = 31_{ten}$ (d) $1010101_{two} = 85_{ten}$

In the binary system, the addition and multiplication tables are easily constructed and there are few number facts to remember. A disadvantage of the binary system is the number of digits required to denote large numbers. For example, the two-digit number 57 in base ten is the six-digit number 111001 in base two. The difficulty can be resolved much more easily by electronic computers than by human computers.

+	0	1
0	0	1
1	0	10

×	0	1
0	0	0
1	0	1

Addition Table   *Multiplication Table*

Base Two

We have seen that it is reasonably easy to change a number from either base eight or base two to base ten notation. Fortunately, there is a simple and routine procedure to change numbers from base ten notation to base eight or base two notations. For example, to change

46 from base ten to base two, we proceed as follows:

STEP 1.   2) 46

STEP 2.   2) 23 $r = 0$

STEP 3.   2) 11 $r = 1$

STEP 4.   2) 5 $r = 1$

STEP 5.   2) 2 $r = 1$

STEP 6.   1 $r = 0$

Explanation of procedure. Using long division (often, it is called "short" division; it would be more appropriate to say that it is a short method for finding the incomplete quotient and the remainder), divide 46 by 2 and then successively divide each incomplete quotient by 2 until a quotient of 1 is obtained; record the remainders after each division. Then start with the final quotient 1 and list successively the remainders in the opposite order than they were obtained; that is, 1 0 1 1 1 0. We assert that $46_{\text{ten}} = 101110_{\text{two}}$.

To verify the technique, consider the steps in the division process.

STEP 1. $46 = 2(23)$

STEP 2. $23 = 2(11) + 1$

Hence, $46 = 2[2(11) + 1]$

and $46 = 2^2(11) + 2$

STEP 3. $11 = 2(5) + 1$

Hence, $46 = 2^2[2(5) + 1] + 2$

and $46 = 2^3(5) + 2^2 + 2$

STEP 4. $5 = 2(2) + 1$

Hence, $46 = 2^3[2(2) + 1] + 2^2 + 2$

and $46 = 2^4(2) + 2^3 + 2^2 + 2$

STEP 5. $46 = 2^5 + 2^3 + 2^2 + 2$

In other words, $46 = 1(2^5) + 0(2^4) + 1(2^3) + 1(2^2) + 1(2) + 0$; it follows that $46 = 101110_{\text{two}}$.

Fortunately, the procedure to change a number from base ten to any base is essentially the same as the one exhibited to change from base ten to base two. This should be expected since the technique depends on the positional notation, the basic properties of addition and multiplication, but not on the base number. Consider the following example in which we change 5,278 in base ten notation to base eight notation.

STEP 1.   8) 5,278

STEP 2.   8)   659 $r = 6$

STEP 3.   8)   82 $r = 3$

STEP 4.   8)   10 $r = 2$

STEP 5.   1 $r = 2$

Note: The process ends when the incomplete quotient is less than the divisor. We conclude that $5{,}278_{ten} = 12236_{eight}$.

Example 4. Change 115 to base two notation.

Solution: STEP 1.   2) 115

STEP 2.   2)   57 $r = 1$

STEP 3.   2)   28 $r = 1$

STEP 4.   2)   14 $r = 0$

STEP 5.   2)   7 $r = 0$

STEP 6.   2)   3 $r = 1$

STEP 7.   1 $r = 1$

Thus, $115_{ten} = 1110011_{two}$.

Example 5. Change 1,723 to base eight notation.

Solution: STEP 1.   8) 1,723

STEP 2.   8)   215 $r = 3$

STEP 3.   8)   26 $r = 7$

STEP 4.   3 $r = 2$

Thus, $1{,}723_{ten} = 3{,}273_{eight}$.

An entertaining as well as instructive use of the binary system is in an effective strategy to play the game of Nim. First, let us explain the game.

Two players play with a collection of sticks, toothpicks, playing cards, or the like; in the game they are usually called *counters*. The counters are placed in several rows; the number of rows and the number of counters in each row are determined by the players. Our exhibition game will contain 18 counters placed into three rows with 9 in the first row, 6 in the second, and 3 in the third.

ROW 1 | | | | | | | | |

ROW 2 | | | | | |

ROW 3 | | |

Each player when it is his turn must remove at least one of the counters from the array; he is allowed to remove more than one as long as he removes them from only *one* of the rows. We define the winner to be the person who removes the last counter from the array. (The student might like to try a few games with the above arrangement before reading the following strategy; the person who goes first with the given arrangement and plays properly can win.)

Count the counters in each of the rows and write the number of counters in base two notation as follows.

ROW 1	| | | | | | | | |	1001_{two}
ROW 2	| | | | | |	110_{two}
ROW 3	| | |	$\underline{11_{two}}$
		1122

Next, perform ordinary (base ten) column addition on the digits in the binary representations of the numbers. In our example above, the sum is 1122. If it is your play and if at least one digit in the sum is

A Sample Game of Nim

Round	First Player		Second Player	
First Round	||||||||| |||||| |||	1001_{two} 110_{two} $\underline{11_{two}}$ 1122	||||| |||||| |||	101_{two} 110_{two} $\underline{11_{two}}$ 222
Second Round	||||| |||||| ||	101_{two} 110_{two} $\underline{10_{two}}$ 221	|||| |||||| ||	100_{two} 110_{two} $\underline{10_{two}}$ 220
Third Round	|||| ||| ||	100_{two} 11_{two} $\underline{10_{two}}$ 121	| ||| ||	1 11_{two} $\underline{10_{two}}$ 22
Fourth Round	| | ||	1 1 $\underline{10_{two}}$ 12	| |	1 1 $\underline{0}$ 2
Fifth Round	|	1 $\underline{0}$ 0		←— Winning position

an odd number, as in this case, then you can win the game in the following manner.

See the table on the previous page. In the left-most column where an odd number appears in the notation for the sum, *remove* a "1" in that column from one of the binary numbers. Now, in the same binary number make changes in the digits 0 and 1 so all other odd numbers (digits) in the sum will become even. Finally, remove the necessary counters from that row so your constructed binary notation represents the number of counters left in the row. Leaving only even numbers as digits in the sum after you play will be a winning position for you. Regardless of the other player's move, it will always result in a losing situation for him. Your opponent must leave at least one digit in the sum that is an odd number and you can continue to effect a winning position when it is your play.

EXERCISES

1. Complete the base eight addition table on page 29.
2. Complete the base eight multiplication table on page 29.
3. Change each of the following numbers to base ten notation.
    (a) 512_{eight} (b) 6534_{eight} (c) 3002_{eight}
4. Change each of the following numbers to base ten notation.
    (a) 347_{eight} (b) 1700_{eight} (c) 3174_{eight}
5. Change each of the following numbers to base ten notation.
    (a) 111_{eight} (b) 435_{eight} (c) 100_{eight}
6. Change each of the following numbers to base ten notation.
    (a) 1776_{eight} (b) 1066_{eight} (c) 1637_{eight}
7. Change each of the following numbers to base ten notation.
    (a) 11101_{two} (b) 101100_{two} (c) 100000_{two}
8. Change each of the following numbers to base ten notation.
    (a) 100111_{two} (b) 101010_{two} (c) 111111_{two}
9. Change each of the following numbers to base ten notation.
    (a) 1001100_{two} (b) 100011_{two} (c) 11011_{two}
10. Change each of the following numbers to base ten notation.
    (a) 10000000_{two} (b) 1100111_{two} (c) 101000_{two}
11. Change each of the following numbers to base eight notation.
    (a) 7,861   (b) 1,776   (c) 23,044
12. Change each of the following numbers to base eight notation.
    (a) 4,663   (b) 8,064   (c) 45,241
13. Change each of the following numbers to base eight notation.
    (a) 7,211   (b) 3,006   (c) 8,111
14. Change each of the following numbers to base eight notation.
    (a) 4,321   (b) 8,888   (c) 10,000

15. (a) Determine if the first player can win at the game of Nim which has the following number of counters in each row: 10 counters in Row 1; 8 counters in Row 2; 6 counters in Row 3. (b) Suggest a first play.

16. (a) Determine if the first player can win at the game of Nim which has the following number of counters in each row: 23 counters in Row 1; 15 counters in Row 2; 12 counters in Row 3. (b) Suggest a first play.

17. (a) Determine if the first player can win at the game of Nim which has the following number of counters in each row: 32 counters in Row 1; 21 counters in Row 2; 16 counters in Row 3. (b) Suggest a first play.

18. (a) Determine if the first player can win at the game of Nim which has the following number of counters in each row: 28 counters in Row 1; 14 counters in Row 2; 7 counters in Row 3. (b) Suggest a first play.

19. (a) Determine if the first player can win at the game of Nim which has the following number of counters in each row: 15 counters in Row 1; 22 counters in Row 2; 11 counters in Row 3. (b) Suggest a first play.

20. (a) Determine if the first player can win at the game of Nim which has the following number of counters in each row: 14 counters in Row 1; 19 counters in Row 2; 9 counters in Row 3. (b) Suggest a first play.

5. COMPUTING IN OTHER BASES (OPTIONAL)

As we have indicated, the techniques for calculating in any base are essentially the same as for base ten. Let us work several examples in base eight. Refer to the base eight addition and multiplication tables on page 29 and consider each example carefully.

Addition

Base Eight		Base Ten
①1 3$_{\text{eight}}$ =		11
3 6$_{\text{eight}}$ =		30
4 1$_{\text{eight}}$ =		33
1 1 2$_{\text{eight}}$ =		74

Base Eight		Base Ten
②3①7 6$_{\text{eight}}$ =		①2①5 4
4 7 5$_{\text{eight}}$ =		3 1 7
7 4 0$_{\text{eight}}$ =		4 8 0
2 0 3 3$_{\text{eight}}$ =		1 0 5 1

Multiplication

Base Eight		Base Ten
236$_{\text{eight}}$ =		158
25$_{\text{eight}}$ =		21
1426$_{\text{eight}}$		158
474$_{\text{eight}}$		316
6366$_{\text{eight}}$ =		3,318

Base Eight		Base Ten
371$_{\text{eight}}$ =		249
72$_{\text{eight}}$ =		58
762$_{\text{eight}}$		1992
3317$_{\text{eight}}$		1245
34152$_{\text{eight}}$ =		14,442

35

Subtraction

Base Eight	Base Ten		Base Eight	Base Ten
6			$4^{①}3$	
$4\ 7^{①}1_{\text{eight}} =$	313		$\not{5}\ \not{4}^{①}3_{\text{eight}} =$	355
$2\ 3\ 4_{\text{eight}} =$	156		$2\ 5\ 6_{\text{eight}} =$	174
$2\ 3\ 5_{\text{eight}} =$	157		$2\ 6\ 5_{\text{eight}} =$	181

The long division algorithm is no more difficult than the addition, subtraction, and multiplication algorithms if we maintain careful attention to both the addition and multiplication tables. We leave the check for each division as an exercise.

Incomplete Division

$$\text{(a)} \quad 7_{\text{eight}} \overline{)\, 4253_{\text{eight}}} \quad \frac{475_{\text{eight}} = q}{}$$

$$34_{\text{eight}}$$
$$65_{\text{eight}}$$
$$61_{\text{eight}}$$
$$43_{\text{eight}}$$
$$43_{\text{eight}}$$
$$0 = r$$

$$\text{(b)} \quad 23_{\text{eight}} \overline{)\, 6142_{\text{eight}}} \quad \frac{246_{\text{eight}} = q}{}$$

$$46_{\text{eight}}$$
$$134_{\text{eight}}$$
$$114_{\text{eight}}$$
$$202_{\text{eight}}$$
$$162_{\text{eight}}$$
$$20_{\text{eight}} = r$$

Let us now consider the techniques for addition, subtraction, multiplication, and division using the binary system.

Addition

Base Two	Base Ten		Base Two	Base Ten
$1001_{\text{two}} =$	9		$11110_{\text{two}} =$	30
$101_{\text{two}} =$	5		$11011_{\text{two}} =$	27
$1110_{\text{two}} =$	14		$111001_{\text{two}} =$	57

Base Two	Base Ten		Base Two	Base Ten
$101_{\text{two}} =$	5		$1001_{\text{two}} =$	9
$111_{\text{two}} =$	7		$10110_{\text{two}} =$	22
$11_{\text{two}} =$	3		$1111_{\text{two}} =$	15
$100_{\text{two}} =$	4		$101_{\text{two}} =$	5
$10011_{\text{two}} =$	19		$110011_{\text{two}} =$	51

Checking the examples of subtraction, multiplication, and incomplete division in base two are left as exercises.

Subtraction

1111_{two}	10110_{two}	101101_{two}
101_{two}	1011_{two}	10110_{two}
1010_{two}	1011_{two}	10111_{two}

Multiplication

$$1111_{two}$$
$$101_{two}$$
$$\overline{1111_{two}}$$
$$1111_{two}$$
$$\overline{1001011_{two}}$$

$$10110_{two}$$
$$1011_{two}$$
$$\overline{10110_{two}}$$
$$10110_{two}$$
$$10110_{two}$$
$$\overline{11110010_{two}}$$

$$11011_{two}$$
$$11000_{two}$$
$$\overline{11011_{two}}$$
$$11011_{two}$$
$$\overline{1010001000_{two}}$$

Incomplete Division

(a) $101_{two} \overline{) 1111_{two}}$ $11_{two} = q$
$$101_{two}$$
$$\overline{101_{two}}$$
$$101_{two}$$
$$0 = r$$

(b) $1101_{two} \overline{) 101110111_{two}}$ $11100_{two} = q$
$$1101_{two}$$
$$\overline{10100_{two}}$$
$$1101_{two}$$
$$\overline{1111_{two}}$$
$$1101_{two}$$
$$\overline{1011_{two}} = r$$

EXERCISES

1. Check part (a) in the example of incomplete division in base eight in the following two ways. (a) Using base eight notation, find the product of the divisor and quotient, add the remainder, and compare with the dividend. (b) Change the divisor and dividend to base ten notation, perform the long division, and compare the quotient and remainder in base ten with that in base eight.

2. Check part (b) in the example of incomplete division in base eight in the following two ways. (a) Using base eight notation, find the product of the divisor and quotient, add the remainder, and compare with the dividend. (b) Change the divisor and dividend to base ten notation, perform the long division, and compare the quotient and remainder in base ten with that in base eight.

3. Check each example of subtraction in the binary system in the following two ways. (a) Add the subtrahend to the difference in base two. (b) Change the numbers to base ten, subtract, and compare answers.

4. Check each example of multiplication in the binary system by two different methods.

5. Check part (a) in the example of incomplete division in the binary system by two different methods.

6. Check part (b) in the example of incomplete division in the binary system by two different methods.

7. Find the following sums by using base two notation. Check your results by using base ten notation.

   (a) 1101_{two}
       $\underline{100_{two}}$

   (b) 1100_{two}
       1111_{two}
       $\underline{1011_{two}}$

   (c) 11111_{two}
       1001_{two}
       $\underline{1111_{two}}$

8. Find the following differences by using base two notation. Check your results by using base ten notation.

   (a) 1101_{two}
       $\underline{11_{two}}$

   (b) 11010_{two}
       $\underline{1111_{two}}$

   (c) 101100_{two}
       $\underline{10011_{two}}$

9. Find the following products by using base two notation. Check your results by using base ten notation.

   (a) 1101_{two}
       $\underline{11_{two}}$

   (b) 11010_{two}
       $\underline{1010_{two}}$

   (c) 101101_{two}
       $\underline{11100_{two}}$

10. Find the following sums in base two.

    (a) 1111_{two}
        101_{two}
        110_{two}
        $\underline{1101_{two}}$

    (b) 1101_{two}
        100_{two}
        1100_{two}
        $\underline{1111_{two}}$

    (c) 11011_{two}
        1101_{two}
        110_{two}
        $\underline{1011_{two}}$

11. Find the following products in base two.

    (a) 1101_{two}
        $\underline{101_{two}}$

    (b) 110111_{two}
        $\underline{11101_{two}}$

    (c) 101011_{two}
        $\underline{1110_{two}}$

12. Find the following sums using base eight notation. Check your results by using base ten notation.

    (a) 476_{eight}
        233_{eight}
        421_{eight}
        $\underline{765_{eight}}$

    (b) 254_{eight}
        377_{eight}
        35_{eight}
        $\underline{62_{eight}}$

    (c) 2345_{eight}
        1000_{eight}
        4010_{eight}
        $\underline{7650_{eight}}$

13. Find the following differences using base eight notation. Check your results by using base ten notation.

    (a) 6744_{eight}
        $\underline{3522_{eight}}$

    (b) 7354_{eight}
        $\underline{2716_{eight}}$

    (c) 7245_{eight}
        $\underline{4766_{eight}}$

14. Find the following products by using base eight notation. Check your results by using base ten notation.

    (a) 134_{eight}
        $\underline{21_{eight}}$

    (b) 354_{eight}
        $\underline{316_{eight}}$

    (c) 2361_{eight}
        $\underline{523_{eight}}$

15. Construct addition and multiplication tables for base six.

16. Perform the following additions in base six.   (See Exercise 15.)

(a) 213_{six}

   351_{six}

   424_{six}

(b) 512_{six}

   222_{six}

   345_{six}

(c) 1240_{six}

   3251_{six}

   4445_{six}

17. Perform the following multiplications in base six.   (See Exercise 15.)

(a) 321_{six}

   12_{six}

(b) 432_{six}

   211_{six}

(c) 324_{six}

   235_{six}

18. Use base ten notation to check your answers in Exercise 16.

19. Use base ten notation to check your answers in Exercise 17.

*20. Check the answers in Exercise 17 by dividing in base six notation.

Georg Cantor (1845–1918)

Georg Cantor was born at St. Petersburg, Russia, on March 3, 1845. His parents originally lived in Denmark but moved to St. Petersburg before Georg was born. However, Cantor is usually referred to as a German since he studied in Germany and spent most of his adult life teaching at Halle. He studied mathematics at Göttingen, Zurich, and at the University of Berlin, where he received his doctorate in 1867.

In his most famous work, *Megenlehre,* Cantor introduced his theory of sets and used the new theory to define and give an abstract development of numbers. He also defined different types of "infinity" and introduced into mathematics transfinite cardinal numbers and an associated transfinite arithmetic. The new field of mathematical research he created led to other new ideas and important theories in mathematics. His work also gave rise to the Russell and the Burali-Forti paradoxes.

Cantor's approach to mathematics accentuated the division between the formalists and the intuitionists, two schools of thought concerning the foundations of mathematics. The distinguished mathematician Leopold Kronecker (1823–1891), one of Cantor's former professors, attacked both Cantor and his new theories with such vehemence that the abuse is said to have contributed to Cantor's several nervous breakdowns. (Kronecker did not save all his scorn for his former pupil; after Lindemann had given his very ingenious proof that π was not an algebraic number, Kronecker is said to have asked Lindemann of what importance the proof could possibly be since irrational numbers did not exist.)

Cantor died in a mental hospital in 1918; it is unfortunate that he did not live to hear David Hilbert exclaim, "No one shall expel us from the paradise which Cantor has created for us."

3

Checks and Pseudo-checks

1. The Missing Digit
2. Divisibility Tests
3. Halve-double-sum Technique
4. Casting Out Nines

*The science of Pure Mathematics, in its modern develop-
ments, may claim to be the most original creation of the
human spirit.*

ALFRED NORTH WHITEHEAD

1. THE MISSING DIGIT

Take a pencil and paper, or ask a friend to do it, and write down any counting number (natural number). The use of at least a five-digit number, though not necessary, makes the following seem more significant. For example, consider the six-digit number 983,264. Now multiply the number by 9.

Multiply: 983,264
                      9
Product   8,849,376

Do not be too concerned if you make a mistake (or if your friend does); you will find out soon enough. Next, circle one of the digits in the product:

$$8, 8\ 4\ 9,\ 3\ \textcircled{7}\ 6$$

Now, *add in any order* the remaining *uncircled digits*.

Add: 8
            8
            4
            9
            3
            6
Sum   38

Add the digits in the resulting sum.

Add: 3
            8
Sum   11

42

Repeat the process of adding digits in the resulting sums until a one-digit number is obtained.

Add: 1
             1
Sum   2

Take the final sum and subtract it from 9.

Subtract: 9
                 2
Difference   ⑦

Did you get the "discarded" digit? If you try this on a friend, he will probably be amazed if you tell him what digit he discarded by having no more information than the digits in the product, except the discarded one. However, do not make any bets on your acumen until you have the answers to the following questions.

---

1. If no mistake is made, does the procedure always produce the discarded digit?
2. If so, why does it?
3. If not, when does it not?

Questions

By trying various examples, you should be able to conjecture intelligent answers to the previous three questions. Of course, it is another thing to *prove* your conjectures are correct. There are two things we should observe. (1) *If* the procedure is always valid and *if* a mistake is not made in addition or subtraction, then a disagreement in answers implies that an error was made in the multiplication. (2) To prove that it does not always produce the discarded digit, we need only to produce one counter-example (that is, one number for which it does not work).

If you prefer not to subtract your final one-digit sum from 9, then multiply it by 8.

Multiply: 2
                 8
Product   16

Add the digits in the product and, if necessary, keep adding the digits in the resulting sums until a one-digit number is obtained.

$Add:$ 1

$\quad\quad\quad\underline{6}$

Sum ⑦

Again, you get the discarded digit! But does this always work?

To find whether or not the last procedure invariably gives the same digit as subtracting the final one-digit sum from 9 is not a difficult task. One way to discover if it does is just to do the computations for each of the nine one-digit numbers that can be obtained. For example, if we select 6, then 9 subtract 6 is ③; furthermore, 8 times 6 is 48 and the sum of 4 and 8 is 12, and the sum of 1 and 2 is ③. We have proved in two cases that the digits are the same; the student will be asked in the exercise set to verify each of the other seven cases.

If we conjectured that "yes" was the answer to Question 1, then we could *not prove* the conjecture by using cases since there is not a finite number of counting numbers. In mathematics, sets with infinitely many elements are generally more interesting than finite sets since it is generally more challenging to answer questions about the elements in an infinite set. However, the student should be able to answer Question 1 correctly after working the first ten exercises in the following exercise set.

EXERCISES

1. Find the product 9×879, circle a "1" in the product, and determine if the procedure described in this section yields the discarded digit.

2. Find the product $9 \times 2{,}478$, circle a "2" in the product, and determine if the procedure described in this section yields the discarded digit.

3. Find the product $9 \times 46{,}467$, circle a "3" in the product, and determine if the procedure described in this section yields the discarded digit.

4. Find the product $9 \times 23{,}326$, circle a "4" in the product, and determine if the procedure described in this section yields the discarded digit.

5. Find the product $9 \times 41{,}273$, circle a "5" in the product and determine if the procedure described in this section yields the discarded digit.

6. Find the product $9 \times 28{,}183$, circle a "6" in the product, and determine if the procedure described in this section yields the discarded digit.

7. Find the product $9 \times 21{,}525$, circle a "7" in the product, and determine if the procedure described in this section yields the discarded digit.

8. Find the product $9 \times 81{,}232$, circle an "8" in the product, and determine if the procedure described in this section yields the discarded digit.

9. Find the product 9 × 32,339, circle a "9" in the product, and determine if the procedure described in this section yields the discarded digit.

10. Find the product 9 × 84,230, circle a "0" in the product, and determine if the procedure described in this section yields the discarded digit.

11. Answer Question 1 on page 43.

12. Let x be any counting number from 1 through 9. For each x, find the product of 8 times the difference $9 - x$. Then, add the digits in the resulting product and, if necessary, keep adding the digits in the resulting sums until a one-digit number is obtained. In each case, is the final number x?

2. DIVISIBILITY TESTS

We say that 2 is a *factor* of 6, 6 is a *multiple* of 2, or 6 is *divisible* by 2. Each assertion means there exists an *integer* such that 2 times the integer is 6; in this case, the integer is 3. In general, an integer a is said to be a *factor* of an integer b if and only if there is an integer x such that $ax = b$. Furthermore, b is called a *multiple* of a if and only if a is a factor of b. Notice that 6 has four positive factors, namely, 1, 2, 3, and 6. For any positive integer a, both 1 and a are factors of a since $a \times 1 = 1 \times a = a$. In other words, every positive integer has itself and 1 as factors. Any positive integer *other than* 1 which has *only* itself and 1 as positive factors is called a *prime number*. For example, 2, 3, 5, 7, 11, 13, 17, 19, 23, and 29 are the first ten prime numbers. As we shall discover later, there are many interesting and important problems concerning the (infinite) set of prime numbers. For example, to prove there is no last prime number is an interesting and challenging problem that we shall deal with later.

Numbers such as 4, 10, 18, 256, 452, and 864 that have 2 as a common factor are called *even* integers; integers that are not even are called *odd* integers. It is a rather well-known fact that *an integer has 2 as a factor if and only if the last digit in the positional notation for the number is* 0, 2, 4, 6, or 8. This is called a *divisibility test* for 2.

factor

multiple

prime number

divisibility test

---

1. How do you prove that any integer with last digit 0, 2, 4, 6, or 8 has 2 as a factor?

2. How do you prove that any integer with 2 as a factor has 0, 2, 4, 6, or 8 as its last digit?

Questions

We shall answer the two preceding questions when we prove the divisibility test for 2 later in the section. However, it is important that you understand the difference between them. Question 1 refers

45

to the "if" part of the divisibility test for 2, and Question 2 refers to the "only if" part of the test.

It is also a familiar fact that *a number has* 5 *as a factor if and only if the last digit in the number is either* 0 *or* 5. For example, 335 and 420 have 5 as a factor, but 343 does not have 5 as a factor. Another familiar divisibility test is that *a number has* 10 *as a factor if and only if its last digit is* 0. Now, let us turn our attention to some other divisibility tests.

Consider the number 378,425,664. From the three divisibility tests already stated, we know that 378,425,664 has 2 as a factor but does not have 5 or 10 as factors. But which of the numbers 3, 4, 6, 8, 9, 11, 12, 15, 18, and 40, for example, are factors of 378,425,664? Of course, one way to determine if the given number is divisible by, say, 18 is to use "long division." The computation below verifies that 378,425,664 does indeed have 18 as a factor. (You should use long division to find if 12 is a factor of the given number. Is it?)

$$
\begin{array}{r}
21{,}023{,}648 \\
18\overline{)378{,}425{,}664} \\
\underline{36} \\
18 \\
\underline{18} \\
42 \\
\underline{36} \\
65 \\
\underline{54} \\
116 \\
\underline{108} \\
86 \\
\underline{72} \\
144 \\
\underline{144} \\
0
\end{array}
$$

Let us find the sum of all the digits in the number 378,425,664.

$$
\begin{array}{rr}
Add\text{:} & 3 \\
 & 7 \\
 & 8 \\
 & 4 \\
 & 2 \\
 & 5 \\
 & 6 \\
 & 6 \\
 & \underline{4} \\
Sum & 45
\end{array}
$$

Using both the digits and the sum of the digits in the given number, we can deduce several important facts using other divisibility tests.

1. Since 45, the sum of the digits in the number, has 9 as a factor, the original number is divisible by 9. (Using long division, verify that the given number is divisible by 9.) In general, *an integer is divisible by 9 if and only if the sum of the digits is divisible by 9.*
2. Since the resulting sum has 3 as a factor, the original number is divisible by 3. In general, *an integer is divisible by 3 if and only if the sum of the digits is divisible by 3.*
3. Since the last *two* digits, 64, of the given number represent a number divisible by 4, the given number is divisible by 4. (Note: $64 \div 4 = 16$.) In general, *an integer is divisible by 4 if and only if the number represented by the digits in the tens' and units' places is divisible by* 4.
4. Since the last *three* digits, 664, of the given number represent a number divisible by 8, the given number is divisible by 8. (Note: $664 \div 8 = 83$.) In general, *an integer is divisible by 8 if and only if the number represented by the digits in the hundreds', tens', and units' positions is divisible by* 8.
5. Since the given number is divisible by 2 and 9, it is divisible by 18. In general, *an integer is divisible by 18 if and only if it is divisible by 2 and 9.*
6. Since the given number is divisible by 2 and 3, it is divisible by 6. In general, *an integer is divisible by 6 if and only if it is divisible by 2 and 3.*
7. Since the given number is divisible by 3 and 4, it is divisible by 12. In general, *an integer is divisible by 12 if and only if it is divisible by 3 and 4.*
8. Consider the digits in the odd-numbered positions from the right in the given number: **378,425,664.** Find their sum.

Add:	3
	8
	2
	6
	4
Sum	23

Consider the digits in the even-numbered positions from the right: **378,425,664.** Find their sum.

Add:	7
	4
	5
	6
Sum	22

Since the difference of the two sums $(23 - 22 = 1)$ does not have 11 as a factor, the given number does not have 11 as a factor. If the difference has 11 as a factor, the number would have 11 as a factor. (*Note:* If the difference is 0, the given number has 11 as a factor.) In general, *an integer is divisible by* 11 *if and only if the difference of the sum of the digits in the odd-numbered positions* (from the right) *and the sum of the digits in the even-numbered positions is divisible by* 11.

9. Since the given number does not have 5 as a factor, it cannot have any multiple of 5, such as 15 or 40, as a factor.

We know that 534,279 is equal to

$$5(10^5) + 3(10^4) + 4(10^3) + 2(10^2) + 7(10) + 9$$

where $10^2 = 10 \times 10$, $10^3 = 10 \times 10 \times 10$, $10^4 = 10 \times 10 \times 10 \times 10$, and $10^5 = 10 \times 10 \times 10 \times 10 \times 10$. In general, if *abc,def* is a six-digit number, then

$$abc,def = a(10^5) + b(10^4) + c(10^3) + d(10^2) + e(10) + f$$

Let us now restate each divisibility test and prove that each is valid for a six-digit number *abc,def*. It should be obvious that the basic features of the proof would not change for an *n*-digit number; the proof just becomes rather tedious to write out.

Test 1. A natural number is divisible by 2 if and only if the units' position is 0, 2, 4, 6, or 8.

Example 1. 238 is divisible by 2 and 769 is not divisible by 2.

Proof of Test 1: (We prove two theorems. First, we prove if the last digit is 0, 2, 4, 6, or 8 then it has 2 as a factor; next, we prove if a number has 2 as a factor then its last digit is 0, 2, 4, 6, or 8.)

PART 1. Let *abc,def* be a six-digit number where *f* is 0, 2, 4, 6, or 8. As a consequence of the positional notation,

$$abc,def = 10^5 a + 10^4 b + 10^3 c + 10^2 d + 10e + f$$

Hence,

$$abc,def = 10(10)^4 a + 10(10)^3 b + 10(10)^2 c + 10(10)d + 10e + f$$
$$= 2[5(10)^4 a + 5(10)^3 b + 5(10)^2 c + 5(10)d + 5e] + f$$

Thus, *abc,def* is the sum of the two numbers

$$2[5(10)^4 a + 5(10)^3 b + 5(10)^2 c + 5(10)d + 5e] \text{ and } f$$

The first number obviously has 2 as a factor. Since *f* is 0, 2, 4, 6, or 8, *f* has 2 as a factor. We recall that if two numbers have a factor in common then so does their sum. Hence, 2 is a factor of the given number abc,def.

PART 2. Assume 2 is a factor of a six-digit number abc,def. From Part 1, we have that

$$f = abc,def - 2[5(10)^4 a + 5(10)^3 b + 5(10)^2 c + 5(10)d + 5e]$$

Since 2 is a factor of abc,def and since 2 is a factor of

$$2[5(10)^4 a + 5(10)^3 b + 5(10)^2 c + 5(10)d + 5e]$$

we know that 2 is a factor of the difference of the two numbers; that is, 2 is a factor of f. Since f must be one of 0, 1, 2, 3, 4, 5, 6, 7, 8, or 9 and since 2 is a factor of only 0, 2, 4, 6, or 8, it follows that f must be one of 0, 2, 4, 6, or 8.

Test 2. A natural number is divisible by 3 if and only if the sum of the digits is divisible by 3.

Example 2. 472,641 is divisible by 3 since $4 + 7 + 2 + 6 + 4 + 1 = 24$ is divisible by 3. The number 64,534 is not divisible by 3 since the sum, 22, of its digits is not divisible by 3.

Proof of Test 2:

PART 1. Let abc,def be a six-digit number and assume 3 is a factor of $a + b + c + d + e + f$. (We need to prove that 3 is a factor of abc,def.) We know that

$$abc,def = 10^5 a + 10^4 b + 10^3 c + 10^2 d + 10e + f$$

Thus,

$$
\begin{aligned}
abc,def &= 100{,}000a + 10{,}000b + 1{,}000c + 100d + 10e + f \\
&= (99{,}999 + 1)a + (9{,}999 + 1)b + (999 + 1)c \\
&\qquad\qquad + (99 + 1)d + (9 + 1)e + f \\
&= (99{,}999a + 9{,}999b + 999c + 99d + 9e) \\
&\qquad\qquad + (a + b + c + d + e + f) \\
&= 3(33{,}333a + 3{,}333b + 333c + 33d + 3e) \\
&\qquad\qquad + (a + b + c + d + e + f)
\end{aligned}
$$

Since 3 is a factor of both

$$(a + b + c + d + e + f) \text{ and } 3(33{,}333a + 3{,}333b + 333c + 33d + 3e)$$

it is a factor of the sum of the two numbers; that is, 3 is a factor of abc,def.

PART 2. Left as an exercise.

Test 3. A natural number greater than ten is divisible by 4 if and only if the number represented by the digits in the tens' and units' places is divisible by 4.

Example 3. 378,569,532 is divisible by 4 since 32 is divisible by 4. We also conclude that 2,576,426 is not divisible by 4 since 26 is not divisible by 4.

Proof of Test 3:
PART 1. Let abc,def be a six-digit number and assume ef is divisible by 4. Since

$$abc,def = 10^5a + 10^4b + 10^3c + 10^2d + 10e + f$$

it follows that

$$abc,def = (100{,}000a + 10{,}000b + 1{,}000c + 100d) + (10e + f)$$
$$= 4(25{,}000a + 2{,}500b + 250c + 25d) + (10e + f)$$

Since 4 is a factor of ef, 4 is a factor of $(10e + f)$. Consequently, 4 is a factor of the sum

$$4(25{,}000a + 2{,}500b + 250c + 25d) + (10e + f)$$

that is, 4 is a factor of abc,def.
PART 2. Left as an exercise.

Test 4. A natural number is divisible by 5 if and only if the digit in the units position is 0 or 5.

Proof of Test 4: Left as an exercise.

Test 5. A natural number is divisible by 6 if and only if the integer is even and the sum of the digits is divisible by 3.

Proof of Test 5: Left as an exercise.

Test 6. A natural number greater than one hundred is divisible by 8 if and only if the number represented by the digits in the hundreds', tens', and units' positions is divisible by 8.

Proof of Test 6: Left as an exercise.

Test 7. A natural number is divisible by 9 if and only if the sum of the digits is divisible by 9.

Proof of Test 7: Left as an exercise.

Test 8. A natural number is divisible by 10 if and only if the digit in the units' position is 0.

Proof of Test 8: Left as an exercise.

Test 9.   A natural number is divisible by 11 if and only if the difference of the sum of the digits in the odd-numbered positions (from the right) and the sum of the digits in the even-numbered positions is divisible by 11.

Example 4.   92,818 is divisible by 11 since $(8+8+9)-(1+2)=22$ is divisible by 11. We also conclude that 867,534,281 is not divisible by 11 since

$$(1+2+3+7+8)-(8+4+5+6)=-2$$

does not have 11 as a factor.

Proof of Test 9:

PART 1.   Let *abc,def* be a six-digit number and assume that $(b+d+f)-(a+c+e)$ has 11 as a factor. Since

$$abc,def = 10^5 a + 10^4 b + 10^3 c + 10^2 d + 10e + f$$

it follows that

$$
\begin{aligned}
abc,def &= 100{,}000a + 10{,}000b + 1000c + 100d + 10e + f \\
&= (100{,}001-1)a + (9{,}999+1)b + (1001-1)c \\
&\qquad\qquad + (99+1)d + (11-1)e + f \\
&= 100{,}001a + 9999b + 1001c + 99d + 11e \\
&\qquad\qquad\qquad - a + b - c + d - e + f \\
&= 11(9091a + 909b + 91c + 9d + e) \\
&\qquad\qquad + [(b+d+f)-(a+c+e)]
\end{aligned}
$$

Since the difference $(b+d+f)-(a+c+e)$ has 11 as a factor and since $11(9091a + 909b + 91c + 9d + e)$ has 11 as a factor, the sum, which is the given number *abc,def*, has 11 as a factor.

PART 2.   Left as an exercise.

The divisibility test for 9 provides a means to explain the procedure discussed in Section 1 to find "the missing digit." We know that the product of the six-digit number 983,264 and 9 is a multiple of 9; that is, 8,849,376 has 9 as a factor. Since the number has 9 as a factor, the sum of the digits must be divisible by 9. Recall that we discarded the digit 7 and then we obtained a sum of 38. It should be clear that the number discarded must be the difference from the sum 38 and the next multiple of 9, which is 45. Thus, the only time the technique is not foolproof is when the sum is a multiple of 9; in this case, we do not know whether a 0 or 9 was discarded. Since the sum of the digits can never be zero, the procedure only fails in one case. Finally, since 38 is divisible by 9 if and only if $3+8=11$ is divisible by 9 and if and only if $1+1=2$ is divisible by 9, the process involved to find the missing digit can be carried down to a one-digit number; however, it is not essential in order to determine the discarded digit.

Although it is not as well known, there is a rather interesting, if not very efficient, divisibility test for 7. It is as follows. Take an n-digit number and remove the digit in the units' position. Double the number removed from the units' position and subtract it from the remaining $(n-1)$-digit number. Continue the process until a two-digit number is obtained. The original number is divisible by 7 if and only if the final two-digit number is divisible by 7. Consider the following examples.

EXAMPLE 1. 4 6 8 ③
             6
          ‾‾‾‾‾‾‾‾‾
          4 6 ②
            4
          ‾‾‾‾‾
          4 2

EXAMPLE 2. 6 1 6 ⑦
               1 4
          ‾‾‾‾‾‾‾‾‾
          6 0 ②
              4
          ‾‾‾‾‾
          5 6

Since 42 has 7 as a factor, 4,683 has 7 as a factor.

Since 56 has 7 as a factor, 6,167 has 7 as a factor.

EXAMPLE 3. 9 2 6 4 ⑤
                 1 0
          ‾‾‾‾‾‾‾‾‾‾‾‾
          9 2 5 ④
              8
          ‾‾‾‾‾‾‾
          9 1 ⑦
          1 4
          ‾‾‾‾‾
          7 7

EXAMPLE 4. 8 2 4 3 ⑥
                 1 2
          ‾‾‾‾‾‾‾‾‾‾‾‾
          8 2 3 ①
              2
          ‾‾‾‾‾‾‾
          8 2 ①
            2
          ‾‾‾‾‾
          8 0

Since 77 has 7 as a factor, 92,645 has 7 as a factor.

Since 80 does not have 7 as a factor, 82,436 does not have 7 as a factor.

The proof of the divisibility test for 7 is quite simple if we do not try the "natural" approach of considering the number with regard to its positional notation. Also, a proof is easier to discover if we first try to prove that if the resulting two-digit number is divisible by 7 then the original n-digit number is divisible by 7.

Suppose the resulting two-digit number is N and that it is divisible by 7. (In Example 1, $N = 42$.) If x is any one-digit number, determine the sum $N + 2x$. (In Example 1, $x = 2$ and $N + 2x = 42 + 4 = 46$.) Now consider the sum

$$(N + 2x)10 + x$$

[In Example 1, $(N + 2x)10 + x = 460 + 2 = 462$.] Since N has 7 as a factor,

$$(N + 2x)10 + x = 10N + 21x$$

has 7 as a factor. Now, the process can be repeated until we obtain the original n-digit number; furthermore, it has 7 as a factor.

EXERCISES

1. (a) If a number N has 3 and 4 as factors, then it has 12 as a factor. If a number M has 3 and 6 as factors, does M necessarily have 18 as a factor? Discuss.
   (b) State a divisibility test for 40. (No proof of the validity is required.)
2. Which of 2, 3, 4, 5, 6, 8, 9, 10, 11, 15, 18, and 40 are factors of 1,141,140?
3. Which of 2, 3, 4, 5, 6, 8, 9, 10, 11, 15, 18, and 40 are factors of 1,022,380?
4. Which of 2, 3, 4, 5, 6, 8, 9, 10, 11, 15, 18, and 40 are factors of 55,074,492?
5. Which of 2, 3, 4, 5, 6, 8, 9, 10, 11, 15, 18, and 40 are factors of 805,950,981?
6. Which of 2, 3, 4, 5, 6, 8, 9, 10, 11, 15, 18, and 40 are factors of 2,968,985,017?
7. Which of 2, 3, 4, 5, 6, 8, 9, 10, 11, 15, 18, and 40 are factors of 2,010,360?
8. Which of 2, 3, 4, 5, 6, 8, 9, 10, 11, 12, 15, 18, and 40 are factors of 61,843,320?
9. Which of 2, 3, 4, 5, 6, 8, 9, 10, 11, 12, 15, 18, and 40 are factors of 737,880?
10. Which of 2, 3, 4, 5, 6, 8, 9, 10, 11, 12, 15, 18, and 40 are factors of 4,820,655,852?
11. Which of 2, 3, 4, 5, 6, 8, 9, 10, 11, 12, 15, 18, and 40 are factors of 4,005,830,664?
12. Which of 2, 3, 4, 5, 6, 8, 9, 10, 11, 12, 15, 18, and 40 are factors of 163,179,720?
13. Complete the proof of Test 2.
14. Complete the proof of Test 3.
15. Prove Test 4.
16. Prove Test 5.
17. Prove Test 6.
18. Prove Test 7.
19. Prove Test 8.
20. Complete the proof of Test 9.
21. (a) Is 91 a factor of 383,838?
    (b) Is 91 a factor of 575,757?

(c) Is 91 a factor of any six-digit number of the form *aba,bab?* Verify your answer.

*22. Let *abc,def* be a six-digit number in base eight where 0, 1, 2, 3, 4, 5, 6, and 7 are the numerals used. State and prove your own divisibility tests for 2, 7, and 10_{eight}.

*23. Prove in base three that a six-digit number is divisible by two if and only if the sum of the digits is divisible by two.

*24. In the divisibility test for 7, prove that if the *n*-digit number has 7 as a factor, then the resulting two-digit number has 7 as a factor. (*Hint:* Prove that if the two-digit number does not have 7 as a factor then the *n*-digit number does not have 7 as a factor.)

3. HALVE-DOUBLE-SUM TECHNIQUE

We have discussed the standard algorithm for finding the product of two natural numbers. What we mean by "standard" is the following procedure.

$$
\begin{array}{rr}
Multiply: & 128 \\
& \underline{46} \\
& 768 \\
& \underline{512} \\
Product & 5{,}888
\end{array}
$$

Of course, this is not the only way to find the product 46×128. Let us discuss a method to multiply counting numbers that requires primarily only a knowledge of how to halve a number (divide by two), how to double a number (multiply by two), and how to add. More specifically, it does not require that we know such products as 6×8.

To find the product 46×128, we proceed as follows:

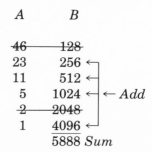

$$
\begin{array}{cc}
A & B \\
\cancel{46} & \cancel{128} \\
23 & 256 \\
11 & 512 \\
5 & 1024 \quad \leftarrow Add \\
\cancel{2} & \cancel{2048} \\
1 & 4096 \\
& \overline{5888}\ Sum
\end{array}
$$

Explanation of the Algorithm. (1) Write 46 in column *A* and write below it one-half of 46, namely 23. (2) Since 23 is an odd number, subtract 1 from 23 to obtain the even number 22; now write one-half of 22 underneath 23. (3) Continue writing in column A either one-half of one less than the preceding number if it is an odd number or one-half the preceding number if it is an even number until the quotient 1 is obtained. (4) Write 128 at the top of column B. Then, multiply 128 by 2 and write the product, 256, underneath 128. (5) Continue the doubling of numbers in column B until there are as many numbers in this column as there are in column A. (6) Find the sum of all numbers in column B which are opposite the odd numbers in column A; the sum is the product 46×128. Remarkable?

Example 1. Find the product 37×421 by the halve-double-sum technique.

Solution:

A	B
37	421
~~18~~	~~842~~
9	1,684
~~4~~	~~3,368~~
~~2~~	~~6,736~~
1	13,472
Product	15,577

In order to understand why the halve-double-sum technique produces the product of two numbers, consider the example where we found the product 46×128. Since any odd number in column A does not have 2 as a factor, a remainder of 1 is obtained in the incomplete division of the number by 2. For the odd numbers in column A, we add the corresponding numbers in column B. Furthermore, we do not add numbers in column B that are opposite even numbers in column A; these are the cases where the remainder is zero. Observe that

$$46 = 0 + 2 + 2^2 + 2^3 + 0(2^4) + 2^5$$

Thus, $46 \times 128 = [0 + 2 + 2^2 + 2^3 + 0(2^4) + 2^5] \times 128$
$$= 2(128) + 2^2(128) + 2^3(128) + 2^5(128)$$
$$= 256 + 512 + 1,024 + 4,096$$
$$= 5,888$$

Obviously, finding the product of two numbers by both the standard algorithm and the halve-double-sum would serve as a check for multiplication. To obtain the same *wrong* answer by both techniques would be quite unusual, though not impossible.

EXERCISES

1. Use the halve-double-sum method to find the product 21×467.
2. Use the halve-double-sum method to find the product 29×122.
3. Use the halve-double-sum method to find the product 48×89.
4. Use the halve-double-sum method to find the product 32×47.
5. Use the halve-double-sum method to find the product 31×402.
6. Check your answers to Exercises 1 through 5 by the standard algorithm for multiplying numbers.
7. Consider two numbers such as 67 and 23. In column *A*, write the quotient (22) and the remainder (1) in the long division of 67 by 3. Underneath, write the quotient and remainder of 22 divided by 3; continue this process until a quotient of zero is obtained. In column *B*, write 23 at the top and thereafter write the product of 3 times the preceding number. (See Example 1 below.) Multiply corresponding remainders in column *A* times the numbers in column *B* and then find their sum.

EXAMPLE 1

A	*B*		
22 *R* 1	$\times$ 23	=	23
7 *R* 1	$\times$ 69	=	69
2 *R* 1	$\times$ 207	=	207
0 *R* 2	$\times$ 621	=	1,242
	Sum		1.541
	(67×23)		

EXAMPLE 2

A	*B*		
9 *R* 2	$\times$ 31	=	62
3 *R* 0	$\times$ 93	=	0
1 *R* 0	$\times$ 279	=	0
0 *R* 1	$\times$ 837	=	837
	Sum		899
	(29×31)		

Is the final sum the product of the two numbers given in each example?
8. Use the technique described in Exercise 7 to find the following products.
    (a) 29×41　　(b) 38×75　　(c) 42×87
9. Use the technique described in Exercise 7 to find the following products.
    (a) 28×421　　(b) 83×279　　(c) 66×95
10. (a) In Exercise 7, replace "3" by "4" and use the resulting procedure to find the product 67×23. (b) Use the procedure described in part (a) to find the product 29×31.

4. CASTING OUT NINES

Now, let us consider a procedure to check the operation of subtraction for two counting numbers.

Minuend	$376,248 \xrightarrow{+} 30 \xrightarrow{+} \textcircled{3}$	
Subtrahend	$138,246 \xrightarrow{+} 24 \xrightarrow{+} 6$	$\left.\right\}$ *Sum:* $12 \xrightarrow{+} \textcircled{3}$
Difference	$237,822 \xrightarrow{+} 24 \xrightarrow{+} 6$	

Explanation of the Procedure. After subtracting two given numbers, add the digits in the minuend (top number), add the digits in the subtrahend (second number from the top), and add the digits in the difference (the answer). Repeat the process in the resulting sums until one-digit numbers are obtained. Then, add the resulting numbers corresponding to the subtrahend and the difference; in the example, the sum is 12. If the sum is not a one-digit number, add the digits in the resulting sums until a one-digit number is obtained. The final number will be the same as the digit corresponding to the minuend *if* the subtraction is correct. In the example, each number is 3.

A check similar to that for subtraction can be given for both addition and multiplication. To exhibit the procedure consider the following examples.

Add:

$$368 \xrightarrow{+} 17 \xrightarrow{\quad+\quad} 8$$
$$429 \xrightarrow{+} 15 \xrightarrow{\quad+\quad} 6$$
$$766 \xrightarrow{+} 19 \xrightarrow{+} 10 \xrightarrow{+} 1$$
$$\underline{321 \xrightarrow{\qquad+\qquad} 6}$$

Sum: $\quad 1884 \xrightarrow{+} 21 \xrightarrow{+} ③ \qquad 21 \xrightarrow{+} ③$

It should be clear that the checking technique for subtraction is used to show that the *sum* of the subtrahend and difference is the minuend.

Multiply:

$$274 \xrightarrow{+} 13 \xrightarrow{+} 4$$
$$\underline{87} \xrightarrow{+} 15 \xrightarrow{+} 6$$
$$1918 \qquad Product: 24 \xrightarrow{+} ⑥$$
$$\underline{2192}$$

Product: $\quad 23,838 \xrightarrow{+} 24 \xrightarrow{+} ⑥$

The preceding techniques are not absolute checks for addition, subtraction, or multiplication. If the results do not agree, then a mistake has been made in computation. Although it is quite unlikely for the final numbers to agree when a mistake in computation has been made, it should be obvious that such a situation is possible. For example, in the addition problem, if the wrong answer 1,974 had been obtained, then

$$1,974 \xrightarrow{+} 21 \xrightarrow{+} ③$$

and the final one-digit numbers would be the same. Since each technique is not an absolute check, it would be more appropriate to call each a *pseudo-check,* but it is not generally done.

Let us consider another problem concerning the sum of a set of numbers where the numbers have a certain specified property. Take your pencil and write in a vertical column any two counting numbers. For example, select 12 and 7. Now, write eight more numbers in the column so that each number after the first two is the sum of the two immediately preceding numbers in the column.

Add:	12
	7
	19
	26
	45
	71
	116 — *seventh number*
	187
	303
	490
Sum	1,276

Add the column of ten numbers. Provided no mistake is made, the sum is the same as 11 times the seventh number from the top in the column.

Multiply:	116
	11
	116
	116
Product	1,276

Often, it is important to obtain the square of a given integer. For example, what is 25×25? The answer can be found by determining the product 20×30 and adding 25.

Multiply:	30		*Multiply:*	25
	20			25
	600			125
Add:	25			50
Product	625		*Product*	625

Since it is not too difficult to multiply mentally a couple of two-digit numbers each having last digit zero, it is significant that the square of any positive integer whose last digit is 5 is the sum of 25 and the product of the number 5 less than the given number and the number 5 more than the given number. As another example,

$$75 \times 75 = (70)(80) + 25 = 5{,}625$$

A verification of the technique follows directly from the well-known algebraic identity

$$x^2 - a^2 = (x - a)(x + a)$$

that is,
$$x^2 = (x - a)(x + a) + a^2$$

To square 55, let $x = 55$ and let $a = 5$. Then, we get

$$55^2 = (50)(60) + 25 = 3{,}025$$

Of course, a similar procedure could be used to square any positive integer. For example, to square 37, let $x = 37$ and, to obtain a number ending in zero, let $a = 3$. Thus,

$$37^2 = (34)(40) + 9 = 1{,}369$$

We conclude the section with a discussion of another problem concerning the squares of integers. Take any *odd* integer and square it. Now subtract 1 from the product. If the result is not divisible by 8, you have made a mistake in squaring the original number. Consider the following example.

Multiply:	237
	237
	1659
	711
	474
Product	56,169
Subtract:	1
Difference	56,168

Since 168 is divisible by 8, we conclude from the divisibility test for 8 that the number 56,168 is divisible by 8.

EXERCISES

1. Find each of the differences and check by the method discussed on page 56.
   (a) *Subtract:* 376,841
                241,382
   (b) *Subtract:* 468,528
                189,237

2. Find each of the differences and check by the method discussed on page 56.
   (a) *Subtract:* 387,684
                129,461
   (b) *Subtract:* 846,821,265
                23,148,237

3. Find each of the sums and check by the method discussed on page 57.

   (a) *Add:*   3,784
                2,561
                8,124
                3,211
                6,824

   (b) *Add:*   2,467
                3,145
                4,567
                9,423
                5,765

4. Find each of the sums and check by the method discussed on page 57.

   (a) *Add:*   2,765
                  384
                2,711
                4,289
                  312

   (b) *Add:*   2,381
                4,265
                  577
                3,648
                4,733

5. Find each of the products and check by the method discussed on page 57.

   (a) *Multiply:*   3,726
                       426

   (b) *Multiply:*   8,427
                       683

6. Find each of the products and check by the method discussed on page 57.

   (a) *Multiply:*   4,826
                       387

   (b) *Multiply:*   7,826
                     3,729

7. Write 38 and 15 in a vertical column with 38 at the top. Then, write eight more numbers in this column so that each number after the first two is the sum of the two immediately preceding numbers in the column. Find the sum and determine if it is 11 times the seventh number in the column.

8. Write 76 and 24 in a vertical column with 76 at the top. Then, write eight more numbers in this column so that each number after the first two is the sum of the two immediately preceding numbers in the column. Find the sum and determine if it is 11 times the seventh number in the column.

9. Find the square of each of the following numbers by the technique discussed on page 59.

   (a) 45   (b) 65   (c) 85   (d) 75   (e) 125

10. Find the square of each of the following numbers by the technique discussed on page 59.

    (a) 33   (b) 81   (c) 49   (d) 62   (e) 78

11. Let x be an odd integer. If $x - 1$ has 8 as a factor, can we conclude whether or not x is a perfect square?

12. From our check, could we determine whether or not 376,859,021,839 is the square of an odd integer?

13. From our check, could we determine whether or not 468,826,041,837 is the square of an odd integer?

14. From our check, could we determine whether or not 784,268,321,833 is a square of an odd integer?

60

15. The "checks" for addition, subtraction, and multiplication discussed on page 57 are sometimes called "casting out nines." Determine why such a name is appropriate.

16. Determine which numbers n less than 30 have the following property. The sum of all the positive factors of n is $2n$. (Remember that 1 and n are factors of n.)

***17.** Consider any sequence of ten numbers where the first two are arbitrary and every other number is the sum of the two preceding numbers in the sequence. Prove that the sum of the ten numbers is eleven times the seventh number in the sequence.

***18.** Prove if x is an odd integer, then $x^2 - 1$ has 8 as a factor.

Karl Weierstrass (1815–1897)

Karl Weierstrass was born at Ostenfelde, Germany, on October 31, 1815. Weierstrass, after some undistinguished academic adventures, decided to attend the Academy at Münster in 1839 to prepare for a career in secondary school teaching. He remained a secondary school teacher until the age of forty when he obtained an instructorship at the University of Berlin. In 1856 he became a professor of mathematics at the University of Berlin; while teaching there, he earned a reputation for being one of the greatest teachers of all time in advanced mathematics.

Just as Isaac Barrow exerted a profound influence on Newton, Cristof Gudermann (1798–1852), a Professor of Mathematics at Münster, was to have a profound influence on the mathematical growth of Weierstrass. It was Gudermann who inspired Weierstrass' important work on power series. Weierstrass, like Cauchy, was meticulous in his mathematical presentations and insisted on a rigorous development of mathematics; it was his approach that made it possible to abolish the inexplicable "infinitesimals" in calculus. He is often called the father of modern analysis. His original example of a continuous function that was not differentiable anywhere (that is, a continuous graph with no tangent line existing at any of its points) clearly emphasized the necessity for rigor to replace the intuitional and geometrical approach to analysis. He studied the concept of uniform convergence and indicated its importance in analysis. He also made fundamental contributions to the theory of complex variables, abelian functions, elliptic functions, and the calculus of variations.

4

The Expanding World of Numbers

1. Rational Numbers
2. Negative Numbers
3. Real Numbers
4. Decimal Notation
5. Complex Numbers (Optional)

Mathematics is the Queen of the Sciences and Number Theory is the Queen of Mathematics.

Carl Friedrich Gauss

1. RATIONAL NUMBERS

The advancement made by man to a stage where numbers were used for a purpose other than counting was a towering achievement and one which required a new synthesis of the number concept. Today, we are so accustomed to using numbers to measure lengths that we may lack sufficient appreciation for the great stride taken in developing this distinctive use of number.

The early geometers not only could bisect a line segment but they also could divide a given segment into any number of equal parts. We recall that if we divide a segment into 5 equal parts as in Figure 4.1, then the shaded segment represents 2 parts of 5 equal sub-

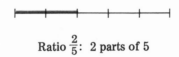

Ratio $\frac{2}{5}$: 2 parts of 5

FIGURE 4.1

divisions. If we let the entire segment represent our unit of length, then the shaded segment is said to have length *two-fifths*. One notation for the number is the fraction "²⁄₅" which, of course, uses a pair of natural numbers to express the *ratio* into which the segment is divided. The number denoted by the *fraction "m/n"* where *m* and *n* are natural numbers is called a positive *rational number*. The number *m* is called the *numerator* of the fraction and the number *n* is called the *denominator*.

rational number

numerator, denominator

The idea of using numbers to assign measure is connected with the idea of associating numbers with points on a line. Recall that the term *line* refers to a straight line which extends indefinitely in opposite directions. A *ray* is that part of a line which extends indefinitely in one direction from some point P on the line. The point P is called the *initial point,* or *origin,* of the ray. We begin to construct what we call a *number line* by marking off equal segments on a ray to the right of the origin as in Figure. 4.2. We associate 0 with the ori-

origin

number line

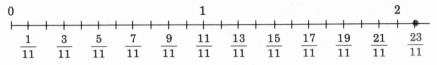

Rational Numbers

FIGURE 4.2

gin P. Next, we associate 1 with the endpoint of the first segment to the right of P and call the segment from 0 to 1 the *unit length.* The number 2 is paired with the endpoint of the second segment, the number 3 is paired with the endpoint of the third segment, etc.

unit length

To find the point on the number line associated with the rational number $^{23}/_{11}$, we divide each of the segments of unit length into eleven equal subdivisions. Next, we count twenty-three segments to the right of the origin and associate $^{23}/_{11}$ with the right-hand endpoint of the twenty-third such segment.

We call the number associated with a point on the number line the *coordinate* of the point. A point on the number line whose coordinate is a rational number is called a *rational point.* Associating rational numbers with points on a line often leads us to use the words *point* and *number* interchangeably. We shall show that there are points on the number line which are not rational points. In fact, we shall eventually discover that the nonrational points are far more numerous than the rational points.

coordinate

rational point

It should be obvious that if we divide the unit segment into twenty-two equal subdivisions then the point associated with $^8/_{22}$ is the same as the one associated with $^4/_{11}$. Notice that

$$\frac{8}{22} = \frac{2 \times 4}{2 \times 11} = \frac{4}{11}$$

In general,

$$\frac{m}{n} = \frac{pm}{pn}$$

where m, n, and p are natural numbers. We should also observe that $8 \times 11 = 22 \times 4$. From our interpretation of rationals and their association with points on a line, we are led to define equality between two rationals x/y and u/v in the following manner:

$$\frac{x}{y} = \frac{u}{v} \qquad \text{if and only if} \qquad xv = yu$$

From our present view of rational numbers, we see that "$^4/_1$" and "4" are two different notations for the same rational number; that is $^4/_1 = 4$. Furthermore, the set of natural numbers is a subset of the set of rational numbers.

Using the number line indicates why the sum of the rationals a/d and b/d is defined as follows:

$$\frac{a}{d} + \frac{b}{d} = \frac{a+b}{d}$$

We want the definition of addition to be consistent with our geometric interpretation of rational numbers. You will be asked to exhibit the consistency in an exercise.

For rationals $\frac{a}{b}$ and $\frac{c}{d}$ since $\frac{a}{b} = \frac{ad}{bd}$ and $\frac{c}{d} = \frac{bc}{bd}$, it follows that

$$\frac{a}{b} + \frac{c}{d} = \frac{ad}{bd} + \frac{bc}{bd} = \frac{ad+bc}{bd}$$

Thus, we have a technique to find the sum of any two given rational numbers. As a result of the closure properties of addition and multiplication for natural numbers, the rational number system is closed with respect to addition.

area   The method used to assign what is called the *area* of a region depends on the type of region involved. At present, we consider only the method used to assign area to rectangular regions. Later we shall find that many fascinating problems evolve when we consider how to assign area to more general regions in the plane.

If one side of a rectangle has length 3 units and the other side has length 2 units, then there are $3 \times 2 = 6$ square regions one unit on a side contained in the rectangle. We say that the area is 6 square units. (See Figure 4.3.) Similarly, if a rectangle has length

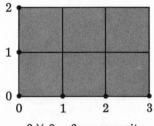

$3 \times 2 = 6$ square units

FIGURE 4.3

m units and width n units, then the area of the rectangle is $m \times n$ square units.

A square with each side having length one unit is our unit of measure for area; it is called a *square unit*. Let us divide one side of a unit square into 3 equal segments and the other side into 2 equal segments and then construct rectangles as in Figure 4.4. Since the

square unit

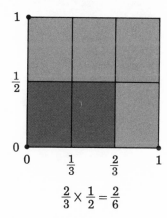

$$\frac{2}{3} \times \frac{1}{2} = \frac{2}{6}$$

FIGURE 4.4

shaded region in Figure 4.4 includes 2 of the 6 rectangular regions of equal size, by our interpretation of rational numbers the area of the shaded region would be $\frac{2}{6}$ of a square unit. As a natural extension of the preceding method to assign area, if the area of a rectangle with length $\frac{2}{3}$ and width $\frac{1}{2}$ is to be the product $\frac{2}{3} \times \frac{1}{2}$ then we should *define* multiplication so that the product will be $\frac{2}{6}$.

Using the above example and other similar examples, we are led to define the product of two rational numbers m/n and p/q as follows:

$$\frac{m}{n} \times \frac{p}{q} = \frac{mp}{nq}$$

It is an immediate consequence of this definition that the set of rational numbers is closed with respect to multiplication.

Even without the familiar applications of rational numbers, mathematicians would surely have invented rational numbers for quite other reasons. Rational numbers would have been created in an attempt to attain closure with respect to the operation of division. Closely related to the goal of having closure with respect to all the rational operations is the goal to have a number system sufficient to solve polynomial equations of the form $a_0x^n + a_1x^{n-1} + a_2x^{n-2} + \cdots + a_{n-1}x + a_n = 0$. A desire to obtain closure with

67

respect to the *algebraic operations* (addition, subtraction, multiplication, division, and taking roots) or the desire to have numbers to solve any polynomial equation would be sufficient motivation to create not only the positive rationals but also zero, the negative rationals, the irrational numbers, and the complex numbers. But, we shall have more to say about this later.

From the definition of division, $a/b \div c/d$ is the rational number x/y, if it exists, such that

$$\frac{c}{d} \times \frac{x}{y} = \frac{a}{b}$$

Our experience with multiplication of positive rationals clearly indicates that

$$\frac{c}{d} \times \frac{ad}{bc} = \frac{a}{b}$$

Thus,

$$\frac{a}{b} \div \frac{c}{d} = \frac{ad}{bc}$$

Notice that since $a/1 = a$ and $b/1 = b$, it follows that

$$a \div b = \frac{a}{1} \div \frac{b}{1}$$
$$= \frac{a}{1} \times \frac{1}{b}$$
$$= \frac{a}{b}$$

Hence, a/b is the quotient of a divided by b.

Proving, for rationals, the commutative and associative properties for both addition and multiplication and proving the distributive property are not very difficult, though a little tedious. Let us prove the commutative property of addition for rationals. It will be obvious that the proof depends on the additive and multiplicative properties for the natural numbers as well as the definitions of equality, addition, and multiplication for the rational numbers.

Theorem. (Commutative Property of Addition.) *For rational numbers a/b and c/d,*

$$\frac{a}{b} + \frac{c}{d} = \frac{c}{d} + \frac{a}{b}$$

Proof: $\dfrac{a}{b} + \dfrac{c}{d} = \dfrac{ad + bc}{bd}$ Definition of addition for rationals

$\qquad\qquad = \dfrac{da + cb}{db}$ Commutative property of multiplication for natural numbers

$\qquad\qquad = \dfrac{cb + da}{db}$ Commutative property of addition for natural numbers

$\qquad\qquad = \dfrac{c}{d} + \dfrac{a}{b}$ Definition of addition for rationals

EXERCISES

1. Use the number line to exhibit the consistency of the definition $\dfrac{a}{d} + \dfrac{c}{d} = \dfrac{a+c}{d}$ with our geometric interpretation of addition.

2. Criticize the following. We know that equals may be substituted for equals and the results are equal. Since the numerator of $6/8$ has 2 as a factor, we conclude, by replacing $6/8$ with its equal $3/4$, that the numerator of $3/4$ has 2 as a factor.

3. Let m and n be natural numbers. (a) Is the set of rational numbers of the form $m/2^n$ closed with respect to addition? (b) Subtraction? (c) Multiplication? (d) Division?

4. Using straightedge and compass only, describe how to divide a unit segment into eleven equal subdivisions.

5. Let a, b, and c be any (positive) rational numbers. Is it true that $a \div (b \div c) = (a \div b) \div c$? Verify your answer.

6. Let a, b, and c be any (positive) rational numbers. Discuss under what conditions $a \div (b \div c) = (a \div b) \div c$?

Let $a/b = 3/7$, $c/d = 4/15$, and $e/f = 21/22$. Use the definitions of addition, multiplication, and equality for rational numbers to verify each statement in Exercises 7 through 10.

7. $\dfrac{a}{b} \times \dfrac{c}{d} = \dfrac{c}{d} \times \dfrac{a}{b}$

8. $\left(\dfrac{a}{b} \times \dfrac{c}{d}\right) \times \dfrac{e}{f} = \dfrac{a}{b} \times \left(\dfrac{c}{d} \times \dfrac{e}{f}\right)$

9. $\left(\dfrac{a}{b} + \dfrac{c}{d}\right) + \dfrac{e}{f} = \dfrac{a}{b} + \left(\dfrac{c}{d} + \dfrac{e}{f}\right)$

10. $\dfrac{a}{b}\left(\dfrac{c}{d} + \dfrac{e}{f}\right) = \left(\dfrac{a}{b} \times \dfrac{c}{d}\right) + \left(\dfrac{a}{b} \times \dfrac{e}{f}\right)$

*11. Prove for any positive rational numbers a/b and c/d that

$$\frac{a}{b} \times \frac{c}{d} = \frac{c}{d} \times \frac{a}{b}$$

*12. Prove for any positive rational numbers a/b, c/d, and e/f that

$$\left(\frac{a}{b} \times \frac{c}{d}\right) \times \frac{e}{f} = \frac{a}{b} \times \left(\frac{c}{d} \times \frac{e}{f}\right)$$

*13. Prove for any positive rational numbers a/b, c/d, and e/f that

$$\left(\frac{a}{b} + \frac{c}{d}\right) + \frac{e}{f} = \frac{a}{b} + \left(\frac{c}{d} + \frac{e}{f}\right)$$

*14. Prove for any positive rational numbers a/b, c/d, and e/f that

$$\frac{a}{b} \left(\frac{c}{d} + \frac{e}{f}\right) = \left(\frac{a}{b} \times \frac{c}{d}\right) + \left(\frac{a}{b} \times \frac{e}{f}\right)$$

2. NEGATIVE NUMBERS

The negative numbers were used to some extent by the Hindu mathematician Bhāshara (1114–1185) and even by the Hindu mathematician Brahmagupta about 500 years earlier. But the early European mathematicians were as uncomfortable with their use as the Persian mathematicians, Omar Khayyam (1044?–1123?) and al-Kowârizmî (circa 825 A.D.). (It is from a treatise by al-Kowârizmî that we obtain our word *algebra*.)

Cardan (1501–1576), in his book entitled *Ars Magna*, was the first to present a clear and reasonably careful treatment of the negative numbers. However, it was not until the seventeenth century that the negative numbers became generally accepted in Europe.

Let us first consider the negative integers. They can be developed in at least two ways. The first way is to *expand* the existing number system as we did when we introduced the (positive) rationals. It should be clear that this technique approximates man's early development of numbers. If we expand the number system to include the negative integers, then we consider the set of positive integers and the set of natural numbers to be one and the same thing. Similarly, "nonnegative integers" and "whole numbers" are two different names for the same set.

Another way to create the negative integers is by what is called an *axiomatic approach*. We shall discuss the axiomatic approach later; essentially, the set of integers (positive, negative, and zero) is constructed as a "new" system using the natural numbers as building blocks. With this approach, the positive integers $\{+1, +2, +3, \ldots\}$ "behave" exactly like the natural numbers but are considered to be new entities. Mathematicians refer to the system of positive integers as being *isomorphic* (same form) to the system of natural numbers; the two systems in all essential aspects are identical. A similar relationship exists between the natural numbers and the rationals $\frac{1}{1}, \frac{2}{1}, \frac{3}{1}, \frac{4}{1}, \ldots$.

We extend the previously constructed number line to the left of the origin and associate the negative rationals with points in such a way that $-\frac{2}{3}$ and $\frac{2}{3}$, for example, are symmetrically placed with respect to 0, the origin. The pairing gives us a point on the number line to associate with each rational number.

When deciding how to *define* addition and multiplication for the set of rational numbers, we do not lose sight of the fact that the set of positive rationals is a subset of the set of all rationals. Therefore, we want our definitions to be consistent with the definitions of addition and multiplication on the set of positive rational numbers. The number line is also used to motivate the definitions. The student is quite familiar with the definitions but a review of the motivations for them is probably in order.

Recall that the sum $8 + 3$ is the number associated with the point 3 units to the *right* of 8. The sum $3 + 8$ is the number associated with the point 8 units to the right of 3; in both cases, the number is 11. The difference $8 - 3$ is the number associated with the point 3 units to the left of 8; it is 5. Thus, to be consistent with the interpretation of subtraction, $3 - 8$ should be the number associated with the point 8 units to the left of 3; it is -5. (See Figure 4.5.)

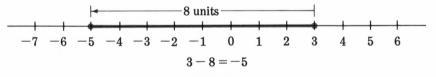

$$3 - 8 = -5$$

FIGURE 4.5

If $3 - 8 = -5$, then by the definition of subtraction $8 + (-5) = 3$. Thus, to *add* -5 to 8 we move 5 units to the *left* of 8. We also see that if the sum $(-5) + 8$ is the number associated with the point 8 units to the right of -5 then $(-5) + 8 = 3$, and the commutative property of addition is preserved.

By our previous interpretations, we observe that $7 - 2$ and $7 + (-2)$ is the same number. Similarly, $3 - 10$ and $3 + (-10)$ is the same number. Also, we conclude that $(-5) - 6$ and $(-5) + (-6)$ is -11.

additive inverse

Finally, consider the difference $(-7) - (-8)$. By the definition of subtraction, the difference should be a number x such that $(-8) + x = -7$. If we start at the point paired with -8, then to get to -7 we need to move 1 unit to the *right;* thus, x should be 1. Consequently, $(-7) - (-8) = 1$, which, of course, is also the sum $(-7) + 8$.

For rational numbers x and y, if $x + y = 0$ then y is called the *additive inverse* of x. Generally, the additive inverse of x is denoted by $-x$. However, we should notice that $-x$ need not be a negative number. For example, if $x = -8$ then the additive inverse of x is 8. Recall that 0 is neither positive nor negative, but the additive inverse of 0 is 0; thus, $-0 = 0$.

Let us consider what the product $(-4)(3)$ should be. To preserve the commutative property of multiplication, we want $(-4)(3)$ to be equal to $(3)(-4)$. If the interpretation of multiplication for *positive integers* as repeated addition is to be preserved, then $(3)(-4)$ should be the sum $(-4) + (-4) + (-4)$. Thus, we are led to define $(-4)(3)$ to be -12.

Another way to motivate the definition for the product $(3)(-4)$ is to use the fact that we wish to preserve the distributive property. The following shows that the preceding definition is consistent with the distributive property. Since $4 + (-4) = 0$, it follows that $3[4 + (-4)] = 3 \times 0$; that is, $3[4 + (-4)] = 0$. Using the distributive property, we obtain

$$3[4 + (-4)] = (3)(4) + (3)(-4)$$

Therefore, $\qquad (3)(4) + (3)(-4) = 0$

or $\qquad\qquad 12 + (3)(-4) = 0$

Consequently, $(3)(-4)$ is the additive inverse of 12; that is,

$$(3)(-4) = -12$$

We use a similar approach to determine how to define the product $(-3)(-4)$. Since the product of any number and zero is zero,

$$(-4)[3 + (-3)] = (-4)(0)$$

$$(-4)(3) + (-4)(-3) = 0$$

and $\qquad\qquad -12 + (-3)(-4) = 0$

Therefore, $(-3)(-4)$ is the additive inverse of -12; that is, $(-3)(-4) = 12$.

When we say that a rational number a is less than a rational number b, we mean that the point on the number line associated with a is to the left of the point associated with b. In general, for any

two numbers a and b, a is said to be *less than* b if and only if there   *less than*
exists a *positive number* x such that $a + x = b$; it is expressed as
$a < b$. If a is less than b we say that b is *greater than* a and denote the   *greater than*
fact by $b > a$. If we wish to state that a is less than or equal to b we
write $a \leq b$. The expressions $a < b$, $b > a$, $a \leq b$, and $b \geq a$ are called
inequalities.   *inequalities*

If P and Q are rational points on the number line with coordinates x and y, respectively, such that $x \leq y$, then the nonnegative
rational number $y - x$ is called the *distance* between P and Q. If P *distance*
has coordinate 2 and Q has coordinate 7, then the distance between P
and Q, denoted by $|PQ|$, is $7 - 2 = 5$; that is, $|PQ| = 5$. (See Figure
4.6.)

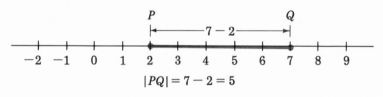

$$|PQ| = 7 - 2 = 5$$

FIGURE 4.6

Let us consider the method for finding the coordinate of the midpoint between two rational points P and Q on the number line. If x
and y are the coordinates of two distinct points P and Q, respectively,
then either $x < y$ or $x > y$. There is no loss in generality in assuming
that P is to the left of Q on the line since the points can be renamed if
necessary; that is, we assume $x < y$. The distance between P and Q
is $y - x$; thus, half the distance is $(y - x)/2$.

If M represents the midpoint of the line segment PQ, its coordinate
t is given by the sum of x and $(y - x)/2$. (See Figure 4.7.) Hence,

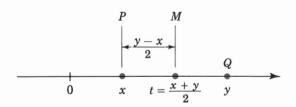

Midpoint: $t = \dfrac{x + y}{2}$

FIGURE 4.7

$$t = x + \frac{(y - x)}{2}$$

Thus, $$t = \frac{x + y}{2}$$

The coordinate of the midpoint of two points on the number line is half the sum of the two coordinates of the given points. If x and y are rational numbers, then $(x + y)/2$ is a rational number; consequently, there is a rational number between any two different rational numbers. In fact, it follows that there are infinitely many rational numbers between any two given rational numbers; to express this fact, we say that the set of rational numbers is *dense*. Although the set of rational numbers is dense, we shall see in the next section that points still exist on the number line that are not associated with rational numbers. However, an important consequence of the density property of the set of rational numbers is that the length of any segment can be approximated to any degree of accuracy by a rational number.

Example 1. If x and y are rational numbers such that $x < y$, find the coordinate of the point R on the number line that is one-fourth the distance from the point P with coordinate x to the point Q with coordinate y.

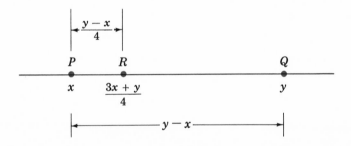

Solution: The length of the segment PQ is $y - x$. One-fourth of the distance from P to Q is $\frac{1}{4}(y - x)$. The coordinate of R is

$$x + \tfrac{1}{4}(y - x)$$

thus, R has $(3x + y)/4$ as coordinate.

EXERCISES

1. Is the set of integers closed with respect to addition? Subtraction? Multiplication? Division?

2. Is the set $\{0, 1, -1\}$ closed with respect to addition? Subtraction? Multiplication? Division?

3. Which of the following is true?
    (a) If $x < y$, then $x \leq y$.
    (b) If $x \leq y$, then $x < y$.

4. Which of the following are true?
    (a) $-11/37 < -1/9$ (b) $-5/7 < -3/5$
    (c) $1/8 - 5/6 < 2/7 - 2/3$ (d) $2/9 - 4/7 < 5/12 - 8/15$

5. (a) Is $(-3/8)(5/7) < (-3/8)(6/7)$?
    (b) Is $23/36 - 5/11 < 5/12 - 9/22$?

6. (a) Is $(-2/5) + (-7/12) < (-8/9) + (1/6)$?
    (b) Is $(-4/5) - (-2/3) < (5/7) - (1/14)$?

7. If x is *any* rational number, is it true that $x \div x = 1$?

8. Find the distance between each of the following pairs of points and give the coordinate of the midpoint of the segment with the two given points as endpoints.
    (a) 11 and -17 (b) $2/3$ and $11/3$
    (c) $2\frac{1}{3}$ and $-4\frac{5}{8}$ (d) $5/7$ and $-13/3$

9. Let points P, Q, and R have coordinates 3, $7\frac{2}{3}$ and $-4\frac{1}{5}$, respectively. (a) Is $|PQ| + |QR| = |PR|$? (b) Under what conditions is $|AB| + |BC| = |AC|$ for any three different points A, B, and C on the coordinate line? (c) Is it true that $|AB| + |BC| \geq |AC|$ for any three points on the coordinate line?

10. If x and y are rational numbers such that $x < y$, prove that $(2x + y)/3$ is the coordinate of the point one-third the distance from the point with coordinate x to the point with coordinate y.

11. Let P and Q be two rational points with coordinates x and y, respectively, such that $x < y$. If the line segment PQ is divided into five equal segments, what are the coordinates of the division points?

12. Let P and Q be two rational points with coordinates x and y, respectively, such that $x < y$. If the line segment PQ is divided into n equal segments where n is a positive integer greater than 1, find the coordinate of the point at the end of the kth segment from P. (See Exercises 10 and 11.)

13. Assume a, b, c, and d are integers different from zero. Prove if a rational number x/y exists such that $a/b + x/y = c/d$ then xbd/y is an integer.

14. Discuss the following "proof." If there are integers x and y such that

$$x - 2 = y$$

then by multiplying both sides by $(x - 2)$ we have

$$(x - 2)^2 = y(x - 2)$$

Subtracting y^2 from both sides of the equality,

$$(x - 2)^2 - y^2 = y(x - 2) - y^2$$

75

Hence, by factoring we obtain

$$(x - 2 - y)(x - 2 + y) = y(x - 2 - y)$$

and by dividing both sides by $(x - 2 - y)$ we get

$$x - 2 + y = y$$

Thus,

$$x - 2 = 0$$

and

$$x = 2$$

Consequently, if $x - 2 = y$, then $x = 2$.

15. Discuss the following "proof" that all rational numbers are equal. Let a and b be two rational numbers. Either $a = b$ or $a \neq b$. If $a \neq b$, then there is no loss in generality to assume that $a < b$. Hence, there is a positive rational number c such that $a + c = b$. Furthermore,

$$(b - a)(a + c) = b(b - a)$$
$$ab - a^2 - ac + bc = b^2 - ab$$
$$ab - a^2 - ac = b^2 - ab - bc$$
$$a(b - a - c) = b(b - a - c)$$

and

$$a = b$$

3. REAL NUMBERS

What is the ratio of the length of the diagonal of a square to the length of one of its sides? Such questions concerning various geometric figures were of great interest to early mathematicians, especially the Pythagoreans. For a long time it was thought that the ratio of the length of the diagonal of a square to the length of a side could be expressed using natural numbers. Suppose it were found that the ratio were 707 to 500; it would mean that the length of the diagonal of the *unit square* (a square with each side one unit in length) would be $707/500$.

Pythagoras was probably the first to demonstrate a proof of the Babylonian theorem which states that the sum of the squares of the lengths of the sides of a right triangle is equal to the square of the length of the hypotenuse; today, we call it the *Pythagorean theorem*. From the Pythagorean theorem, it follows that if $707/500$ were the length of the diagonal of the unit square, then the sum $1^2 + 1^2$ would be $(707/500)^2$. It is a simple arithmetic task to show that

$$\left(\frac{707}{500}\right)^2 = \frac{499,849}{250,000} = \frac{1,999,396}{1,000,000} \neq 2$$

Notice that the square of the given rational is "close" to 2; thus, it might appear that a more intensive search would produce a rational whose square is 2.

In an algebraic setting, the geometric problem of finding the length of the diagonal of the unit square is equivalent to finding a positive solution to the equation $x^2 = 2$. In terms of the basic number properties, it is related to the problem of determining if the rational number system is closed with respect to the operation of taking square roots.

From our past experiences we know there is no rational number whose square is 2. Although the Pythagoreans discovered this fact, our proof that no rational number has 2 as its square is essentially the one given by Euclid sometime prior to the second century B.C. The proof is a classic in mathematics, and although it does involve some logical subtleties, it is not too difficult to understand. Furthermore, it exhibits an excellent piece of deductive reasoning using only basic number facts.

Theorem. *There is no rational number whose square is 2.*

Proof: (Recall that any rational number can be expressed as a fraction in lowest terms; that is, any rational number can be expressed in the form p/q where p and q are integers, q is not zero, and p and q have no common factors except 1 and -1.)

Assume that there is a rational number whose square is 2. Let p/q be the fraction in lowest terms representing this number. Thus,

$$\left(\frac{p}{q}\right)^2 = 2$$

Hence,

$$p^2 = 2q^2 \tag{A}$$

Since q is an integer, q^2 is an integer and $2q^2$ is an even integer. Since $p^2 = 2q^2$, p^2 is even. (Since the square of every odd integer is odd, p is an even integer.) Since p is even, it can be expressed as $p = 2t$ where t is some integer. Substituting in Equation (A),

$$(2t)^2 = 2q^2$$
$$4t^2 = 2q^2$$
$$2t^2 = q^2$$

Since $2t^2$ is an even integer, by an argument similar to the one above we conclude that q is an even integer. Therefore, p and q have a common factor of 2, a contradiction to our original assumption.

Hence, our assumption that there is a rational number whose square is 2 is false, and the theorem is proved.

By now we should anticipate how we meet the apparent impasse created by the insufficiency of the rational number system for solving such equations as $x^2 = 2$. The number system is expanded by creating what are called *irrational numbers*. The irrational numbers are the numbers associated with the points on the number line which are not rational. We use "$\sqrt{2}$" to denote the positive irrational number whose square is 2. It can be proved that if n is not the square of a natural number, then no rational number exists whose square is n. Furthermore, it can be proved that if n is not the cube of a natural number, then no rational number exists whose cube is n. Such theorems are endless and we can prove that $\sqrt[4]{18}$, $\sqrt[5]{17}$, $\sqrt[8]{39}$, $\sqrt[9]{41}$, etc. are irrational numbers. As a consequence of the fact that $\sqrt[n]{2}$ is irrational for each $n \geq 2$, it follows that the set of irrational numbers is an infinite set.

*irrational
numbers*

The collection of all the rational and irrational numbers is called the set of *real numbers*. The real numbers are assumed to be in one-to-one correspondence with the points on the number line; that is, it is assumed that there is exactly one point on the number line associated with each real number, and there is exactly one real number associated with each point on the number line. Thus, the coordinate line is often called the *real number line*.

real numbers

*real number
line*

All of the irrational real numbers *which we have discussed* are called algebraic numbers. An *algebraic number* is a real number which is the root of a polynomial equation with *rational numbers* as *coefficients*. Observe that each rational number p/q is an algebraic number since it is a root of $qx = p$. It is interesting to discover that there are a great many (irrational) real numbers which are not algebraic. The real numbers which are not algebraic are called *transcendental numbers*.

*algebraic
number*

*transcendental
numbers*

In geometry we learn that the circumference of a circle is πd where d is the diameter of the circle. Therefore, the ratio of the circumference of a circle to its diameter is the number we call *pi*. We recall that although π can be approximated to any degree of accuracy by a rational number, it is an irrational number. It is not easy to prove that π is an irrational number. The first proof of the irrationality of π was given by Lambert in 1761; the "late" date should be some indication of the difficulties involved. The number π is not only irrational but it is also transcendental. Generally, to prove a number is transcendental is no minor task; the first proof that π is a transcendental number was given in 1882 by Lindemann, a student of Weierstrass.

The first mathematician to prove that certain real numbers were transcendental was Joseph Liouville. In 1844 he proved a whole class of numbers to be transcendental; they are of the form

$$\frac{1}{n} + \frac{1}{n^2} + \frac{1}{n^6} + \frac{1}{n^{24}} + \frac{1}{n^{120}} + \cdots$$

where n is a real number greater than 1 and the exponents are successive factorials. Liouville's proof was given nearly forty years before it was proved that π was transcendental. Also, a very well-known number in analysis denoted by e and approximately equal to 2.71828 was proved transcendental before π was proved transcendental. Hermite, a renowned French mathematician, proved in 1873 that e is transcendental.

At first glance it might appear that to prove the theorem of Liouville obtaining an entire class of transcendental numbers would be more difficult than to prove one number, such as π, to be transcendental. It is not the last time we shall find that mathematicians have solved a problem that appears more difficult than a similar unsolved problem. There can be several reasons for the "difficult" problem being solved first, but often it is a case of the "mathematician picking the problem" instead of the "problem picking the mathematician;" the former can have its advantages.

How many transcendental numbers are there? After we know that π is transcendental, it is not too difficult to prove that any rational multiple of π is also transcendental. Thus, we know that the set of transcendental numbers is not finite. Since the student is not very likely to be familiar with many "different" types of transcendental numbers, it might be startling to learn that the transcendental numbers are more numerous than the algebraic numbers. Of course, we are rather casual about using the term "more numerous" for infinite sets since we have not made any clear definition concerning *size* for infinite sets. At present, we shall rely on an intuitive understanding of the matter.

We assume that the student has a working knowledge of the real number system. The next section on decimals will expand our knowledge of the real number system somewhat, but a rigorous development of the real number system will have to wait. The student will find that some of the most difficult problems in mathematics are at the foundations and at the frontiers of the subject. The mathematical "sailing" is usually much easier and smoother "in the middle;" things tend to get turbulent at the extremities.

EXERCISES

1. Perform the indicated operations.
   (a) $(2 + \sqrt{3}) + (7 + 5\sqrt{3})$
   (b) $(6 + 2\sqrt{3}) + (8 - 2\sqrt{3})$
   (c) $(2 + \sqrt{3})(7 + 5\sqrt{3})$
   (d) $(8 + 2\sqrt{3})(8 - 2\sqrt{3})$
   (e) $(5 + 3\sqrt{3}) \div (4 - 2\sqrt{3})$

2. Perform the indicated operations.
   (a) $(4 + 3\sqrt{5}) + (-9 + 6\sqrt{5})$
   (b) $(11 + 7\sqrt{5}) + (8 - 7\sqrt{5})$
   (c) $(4 + 3\sqrt{5})(-9 + 6\sqrt{5})$
   (d) $(8 + 7\sqrt{5})(8 - 7\sqrt{5})$
   (e) $(3 - 2\sqrt{5}) \div (4 + 5\sqrt{5})$

3. Is the set of irrational numbers closed with respect to addition?

4. Is the set of irrational numbers closed with respect to multiplication?

5. Is the sum of a rational and an irrational number ever a rational number? Why?

6. Let a and b be rational numbers. Is the set of numbers of the form $a + b\sqrt{3}$ closed with respect to addition?

7. Let a and b be rational numbers. Is the set of numbers of the form $a + b\sqrt{3}$ closed with respect to multiplication?

8. Let a and b be rational numbers such that $ab \neq 0$. Is the set of numbers of the form $a + b\sqrt{3}$ closed with respect to division?

*9. Prove that there is no rational number whose square is 3.

*10. Using as a pattern the proof that there is no rational number whose square is 2, where would the proof "break down" if we tried to prove that there is no rational number whose square is 4?

4. DECIMAL NOTATION

Another notation for the rationals is the mixed numeral notation. For example, "$8^3/_5$" denotes the sum $8 + {}^3/_5$. Since

$$8 + {}^3/_5 = {}^{40}/_5 + {}^3/_5 = {}^{43}/_5$$

the fractional notation "$^{43}/_5$" denotes the same rational as the mixed numeral "$8^3/_5$". Because mixed numerals are only a slight modification of fractions, they present no more basic difficulties in computation than do fractions. Mixed numerals are useful in applications and have some advantages over fractions. For example, it is much easier to determine which of the rationals $^{169}/_{19}$ and $^{136}/_{15}$ is greater when each is written in its corresponding mixed numeral notation $8^{17}/_{19}$ and $9^1/_{15}$.

However, computing with rationals written in either fractional or mixed numeral notation can become an unpleasant task. For example, consider finding the sum

$$\frac{1,736,201}{5,003,104} + \frac{236,111}{561,306}$$

Fortunately, we have another notation for rationals which lends itself quite well to computational work and eliminates the need for such fractions in most practical applications. This notation, developed in the sixteenth century by Simon Stevin of Belgium, is the *decimal notation*.

The decimal notation is an extension of the positional notation for natural numbers. We know that any natural number greater than 1 can be written as

$$a_n 10^n + a_{n-1} 10^{n-1} + \cdots + a_2 10^2 + a_1 10 + a_0$$

where each of $a_n, a_{n-1}, \ldots, a_2, a_1, a_0$ is one of the numbers 0, 1, 2, 3, 4, 5, 6, 7, 8, or 9. For example, $3,786 = 3(10^3) + 7(10^2) + 8(10) + 6$. Similarly, if each of $b_1, b_2, b_3, \ldots, b_n$ is one of the numbers 0, 1, 2, 3, 4, 5, 6, 7, 8, or 9, then

$$b_1(10^{-1}) + b_2(10^{-2}) + b_3(10^{-3}) + \cdots + b_n(10^{-n})$$

or

$$\frac{b_1}{10} + \frac{b_2}{10^2} + \frac{b_3}{10^3} + \cdots + \frac{b_n}{10^n}$$

is a rational number between 0 and 1. For example,

$$3(10^{-1}) + 5(10^{-2}) + 7(10^{-3}) = \frac{3}{10} + \frac{5}{10^2} + \frac{7}{10^3}$$

$$= \frac{3}{10} + \frac{5}{100} + \frac{7}{1,000}$$

$$= \frac{300}{1,000} + \frac{50}{1,000} + \frac{7}{1,000}$$

$$= \frac{357}{1,000}$$

A fraction whose denominator is a power of 10 is called a *decimal fraction*. Corresponding to a decimal fraction such as "$357/1000$" is the decimal ".357," or "0.357." In general, "$0.b_1 b_2 b_3 \ldots b_n$" is the *decimal notation* for the rational number given by

$$b_1(10^{-1}) + b_2(10^{-2}) + b_3(10^{-3}) + \cdots + b_n(10^{-n})$$

We see that the mixed numeral "$38\,213/1000$" represents the same rational number as the decimal "38.213." The "period" between "8"

decimal point

and "2" is the *separatrix* in the notation and is called the *decimal point.* (The use of a "period" as separatrix is not universal; some countries use a "raised" period and in others a comma is used.) The first position to the right of the decimal point (in base ten) is called the *tenths' position,* the second is called the *hundredths' position,* the third is called the *thousandths' position,* etc. (See Figure 4.8.)

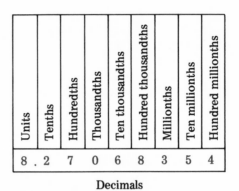

Decimals

FIGURE 4.8

We are familiar with the fact that we add and multiply rationals using decimal notation in much the same way we add and multiply natural numbers. It is not difficult to verify the standard techniques by using the properties of a positional notation and basic number properties. We should point out that since the three-place decimal "0.213" and the five-place decimal "0.41826" represent the rationals $213/10^3$ and $41,826/10^5$, the product is

$$\frac{213}{10^3} \times \frac{41,826}{10^5} = \frac{231 \times 41,826}{10^8}$$

Thus, the product can be represented by an eight-place decimal. To find it, we need only multiply the natural numbers 213 and 41,826 and insert the decimal point in the appropriate place.

terminating decimals

Until now, we have given meaning only to finite sums, the sum of a finite number of rational numbers. Hence, we are still restricted to finite *n*-place decimals called *terminating decimals.* The restriction presents a problem when we show as a consequence of the definition of the decimal notation that although each terminating decimal must represent a rational number not every rational number can be represented by a terminating decimal.

With a few basic number facts it is easy to prove that a rational need not have a terminating decimal representation. Suppose, for example, there is an n-place decimal which represents $1/3$. Then, there must be natural numbers a and n such that

$$\frac{a}{10^n} = \frac{1}{3}$$

Thus,
$$3a = 10^n$$

The last equality states that 3 is a factor of 10^n. However, the divisibility test for 3 shows that 3 is *not* a factor of 10^n for any natural number n. Hence, $1/3$ cannot be represented by a terminating decimal.

We can meet the barrier of not having an n-place decimal to represent such rationals as $1/3$ in two ways. One way is to use decimal approximations of such rationals. Since, as we know, a decimal approximation of a rational can be obtained to any degree of accuracy, this could be a satisfactory solution to the problem.

If we wish to find a decimal representation of a rational number which differs from $1/3$ by less than $1/10^4$, then we use the long division process and obtain the incomplete quotient and remainder in the long division of 10^4 by 3.

$$3 \underline{ 10{,}000}$$
$$q = 3{,}333, \; r = 1$$

Thus,
$$10{,}000 - 3(3{,}333) = 1$$

$$1 - (3)\,\frac{3{,}333}{10{,}000} = \frac{1}{10{,}000}$$

$$\frac{1}{3} - \frac{3{,}333}{10{,}000} = \frac{1}{3(10{,}000)} < \frac{1}{10^4}$$

A more fruitful and elegant way than decimal approximations to escape the insufficiency of terminating decimals to represent rational numbers is to create infinite decimals. An *infinite decimal* represents an "infinite sum;" but with this approach it would be necessary to define *infinite sum* and prove several theorems pertinent to the new concept. We shall not attempt the task now; it is postponed until we develop the needed mathematical "tools." However, let us state now some important facts concerning infinite decimals.

An infinite or terminating decimal can be obtained to represent any rational number, and the decimal is found by the long division process. Since each remainder in the division algorithm is always a whole number less than the divisor, the remainder must repeat in the algorithm and the decimal must be repeating; the number of digits in the repeating part is less than the divisor. For example, the repeating decimal representation for $3/7$ is found as follows:

$$
\begin{array}{r}
0.4285714 \\
7{\overline{)3.0000000}} \\
\underline{2\ 8} \\
20 \\
\underline{14} \\
60 \\
\underline{56} \\
40 \\
\underline{35} \\
50 \\
\underline{49} \\
10 \\
\underline{7} \\
\mathbf{30}
\end{array}
$$

Since the process begins to repeat when a remainder of 3 is obtained, $\frac{3}{7} = 0.428571\overline{428571}.\ .\ .$ where the overbar indicates the repeating digits.

It is also true that each repeating decimal denotes a rational number. Thus, we see that if irrational numbers can be represented by decimals then the representation will be by nonterminating and nonrepeating decimals. In fact, we can prove that any infinite decimal represents a real number. Fortunately, we can also prove that any real number can be written as a decimal. (Careful, we did not say in only one way. But, a one-to-one pairing between decimals and real numbers can be obtained if we rule out the use of infinite repeating decimals where the repeating digits are nines.) It is a delightful bonus to discover that the decimal notation created for the purpose of representing the rationals can be extended and used to represent each number in the real number system.

Assuming that the techniques of computing with infinite decimals and finite decimals are similar, we can exhibit a simple technique to find a fractional representation for any rational number written as a repeating decimal. For example, to find the fractional notation for $0.64\overline{64}\ .\ .\ .$, let

$$
x = 0.6464\overline{64}.\ .\ .
$$

Multiplying by 100, $100x = 64.6464\overline{64}.\ .\ .$
$$x = 0.646464.\ .\ .$$
Subtracting, $99x = 64$

Thus, $x = \dfrac{64}{99}$

As another example, to find the fractional notation for the rational $2.134343\overline{34}. \ldots$, let

$$x = 2.134343\overline{34}. \ldots$$

Then, $\qquad\qquad 10x = 21.3434\overline{34}. \ldots$

and $\qquad\qquad 1{,}000x = 2{,}134.3434\overline{34} - 21.3434\overline{34}. \ldots$

Thus, $\qquad 1{,}000x - 10x = 2{,}134.3434\overline{34}. \ldots$

and $\qquad\qquad\qquad 990x = 2{,}113$

Therefore, $\qquad\qquad\qquad x = \dfrac{2{,}113}{990}$

The technique just described can be used in other bases since the validity of each step depends on basic properties of the number system and not on the base number. Of course, in base seven, for example, we should recall that $100_{\text{seven}} = 49_{\text{ten}}$ and $100_{\text{seven}} - 1 = 66_{\text{seven}}$. In order to find the fractional representation in base seven for the repeating decimal $0.5151\overline{51}. \ldots$ in base seven, we proceed as follows:

Let $\qquad\qquad x = \ \ 0.5151\overline{51} \ \ldots \ \text{(base seven)}$

Then, $\qquad (100_{\text{seven}})x = 51.5151\overline{51} \ \ldots \ \text{(base seven)}$

$$\underline{\qquad\qquad\qquad x = \ \ 0.5151\overline{51} \ \ldots \ \text{(base seven)}\qquad}$$

Subtracting, $\quad (66_{\text{seven}})x = 51_{\text{seven}}$

Thus, $\qquad\qquad\qquad x = \dfrac{51_{\text{seven}}}{66_{\text{seven}}}$

Since $51_{\text{seven}} = 36_{\text{ten}}$ and $66_{\text{seven}} = 48_{\text{ten}}$, the repeating decimal $0.5151\overline{51}. \ldots$ (base seven) represents the same number as $36/48 = 3/4 = 0.75$ in base ten. Here we see that the number represented by a finite decimal in one base may be represented by an infinite repeating decimal in another base.

EXERCISES

Express each of the following rational numbers as a terminating or repeating decimal.

1. $\dfrac{3}{8}$ $\qquad\qquad\qquad$ 2. $\dfrac{4}{9}$ $\qquad\qquad\qquad$ 3. $\dfrac{5}{11}$

Express each of the following rational numbers as a terminating or repeating decimal.

4. $\dfrac{9}{16}$ **5.** $\dfrac{6}{7}$ **6.** $\dfrac{5}{17}$

Express each of the following rational numbers in fractional notation.

7. 0.125   **8.** $0.317\overline{317}$. . .   **9.** $0.41\overline{41}$. . .

Express each of the following rational numbers in fractional notation.

10. $0.25\overline{25}$. . .   **11.** $0.5618\overline{18}$. . .   **12.** $0.3215\overline{15}$. . .

13. Using familiar properties of decimals, explain why each of the following is true.
   (a) The sum of two rationals is a rational number.
   (b) The sum of a rational and an irrational is an irrational number.

14. Using the familiar properties of decimals, explain how the sum of two irrational numbers can be rational or irrational. (*Hint:* 0.1010010001000010000010. . . is an irrational number. Though we do not need the fact to work the exercise, it is interesting to know that the number is also transcendental.)

15. In base two, discuss the meaning of "101.10111_{two}."

16. Can the rational number represented by "101.1011_{two}" be represented by a terminating decimal in base ten?

17. If p is a prime number different from 2 and 5, is it possible for the decimal representation (base ten) of $1/p$ to be a terminating decimal? Justify your answer.

18. What is the *ternary* (base three) decimal representation for the rational number one-third?

*19. Express the rational $0.2121\overline{21}$. . . (base 7) in base ten notation.

20. Would every number denoted by a terminating decimal in base two have a terminating decimal representation in base ten? Justify your answer.

*21. Express the rational $0.101101\overline{101}$. . . (base 2) in base ten notation.

5. COMPLEX NUMBERS (OPTIONAL)

Although the remainder of the text is going to be devoted almost entirely to topics concerned with the real number system, we would be remiss in our discussion of the number systems if we ignored the capstone, the complex numbers.

For several hundred years, it was the mathematicians' quest to derive formulas that would give the roots of polynomial equations of each degree. For the linear equation $ax + b = 0$ where $a \neq 0$, a real (number) solution r_1 always exists and it is given by $r_1 = -b/a$.

Hindu and Arabian mathematicians developed the quadratic formula and found that the quadratic equation

$$ax^2 + bx + c = 0 \qquad \text{where } a \neq 0$$

always has real solutions provided $b^2 - 4ac \geq 0$. The solutions are given by

$$x = \frac{-b \pm \sqrt{b^2 - 4ac}}{2a}$$

that is, the two solutions are

$$r_1 = \frac{-b + \sqrt{b^2 - 4ac}}{2a} \qquad \text{and} \qquad r_2 = \frac{-b - \sqrt{b^2 - 4ac}}{2a}$$

As we know, no real number exists whose square is negative. Until the sixteenth century, there had never been any compelling reasons to consider any "number" x such that x^2 is negative so "solutions" to a quadratic equation where $b^2 - 4ac < 0$ were not seriously considered.

In 1515, Scipio del Ferro discovered that the equation $x^3 + px = q$ had a solution given by

$$x = \sqrt[3]{\sqrt{\frac{p^3}{27} + \frac{q^2}{4}} + \frac{q}{2}} - \sqrt[3]{\sqrt{\frac{p^3}{27} + \frac{q^2}{4}} - \frac{q}{2}}$$

Since every cubic equation $ay^3 + by^2 + cy + d = 0$ where $a \neq 0$ can be transformed by the linear substitution $y = x - (b/3a)$ into a cubic equation of the form $x^3 + px = q$, the solution is quite significant. Although the solution is not easy to derive, once obtained it can be shown to be a solution in a straightforward manner using only elementary algebra. Let

$$u = \sqrt{\frac{p^3}{27} + \frac{q^2}{4}} \qquad \text{and} \qquad v = \frac{q}{2}$$

Thus, $(u^2 - v^2)^{1/3} = p/3$. We wish to prove that

$$[(u+v)^{1/3} - (u-v)^{1/3}]^3 + p[(u+v)^{1/3} - (u-v)^{1/3}] = q$$

The proof follows.

$(u+v) - 3(u+v)^{2/3}(u-v)^{1/3} + 3(u+v)^{1/3}(u-v)^{2/3} - (u-v)$
$\qquad\qquad\qquad\qquad\qquad\qquad + p(u+v)^{1/3} - p(u-v)^{1/3}$
$= 2v - 3(u+v)^{1/3}(u^2-v^2)^{1/3} + 3(u^2-v^2)^{1/3}(u-v)^{1/3}$
$\qquad\qquad\qquad\qquad\qquad\qquad + p(u+v)^{1/3} - p(u-v)^{1/3}$
$= 2v + (u+v)^{1/3}[p - 3(u^2-v^2)^{1/3}] + (u-v)^{1/3}[3(u^2-v^2)^{1/3} - p]$
$= 2v + (u+v)^{1/3}[p-p] + (u-v)^{1/3}[p-p]$
$= 2v$
$= q$

In 1535, the Italian Nicoli Fontana, who received the nickname Tartaglia because of a speech stammer, rediscovered the solution of Ferro. He communicated his solution to Gerolamo Cardano (1501–1576) who published the result in 1545 in his book on algebra. Although Cardano was not primarily responsible for the discovery of the formula for solving the cubic equation, it is generally referred to as Cardano's or Cardan's, formula.

In 1572, Raffael Bombelli studied the cubic equation $x^3 - 15x = 4$. This equation has three real solutions; they are $r_1 = 4$, $r_2 = -2 + \sqrt{3}$, and $r_3 = -2 - \sqrt{3}$, as the student may verify. Using the cubic formula where $p = -15$ and $q = 4$, we obtain the expression

$$x = \sqrt[3]{\sqrt{-121} + 2} - \sqrt[3]{\sqrt{-121} - 2}$$

Bombelli's example showed that the cubic formula published by Cardan led to the theretofore meaningless expression $\sqrt{-121}$. Prior to this time when such an expression resulted in solving quadratic equations, it was ignored and considered to have no mathematical meaning or practical application. However, Bombelli noticed that treating $\sqrt{-121}$ in a formal algebraic manner led to very desirable results. Formally,

$$\sqrt{-121} = \sqrt{(121)(-1)} = \sqrt{121}\ \sqrt{-1} = 11\sqrt{-1}$$

Furthermore,

$$(2 + \sqrt{-1})^3 = 2^3 + 3(2)^2(\sqrt{-1}) + 3(2)(\sqrt{-1})^2 + (\sqrt{-1})^3$$
$$= 8 + 12\sqrt{-1} - 6 - \sqrt{-1}$$
$$= 11\sqrt{-1} + 2$$

Thus,

$$\sqrt[3]{\sqrt{-121} + 2} = 2 + \sqrt{-1}$$

Similarly, we can "prove" that

$$\sqrt[3]{\sqrt{-121} - 2} = -2 + \sqrt{-1}$$

Consequently, substituting in the cubic formula,

$$x = (2 + \sqrt{-1}) - (-2 + \sqrt{-1})$$
$$= 2 + \sqrt{-1} + 2 - \sqrt{-1}$$
$$= 4, \quad \text{a real root of the given equation!}$$

Having discovered that the "complex numbers" could be put to a practical use, obtaining a real solution to a cubic equation, Bombelli was moved to develop a theory of complex numbers. While he started the numbers along the road to respectability, it was not until the nineteenth century that they gained full acceptance into the mathematical community.

Ferrari, one of Cardan's students, discovered that the problem of solving the biquadratic (or quartic) equation

$$ax^4 + bx^3 + cx^2 + dx + e = 0 \qquad \text{where } a \neq 0$$

could be reduced to that of solving a cubic equation. The result also was published in Cardan's book *Ars magna*.

There is another important problem connected with the quest to solve polynomial equations. The equation $x + 5 = 0$ does not have a solution in the set of positive integers but it does have a solution in the set of integers. The equation $2x + 5 = 8$ does not have a solution in the set of integers, but it does have a solution in the set of rational numbers. The equation $x^2 = 2$ does not have a solution in the set of rational numbers, but it does have two solutions in the set of real numbers. Finally, the equation $x^2 = -4$ does not have a solution in the set of real numbers, but it does have two solutions in the set of complex numbers. Thus, one *needs* complex numbers to solve even rather simple polynomial equations. But, is the set of complex numbers sufficient to solve *any* polynomial equation? Do we need to again expand our number system in order to be able to solve any polynomial equation?

In the middle of the eighteenth century, D'Alembert suspected that any algebraic equation must possess one real or complex root (solution), but he was unable to prove his conjecture. About fifty years later in 1799, Gauss proved in his doctoral thesis that any equation of the form

$$a_0x^n + a_1x^{n-1} + a_2x^{n-2} + \cdots + a_{n-1}x + a^n = 0$$

where the coefficients are real or complex numbers has at least one root in the complex number field. The theorem is of such importance that it is called the *Fundamental Theorem of Algebra*. Having proved the Fundamental Theorem of Algebra, it is not too difficult to prove that any nth degree polynomial equation has at most n roots, each of which is a real or complex number.

Fundamental Theorem of Algebra

There have been many proofs given of the Fundamental Theorem of Algebra since Gauss first proved it. With the "tools" from the branch of mathematical analysis called *complex variable*, it is possible to give a very "short" proof. (We shall find that the use of the theory from one field of mathematics to develop important theory in another branch is a common occurrence.) In all the proofs of the Fundamental Theorem of Algebra, the concept of *continuity*, a basic idea of analysis, is used either directly or indirectly.

Mathematicians continued their search to find a formula to solve not only the general fifth-degree equation but also equations of higher degree. Abel proved in 1825 that no formula exists to solve the general fifth-degree equation.   Shortly thereafter, the French mathematician, Evariste Galois, proved that *no formula could exist* for solving a general equation of any degree higher than four.   Of course, it was necessary for Galois to give a precise definition of *formula* before such a result could be proved.   Essentially, a formula for the solution of an equation is an expression involving a finite number of algebraic operations on the coefficients.   The brilliant Galois had a profound influence on the development of modern mathematics.   It is difficult to imagine the total influence he might have had on mathematics if he had not been killed in an unfortunate duel in 1832 before the age of 21.

Let us conclude the section with a diagram of the "family tree" of the basic number systems created by man.

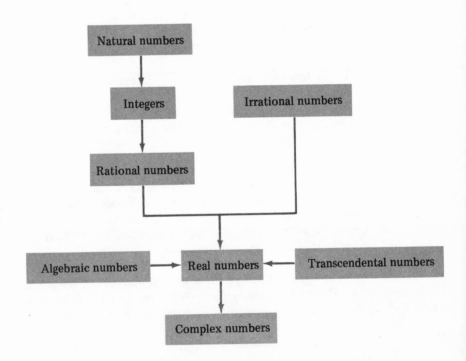

EXERCISES

Use the quadratic formula to solve each equation in Exercises 1 through 6.

1. $x^2 - 5x - 6 = 0$ 2. $x^2 - 2x - 6 = 0$
3. $x^2 - x - 1 = 0$ 4. $x^2 + x + 1 = 0$
5. $x^2 + 2x + 4 = 0$ 6. $x^2 + 4x + 8 = 0$

7. Show by substitution that 4, $-2 + \sqrt{3}$ and $-2 - \sqrt{3}$ are three real roots of the equation $x^3 - 15x = 4$.

8. Show that $(-2 + \sqrt{-1})^3 = 11\sqrt{-1} - 2$.

9. If $ay^3 + by^2 + cy + d = 0$ and $a \neq 0$, let $y = x - b/3a$ and obtain an equation of the form $x^3 + px = q$. What are p and q in terms of a, b, c, and d?

Pierre Fermat (1601–1665)

Pierre Fermat was born in France in August, 1601, in a century that gave the world many truly great men. Although Newton might head the list of the great mathematicians of the seventeenth century, Fermat, as a pure mathematician, has been ranked as his equal. Technically, Fermat was not a mathematician, at least not a professional mathematician; he was a lawyer and a civil servant who did mathematics for the fun of it. Since science and mathematics were his avocation and not his vocation, he is often called history's greatest scientific amateur.

Fermat developed analytic geometry independently of Descartes, but since he failed to publish his discoveries, Descartes received most of the credit for its creation. Fermat discovered the basic ideas of differential calculus; he also shares the credit with Pascal for initiating the mathematical theory of probability. It is difficult to imagine where Fermat found the time to make all of his contributions to analysis, geometry, and probability; still, many of his greatest contributions were in yet another field—number theory. (It does seem significant that many of the truly great mathematicians had an unusual fondness for this subject.) Although he discovered and proved many important theorems in number theory, none is as famous as his "last" theorem. Fermat's Last Theorem states that if n is any positive integer greater than 2, then no positive integers x, y, and z exist such that $x^n + y^n = z^n$. Fermat claimed he had a proof and noted in a book that the proof was too long to exhibit in the margin. Although the theorem has been proved true for specific cases (Euler, for example, proved it true for $n = 3$), no one has ever been able to give a satisfactory proof of the theorem, and no one has ever been able to find a counterexample. Fermat's Last Theorem remains one of the most famous unsolved problems in mathematics!

5

Number Patterns

1. Arithmetic Sequences
2. Geometric Sequences
3. A Look at the Primes
4. Making Conjectures
5. Perfect Numbers
6. Other Types of Sequences (Optional)

1. ARITHMETIC SEQUENCES

Consider the set of odd positive integers: 1, 3, 5, 7, 9, 11, 13, ... What is the 50th term in the sequence? The second term is obtained by adding two to the first term; the third term is obtained by adding two twos to the first term; the fourth term is obtained by adding three twos to the first term; and the 50th term is obtained by adding 49 twos to the first term. Thus, the 50th odd positive integer is $1 + (49)2 = 99$. In general, the nth term of the sequence is $1 + (n-1)2$; that is, $2n - 1$.

Suppose we wish to find the sum S of the first 50 odd integers. It can be done in several ways. One way, though not very efficient, is to list in a column all the odd numbers from 1 to 99 and then add. Besides the possibility of making a mistake in addition, just writing all the numbers down would not be a very pleasant task. A second and more efficient method would be to look at a tile floor. (See Figure 5.1.)

If we start in the lower left-hand corner and add the 3 adjacent squares to the first square, then we get a new square that is 2 by 2. Thus,

$$1 + 3 = 2^2$$

To get the next larger square which is 3 by 3, we add the 5 adjacent tiles to the preceding square. Thus,

$$1 + 3 + 5 = 3^2$$

Likewise, $$1 + 3 + 5 + 7 = 4^2$$

$$1 + 3 + 5 + 7 + 9 = 5^2$$

and $$1 + 3 + 5 + 7 + 9 + 11 = 6^2$$

Continuing, we conclude that

$$1 + 3 + 5 + \cdots + 97 + 99 = 50^2$$

Hence, the sum of the first 50 odd integers is 2,500. In general, the sum of the first n odd integers is n^2.

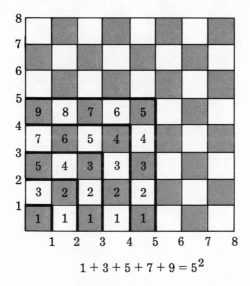

$$1 + 3 + 5 + 7 + 9 = 5^2$$

FIGURE 5.1

A third way to find the sum uses the fact that the order in which numbers are added does not affect the sum. Hence, if

$$S = 1 + 3 + 5 + \cdots + 95 + 97 + 99 \qquad (1)$$

then $\qquad S = 99 + 97 + 95 + \cdots + 5 + 3 + 1 \qquad (2)$

Since $A = B$ and $C = D$ implies $A + C = B + D$, we can add the equalities (1) and (2) and obtain

$$2S = 100 + 100 + 100 + \cdots + 100 + 100 + 100$$

Since there are fifty terms in the sum each of which is 100,

$$2S = 50(100)$$

and $\qquad S = (25)(100) = 2{,}500$

The third technique for finding the sum of the first 50 odd integers is quite significant since it lends itself to generalization. Suppose we wish to find the sum of the first 100 positive integers. If

$$T = 1 + 2 + 3 + \cdots + 97 + 98 + 99 + 100$$

then $\qquad T = 100 + 99 + 98 + \cdots + 4 + 3 + 2 + 1$

Adding the equalities,

$$\underbrace{2T = 101 + 101 + 101 + \cdots + 101 + 101 + 101 + 101}_{\text{100 terms}}$$

Thus,
$$2T = 100(101)$$
$$T = 50(101) = 5{,}050$$

Could the last technique be used to find the sum of the first 50 perfect squares? To answer this question, let us try it on the sum of just the first 5 perfect squares.

If $\qquad\qquad S = 1^2 + 2^2 + 3^2 + 4^2 + 5^2$

then $\qquad\qquad S = 5^2 + 4^2 + 3^2 + 2^2 + 1^2$

that is, $\qquad\qquad S = 1 + 4 + 9 + 16 + 25$

and $\qquad\qquad S = 25 + 16 + 9 + 4 + 1$

Adding the last two equalities, we get
$$2S = 26 + 20 + 18 + 20 + 26$$

Obviously, not all terms of the sum are the same and our new-found technique "breaks down." But on what kind of sums does the technique work? In other words, what will ensure that when we write down in reverse order the terms of a given sequence of numbers and add the corresponding terms of the original sequence with the new sequence that each term of the resulting sum is the same? A careful study of the situation will show that each term will be the same if the *arithmetic sequence* difference between each pair of consecutive terms is the same. Such a sequence of terms is called an *arithmetic sequence* (progression).

common difference For an arithmetic sequence with the first term a, the second term is $a + d$ where d is the *common difference* between the terms. The third term is $a + 2d$, the fourth term is $a + 3d$, the fifth is $a + 4d$, and the nth term is $a + (n - 1)d$. For example, 4, 7, 10, 13, 16, . . . is an arithmetic sequence where the first term a is 4 and the common difference d is 3; furthermore, the 14th term is $4 + (13)3 = 4 + 39 = 43$.

Example 1. If 3 is the first term of an arithmetic sequence with common difference $3/4$, find the 21st term.

Solution: The 21st term is $3 + (20)(3/4) = 3 + 15 = 18$.

Example 2. If the first term of an arithmetic sequence is 4 and the 23rd term is 50, what is the common difference?

Solution: $50 = 4 + (22)d$, $22d = 46$, and $d = 23/11$.

Example 3. Given an arithmetic sequence with common difference 3, if the first term is 2 and the nth term is 137, find the number of terms in the sequence.

Solution:

$$137 = 2 + (n-1)(3)$$
$$3n - 3 = 135$$
$$3n = 138$$
$$n = 46$$

A formula for the sum of an arithmetic sequence can be found by using the technique to find the sum of the first one hundred positive integers. The sum S of n terms of an arithmetic sequence with first term a and common difference d is

$$S = a + [a+d] + [a+2d] + \cdots + [a+(n-2)d] + [a+(n-1)d]$$

Thus, writing the terms of the sum in reverse order we get

$$S = [a+(n-1)d] + [a+(n-2)d] + \cdots + [a+2d] + [a+d] + a$$

Adding the last two equalities,

$$2S = \underbrace{[2a+(n-1)d] + [2a+(n-1)d] + \cdots + [2a+(n-1)d]}_{n \text{ terms}}$$

Hence,
$$2S = n[2a+(n-1)d]$$

and
$$S = \frac{n}{2}[2a+(n-1)d]$$

Consequently, $S = (n/2)[2a+(n-1)d]$ is the formula for the sum of n terms of any arithmetic sequence with the first term a and common difference d.

Example 4. Find the sum of the first fifty terms of the arithmetic sequence in Example 1.

Solution:
$$S = {}^{50}/_2\,[2(3) + 49(^3/_4)]$$
$$= 25[6 + {}^{147}/_4]$$
$$= 1{,}068^3/_4$$

As another example of an arithmetic sequence, suppose a man secures a job with a starting salary of $10,000 a year. If he gets a $600 raise each year, what is his total gross income for 20 years? His salary schedule is an arithmetic sequence where $a = 10{,}000$, $d = 600$, and $n = 20$. Thus,

$$S = {}^{20}/_2[20{,}000 + (19)(600)]$$
$$= 10[20{,}000 + 11{,}400]$$
$$= 314{,}000 \text{ dollars}$$

is his total gross income for the twenty-year period.

We can easily prove that the sum of the first n positive integers is

$n(n+1)/2$. The first n positive integers form an arithmetic sequence where $a = 1$, $d = 1$ and the number of terms is n. If S is the sum, then

$$S = \frac{n}{2}\left[2 + (n-1)(1)\right]$$

$$= \frac{n}{2}\left[2 + n - 1\right]$$

$$= \frac{n(n+1)}{2}$$

Let us give a geometric argument for finding the sum of the first six positive integers. It should be clear that the procedure can be generalized for any positive integer n. On a piece of rectangular graph paper place dots as in Figure 5.2a. If S is the number of dots,

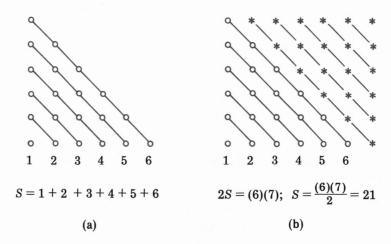

$$S = 1 + 2 + 3 + 4 + 5 + 6$$

$$2S = (6)(7); \quad S = \frac{(6)(7)}{2} = 21$$

(a)

(b)

FIGURE 5.2

then it should be clear by observing how many dots are on each line segment that $S = 1 + 2 + 3 + 4 + 5 + 6$. In Figure 5.2b, we notice that the total number of stars is also S; thus, the total number of points indicated is $2S$. Obviously, the configuration in Figure 5.2b is a rectangle consisting of 6 rows with 7 points in each row. Hence, the total number of points in the configuration is $(6)(7)$. Consequently, $2S = (6)(7)$ and $S = (6)(7)/2$.

EXERCISES

1. (a) In an arithmetic sequence with first term 4 and common difference 5, what is the 50th term?
   (b) What is the sum of the first 50 terms?

2. (a) If 5, 8, 11, . . . , 65 is an arithmetic sequence, what is the common difference?
   (b) How many terms are there in the sequence if 65 is the last term?
   (c) What is the sum of the sequence?
   (d) Show for any arithmetic sequence with last term l that the sum S is given by $S = (n/2)(a + l)$.

3. In an arithmetic sequence with first term 3 and common difference $4/3$, what is the 50th term? What is the sum of the first 50 terms?

4. In an arithmetic sequence, if the first term is 5 and the 31st term is 98, what is the common difference?

5. (a) In an arithmetic sequence with first term 6 and common difference $2/3$, what is the 20th term?
   (b) What is the sum of the first 20 terms?

6. (a) If 5, $11/3$, . . . , -11 is an arithmetic sequence, what is the common difference?
   (b) How many terms are there in the sequence if -11 is the last term?

7. What is the sum of the first thirty multiples of 3?

8. For the following arithmetic sequence, answer the given questions: 8, 11, 14, ... (a) What is d? (b) What is S if $n = 30$? (c) What is the 50th term?

9. For the following arithmetic sequence, answer the given questions: 5, y, 12, ... (a) What is y? (b) What is d? (c) What is S if $n = 20$?

10. For the following arithmetic sequence, answer the given questions: 4, 7, 10, . . . , 175. (a) What is d? (b) What is n? (c) What is S?

11. For the following arithmetic sequence, answer the given questions: 2 $10/3$, ... (a) What is d? (b) What is the third term? (c) What is the 27th term?

12. For the following arithmetic sequence, answer the given questions: 8, s, t, u, 18, ... (a) What is s? (b) What is t? (c) What is u? (d) What is S if $n = 10$?

13. For the following arithmetic sequence, answer the given questions: 4, u, v, -2, ... (a) What is u? (b) What is v? (c) What is S if $n = 20$?

14. For the following arithmetic sequence, answer the given questions: -3, 1,5, . . . , 85. (a) What is d? (b) What is n? (c) What is S?

15. (a) If 2 is the first term of an arithmetic sequence and 52 is the 21st, what is d? (b) What is the sum of the first 21 terms?

16. A man secures a job with a starting salary of $8,300. If he receives a $500 a year raise each year, how much would his salary be during the 15th year?

17. In Exercise 16, what would be the man's total earnings for the fifteen years?

18. If a boy saved one cent the first day, two cents the second, three cents the third, four cents the fourth, etc., how long would it take him to save $40.95?

19. The numbers 1, 3, 6, 10, 15, . . . are called *triangular numbers*. The following figures indicate the origin of the name.

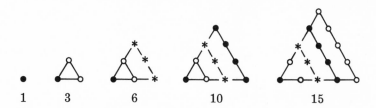

1   3   6   10   15

(a) Is the sequence of triangular numbers an arithmetic sequence?
(b) What are the sixth, seventh, eighth, ninth, and tenth triangular numbers?
(c) Show that the nth triangular number is the sum of the first n positive integers? (Give a geometric argument.)
(d) What is the sum of the first and second triangular numbers? Also, give the sums of the second and third, third and fourth, and fourth and fifth triangular numbers.
(e) What is the sum of the $(n-1)$st and the nth triangular numbers? Verify your answer geometrically and give an algebraic proof.

20. Find the sum of the first 10 triangular numbers. (See Exercise 19.)

21. (a) Verify the following: $2 + 4 + 2 = 2^3$; $3 + 6 + 9 + 6 + 3 = 3^3$; $4 + 8 + 12 + 16 + 12 + 8 + 4 = 4^3$; and $5 + 10 + 15 + 20 + 25 + 20 + 15 + 10 + 5 = 5^3$.
(b) Prove for any positive integer n that the sum $n + 2n + 3n + 4n + \cdots + (n-1)n + n^2 + (n-1)n + \cdots + 4n + 3n + 2n + n$ is n^3. *Hint:* Factor an n from the first n terms, factor an n from the last $(n-1)$ terms, and consider the two sums separately.

2. GEOMETRIC SEQUENCES

What is a large number? Bigness and smallness in numbers are quite relative and the answer to the question would depend on the position of the observer. Suppose the distance from the earth to the sun is measured as 93,000,000 miles and suppose the measurement is incorrect by 100,000 miles. The percentage of error in the measurement is only about one-half the percentage of error in the length of a yard stick that is 36.08 inches long. From the viewpoint of percentage of error, 0.08 inches is a bigger error than 100,000 miles.

How big is the national debt of the United States? In relation to the gross national product, some would say that it is not so very large. However, suppose we look at the size of the debt from a different viewpoint. In January 1973, the national debt was somewhat more than $440,000,000,000 (four hundred forty billion dollars). If a person were to count a dollar a second, sixty seconds each minute, sixty minutes each hour, twenty-four hours each day, and three hundred and sixty-five days each year without stopping to eat, sleep, etc., how long would it take to count the national debt? Ten minutes? Ten hours? Ten days? Perhaps ten years? Take a guess.

Since there are 60 seconds in a minute and 60 minutes in an hour, there are $60 \times 60 = 3{,}600$ seconds in an hour. Since there are 24 hours in a day, there are $24 \times 3{,}600 = 86{,}400$ seconds in a day and $365 \times 86{,}400 = 31{,}536{,}000$ seconds in a (nonleap) year. Thus, in one year, a person could count $31,536,000 at a dollar a second. Since the total national debt divided by the number of dollars that can be counted per year is

$$440{,}000{,}000{,}000 \div 31{,}536{,}000 = 13{,}952 \text{ approx.}$$

it would take in excess of 13,952 years to count the debt by the method described.

Another problem which has to do with the size of numbers is the following. If Mr. Smith were paid a salary of $10,000 a day for 31 days and Mr. Jones earned 1 cent the first day, 2 cents the second day, 4 cents the third day, 8 cents the fourth day, 16 cents the fifth day, 32 cents the sixth day, and 2^{n-1} cents the nth day, which thirty-one day total salary is the best? Since we bother to ask the question one might guess that Mr. Jones has the best salary. How much do you think Mr. Smith would have to make each day to have the same total salary as Mr. Jones? To determine how much Mr. Smith needs to make each day, we must find what Mr. Jones' total salary would be.

If S is Mr. Jones' salary, then

$$S = 1 + 2 + 2^2 + 2^3 + \cdots + 2^{29} + 2^{30} \text{ cents} \qquad (1)$$

Of course, one could find the sum by adding the thirty-one given numbers. However, the following procedure makes this unnecessary. Multiplying both sides of Equation (1) by 2, we obtain

$$2S = 2 + 2^2 + 2^3 + 2^4 + \cdots + 2^{30} + 2^{31} \qquad (2)$$

Subtracting, $\quad S = 1 + 2 + 2^2 + 2^3 + \cdots + 2^{29} + 2^{30} \quad$ from Eq. (2), we get $\qquad S = 2^{31} - 1$ cents

Since $\quad 2^4 = 16, \quad 2^8 = (2^4)^2 = (16)^2 = 256, \quad 2^{16} = (2^8)^2 = 256 \times 256 = 65,536,$ and $2^{31} = (2^{15})(2^{16}) = 32,768 \times 65,536 = 2,147,483,648,$ it follows that

$$(2^{31} - 1) \text{ cents} = 2,147,483,647 \text{ cents} = \$21,474,836.47$$

Since \$21,474,836.47 divided by 31 is approximately \$692,736.66, Mr. Smith would need to make \$692,736.66 a day (more than two-thirds of a million dollars a day) in order to have a thirty-one day salary equal to that of Mr. Jones!

geometric
sequence

common ratio

The salary schedule for Mr. Jones forms what is called a *geometric sequence*. In general, if a is the first term of a sequence and if each successive term is obtained by multiplying the preceding term by a fixed number r, then the sequence is called *geometric sequence*. The number r is called the *common ratio*. In a geometric sequence, a is the first term, ar is the second term, ar^2 is the third term, ar^3 is the fourth term, and ar^{n-1} is the nth term. In the geometric sequence

$$1, \quad 2, \quad 2^2, \quad 2^3, \quad 2^4, \quad \ldots, \quad 2^{29}, \quad 2^{30}$$

$a = 1$, $r = 2$, and $n = 31$. The procedure used to find the sum of this geometric sequence can be used to find the sum of any geometric sequence with a finite number of terms.

Consider the geometric sequence $a,\ ar,\ ar^2,\ ar^3,\ \ldots,\ ar^{n-2},$ ar^{n-1} with n terms and let

$$S = a + ar + ar^2 + ar^3 + \cdots + ar^{n-2} + ar^{n-1} \qquad (1)$$

Multiplying both sides of Equation (1) by the common ratio r, we obtain

$$rS = ar + ar^2 + ar^3 + ar^4 + \cdots + ar^{n-1} + ar^n \qquad (2)$$

Subtracting Equation (1) from Equation (2), we get

$$rS - S = ar^n - a$$

$$S(r - 1) = ar^n - a$$

and $\qquad S = \dfrac{ar^n - a}{r - 1} \qquad$ provided $r \neq 1$

If $r = 1$, each of the n terms of the sequence is a and the sum is na.

Example 1. Let $r = -\frac{1}{2}$ be the common ratio of a geometric sequence with first term 64. (a) Find the eighth term. (b) Find the sum of the first eight terms.

Solution: (a) The eighth term is $64(-\frac{1}{2})^7 = -\frac{1}{2}$.

(b) $S = \dfrac{(64)(-\frac{1}{2})^8 - 64}{(-\frac{1}{2}) - 1} = \dfrac{\frac{1}{4} - 64}{-\frac{3}{2}} = \dfrac{85}{2}$

A geometric sequence is obtained when money is deposited at compound interest. Suppose one deposits P dollars at an interest rate of 6 percent per year. At the end of one year the total amount on deposit is

$$P + 0.06P = (1.06)P$$

If the money is left on deposit, then at the end of the second year the amount of money on deposit is the total on deposit at the end of the first year plus the second year's interest; that is,

$$\begin{aligned}(1.06)P + (0.06)[(1.06)P] &= (1.06)P(1 + 0.06)\\ &= (1.06)P(1.06)\\ &= (1.06)^2 P\end{aligned}$$

At the end of three years, the amount is

$$(1.06)^3 P$$

and at the end of n years it is

$$(1.06)^n P$$

Notice that P, $(1.06)P$, $(1.06)^2 P$, . . . is a geometric sequence with first term P and common ratio 1.06.

You might like to know how long it takes to double your money if it is deposited at 6 percent interest and compounded annually. This involves determining the number n such that $(1.06)^n P = 2P$, or

$$(1.06)^n = 2$$

The answer can be found easily in interest tables. (See Appendix D for interest tables.) In an interest table, you will find that

$$(1.06)^{12} = 2.01219647$$

thus, in twelve years you would double your money with this type of investment.

Another method of solution is to use logarithms. If

$$(1.06)^n = 2$$

then
$$\log_{10}(1.06)^n = \log_{10} 2$$
$$n \log_{10}(1.06) = \log_{10} 2$$

Using logarithm tables, $\qquad 0.0253n = 0.3010$

$$n = \frac{3010}{253} \approx 11.9$$

Consequently, 12 years would more than double the savings.

Suppose we have a geometric sequence with a common ratio between -1 and 1. Note that the sum of n terms of the sequence can be expressed as follows:

$$S = \frac{a - ar^n}{1 - r} = \frac{a}{1 - r} - \frac{ar^n}{1 - r}$$

When $-1 < r < 1$, we see for "large" n that $ar^n/(1 - r)$ can be made arbitrarily small. For example, consider the geometric sequence 1, $1/2, 1/2^2, \ldots, 1/2^{n-1}$. The sum is

$$1 + \frac{1}{2} + \frac{1}{2^2} + \cdots + \frac{1}{2^{n-1}} = \frac{1}{1 - \frac{1}{2}} - \frac{(\frac{1}{2})^n}{1 - \frac{1}{2}} = 2 - \frac{1}{2^{n-1}}$$

For "large" n, $1/2^{n-1}$ can be made as small as we please. Hence, the sum can be made as close to 2 as we want by selecting n sufficiently large.

We call

$$1 + \frac{1}{2} + \frac{1}{2^2} + \frac{1}{2^3} + \cdots + \frac{1}{2^{n-1}} + \cdots$$

infinite
geometric
series

an *infinite geometric series*. Since the sum of n terms can be made arbitrarily close to 2 by choosing n large enough, we say that the *sum* of the infinite geometric series is 2.

In general, an *infinite geometric series* has the form

$$a + ar + ar^2 + ar^3 + ar^4 + \cdots + ar^{n-1} + \cdots$$

If $-1 < r < 1$, the *sum* is $a/(1 - r)$. It is more tedious than difficult to prove that infinite geometric series "behave" like finite sums. For example, if b is a real number and $-1 < r < 1$, then we can prove that

$$b(a + ar + ar^2 + ar^3 + \cdots) = ba + bar + bar^2 + bar^3 + \cdots$$

This is the distributive property for an infinite geometric series. In addition to the distributive property, we can also prove the associative and commutative properties for such infinite geometric sums.

Observe that the repeating decimal $0.333\bar{3}$. . . (with period one) represents the infinite geometric series

$$\frac{3}{10} + \frac{3}{10^2} + \frac{3}{10^3} + \frac{3}{10^4} + \cdots + \frac{3}{10^{n-1}} + \cdots$$

where $\frac{3}{10}$ is the first term and $\frac{1}{10}$ is the common ratio. The sum is

$$\frac{a}{1 - r} = \frac{\frac{3}{10}}{1 - \frac{1}{10}} = \frac{\frac{3}{10}}{\frac{9}{10}} = \frac{1}{3}$$

Similarly, the infinite repeating decimal $0.41414\overline{1}$. . . (with period two) represents the infinite geometric series

$$\frac{41}{10^2} + \frac{41}{10^4} + \frac{41}{10^6} + \cdots$$

where $^{41}/_{100}$ is the first term and $1/10^2$ is the common ratio. Thus, the sum is

$$\frac{^{41}/_{100}}{1 - ^{1}/_{100}} = \frac{41}{100 - 1} = \frac{41}{99}$$

As a final example, observe that $3.213131\overline{3}$. . . represents the sum $3.2 + 0.013131\overline{3}$. . . . Hence,

$$3.213131\overline{3}. . . = \frac{32}{10} + \left(\frac{13}{10^3} + \frac{13}{10^5} + \frac{13}{10^7} + \cdots\right)$$

Thus, $\quad 3.213131\overline{3}. . . = \frac{16}{5} + \frac{^{13}/_{1000}}{1 - ^{1}/_{100}} = \frac{16}{5} + \frac{13}{990} = \frac{3,181}{990}$

It should be obvious that an infinite repeating decimal with period p represents either an infinite geometric series or the sum of a rational number and a geometric series where the series has common ratio $1/10^p$. Furthermore, since the first term a and ratio r are rational numbers, the sum $a/(1 - r)$ is a rational number. Hence, every repeating infinite decimal represents a rational number.

From the definition of infinite decimals and the definition of the sum of an infinite geometric series, we see that

$$0.9999. . . = \frac{9}{10} + \frac{9}{10^2} + \frac{9}{10^3} + \frac{9}{10^4} + \cdots$$

$$= \frac{^{9}/_{10}}{1 - ^{1}/_{10}}$$

$$= 1$$

Hence, $1 = 0.999\overline{9}$. . . ; thus $1.0000\overline{0}$. . . ; and $0.9999\overline{9}$. . . are two different decimal representations for the same rational number. However, if we rule out the use of such repeating nines in the decimal notation, then each rational number, fortunately, can be written as a decimal in one and only one way.

Corresponding to the step up the mathematical ladder from repeating decimals to nonrepeating decimals is the step from infinite geometric series to the more general mathematical concept of *infinite series*. Infinite series provide a way to put the real number system on a sound foundation. Also, infinite series have many other practical applications and the theory of infinite series forms a very large and important body of mathematics.

EXERCISES

1. For each of the following geometric sequences find the common ratio and the 7th term.
   (a) $3, -3, 3, \ldots$ (b) $2, 6, 18, \ldots$ (c) $4, -2, 1 \ldots$

2. For each of the following geometric sequences find the common ratio and the 6th term.
   (a) $3, 6, 12, \ldots$ (b) $81, -27, 9, \ldots$ (c) $60, 30, 15, \ldots$

3. For each of the following geometric sequences, find the common ratio and the 6th term.
   (a) $\frac{2}{3}, \frac{1}{3}, \frac{1}{6}, \ldots$ (b) $8, -2, \frac{1}{2}, \ldots$ (c) $3, 3.6, 4.32, \ldots$

4. Find the sum of the first ten terms of each of the following geometric sequences.
   (a) $81, -27, 9, \ldots$ (b) $8, -2, \frac{1}{2}, \ldots$

5. For each of the following geometric sequences answer the given questions.
   (a) $4, -2, 1, \ldots$ What is the sum S if $n = 10$?
   (b) $2, x, 9, \ldots$ What is x if x is positive?
   (c) $16, x, y, 54, \ldots$ What are x and y?

6. For each of the following geometric sequences answer the given questions.
   (a) $81, -27, 9, \ldots$ What is the sum S if $n = 8$?
   (b) $49, x, 16, \ldots$ What is x if x is positive?
   (c) $125, x, y, 8, \ldots$ What are x and y?

7. For each of the following geometric sequences, answer the given questions.
   (a) $2, x, 7, \ldots$ What is x if x is positive?
   (b) $3, x, y, \frac{8}{9}, \ldots$ What are x and y?

8. For each of the following geometric sequences, answer the given questions.
   (a) $5, x, 12, \ldots$ What is x if x is positive?
   (b) $-4, x, y, \frac{27}{16}, \ldots$ What are x and y?

9. What is the sixth term of each sequence in Exercise 7?

10. What is the sixth term of each sequence in Exercise 8?

11. If the first three terms of a geometric sequence are $x, x + 3, 2x - 2$ where each is positive, find the common ratio and the first three terms.

12. Let 2 be the first term of a geometric sequence of positive numbers. If $2 + b$ is the second term and $4 + b$ is the third term, what number does b represent?

13. (a) Let P be the amount of money put on deposit in a savings account with i as the annual interest rate. If the original investment and interest are left on deposit, show that the interest on the savings in the nth year is $P(1 + i)^{n-1}i$.

(b) Use the result in part (a) and the formula for the sum of geometric series to show that the value of the investment at the end of n years is $P(1 + i)^n$.

14. Let P be the principal invested at an annual interest rate i. If the interest is compounded 4 times per year for n years, prove that the amount A on deposit at the end of n years is given by $A = P(1 + i/4)^{4n}$.

15. (a) If $1,000 is invested with a 5 percent interest rate which is compounded quarterly, what is the value of the investment at the end of the year? (See Exercise 14.)
(b) What simple interest would be equivalent to the 5 percent interest compounded quarterly?

16. How many years would it take to double your investment if money were deposited at 6 percent compounded quarterly? (See Exercise 14.)

17. How many years would it take to double your investment if money were deposited at 5 percent compounded quarterly? (See Exercise 14.)

18. How many years would it take to double your investment if money were deposited at 3 percent compounded quarterly? (See Exercise 14.)

19. How long must a given sum of money be invested at 5 percent interest compounded annually in order to receive the equal return of a ten year investment at 3 percent interest rate compounded quarterly? (See Exercise 14.)

20. Suppose $5,000 is deposited at 5 percent compounded quarterly. If no money is added or withdrawn from the account, what would be the total amount on deposit at the end of 5 years? (See Exercise 14.)

3. A LOOK AT THE PRIMES

As we said earlier, any positive integer, except 1, which has only itself and 1 as positive factors, is a prime number. The first fifteen primes are 2, 3, 5, 7, 11, 13, 17, 19, 23, 29, 31, 37, 41, 43, and 47. Since every even number has 2 as a factor, 2 is the only even prime. Every positive integer, except 1, which is not a prime is called *composite*. For example, 4, 6, 8, 10, 12, 14, 15, etc., are composite numbers. Many statements which are true for the prime numbers are not true for 1 and many statements which are true for the composites are not true for 1. For example, the important Fundamental Theorem of Arithmetic, which states that a composite number can be expressed as the product of primes in one and only one way, would not be true if 1 were either prime or composite. Hence, for convenience the set of primes and the set of composites are defined in such a way as to exclude 1 from both sets.

composite

The questions one can ask concerning the prime numbers are legion. Many interesting questions arise by careful consideration of a table containing the primes less than 1,000. (See Table 1.)

---

1. Is there a formula that will give all the prime numbers? (Is there a formula from which Table 1 could be easily constructed?)

2. Is the set of primes a finite or infinite set?

3. If the set of primes is finite, how many prime numbers are there?

4. How many primes are there between 1,000 and 2,000?

5. Since every even number greater than 2 is composite, every prime greater than 2 must be odd and differ from the next prime by at least two. How many pairs of primes are there whose difference is exactly two?

6. Is it possible to find a million consecutive positive integers none of which is a prime?

Let us answer the last question first. Consider the number $N = 6 \times 5 \times 4 \times 3 \times 2 \times 1$; of course, N is 720, but for our purposes it is better to leave it expressed as a product. Since N has 2 as a factor, $N + 2$ has 2 as a factor. (This follows from the well-known fact that if two integers a and b have an integer x as a factor, then their sum $a + b$ also has x as a factor.) Similarly, since N has 3 as a factor, $N + 3$ has 3 as a factor. Continuing, $N + 4$ has 4 as a factor, $N + 5$ has 5 as a factor, and $N + 6$ has 6 as a factor. Thus, none of the five consecutive numbers

$$N + 2, \quad N + 3, \quad N + 4, \quad N + 5, \quad N + 6$$

is a prime since each has a positive factor other than itself and 1. The reader can observe in Table 1 that 722, 723, 724, 725, and 726 are not primes.

In the preceding argument we could have used $M = 10 \times 9 \times 8 \times 7 \times 6 \times 5 \times 4 \times 3 \times 2 \times 1$ and none of the nine consecutive numbers

$$M + 2, \ M + 3, \ M + 4, \ M + 5, \ M + 6, \ M + 7, \ M + 8, \ M + 9, \ M + 10$$

would be a prime. In general, let n be a positive integer and consider the product of the positive integers less than or equal to n. Usually, the product $n \times (n - 1) \times (n - 2) \times \cdots \times 3 \times 2 \times 1$ is denoted by $n!$ (read "n factorial"); thus, $6! = 6 \times 5 \times 4 \times 3 \times 2 \times 1$. It follows that none of the $n - 1$ consecutive numbers

$$n! + 2, \quad n! + 3, \quad n! + 4, \quad n! + 5, \quad \ldots, \quad n! + n$$

is a prime. Since n could be a million and one, this means that there

Table 1. Primes and Twin Primes

	2	3	5	7	11	13	17	19	23	29
25	31	37	41	43	47	53	59	61	67	71
	73	79	83	89	97					
	101	103	107	109	113	127	131	137	139	149
21	151	157	163	167	173	179	181	191	193	197
	199									
16	211	223	227	229	233	239	241	251	257	263
	269	271	277	281	283	293				
16	307	311	313	317	331	337	347	349	353	359
	367	373	379	383	389	397				
17	401	409	419	421	431	433	439	443	449	457
	461	463	467	479	487	491	499			
14	503	509	521	523	541	547	557	563	569	571
	577	587	593	599						
16	601	607	613	617	619	731	641	643	647	653
	659	661	673	677	683	691				
14	701	709	719	727	733	739	743	751	757	761
	769	773	787	797						
15	809	811	821	823	827	829	839	853	857	859
	863	877	881	883	887					
14	907	911	919	929	937	941	947	953	967	971
	977	983	991	997						

are indeed a million consecutive composite numbers.

Since we can find a billion (or a billion-billion) consecutive composite numbers, we might be tempted to conjecture that the set of primes is a finite set and that there is a last (largest) prime. However, this is not true and a proof that the set of prime numbers is an infinite set was given two thousand years ago by Euclid.

Let us prove that there is no last prime. Although the proof is neither long nor complicated, it requires a familiarity with some basic ideas of logic. The proof is an indirect one (reductio ad absurdum). We show that the assumption that there is a last prime leads to contradictory statements. A resulting contradiction makes the assumption untenable and we conclude there is no last prime.

Theorem. *The set of prime numbers is not a finite set.*

Proof: Assume there is a last (largest) prime and let it be t. Now, consider the number x which is the sum of 1 and the product of *all* primes from 2 to t; that is, let

$$x = 1 + (2 \times 3 \times 5 \times 7 \times \cdot \cdot \cdot \times t)$$

Since x is greater than the last prime t, we conclude that x is a composite number and, hence, must have some prime p as a factor. Now, p must be one of the primes in the product $(2 \times 3 \times 5 \times 7 \times \cdot \cdot \cdot \times t)$ since there are no other primes. Next, using the fact that if two numbers have a common factor then their difference also has the number as a factor, we conclude that

$$x - (2 \times 3 \times 5 \times 7 \times \cdot \cdot \cdot \times t)$$

has p as a factor. But, this difference is equal to 1, and p is *not* a factor of 1. Since the assumption that there is a finite number of primes leads to a contradiction, it follows that the set is an infinite set.

As seen in Table 1, there are 168 primes less than 1,000. Between 1,000 and 2,000 there are 135 primes and between 2,000 and 3,000 there are 127 primes. Unfortunately, a formula has never been discovered which will give the exact number of primes less than any integer n. (There is a rather complicated formula using the Riemann integral which can be used to approximate the number of primes less than a positive integer n. It can be found in almost any book on number theory.)

Let us complete this section by discussing Question 5. If p and q *twin primes* are primes and if they differ by two, then they are called *twin primes.* For example, 3 and 5, 5 and 7, 11 and 13, 17 and 19, and 29 and 31 are pairs of twin primes. Although mathematicians have solved many deep and difficult problems concerning the set of primes, it remains an open question whether or not the set of twin primes is a finite set; it is another famous unsolved problem.

EXERCISES

1. Express each of the following numbers as the product or powers of primes.
   (a) 28   (b) 64   (c) 320
   (d) 420   (e) 426   (f) 1,800

2. Express each of the following numbers as the product or powers of primes.

(a) 384   (b) 628   (c) 895
(d) 424   (e) 273   (f) 909

3. List all of the factors of each of the following numbers.

(a) 28   (b) 64   (c) 320
(d) 420   (e) 6,128   (f) 884

4. From the first 50 primes, list each pair whose difference is 2.

5. Can every even integer greater than 5 and less than 101 be expressed (in at least one way) as the sum of two odd primes?

6. (a) Is $n^2 - n + 41$ a prime number for $n = 1, 2, 3, 4, 5, 6, 7, 8, 9, 10$?
   (b) Is $n^2 - n + 41$ a prime number for every positive integer n?

7. (a) Can you express each odd integer between 4 and 100 as the sum of a power of 2 and a prime number?
   (b) Can you express each odd integer between 144 and 150 as the sum of a power of 2 and a prime number?

8. (a) Find a prime number p such that p, $p + 2$, and $p + 4$ are all prime numbers.
   (b) Is it possible to find more than one prime triple as described in part (a)?

9. List twelve consecutive composite numbers.

10. (a) Find at least 5 positive integers for N such that $N^2 + 1$ is a prime number.
    (b) It is unknown whether or not the set of primes of the form $N^2 + 1$ is an infinite set. How many primes are there of the form $N^2 - 1$?

11. (a) Find five positive integers for q which make $2^q - 1$ a prime.
    (b) If q is a composite number, what can you conclude about $2^q - 1$?

12. Let $p_1, p_2, p_3, \ldots$ be the sequence of primes; that is, $p_1 = 2$, $p_2 = 3$, $p_3 = 5$, etc. Notice that $(2 \times 3) - 1 = 5$ and $(2 \times 3) + 1 = 7$ are both primes.
    (a) If
    $$(p_1 \times p_2 \times p_3 \times \cdots \times p_n) - 1$$
    and
    $$(p_1 \times p_2 \times p_3 \times \cdots \times p_n) + 1$$
    were always primes, what unsolved problem would be solved?
    (b) Is it true that $(p_1 \times p_2 \times p_3 \times \cdots \times p_n) - 1$ is always a prime? (*Hint:* Try several examples.)
    (c) Is it true that $(p_1 \times p_2 \times p_3 \times \cdots \times p_n) + 1$ is always a prime?

4. MAKING CONJECTURES

New mathematical ideas and facts can be created in many ways. For example, we can generalize existing ideas and concepts, we can reason by analogy and create new structures similar to old structures, and we can observe patterns of various kinds and make conjectures. It is the latter method of development that we consider in this section.

Observing patterns, reasoning inductively, and making conjectures can lead us down several avenues. For example, we found in the last section that $n^2 - n + 41$ is a prime for $n = 1, 2, 3, 4, 5, 6, 7, 8, 9$, and 10. In fact, the expression yields a prime for each of the first forty positive integers. An intelligent conjecture to make (though incorrect) is that the expression always gives a prime. Obviously, for $n = 41$, $n^2 - n + 41 = (41)^2 = 1,681$ is not a prime. Thus, we can see that a false statement can be obtained by making what appears to be a reasonable conjecture.

In Exercise 5 of the last section, we found that each of the even integers greater than 4 and less than 101 could be expressed as the sum of two odd primes. With sufficient time, we could show that each even number between 100 and 200 could be expressed as the sum of two odd primes. Thus, we might be led to conjecture that *every* even integer greater than 4 could be expressed as the sum of two odd primes. In the process, we would not only discover a famous conjecture in mathematics called *Goldbach's conjecture* but would uncover a famous unsolved problem.

Of course, making a conjecture that is correct is most rewarding. Making one that we are able to *prove* correct is the real "payoff." We see that a conjecture we make may be false; it is often shown false by counterexample. A conjecture we make that is true may result in a theorem we can prove, it may result in a theorem we are presently unable to prove, or it may result in a theorem that no mathematician is presently able to prove. In the exercise set that follows, you will be asked to make several conjectures but will be called on to prove very few. The adventuresome student is encouraged to take on the challenge independently and to try to prove some of the conjectures.

EXERCISES

1. (a) List all positive factors of 20.
   (b) List all positive factors of 45.
   (c) What is the greatest factor that 20 and 45 have in common?
2. (a) List all positive factors of 18.
   (b) List all positive factors of 30.
   (c) What is the greatest factor that 18 and 30 have in common?
3. (a) List all positive factors of 360.
   (b) List all positive factors of 234.
   (c) What is the greatest factor that 360 and 234 have in common?

4. (a) List all positive factors of 693.
   (b) List all positive factors of 1,260.
   (c) What is the greatest factor that 693 and 1,260 have in common?

5. (a) Find the product 20×45.
   (b) Find the quotient $(20 \times 45) \div G$ where G is the greatest factor that 20 and 45 have in common. (See Exercise 1.)
   (c) Is the quotient in part (b) a multiple of both 20 and 45?
   (d) Do 20 and 45 have any multiple in common less than that found in part (b)?

6. (a) Find the product 18×30.
   (b) Find the quotient $(18 \times 30) \div G$ where G is the greatest factor that 18 and 30 have in common. (See Exercise 2.)
   (c) Is the quotient in part (b) a multiple of both 18 and 30?
   (d) Do 18 and 30 have any multiple in common less than that found in part (b)?

7. (a) Find the product 360×234.
   (b) Find the quotient $(360 \times 234) \div G$ where G is the greatest factor that 360 and 234 have in common. (See Exercise 3.)
   (c) Is the quotient in part (b) a multiple of both 360 and 234?
   (d) Do 360 and 234 have any multiple in common less than that found in part (b)?

8. (a) Find the product $693 \times 1,260$.
   (b) Find the quotient $(693 \times 1,260) \div G$ where G is the greatest factor that 693 and 1,260 have in common. (See Exercise 4.)
   (c) Is the quotient in part (b) a multiple of both 693 and 1,260?
   (d) Do 693 and 1,260 have any multiple in common less than that found in part (b)?

9. Use Exercises 1 through 9 to make a conjecture. (No proof required.)

10. (a) Try to express each positive integer greater than 2 and less than 30 as the sum of two consecutive integers.
    (b) Make conjectures as a result of your answers in part (a).
    (c) Try to prove or disprove your conjectures in part (b).

11. (a) Can you find a positive integer n such that

$$1 + n(n + 1)(n + 2)(n + 3)$$

is a perfect square?
    (b) Find seven integers, if possible, that make the expression in part (a) a perfect square.
    (c) Make a conjecture as a result of your answers to part (b).
    (d) Try to prove or disprove your conjecture.

12. If $s(n)$ represents the sum of all of the factors of n, find each of the following. (Recall that 1 and n are factors of n and see Exercise 1 in the previous section.)
    (a) $s(28)$ (b) $s(64)$ (c) $s(320)$ (d) $s(420)$

13. Two positive integers are said to be *relatively prime* if they have no factors in common except 1. For example, 2 and 7 are relatively prime;

3 and 8 are relatively prime; and 14 and 15 are relatively prime.

(a) Is it true that two different prime numbers are relatively prime?

(b) Need two numbers be primes to be relatively prime?

14. Let $s(n)$ represent the sum of all of the factors of a positive integer n. For each of the following pairs of integers m and n find $s(m)$, $s(n)$, and $s(mn)$.

(a) $m = 2$ and $n = 3$ (b) $m = 5$ and $n = 7$

(c) $m = 4$ and $n = 7$ (d) $m = 4$ and $n = 15$

(e) $m = 4$ and $n = 6$ (f) $m = 6$ and $n = 21$

15. (a) If p is a prime number, what is $s(p)$? (*Hint:* See Exercise 12.)

(b) If p and q are different primes, is it true that $s(p)s(q) = s(pq)$? Verify your answer.

(c) If p is a prime, is $s(p^2) = [s(p)]^2$?

16. (a) If m and n are any positive integers, is it true that $s(m)s(n) = s(mn)$? Verify your answer.

(b) Use enough examples to make a conjecture as to when $s(m)s(n) = s(mn)$. (You need not prove your conjecture.)

17. If $d(n)$ represents the total number of factors of n, find each of the following: (See Exercise 12.)

(a) $d(28)$ (b) $d(64)$ (c) $d(320)$ (d) $d(420)$

18. If $s(n)$ represents the sum of all factors of n and if $d(n)$ represents the number of factors of n, find each of the following:

(a) $s(27)$ (b) $s(39)$ (c) $s(632)$ (d) $s(1,900)$

(e) $d(27)$ (f) $d(39)$ (g) $d(632)$ (h) $d(1,900)$

19. Let $d(n)$ represent the number of all of the factors of a positive integer n. For each of the following pairs of integers m and n find $d(m)$, $d(n)$, and $d(mn)$.

(a) $m = 2$ and $n = 3$ (b) $m = 5$ and $n = 7$

(c) $m = 4$ and $n = 7$ (d) $m = 4$ and $n = 15$

(e) $m = 4$ and $n = 6$ (f) $m = 6$ and $n = 21$

20. (a) If p is a prime number what is $d(p)$? (*Hint:* See Exercise 19.)

(b) If p and q are different primes, is it true that $d(p)d(q) = d(pq)$? Verify your answer.

(c) If p is a prime number, is $d(p^2) = [d(p)]^2$?

21. (a) If m and n are any positive integers, is it true that $d(m)d(n) = d(mn)$? Verify your answer.

(b) Use enough examples to make a conjecture as to when $d(m)d(n) = d(mn)$. (You need not prove your conjecture.)

22. (a) If $N = p^q$ where p is a prime and q is a positive integer, prove that the sum of all of the factors of N is given by

$$s(N) = \frac{p^{q+1} - 1}{p - 1}$$

(b) If $N = p_1^q p_2^r$ where p_1 and p_2 are primes and q and r are positive integers, show that

$$s(N) = \frac{p_1^{q+1} - 1}{p_1 - 1} \times \frac{p_2^{r+1} - 1}{p_2 - 1}$$

(c) Generalize the results in parts (a) and (b) and verify your formula by using it to find $s(28)$, $s(64)$, $s(320)$, $s(420)$, $s(426)$, and $s(1,800)$. (See Exercise 12.)

23. (a) If $N = p^q$ where p is a prime and q is a positive integer, prove that the total number of factors of N is given by $d(N) = (q + 1)$.
(b) If $N = p_1^q p_2^r$ where p_1 and p_2 are primes and q and r are positive integers, prove that $d(N) = (q + 1)(r + 1)$.
(c) Generalize the results in parts (a) and (b) and verify your formula by using it to find $d(28)$, $d(64)$, $d(320)$, $d(420)$, $d(426)$, and $d(1,800)$. (See Exercise 17.)

24. Use the indicated formula in Exercise 22 to find each of the following:
(a) $s(27)$ (b) $s(39)$ (c) $s(632)$

25. Use the indicated formula in Exercise 23 to find each of the following:
(a) $d(27)$ (b) $d(39)$ (c) $d(632)$

26. (a) Let $\phi(n)$ be the number of positive integers less than n and relatively prime to n. (See Exercise 13.) For example, since 1 and 5 are the only positive integers less than 6 which are relatively prime to 6, we have that $\phi(6) = 2$. Find $\phi(7)$, $\phi(15)$, $\phi(28)$, $\phi(60)$, and $\phi(64)$.
(b) Use your answers to part (a) to check the following formula known as Euler's *phi-function*. Let n be a positive integer and let p_1, p_2, p_3, . . . , p_k be the prime factors of n; then,

$$\phi(n) = n \left(1 - \frac{1}{p_1}\right)\left(1 - \frac{1}{p_2}\right)\left(1 - \frac{1}{p_3}\right) \cdots \left(1 - \frac{1}{p_k}\right)$$

27. Determine each of the following by two methods. (See Exercise 26.)
(a) $\phi(27)$ (b) $\phi(39)$ (c) $\phi(632)$ (d) $\delta(200)$

5. PERFECT NUMBERS

As we mentioned earlier, the Pythagoreans attributed a mystical quality to numbers. Besides separating the positive integers into the classes of primes and composites, they also had such distinguishing classifications as triangular, square, friendly, and perfect numbers. Today, any such classification for numbers has a precise definition, which is applied to numbers on a nonemotional basis. Few would consider any numbers as really *friendly* or *perfect* in the literal sense; perhaps lucky or unlucky, but that is another thing. (Or is it?)

Let us state precisely what a perfect number is and consider some of the problems associated with the set of perfect numbers. This set is not of overwhelming importance in any practical applications of mathematics, but it does give us a vehicle to show how ideas are created and expanded in mathematics. Some of the problems concerning perfect numbers were solved more than two thousand years ago by the Pythagoreans. Although great strides were made in the last two centuries in settling some of the unanswered questions pertaining to these numbers, several questions remain unanswered today.

Consider the factors of the positive integer 6; they are 1, 2, 3, and 6. If $s(6)$ (read, "s of 6") represents the sum of the positive factors of 6, then $s(6) = 1 + 2 + 3 + 6 = 12$. Note that the sum of the factors of 6 is twice six; that is, $s(6) = 2 \times 6$. This distinguishing feature qualifies 6 as a perfect number. In general, if $s(n)$ represents the sum of the positive factors of a positive integer n, then n is called a

perfect
number

perfect number if and only if $s(n) = 2n$; that is, the sum of all of the positive factors is twice the number.

If the set of perfect numbers is to have any real interest, then the set should contain more than the integer 6. We can prove by brute strength (and some awkwardness) that there are other perfect numbers. For example, 28 is also a perfect number as is shown by the following.

Positive factors of 28: 1, 2, 4, 7, 14, and 28.

$$s(28) = 1 + 2 + 4 + 7 + 14 + 28 = 56 = 2 \times 28$$

The first five perfect numbers are:

$$6, \quad 28, \quad 496, \quad 8{,}128, \quad \text{and} \quad 33{,}550{,}336$$

If these were all of the perfect numbers or if we knew that there were only a finite number of them, the set might lose some of its charm and challenge. Suppose there are only five perfect numbers; we could prove that, say, all perfect numbers were even by just showing each had 2 as a factor. Furthermore, the statement—every perfect number has 6 or 8 as its last digit—would be obvious if those listed were the only perfect numbers. Sets not having a finite number of elements (that is, *infinite sets*) usually present more interest and challenge than finite sets since a statement about all the elements in the set cannot be proved true or false by trial and error. (Even for a finite set, a mathematician would find "trial and error" a somewhat pedestrian way to prove a statement. If it were necessary to resort to this approach, he might very well dignify the approach by calling it a "proof by cases.") Of course, if it is unknown whether or not a set is finite, this presents another problem to be solved as well as nullifying a "proof by cases."

After discovering the first five perfect numbers, a little thought coupled with some intellectual curiosity should cause us to seek the answers to several questions concerning the set of perfect numbers. Each arises rather naturally by giving careful consideration to the first five perfect numbers listed above.

1. Is the set of perfect numbers finite or infinite?
2. Are there any odd perfect numbers?
3. Can one obtain a formula that will give all the perfect numbers?
4. If there are more than five perfect numbers, what is the sixth?
5. Is it true that the last digits in the sequence of even perfect numbers alternate between 6 and 8?
6. If the last digits do not alternate between 6 and 8, then does each perfect number still have 6 or 8 as its last digit?

Let us express each of the first five perfect numbers as the product of primes and powers of primes.

$$6 = 2 \times 3$$
$$28 = 4 \times 7 = 2^2 \times 7$$
$$496 = 16 \times 31 = 2^4 \times 31$$
$$8128 = 64 \times 127 = 2^6 \times 127$$
$$33{,}550{,}336 = 4096 \times 8191 = 2^{12} \times 8191$$

We see that each of the five perfect numbers is a product of two numbers: the first number is a power of 2 and the second number is a *prime which is twice the first factor less one.* Thus,

$$6 = 2(2^2 - 1)$$
$$28 = 2^2(2^3 - 1)$$
$$496 = 2^4(2^5 - 1)$$
$$8128 = 2^6(2^7 - 1)$$
$$33{,}550{,}336 = 2^{12}(2^{13} - 1)$$

where the second factor is a prime.

The careful observer looking for a pattern might (wisely, but incorrectly) think that $2^8(2^9 - 1)$ or $2^{10}(2^{11} - 1)$ would be a perfect number. We shall see that the reason they are not perfect is that $2^9 - 1$ and $2^{11} - 1$ are *not* primes. If we remember some basic facts from algebra, it is trivial to see that $2^9 - 1$ is not a prime number. Recalling that $x^3 - y^3$ has $x - y$ as a factor, we observe that

$$2^9 - 1 = (2^3)^3 - 1^3$$

is the difference of two cubes and has $2^3 - 1 = 7$ as a factor. In fact, a similar argument will show that $2^q - 1$ cannot be a prime *unless* q is a prime number. Now, since 11 is a prime number it is not so obvious that $2^{11} - 1$ is not a prime. By doing a little arithmetic, we can prove that

$$2^{11} - 1 = 2047 = (23)(89)$$

Hence $2^{11} - 1$ has factors other than itself and one and is not a prime.

In the above discussion, we assumed that the second factor $2^q - 1$ must be a prime number for the product to be a perfect number. This is actually the case for any even perfect number, but it is not trivial to prove. However, it is fairly easy to prove that if

$$N = 2^{p-1}(2^p - 1) \quad \text{where } 2^p - 1 \text{ is a prime}$$

then N is a perfect number. We first exhibit the validity of this statement by using a numerical example; it will serve as a pattern for the proof of the general statement. (A wise approach for the mathematically uninitiated to take for such a problem.)

Example. Let us prove that if $N = 2^4(2^5 - 1)$ where $2^5 - 1$ is the prime 31, then N is a perfect number. First, we need to know each of the factors of $496 = 2^4(2^5 - 1)$ in order to find the sum of the factors. The following is a significant and routine method to find all of the factors. Since $2^5 - 1$ is a prime number, the only factors of $2^4(2^5 - 1)$ are 1, 2, 2^2, 2^3, 2^4, and each of these numbers times the prime $2^5 - 1$. Thus, the factors are

$$1, 2, 2^2, 2^3, 2^4, 2^5 - 1, 2^6 - 2, 2^7 - 2^2, 2^8 - 2^3, \text{ and } 2^9 - 2^4$$

If we add these factors, something very desirable happens; namely, 1, 2, 2^2, 2^3, and 2^4 add out. Thus,

$$s(496) = 2^5 + 2^6 + 2^7 + 2^8 + 2^9 \quad \text{(A geometric progression)} \qquad (1)$$

Multiplying each side by 2, we get

$$2s(496) = 2^6 + 2^7 + 2^8 + 2^9 + 2^{10} \qquad (2)$$

Subtracting Equation (1) from (2), we get

$$\begin{aligned} s(496) &= 2^{10} - 2^5 \\ &= 2^5(2^5 - 1) \\ &= 2[2^4(2^5 - 1)] \\ &= 2 \times 496 \end{aligned}$$

Thus, 496 is perfect.*

Now let us prove the general statement. If $N = 2^{p-1}(2^p - 1)$ where $2^p - 1$ is a prime, then all the factors are obtained as follows. The factors of 2^{p-1} are

$$1, 2, 2^2, 2^3, 2^4, \ldots, 2^{p-1}$$

---

* We could have used the formula for the sum of a geometric progression.

and the factors of the prime $2^p - 1$ are

$$1 \quad \text{and} \quad 2^p - 1$$

Thus, all possible factors of N are

$$1, \, 2, \, 2^2, \, \ldots, \, 2^{p-1}, \, (2^p - 1), \, 2(2^p - 1), \, 2^2(2^p - 1), \, \ldots, \, 2^{p-1}(2^p - 1)$$

Now, the sum $s(N)$ of all factors of N is

$$s(N) = 2^p + 2^{p+1} + 2^{p+2} + \cdots + 2^{2p-2} + 2^{2p-1} \tag{1}$$

Thus, $\qquad 2s(N) = 2^{p+1} + 2^{p+2} + 2^{p+3} + \cdots + 2^{2p-1} + 2^{2p} \tag{2}$

Subtracting Equation (1) from (2), we get

$$\begin{aligned}
s(N) &= 2^{2p} - 2^p \\
&= 2^p(2^p - 1) \\
&= 2[2^{p-1}(2^p - 1)] \\
&= 2N
\end{aligned}$$

Hence, N is a perfect number.

We have proved that every number of the form $2^{p-1}(2^p - 1)$ where $2^p - 1$ is a prime is a perfect number. It would be of interest to know if every *even* perfect number is of this form. In other words, we would like to be able to state that an even number was perfect if and only if it had the given form. In fact, the statement is true. Although a proof is not extremely difficult, we shall not give it here. In the exercise set, we outline a proof.

If we could prove that there were an infinite number of prime numbers of the form $2^p - 1$, we could conclude that the set of even perfect numbers is infinite. Father Marin Mersenne (1588–1648) asserted in 1644 that the only primes p less than or equal to 257 for which $2^p - 1$ is a prime are

$$p = 2, \, 3, \, 5, \, 7, \, 13, \, 17, \, 19, \, 31, \, 67, \, 127, \, 257$$

Primes of the form $2^p - 1$ came to be called *Mersenne primes*. One can only speculate on the ingenuity required of Mersenne to produce these 11 numbers. For example, $2^{67} - 1$ is a 21 digit number! Without the aid of modern computers, it is highly unlikely that one would discover by trial and error that $2^{257} - 1$ was a prime.

Mersenne primes

Mersenne's assertion concerning these primes (which would give the first 11 perfect numbers) stood as fact for nearly 300 years. In October of 1903, an American mathematician by the name of Cole submitted a paper to be delivered at the American Mathematical Society's meeting at Brown University with the modest title "On the Factorization of Large Numbers." The story goes that upon being called on to deliver his paper, Professor Cole went to the board in front of this most august body of American mathematicians and proceed to raise 2 to the 67th power; then, he subtracted 1 from the resulting 21 digit number and let the answer stand. He then proceeded without having spoken a word to a clean part of the board and multiplied out the product

$$193{,}707{,}721 \times 761{,}838{,}257{,}287$$

He then, with a flourish, inserted an equals sign between his two answers to indicate that they were the same. Cole had just proved that $2^{67} - 1$ was not a prime by producing a pair of factors, and Mersenne's conjecture of 1644 was demolished. The American mathematician Eric Temple Bell reports that this was one of the few times an audience of the Society ever gave the presenter of a paper a standing ovation.

Of course, the fact that $2^{67} - 1$ is not a prime is an interesting fact but not one that could be considered exciting. An alert mathematician (probably Bell) realized that what was really important was to determine by what ingenious method Cole found the factors of $2^{67} - 1$. The story goes that Professor Cole indicated it had cost him twenty years of Sunday afternoons to prove Mersenne wrong—essentially, trial and error. (Probably, we should say "disproof by cases.")

It has been proved that Mersenne was correct for most of his given numbers. It is true for

$$p = 2, 3, 5, 7, 13, 17, 19, 31, 61, 89, 107, 127, \text{ and } 257$$

that $2^p - 1$ is a prime number. It is unknown whether or not there are an infinite number of Mersenne primes. Hence, it is unknown if there are an infinite number of even perfect numbers.

If it turned out that there were only a finite number of even perfect numbers, the set of perfect numbers might still be proved to be infinite by showing that there is an infinite number of odd perfect numbers. At present, this seems quite unlikely since no one has ever proved the existence of any odd perfect number —another unsolved problem.

Since the sixth perfect number is $2^{p-1}(2^p - 1)$ where $p = 17$, it follows that

$$2^{16}(2^{17} - 1) = 8{,}589{,}869{,}056$$

is the next even perfect number; hence, the last digits in the sequence of perfect numbers do not alternate between 6 and 8 since the fifth also ended in 6. However, the great Swiss mathematician Euler proved that each even perfect number must indeed have 6 or 8 as its last digit.

We should remark that $2^{257} - 1$ is not the largest known Mersenne prime. Many more are known; some unbelievably large. For example,

$$2^{11,213} - 1$$

is a prime. Consider the fantastic size of the associated perfect number; it would be at least a 6,750-digit number requiring approximately $2\frac{1}{3}$ pages of a book this size to reproduce in decimal notation.

EXERCISES

1. What is the sum of the reciprocals of all the factors of 6?
2. What is the sum of the reciprocals of all the factors of 28?
3. What is the sum of the reciprocals of all the factors of any given perfect number? Prove that your answer is correct.
4. Two numbers p and q are called *friendly* (or *amicable*) if $s(p) = s(q) = p + q$. Show that 220 and 284 are friendly numbers
5. Show that $p = 1,184$ and $q = 1,210$ are friendly numbers. (See Exercise 4.)
6. If there exists a positive integer k greater than 2 such that $s(n) = kn$, then n is called *multiperfect*. (a) Is 120 a multiperfect number? (b) Is 132 a multiperfect number?
7. In Section 4 we proved that every odd positive integer could be expressed as the sum of two consecutive integers. (a) Can any even positive integer be expressed as the sum of two consecutive integers? (b) Try to express every even positive integer less than thirty-five as the sum of any number of consecutive integers.
8. Use Exercise 7 above to make a conjecture concerning which positive integers cannot be expressed as the sum of consecutive integers.
9. Notice that the sum of any number of consecutive positive integers can be expressed by the difference

   $$(1 + 2 + 3 + \cdots + n) - (1 + 2 + 3 + \cdots + m) \text{ where } n > m \geq 1.$$

   For example,
   $5 + 6 + 7 + 8 + 9 + 10 = (1 + 2 + \cdots + 10) - (1 + 2 + 3 + 4).$
   (a) Show that the sum of any given number of consecutive positive integers must have the form $\dfrac{(n - m)(n + m + 1)}{2}$ where $n - m \neq 1$.
   (b) Explain why $\dfrac{(n - m)(n + m + 1)}{2}$ cannot equal a power of 2 where $n - m \neq 1$.
10. Let N be any even integer which is not a power of 2.
    (a) Explain why $N = 2^q x$ where x is an odd integer greater than 1.

(b) Show that if $2^{q+1} > x$ then $\dfrac{(n-m)(n+m+1)}{2} = N$ where $n = \dfrac{2^{q+1}+x-1}{2}$ and $m = \dfrac{2^{q+1}-x-1}{2}$.

11. Is 30,240 a multiperfect number? (See Exercise 6.)

12. Use the fact that if m and n are relatively prime, then $s(m) \times s(n) = s(mn)$ to prove that if $2^p - 1$ is a prime and $N = 2^{p-1}(2^p - 1)$, then $s(N) = 2N$.

*13. (a) Answer each question in the following argument. Let m be an even positive integer such that $s(m) = 2m$. Now $m = 2^{p-1}q$ where p is greater than 1 and q is an odd integer. (1) Why? Since we can prove that $s(uv) = s(u)s(v)$ for two integers u and v with no factor in common other than 1, it follows that

$$s(m) = s(2^{p-1})s(q) \qquad (2) \quad \text{Why?}$$

Hence, $\qquad\qquad s(m) = (2^p - 1)s(q) \qquad (3) \quad \text{Why?}$

Thus, $\qquad\qquad\quad 2m = (2^p - 1)s(q) \qquad (4) \quad \text{Why?}$

and $\qquad\qquad\quad 2^p q = (2^p - 1)s(q) \qquad (5) \quad \text{Why?}$

Since 2^p and $2^p - 1$ have no factors in common except 1,

$$2^p \text{ is a factor of } s(q) \qquad (6) \quad \text{Why?}$$

Consequently,

$$2^p w = s(q) \text{ for some integer } w \qquad (7) \quad \text{Why?}$$

and $\qquad\qquad\quad q = (2^p - 1)w \qquad\qquad (8) \quad \text{Why?}$

Now,

$$w \text{ is a factor of } q \text{ and } w \ne q \qquad (9) \quad \text{Why?}$$

Since

$$w + q = w + (2^p - 1)w$$
$$= 2^p w$$

we have that $w + q = s(q)$.

Since the sum of *all* of the factors of q is $q + w$, q has only two different factors; thus, q is a prime and $w = 1$. Thus, $q = 2^p - 1$ is a prime and $m = 2^{p-1}(2^p - 1)$.

(b) State the theorem proved in part (a).

6. OTHER TYPES OF SEQUENCES (OPTIONAL)

In Section 1 we discussed two sequences of numbers which were not arithmetic sequences. They were the sequence of triangular numbers 1, 3, 6, 10, 15, 21, 29, . . . (see Exercise 19) and the sequence of squares 1, 4, 9, 16, 25, 36, 49, ... Since they are neither arithmetic nor geometric sequences we do not yet have a formula to determine the sum, say, of the first 50 terms of either sequence. Let us consider a method that not only can be used to find the sum of the first ten squares but also can be generalized to find the sum of the first n squares where n is any positive integer.

From algebra, we know that $k^3 - (k-1)^3 = 3k^2 - 3k + 1$ is an identity; thus, the statement is true for any integer k we wish to substitute.

For $k = 10$,	$10^3 - 9^3 = 3(10)^2 - 3(10) + 1$	(1)
For $k = 9$,	$9^3 - 8^3 = 3(9)^2 - 3(9) + 1$	(2)
For $k = 8$,	$8^3 - 7^3 = 3(8)^2 - 3(8) + 1$	(3)
For $k = 7$,	$7^3 - 6^3 = 3(7)^2 - 3(7) + 1$	(4)
For $k = 6$,	$6^3 - 5^3 = 3(6)^2 - 3(6) + 1$	(5)
For $k = 5$,	$5^3 - 4^3 = 3(5)^2 - 3(5) + 1$	(6)
For $k = 4$,	$4^3 - 3^3 = 3(4)^2 - 3(4) + 1$	(7)
For $k = 3$,	$3^3 - 2^3 = 3(3)^2 - 3(3) + 1$	(8)
For $k = 2$,	$2^3 - 1^3 = 3(2)^2 - 3(2) + 1$	(9)
For $k = 1$,	$1^3 - 0^3 = 3(1)^2 - 3(1) + 1$	(10)

If we add the equalities (1) through (10), we get

$$10^3 - 0^3 = 3(1^2 + 2^2 + 3^2 + 4^2 + 5^2 + 6^2 + 7^2 + 8^2 + 9^2 + 10^2)$$
$$- 3(1 + 2 + 3 + 4 + 5 + 6 + 7 + 8 + 9 + 10) + 10$$

If we let S be the sum of the first ten squares and use the formula for the sum of the first n positive integers, we get

$$1{,}000 = 3S - 3 \frac{(10)(11)}{2} + 10$$

Solving for $3S$, $\quad 3S = 1{,}000 - 10 + 165 = 1{,}155$

Hence $\quad S = 385$

Now, let S be the sum of the first n squares and let us derive a formula which will give S for any n. Since

$$k^3 - (k-1)^3 = 3k^2 - 3k + 1$$

For $k = n$,	n^3	$- (n-1)^3 =$	$3(n)^2$	$-$	$3n$	$+1$
For $k = n-1$,	$(n-1)^3$	$- (n-2)^3 =$	$3(n-1)^2$	$-$	$3(n-1)$	$+1$
For $k = n-2$,	$(n-2)^3$	$- (n-3)^3 =$	$3(n-2)^2$	$-$	$3(n-2)$	$+1$
For $k = n-3$,	$(n-3)^3$	$- (n-4)^3 =$	$3(n-3)^2$	$-$	$3(n-3)$	$+1$

. . . .

For $k = 3$,	3^3	$- \quad 2^3 \quad =$	$3(3)^2$	$-$	$3(3)$	$+1$
For $k = 2$,	2^3	$- \quad 1^3 \quad =$	$3(2)^2$	$-$	$3(2)$	$+1$
For $k = 1$,	1^3	$- \quad 0^3 \quad =$	$3(1)^2$	$-$	$3(1)$	$+1$
Adding,	n^3	$- \quad 0^3 \quad =$	$3S$	$- 3\dfrac{n(n+1)}{2} + n$		

Thus,
$$3S = n^3 + \frac{3n(n+1)}{2} - n$$

$$3S = \frac{2n^3 + 3n(n+1) - 2n}{2}$$

$$S = \frac{n(2n^2 + 3n + 3 - 2)}{6}$$

$$S = \frac{n(2n^2 + 3n + 1)}{6}$$

$$S = \frac{n(n+1)(2n+1)}{6}$$

Thus, the sum of the first n squares is $n(n+1)(2n+1)/6$. (The student should remember this formula.)

Let us consider the sequence of triangular numbers 1, 3, 6, 10, 15, 21, 28, ... From Exercise 19 of Section 1, we know that the nth triangular number is $n(n+1)/2$; thus, the 50th triangular number is $50(51)/2 = 1{,}275$. Let S be the sum of the first fifty triangular numbers and let us determine S in three different ways.

METHOD 1. (See Exercise 19e, page 100.)

Let

$$S = 1 + 3 + 6 + 10 + 15 + 21 + 28 + 36 + \cdots + 1{,}225 + 1{,}275$$

Thus,

$$S = \quad 2^2 \ + \ 4^2 \ + \ 6^2 \ + \ 8^2 \ + \cdots + \quad 50^2$$

(Equation A)

Also,

$$S = 1 + 3 + 6 + 10 + 15 + 21 + 28 + \cdots + 1{,}176 + 1{,}225 + 1{,}275$$

$$S = 1^2 + \ 3^2 \ + \ 5^2 \ + \ 7^2 \ + \cdots + \quad 49^2 \quad + 1{,}275$$

(Equation B)

Adding Equations A and B, we obtain

$$2S = 1^2 + 2^2 + 3^2 + 4^2 + \cdots + 49^2 + 50^2 + 1{,}275$$

Using the formula for the sum of the first 50 squares,

$$2S = \frac{50(51)(101)}{6} + 1{,}275$$

$$2S = (25)(17)(101) + 1{,}275$$
$$2S = 42{,}925 + 1{,}275$$
$$2S = 44{,}200$$
$$S = 22{,}100$$

METHOD 2.

Let

$$S = 1 + 3 + 6 + 10 + 15 + 21 + 28 + 36 + \cdots + 1{,}225 + 1{,}275$$

Thus,

$$S = \quad 2^2 \quad + \quad 4^2 \quad + \quad 6^2 \quad + \quad 8^2 \quad + \cdots + \quad 50^2$$

$$S = 2^2 + 2^2(2)^2 + 2^2(3)^2 + 2^2(4)^2 + \cdots + 2^2(25)^2$$
$$S = 2^2(1^2 + 2^2 + 3^2 + 4^2 + \cdots + 25^2)$$

Using the formula for the sum of the first 25 squares,

$$S = \frac{4(25)(26)(51)}{6}$$

$$S = 2(25)(26)(17)$$
$$S = 22{,}100$$

METHOD 3.

Let

$$S = 1 + 3 + 6 + 10 + 15 + 21 + 28 + 36 + \cdots + 1{,}275$$

Using the fact that the nth triangular number is $n(n+1)/2$, we have

$$S = \frac{1(2)}{2} + \frac{2(3)}{2} + \frac{3(4)}{2} + \frac{4(5)}{2} + \frac{5(6)}{2} + \frac{6(7)}{2} + \cdots + \frac{50(51)}{2}$$

Hence,

$$S = \tfrac{1}{2}[1(1+1) + 2(2+1) + 3(3+1) + 4(4+1) + \cdots + 50(50+1)]$$
$$= \tfrac{1}{2}[(1^2+1) + (2^2+2) + (3^2+3) + (4^4+4) + \cdots + (50^2+50)]$$
$$= \tfrac{1}{2}[(1+2+3+4+ \cdots +50) + (1^2+2^2+3^2+4^2+ \cdots +50^2)]$$

Using the formulas for the sum of the first fifty integers and the first fifty squares,

$$S = \frac{1}{2}\left[\frac{50(51)}{2} + \frac{50(51)(101)}{6}\right]$$
$$= \frac{1}{2}[(25)(51) + (25)(17)(101)]$$
$$= \frac{1}{2}[1{,}275 + 42{,}925]$$
$$= \frac{1}{2}[44{,}200]$$
$$= 22{,}100$$

One advantage of the last method for finding the sum of the first fifty triangular numbers is that it generalizes quite readily and can be used to determine a formula for the sum of the first n triangular numbers; the derivation is left as an exercise for the student.

EXERCISES

1. Find the sum of the first 30 triangular numbers.

2. Find a formula for the sum of the first n triangular numbers.

3. Find the following sum: $\dfrac{1}{1 \cdot 2} + \dfrac{1}{2 \cdot 3} + \dfrac{1}{3 \cdot 4} + \cdots + \dfrac{1}{99 \cdot 100}$

   Hint: $\dfrac{1}{1 \cdot 2} = 1 - \dfrac{1}{2}$ and $\dfrac{1}{2 \cdot 3} = \dfrac{1}{2} - \dfrac{1}{3}$

4. Find the following sum: $\dfrac{1}{1 \cdot 3} + \dfrac{1}{3 \cdot 5} + \dfrac{1}{5 \cdot 7} + \cdots + \dfrac{1}{99 \cdot 101}$

   Hint: $\dfrac{1}{(2n-1)(2n+1)} = \dfrac{1}{2}\left(\dfrac{1}{2n-1} - \dfrac{1}{2n+1}\right)$ and see Exercise 3.

5. Use the identity $k^4 - (k-1)^4 = 4k^3 - 6k^2 + 4k - 1$ and the technique for finding the sum of the first ten squares to find the sum of the first ten cubes.

6. Find a formula for the sum of the first n cubes. (See Exercise 5.)

7. Use an identity involving $k^5 - (k-1)^5$ to find the sum

$$1^4 + 2^4 + 3^4 + 4^4 + \cdots + 19^4 + 20^4$$

(See Exercise 5.)

8. The numbers in the sequence 1, 5, 12, 22, . . . are called *pentagonal numbers*. The following figures indicate the origin of this name:

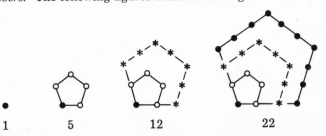

1   5   12   22

(a) What is the fifth pentagonal number?

(b) What is the sixth pentagonal number?

9. Notice that the nth triangular number is the sum of the first n terms of the arithmetic sequence of positive integers. Also, the nth square number is the sum of the first n terms of the arithmetic sequence of odd integers $1, 3, 5, 7, \ldots , 2n - 1$.

(a) Show that the nth pentagonal number is the sum of the first n terms of the arithmetic sequence $1, 4, 7, 10, 13, 16, \ldots , 3n - 2$. (See Exercise 8.)

(b) What is the nth pentagonal number?

10. The nth *hexagonal number* is the sum of the first n terms of the arithmetic sequence $1, 5, 9, 13, 17, \ldots , 4n - 3$.

(a) Draw figures similar to those given for the triangular and pentagonal numbers which will give the first four hexagonal numbers.

(b) What is the nth hexagonal number?

11. (a) Use Exercise 23 from Section 1 and the figure below to conclude that

$$(1 + 2 + 3 + 4 + 5 + 6)^2 = 1^3 + 2^3 + 3^3 + 4^3 + 5^3 + 6^3$$

1	2	3	4	5	6
2	4	6	8	10	12
3	6	9	12	15	18
4	8	12	16	20	24
5	10	15	20	25	30
6	12	18	24	30	36

Hint: Adding all of the numbers by rows we get

$(1 + 2 + \cdots + 6) + 2(1 + 2 + \cdots + 6)$
$\qquad + 3(1 + 2 + \cdots + 6) + \cdots + 6(1 + 2 + \cdots + 6)$

Factor the common factor from this sum.

(b) Generalize the results in part (a) to (again) find the sum of the first n cubes.

12. Find three triangular numbers which are also perfect squares.

13. Find the following sum: $1 \cdot 2 \cdot 3 + 2 \cdot 3 \cdot 4 + \cdots + 10 \cdot 11 \cdot 12$

Hint: $n(n + 1)(n + 2) =$

$$\frac{n(n + 1)(n + 2)(n + 3) - (n - 1)(n)(n + 1)(n + 2)}{4}$$

14. Find the following sum: $1 \cdot 2 + 2 \cdot 3 + \cdots + 99 \cdot 100$

Hint: $n(n + 1) = n^2 + n$

Henri Poincaré (1854–1912)

Henri Poincaré was born at Nancy, France, in 1854. He received his doctorate from the University of Paris in 1879. One of the greatest French mathematicians of the nineteenth century, his early research accomplishments were of such magnitude that he was appointed to the Academy of Sciences at the age of thirty-two. In a little over thirty years he published thirty books on mathematics, physics, and celestial mechanics and over 500 papers on mathematics. He made significant contributions to the modern theories of relativity, probability, and topology. In addition, Poincaré wrote some very excellent books for the layman on the foundations of mathematics. He shared Kronecker's doubts about the validity of some of the developments in logic and set theory in the nineteenth century. Some of the results stemming from the introduction of set theory prompted Poincaré to remark, ''Later generations will regard set theory as a disease from which one has recovered.''

Like that of Euler and Gauss, Poincaré's work constantly reflected brilliance and originality. Unlike Euler and Gauss, he did not possess their phenomenal ability to perform arithmetic calculations mentally; Poincaré exemplifies that one need not be a great arithmetician to be a great mathematician. He did, however, have a prodigious memory and a comprehensive understanding of the many fields of mathematics. As Gauss is called the first universalist, Poincaré is often called the last.

6

A Look at Topology

1. Houses, Maps, and Vests
2. Networks
3. The Regular Polyhedra

Mathematicians do not study objects but the relations between objects. Matter does not engage their attention. They are interested in form alone.

HENRI POINCARÉ

1. HOUSES, MAPS, AND VESTS

Topology, a subject that is twentieth century mathematics for the most part, emerged as a new branch of mathematics in the middle of the nineteenth century. The origins of this field can be found in some of the work done by Descartes in 1640 and Euler in 1750; but it was the contributions of Riemann, Cantor, and Poincaré that finally established topology as a separate field of mathematics.

Topologists are interested in properties of figures which remain invariant when the figures are deformed in a "continuous" manner. Such deformations as stretching, bending, and twisting are allowed as long as distinct points remain distinct. The early work in topology was quite geometrical and intuitive; today, it is quite abstract and is developed on a logical and rigorous basis.

Let us embark on our study of topology by considering four interesting problems. In the next two sections we shall discuss each of them in detail. The first problem we consider is called the Five Room House Problem. The student may be familiar with the problem, though probably not with its complete solution. Consider the diagram of a five room house in Figure 6.1. From each room there is not only a doorway leading to each adjoining room, but there is also a doorway leading outdoors through each outside wall.

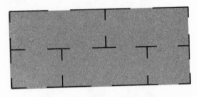

Five Room House

FIGURE 6.1

Can an individual start either in a given room of the house or outdoors and walk through every doorway of the house once and only once? (No trickery, such as going in and out of windows.)

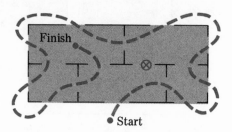

Five Room House Path
FIGURE 6.2

In Figure 6.2, a path is shown that goes through all but one doorway once and only once. After some reflection, the reader might realize that since there is only a finite number of doorways, the problem could be solved by trial and error. However, if he were aware of how many different paths need be tried to solve the problem by trial and error, it would be clear that the number of trials is much too great for this to be a sensible approach. In fact, the problem of finding the *number* of paths necessary to be tried would probably be a more difficult task than the student would care to (or should) attempt at this time.

Let us now consider a map problem. Suppose we wish to make a plane map of some geographical region, such as a collection of adjoining states. Also, suppose we wish to color the map so that no two regions (states) with a common boundary have the same color. As is customary, we shall allow regions with no common boundary or those meeting in a finite number of points to be distinguished with the same color.

How many different colors are necessary to distinguish the regions in any such plane map?

Question 2

In Figure 6.3, we exhibit three "maps" to be colored: one requires two colors, one requires three colors, and one requires four colors. Thus, at least four colors are *necessary* to color some plane maps.

131

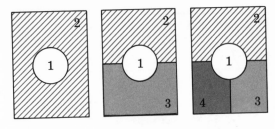

Map Coloring

FIGURE 6.3

Questions

3. Can you draw a map that needs more than four colors to distinguish the regions? (Try it.)
4. How many colors do you think are sufficient (enough) to fill in any plane map?

Another problem of perennial interest is called the Public Utility Problem. It consists of three houses and three public utility outlets (gas, electricity, and water) situated as in Figure 6.4. The object is to connect each of the utilities with each of the three houses without "crossing" any of the lines or mains. In other words, we want to connect each of the three squares with each of the three rectangles by nine continuous curves, none of which intersect. Several attempts might serve to give some clue as to whether or not the problem has a solution.

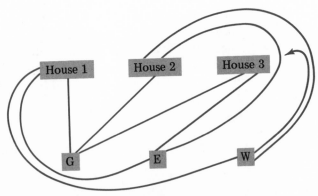

Public Utility Problem

FIGURE 6.4

The house, map, and utility problems are what mathematicians call *topological* problems. In the next section we shall have more to say about the topological questions posed here. However, we conclude this section by asking and answering a question of a topological nature.

Can a man remove his vest without removing his coat? If so, how?	**Question 5**

The answer to Question 5 is "yes," and the vest can be removed in the following manner. (1) Unbutton the vest and coat. (2) Lift the right front part of the coat and put the right side of the coat through the armhole of the vest from the outside. (3) Work the armhole around the body by pulling the back of the coat through the armhole. (4) Work it over the left shoulder and down and off the left arm. (5) Push the vest which is now hanging on the left shoulder, halfway down the left coat sleeve. (6) Reach up the left sleeve and pull the vest free by pulling it down through the left sleeve.*

EXERCISES

1. (a) Try to exhibit a solution to the Five Room House Problem.
   (b) Try to exhibit a solution to the Public Utility Problem.

2. Can you draw a plane map that requires more than four colors to distinguish the regions?

In Exercises 3 through 13, try to determine if the figure can be drawn without lifting your pencil and without retracing any lines. For the figures for which this is possible, exhibit how it can be done.

3.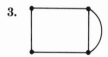

4.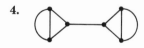

5.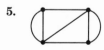

6.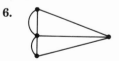

---

* Of course, if one is foolish (or clever) enough to wear the vest over the coat, the answer is still "yes" and the method to remove the vest is obvious.

7.

8.

9.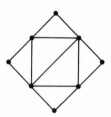

10.

11.

12.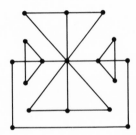

13.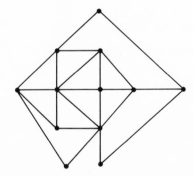

2. NETWORKS

Let us restate the Five Room House Problem discussed in Section 1. Suppose we have a five room house resembling the diagram in Figure 6.5. From each room there is a doorway leading to each adjoining room and a doorway leading outdoors through each outside wall. We

134

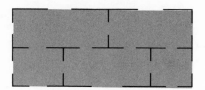

Five Room House

FIGURE 6.5

wish to determine whether or not an individual can start either in a given room of the house or outdoors and walk through each doorway of the house once and only once. To solve this problem, we begin by considering a different, though related, problem.

Consider the six drawings in Figure 6.6. Such configurations which are made up of line segments and continuous arcs are generally called *networks*. We want to determine which networks can be

networks

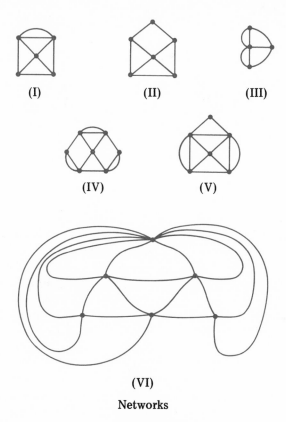

(I)   (II)   (III)

(IV)   (V)

(VI)

Networks

FIGURE 6.6

traversible

drawn (or traced) *without* lifting the drawing implement from the paper and *without* retracing any of the lines or curves in the network. If this is possible to do, then we say that we can traverse the network or that the network is *traversible.*

Questions

1. Which of the networks in Figure 6.6 can be traversed? (Try to determine the answer before continuing.)

2. Can one determine by means other than trial and error if a network can be traversed?

3. If so, how?

arc

arc ends

In order to answer the three questions, let us introduce some important terminology. An *arc* is either a line segment or a curve of finite length in the plane that does not intersect itself. The two ends of a given arc are called *arc ends.* Networks II and III in Figure 6.7

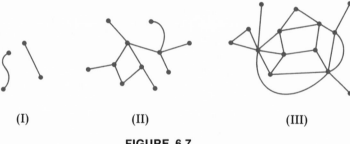

(I)   (II)   (III)

FIGURE 6.7

connected networks

continuous path

finite network

vertex

are called *connected networks.* A network is connected if it is possible "to move" from any point in the network to any other point in the network by "traveling along" the arcs of the network. In other words, you can go from any point in a connected network to any other point in the network by what is usually called a *continuous path.* All of the networks in Figure 6.6 are connected; Network I in Figure 6.7 is not connected. We shall not only restrict our study to connected networks but also to what are called finite networks. A *finite network* is one having a specific number of arcs which we could (eventually) count. (All networks in Figures 6.6 and 6.7 are finite.) In what follows, we use "network" to mean a *connected and finite network.*

In a network, the endpoint of an arc where other arcs may be joined is called a *vertex* of the network. Notice that Network II in Figure 6.7 has 11 vertices; Network III has 14 vertices. (Count them.) Another important concept in our study of networks is called the order of a vertex; the *order of a vertex* is the number of arc ends at a given vertex in a network. In Figure 6.8, we have labeled the order of each vertex in the given networks. Before continuing, you should return to Figures 6.6 and 6.7 and determine the order of each vertex in the connected networks given there.

order of a vertex

We shall let a_1 (read, "a sub-one") be the *number* of vertices of order one in a network. Similarly, a_2 is the number of vertices of order two, a_3 is the number of vertices of order three, etc. (The student should carefully study Figure 6.8 to make certain that this notation is understood before proceeding.) Also, we let A be the *number of vertices of odd order* in a given network and let B be the *total number of arc ends*. Notice that B is the *total of the orders of all*

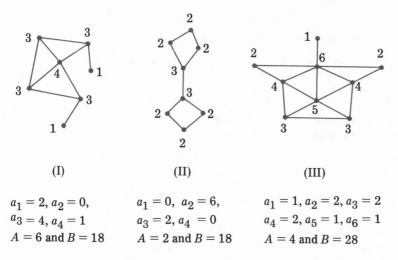

(I)

$a_1 = 2, a_2 = 0,$
$a_3 = 4, a_4 = 1$
$A = 6$ and $B = 18$

(II)

$a_1 = 0, \ a_2 = 6,$
$a_3 = 2, a_4 = 0$
$A = 2$ and $B = 18$

(III)

$a_1 = 1, a_2 = 2, a_3 = 2$
$a_4 = 2, a_5 = 1, a_6 = 1$
$A = 4$ and $B = 28$

Finite Connected Networks

FIGURE 6.8

of the vertices. Verify for Network I in Figure 6.8 that $A = 6$ and $B = 18$; in Network II, $A = 2$ and $B = 18$; and in Network III, $A = 4$ and $B = 30$. It should be obvious that since every arc of a network has two ends that the number of arc ends B must be an even number for each network; in fact, it is twice the number of arcs in the network. By checking the connected networks given in the figures, we discover that A is also an even number in each case. In general, A must be an even number for any network, but this fact is not as obvious as the fact that B must be an even number. Hence, we shall prove it as a theorem.

Theorem. The number of odd vertices A in any connected network is an even number.

Proof: Since a_1 is the number of vertices of order 1, a_3 is the number of vertices of order 3, a_5 is the number of vertices of order 5, etc., the number A of vertices of odd order is

$$A = a_1 + a_3 + a_5 + a_7 + a_9 + \cdots \quad \text{(a finite sum)}$$

If k is the order of a vertex, then ka_k is the total number of arc ends existing at the vertices of order k. (For example, if $a_4 = 7$, then there are seven vertices of order four. Since there are four arc ends at each of the seven vertices, the total number of arc ends accounted for at the vertices of order four is $4 \times 7 = 28$.) Thus, the total number of arc ends B in any network is given by

$$B = a_1 + 2a_2 + 3a_3 + 4a_4 + 5a_5 + 6a_6 + 7a_7 + \cdots$$

Now, subtract A from B:

$$\begin{aligned} B - A &= 2a_2 + 2a_3 + 4a_4 + 4a_5 + 6a_6 + 6a_7 + \cdots \\ &= 2(a_2 + a_3 + 2a_4 + 2a_5 + 3a_6 + 3a_7 + \cdots) \end{aligned}$$

Since every term in $B - A$ has 2 as a factor, the number $B - A$ is an even number. Furthermore, since the difference of two even numbers is an even number,

$$B - (B - A) = A \quad \text{is an even number}$$

Thus, the number of odd vertices in any connected network is an even number.

We shall now prove another theorem which is not only vital to the solution of the Five Room House Problem but also to the solutions of other related network problems.

Theorem. If a connected network can be traversed, then it has at most two vertices of odd order.

Proof: On a continuous path the "interior" vertices must be "passed through," and every "pass through" accounts for two arc ends, one obtained when entering the vertex and one when leaving. Thus, if a network is traversed, each vertex other than where one begins or ends must be a vertex of even order. Since each interior vertex must be of even order, this leaves at most the beginning (initial vertex) and the end (terminal vertex) for vertices of odd order.

Since every network has an even number of vertices of odd order, we can conclude that the *number of vertices of odd order of any travers-*

ible network must be two or zero; this is sufficient information to solve the Five Room House Problem. In fact, it can be proved that any network can be traversed if the number of its vertices of odd order is zero or two. It can also be proved that if there are no vertices of odd order, then the network can be traversed by starting at any vertex. If there are two vertices of odd order, then the network can be traversed only by starting at one of the vertices of odd order and ending at the other vertex of odd order. (The last fact should be obvious since every interior vertex must be of even order.)

Since Network VI in Figure 6.6 has four vertices of odd order, we conclude immediately that this network cannot be traversed. As we observe by looking at Figure 6.9, the Five Room House Problem has a

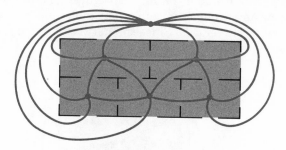

Five Room House Network

FIGURE 6.9

solution if and only if the associated network can be traversed. Since the associated network is Network VI, it is impossible to walk through each doorway of the five room house once and only once on a continuous walk through the house. The reader should check the other networks in Figure 6.6 and use the theorems to determine which can be traversed.

A much older and exceedingly more famous problem than the Five Room House Problem is called the Seven Bridges of Königsberg Problem. In the eighteenth century, the town of Königsberg was located in Prussia where two branches of the Pregel river meet. At that time, seven bridges crossed the river in a manner similar to that shown in Figure 6.10. A famous problem of the day was to determine if a person could start at a given point in Königsberg and cross every bridge once and only once on a continuous walk through the city.

In 1735, Leonhard Euler (1707–1783), a Swiss mathematician and one of the most productive mathematicians who ever lived, proved in much the same way that we settled the Five Room House Problem that the bridges of Königsberg could not be crossed once and

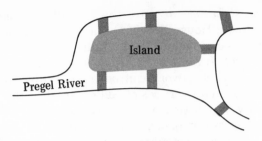

Seven Bridges of Königsberg

FIGURE 6.10

only once by a continuous path. In Figure 6.11, we see that the Königsberg Bridge Problem is equivalent to finding if Network III in Figure 6.6 can be traversed. Since the network has four odd vertices, we know that it is not traversible.

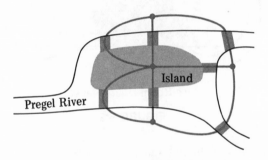

Seven Bridges of Königsberg Network

FIGURE 6.11

As one might guess, network theory is closely associated with the map coloring problem discussed in Section 1. There you were asked to try to construct a plane map that needed more than four colors to fill in; you surely failed in this task. If you did not fail, you have a solution to a famous unsolved topological problem called the Four Color Problem. The problem probably got its first serious thought in 1840 by August F. Moebius (1790–1868), one of the founders of the field of topology. Arthur Cayley (1821–1895), an English mathematician who made many significant contributions to the field of algebra, communicated the Four Color Problem (without solution) to the London Mathematical Society in 1878; this helped to promote interest in the problem. In 1890, P. J. Heawood proved the significant fact that five colors were enough to color any map on a sphere; this can be used to show that five colors are sufficient to fill in any plane map.

Although no one has ever produced a plane map that needs more than four colors to complete, neither has anyone been able to prove that four colors are sufficient to color any plane map.

One thing so fascinating and remarkable about such a famous unsolved problem as the Four Color Problem is that its solution has eluded mathematicians for over a hundred years, even with the sophisticated mathematical tools that have been created during this time and with the large reservoir of mathematical knowledge available to draw on. Perhaps even more remarkable is the fact that mathematicians have solved what might appear to be a much more difficult problem. It can be proved that seven colors are sufficient to color any map on the surface of a torus (doughnut). In fact, since a map can be constructed on a torus which requires seven colors to complete, one can prove that seven colors are both necessary and sufficient to color any map on such a surface.

EXERCISES

1. Consider the "bridges problem" as depicted in Figure 6.12a. Can each bridge be crossed once and only once on a walk through the city?

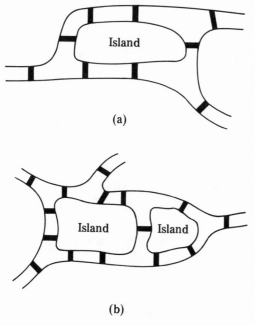

(a)

(b)

FIGURE 6.12

2. The following problem was proposed and solved by Euler. Can each of the fifteen bridges as depicted in Figure 6.12b be crossed once and only once by a continuous path? What is the answer?

3. Label Networks II and III in Figure 6.7 as the networks are labeled in Figure 6.4.

4. For any of the networks in Figure 6.6 that can be traversed, give a method to do it.

For each of the networks in Exercises 5 through 8, provide the following information. (a) The number of vertices of order 3. (b) The number of vertices of odd order. (c) The total number of arc ends. (d) Label the order of each vertex. (e) Give a method to traverse the network if it is traversible.

5.

6.

7.

8.

9. Which of the following networks are traversible?

(a)

(b)

(c)

(d)

(e)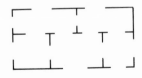

(f)

10. (a) Can a person walk through each door once and only once of the following five room house?

(b) If the answer to part (a) is "yes," draw a path that will do it.

11. (a) Can a person walk through each door once and only once of the following seven room house?

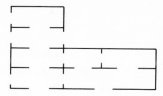

(b) If the answer to part (a) is "yes," draw a path that will do it.

12. (a) Can a person walk through each door once and only once of the following seven room house?

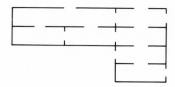

(b) If the answer to part (a) is "yes," draw a path that will do it.

13. (a) Can a person walk through each door once and only once of the following seven room house?

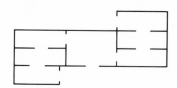

(b) If the answer to part (a) is "yes," draw a path that will do it.

14. (a) Can a person walk through each door once and only once of the following eight room house?

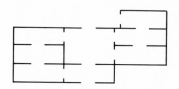

(b) If the answer to part (a) is "yes," draw a path that will do it.

15. (a) Can a person walk through each door once and only once on a tour through *both* of the following houses?

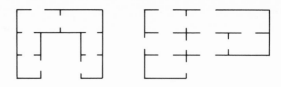

(b) If the answer to part (a) is "yes," draw a path that will do it.

For each of the "houses" depicted in Exercises 16 through 20, either show how a person could walk through each door once and only once by a continuous path or explain why this is not possible.

16.

17.

18.

19.

20.

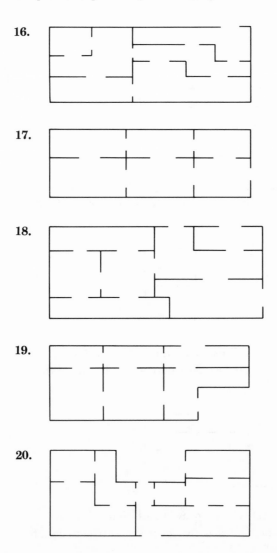

21. (a) Exhibit a map on a torus that requires three colors to distinguish the regions. (b) Four colors. (c) Five colors. (d) Six colors. (e) Seven colors.

22. Take a strip of paper such as indicated in the following figure. It is called a two-sided surface. Twist one end one-half turn and attach the two ends together. This is called *Moebius strip*. Explain why you think it is called a one-sided surface.

Strip   Two–sided   One–sided

3. THE REGULAR POLYHEDRA

Most of us are familiar with a pair of dice. They are a pair of cubes on which the faces are numbered with dots from one to six. When a pair is rolled, the usual interest is in the sum of the numbers on the top faces when the dice stop rolling; the sum is a number from two to twelve. Although there are several rules for the game, basically, the betting is on whether the sum of the numbers on the two top faces at the end of each roll will or will not be a certain number.

Instead of proceeding now to consider the odds involved in a dice game, let us look carefully at the dice. One die is a cube; this is a solid with six square faces, all of which are of equal size. A plane figure, such as a triangle, square, pentagon, etc., whose sides are connected line segments is called a *polygon*. A solid, such as a cube or pyramid, whose faces are polygons is called a *polyhedron*. If, as for the cube, the faces of the polyhedron are congruent regular polygons (that is, congruent faces with equal sides and interior angles), then the solid is called a *regular polyhedron*. If we were to insist only that a pair of "dice" be regular polyhedra, then the total number of such solids would be of immediate interest. Whether or not one is interested in dice, the following questions have significant mathematical interest.

polygon

polyhedron

regular polyhedron

---

1. Are there a finite or infinite number of regular polyhedra?
2. If the number is finite, how many regular polyhedra are there?
3. How many faces would each regular polyhedron have?
4. For each regular polyhedron, what kind of polygonal face would it have?

Questions

Let us begin by looking at several convex polyhedra. A polyhedron is *convex* if it has no holes or indentations; that is, each point on the line segment connecting any two points of the solid lies on the surface or is an interior point of the solid. A careful consideration of several convex polyhedra will lead to an interesting (and famous) result; it will provide us with the means to answer the four questions stated above. (Notice that at first we do not assume the polyhedra are regular.)

Let V be the number of vertices of a given polyhedron, let E be the number of edges, and let F be the number of faces. For each polyhedron in Figure 6.13, the student should determine V, E, and F, and then make the following observations.

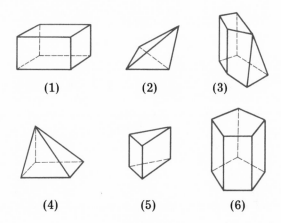

(1)   (2)   (3)

(4)   (5)   (6)

Polyhedra

FIGURE 6.13

Figure 1. $V = 8; E = 12; F = 6;$
$$V + F = 14 \quad \text{and} \quad E + 2 = 14$$

Figure 2. $V = 4; E = 6; F = 4:$
$$V + F = 8 \quad \text{and} \quad E + 2 = 8$$

Figure 3. $V = 9; E = 14; F = 7:$
$$V + F = 16 \quad \text{and} \quad E + 2 = 16$$

Figure 4. $V = 5; E = 8; F = 5:$
$$V + F = 10 \quad \text{and} \quad E + 2 = 10$$

Figure 5. $V = 6; E = 9; F = 5:$
$$V + F = 11 \quad \text{and} \quad E + 2 = 11$$

Figure 6. $V = 10$; $E = 15$; $F = 7$:

$$V + F = 17 \qquad \text{and} \qquad E + 2 = 17$$

In each case, we see that $V + F = E + 2$. This is no accident. The remarkable statement of equality is true for any convex polyhedron and is known as *Euler's Formula*. Let us give a (topological) proof that $V + F = E + 2$ by using the box in Figure 6.14. The proof can be generalized to prove that $V + F = E + 2$ for any convex polyhedron.

Euler's Formula

Consider an *open* box such as in (1) of Figure 6.14; it is a box with one side (face) missing. Suppose the box is made from some material that allows it to be flattened out in the plane as appears in (2) of Figure 6.14. Although the shapes of the faces are changed by the deformation, the number of faces (now represented by plane polygonal figures) remain unchanged. Furthermore, the number of edges (the sides of the polygons), and the number of vertices remain unchanged. Since each face is a polygonal figure in the plane, it can be "triangularized" as in (3) of Figure 6.14.

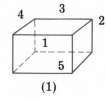

(1)

Consider back removed

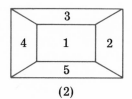

(2)

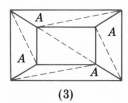

(3)

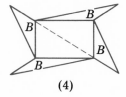

(4)

(5)

$$V + F - E = 1$$

FIGURE 6.14

Now, consider what happens to $V + F - E$ as we "remove" triangles of Type A in (3) of Figure 6.14. Since we remove one "edge" and one "face" in removing a triangle of Type A, F is reduced by one and E is reduced by one. Consequently, the difference $F - E$ is unaffected and $V + F - E$ remains the same. When removing a triangle of Type B as in (4) of Figure 6.14, E is reduced by two, F is reduced by one, and V is reduced by one. Reducing each V and F by one reduces the sum $V + F$ by two; again, $V + F - E$ remains unchanged. Continuing the process of removing triangles, we finally obtain one triangle as in (5) of Figure 6.14. Since every triangle removed must be of Type A or Type B, $V + F - E$ has remained unchanged. Furthermore, since for the final triangle $V = 3$, $F = 1$, and $E = 3$, we have that $V + F - E = 1$. For the box (polyhedron) with one face missing, $V + F - E = 1$. Inserting the missing face adds one to this total and we get

$$V + F - E = 2$$

Obviously, the above procedure could be used for any of the polyhedra in Figure 6.13, and we could obtain the same results. Indeed, the formula would be valid for any convex polyhedron.

Now, suppose we have any *regular polyhedron*. (The cube is an example.) Let u be the number of edges on each face of the regular polyhedron and let v be the number of edges at each vertex. Notice that since the polyhedron is *regular* the numbers u and v are determined; for example, for the cube $u = 4$ and $v = 3$.

Since each edge borders on exactly two faces, the product uF must be $2E$; that is,

$$uF = 2E \qquad (1)$$

For the cube $F = 6$, $E = 12$, and $uF = (4)(6) = 24 = 2E$. Similarly, since each edge has an end at two different vertices,

$$vV = 2E \qquad (2)$$

For the cube, $v = 3$, $V = 8$, and $vV = (3)(8) = 24 = 2E$.

From Equations (1) and (2), we conclude that for a regular polyhedron

$$F = \frac{2E}{u} \qquad (3)$$

and

$$V = \frac{2E}{v} \qquad (4)$$

Since $V + F - E = 2$ for *any* polyhedron, we have

$$\frac{2E}{v} + \frac{2E}{u} - E = 2$$

$$\frac{2E}{v} + \frac{2E}{u} = E + 2$$

or, dividing by $2E$,

$$\frac{1}{v} + \frac{1}{u} = \frac{1}{2} + \frac{1}{E} \tag{5}$$

Using the fact that Equation (5) must be true for any regular polyhedron, we can make some rather remarkable deductions by using only elementary ideas of arithmetic and geometry. First, since each face is a polygon, we know that u must be greater than or equal to three. (The polygon with the least number of sides is a triangle.) Second, in order to get a three-dimensional solid, it also follows that v is greater than or equal to three. (To "get out" of the plane, the number of edges at a vertex must be at least three.) Third, since E is a positive integer $\frac{1}{2} + 1/E$ must be *greater than* $\frac{1}{2}$. If u and v were both 4 then $1/u + 1/v = \frac{1}{4} + \frac{1}{4} = \frac{1}{2}$; this is impossible. In fact, it is impossible for both u and v to be greater than or equal to 4 at the same time since the sum $1/u + 1/v$ would *not* be greater than $\frac{1}{2}$. Thus, either u or v *must be* 3. Fourth, if u, for example, were 3 then v could not be as great as 6 since the sum $1/u + 1/v$ would not be greater than $\frac{1}{2}$. (Note that $\frac{1}{3} + \frac{1}{6} = \frac{1}{2}$.) Therefore, the only possible combinations for u and v are the following:

CASE 1.	$u = 3$	and	$v = 3$
CASE 2.	$u = 4$	and	$v = 3$
CASE 3.	$u = 3$	and	$v = 4$
CASE 4.	$u = 5$	and	$v = 3$
CASE 5.	$u = 3$	and	$v = 5$

Let us consider each of these possible cases for u and v. In each case, V, F, and E will have to be positive integers in order to determine a polyhedron.

CASE 1. If $u = 3$ and $v = 3$, then

$$\frac{1}{3} + \frac{1}{3} = \frac{1}{2} + \frac{1}{E}$$

$$\frac{2}{3} - \frac{1}{2} = \frac{1}{E}$$

$$\frac{1}{6} = \frac{1}{E}$$

and

$$E = 6$$

Since $E = 6$,

$$F = \frac{2E}{u} \quad \text{and} \quad V = \frac{2E}{v}$$

$$F = \frac{12}{3} \quad \text{and} \quad V = \frac{12}{3}$$

$$F = 4 \quad \text{and} \quad V = 4$$

Hence, Case 1 yields integer solutions for E, F, and V. In fact, we can construct a regular polyhedron with four faces, four vertices, and six edges. Since $u = 3$, each face is a triangle. This four-sided regu-

tetrahedron

lar polyhedron is called a *tetrahedron*. (See Figure 6.15.)

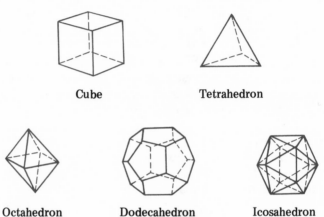

Cube   Tetrahedron

Octahedron   Dodecahedron   Icosahedron

The Regular Polyhedra

FIGURE 6.15

The following table shows that each of the five cases yields integer solutions for E, F, and V. In each case we can construct a regular polyhedron; pictures of the five regular polyhedra are shown in Figure 6.15. (The student will be asked to verify the arithmetic calculations for each remaining case as we did for Case 1.)

The Regular Polyhedra

1	3	3	6	4	4	Tetrahedron
2	4	3	12	8	6	Cube
3	3	4	12	6	8	Octahedron
4	5	3	30	20	12	Dodecahedron
5	3	5	30	12	20	Icosahedron

Of the five regular solids, the student undoubtedly has seen the cube and very likely has seen the dodecahedron; the latter is often used to make desk calendars by placing a calendar month on each of the 12 sides. An interesting as well as challenging problem is to determine how a model of each regular polyhedron can be made out of a single piece of construction paper. In Figure 6.16, we show how it can be done for each of the regular polyhedra.

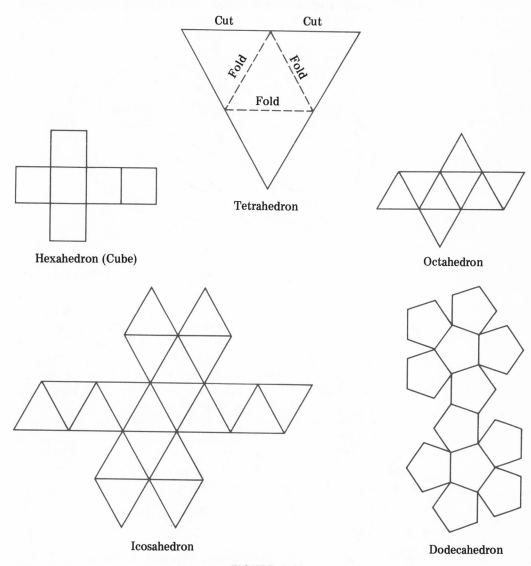

FIGURE 6.16

Let us return to the Public Utility Problem discussed in Section 2. (See Figure 6.17.) Recall that the object is to connect each utility with each of the three houses without "crossing" any lines or mains. First, interpret Euler's Formula as it relates to networks in the plane. If V is the number of vertices and E is the number of arcs in any connected network in the plane, then the number of regions F into which the network divides the plane is given by $F = E + 2 - V$. (In our previous proof, the missing face can be considered to be the "outside" region.)

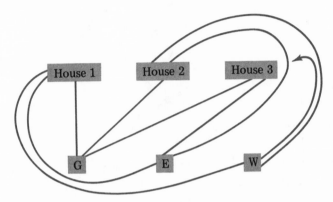

Public Utility Problem

FIGURE 6.17

We can now show that assuming there is a solution to the Public Utility Problem leads to a contradiction. Suppose a solution to the Public Utility Problem exists. The solution will consist of a connected network where $V = 6$ and $E = 9$. From $F = E + 2 - V$, we obtain that $F = 5$. Because of the nature of the joins, there are no three vertices with each pair joined by an arc; therefore, the network contains no regions bounded by three arcs. Neither is any pair of vertices joined by two different arcs; hence, the network contains no regions bounded by two arcs. Consequently, each region must be bounded by at least four arcs.

Since there are 5 regions and since each arc borders on 2 regions, $2E$ cannot be less than $(4)(5) = 20$. Thus,

$$2E \geq 20$$

and
$$E \geq 10$$

But $E \geq 10$ is a contradiction since a solution requires that E be 9.

EXERCISES

1. Perform the arithmetic calculations necessary to verify each number listed in the regular polyhedra table for Case 2.

2. Perform the arithmetic calculations necessary to verify each number listed in the regular polyhedra table for Case 3.

3. Perform the arithmetic calculations necessary to verify each number listed in the regular polyhedra table for Case 4.

4. Perform the arithmetic calculations necessary to verify each number listed in the regular polyhedra table for Case 5.

5. Without cutting the paper in more than one piece, make models of a cube and a tetrahedron.

6. Without cutting the paper in more than one piece, make a model of an octahedron.

7. Without cutting the paper in more than one piece, make a model of a dodecahedron.

8. Without cutting the paper in more than one piece, make a model of an icosahedron.

9. (a) Can you show that at least four colors are necessary in order to color any convex polyhedron so that no two adjacent faces are the same color? Five colors?

   (b) How many colors do you think it would take to color any convex polyhedron? (State your conjecture; no proof requested.)

10. For a polyhedron, let F_n be the number of faces with n edges.

    (a) In Figure 6.13, for polyhedron (3) what are F_3, F_4, F_5, F_6, and F_7?

    (b) In Figure 6.13, for polyhedron (6) what are F_3, F_4, F_5, F_6, and F_7?

11. **Theorem.** Any convex polyhedron having each vertex of order three must have at least one face with fewer than six edges. (Answer each question below in the proof of this theorem. See Exercise 10.)

    Proof: If F is the number of faces on a polyhedron, then

    $$F = F_3 + F_4 + F_5 + F_6 + \cdots$$

    where the sum on the right is finite.   (1) Why?

    If V is the total number of vertices and E is the number of edges for the polyhedron, then

    $$3V = 2E \qquad \text{(2) Why?}$$

    Furthermore,

    $$3F_3 + 4F_4 + 5F_5 + 6F_6 + \cdots = 2E \qquad \text{(3) Why?}$$

    Since $V = \tfrac{2}{3}E$, we conclude from Euler's formula that

    $$3F = 6 + E \qquad \text{(4) Why?}$$

153

Thus, $$6F = 12 + 2E$$

and $$6F = 12 + 3F_3 + 4F_4 + 5F_5 + 6F_6 + \cdots \qquad \text{(5) Why?}$$

Furthermore,

$$6(F_3 + F_4 + F_5 + F_6 + \cdots)$$
$$= 12 + 3F_3 + 4F_4 + 5F_5 + 6F_6 + \cdots \qquad \text{(6) Why?}$$

Hence,

$$3F_3 + 2F_4 + F_5 = 12 + F_7 + 2F_8 + 3F_9 + \cdots \qquad \text{(7) Why?}$$

Since $3F_3 + 2F_4 + F_5$ is at least 12, it follows that one of F_3, F_4, or F_5 must not be zero.

12. Can you give an example of a polyhedron (draw, name, or construct) where the order of each vertex is three and where $F_3 \neq 0$ and $F_n = 0$ for n greater than 3? (As in Exercise 10, F_n is the number of faces with n edges.)

13. Can you give an example of a polyhedron where the order of each vertex is three and where $F_3 = 0$, $F_4 \neq 0$, and $F_n = 0$ for n greater than 4?

14. Can you give an example of a polyhedron where the order of each vertex is three and where $F_3 = 0$, $F_4 = 0$, $F_5 \neq 0$, and $F_n = 0$ for n greater than 5?

15. Can you give an example of a polyhedron where the order of each vertex is three and where $F_3 \neq 0$, $F_4 \neq 0$, but $F_n = 0$ for n greater than 4?

16. Can you give an example of a polyhedron where the order of each vertex is three and where $F_3 = 0$, $F_4 \neq 0$, $F_5 \neq 0$, and $F_n = 0$ for n greater than 5?

17. For any convex polyhedron, prove that $3V$ is greater than or equal to $E + 6$. *Hint:* $3F \leq 2E$. Why?

18. For any convex polyhedron, prove that $3F \geq E + 6$.

19. Prove for any convex polyhedron that $6V \geq 2E + 12$ and $2E + 12 \geq 3F + 12$ and conclude that $6V \geq 3F + 12$.

20. Prove for any convex polyhedron that $6F \geq 3V + 12$.

21. Use Exercise 19 to prove that a convex polyhedron must have at least four vertices.

22. Use Exercise 20 to prove that a convex polyhedron must have at least four faces.

23. Prove that a convex polyhedron must have at least six edges.

24. Draw or construct a polyhedron that is not convex.

25. Show by example that $V + F - E$ need not be 2 if a polyhedron is not convex.

*26. Prove that no convex polyhedron has exactly seven edges.

*27. Prove that if a polyhedron exists where the order of each vertex is three and where $F_3 \neq 0$, $F_4 = 0$, $F_5 \neq 0$, and $F_n = 0$ for n greater than 5, then the number of pentagonal faces must be 3, 6, or 9.

Blaise Pascal (1623–1662)

Blaise Pascal was born in the French province of Auvergne at Clermont-Ferrand on June 19, 1623. He was a child prodigy, one who developed many theorems of euclidean geometry on his own by the age of twelve. His father, who was a mathematician, not only encouraged his son in his academic pursuits but moved to Paris to enable the boy to get a better education and to capitalize on his abilities. At 14 years of age, Pascal was meeting regularly with a group of French mathematicians, including such men as Roberval and Mersenne; the meetings led to the birth of the French Academy in 1666. In 1642, when he was only 19, Pascal invented the first mechanical adding machine.

Pascal also made great contributions to the field of probability. Along with Fermat, he created the theory of probability. Their work was originally motivated by a question on gambling put to Pascal by Chevalier de Méré. Pascal communicated the problem by letter to Fermat. Both solved the problem, but by somewhat different techniques. Fermat and Pascal continued to correspond and out of their correspondence emerged some of the basic concepts of probability.

Pascal might have continued to distinguish himself as a great mathematician, but he was plagued with poor health and other interests began to occupy more and more of his time. Already something of a religious mystic, Pascal, at twenty-five, turned his back on his abilities in science and mathematics and spent much of his remaining life in religious contemplation. He died in 1662 at the age of thirty-nine.

7

Probability and Statistics

1. Introduction
2. Counting Collections
3. Basic Ideas of Probability
4. Introduction to Statistics
5. Measures of Central Tendency and Dispersion

In most sciences one generation tears down what another has built, and what one has established another undoes. In mathematics alone each generation builds a new story to the old structure.

HERMANN HANKEL

1. INTRODUCTION

The birth of probability occurred about the same time as that of calculus, in the mid-seventeenth century. Although the original problems which motivated the creation of each subject were quite unrelated, the student will find that calculus has come to play an important role in the development of probability, and conversely. It has been the rule and not the exception that two different branches of mathematics eventually provide mutual support for their common development.

As with calculus, some of the ideas of probability predate the time usually designated as the beginning of the subject. However, probability was given its first great push forward as the result of a problem proposed to Blaise Pascal by a gambler. Pascal relayed the gambling problem to Fermat; each solved the problem independently and the ensuing correspondence between the two provided the basis for the early developments of the subject. In fact, their correspondence was used as the basis of the first treatise on probability; it was written in 1657 by Huygens. Later, a book entitled *Ars Conjectandi,* written by Jacob Bernoulli and published in 1713, was a significant contribution to the field and its sustained growth.

Probability has expanded its horizons far beyond its early associations with a gambling problem. Probability and its sister subject, *statistics,* have been applied to many other fields such as business, biology, sociology, and psychology in an unending number of applications. Of course, the modern probabilist is attentive to the theory as well as to the applications.

Other pioneers in the field of probability were DeMoivre, Laplace, and the mathematical genius, Gauss. Two important contributors from the last century were Chebychev and Markov. In this century, the Russian mathematician Kolmogorov helped establish the subject on a sound foundation with the publication in 1933 of his book entitled *Foundations of the Theory of Probability.*

It should become clear that not only is a satisfactory definition of mathematics difficult to devise but satisfactory definitions of the various branches of mathematics present similar difficulties. (Knowing some probability theory is one of the best ways to know what the subject is all about.) However, some definition of probability seems in order if for no other reason than to distinguish it from the closely related field of statistics. Roughly speaking, probability provides a method to predict from a known collection of objects the probable characteristics of a specified sampling from the collection. For example, suppose our known collection consists of 12 red balls, 4 green balls, 3 white balls, and 1 black ball. Probability will provide us with an indication of the most frequent characteristics of a sampling of 10 balls selected at random from the collection.

The approach in statistics tends to be the reverse of that in probability. Statistics provides a method to determine from a known sample of an unknown collection the characteristics of the original collection. For example, the statistician will (attempt to) determine from a sample of television viewers what the collection of all television viewers prefer to watch.

2. COUNTING COLLECTIONS

An integral part of probability is the problem of counting collections. To be efficient and successful in counting collections, more sophisticated tools than counting objects one at a time are needed. Let us begin by asking three questions.

Questions

1. How many two-digit numbers can be formed from the six digits 3, 4, 5, 6, 7, and 8 provided a digit can be repeated? The set of such two-digit numbers would include, for example, 37, 83, and 55.

2. If a political party has six men from which to choose presidential and vice-presidential candidates, how many different tickets can they present to the voters? (Notice that although Smith for president and Jones for vice-president is a different ticket from Jones for president and Smith for vice-president, a Smith-Smith ticket is impossible unless, of course, two different men are named Smith.)

3. Suppose an automobile manufacturer has six different makes of cars to advertise. If an advertising agency decides that only two makes should be advertised on a television special, how many choices does the manufacturer have when deciding which two should be picked? (Although pairs are to be picked by the manufacturer from six objects as in questions (1) and (2), the order in the pairing is immaterial.)

Even though the student might not be able to answer the three questions correctly at the present time, it should be obvious that the answers are not the same. We now develop methods to answer not only these but also other similar questions.

ordered pair

Let S be a set with m distinct elements. If a and b are elements in S, then (a, b) is called an *ordered pair* from S. The element a is called the *first element* and b is called the *second element*. The word "ordered" is used since we distinguish between the pair (a, b) and the pair (b, a). Two ordered pairs (a, b) and (c, d) are equal if and only if $a = c$ and $b = d$. Hence, for (a, b) to be the same as (b, a) we must have $a = b$. The set of all ordered pairs that can be formed

cartesian product

from a set S is called the *cartesian product of S with itself* and it is denoted by $S \times S$. Symbolically,

$$S \times S = \{(x, y) \mid x \in S \text{ and } y \in S\}$$

As an example, if $S = \{1, 2, 3\}$, then

$$S \times S = \{(1,1), (1,2), (1,3), (2,1), (2,2), (2,3), (3,1), (3,2), (3,3)\}$$

Consider the following diagram which exhibits the pairing of elements in $S \times S$.

$$1 \Longleftarrow \begin{matrix} 1 \\ 2 \\ 3 \end{matrix} \qquad 2 \Longleftarrow \begin{matrix} 1 \\ 2 \\ 3 \end{matrix} \qquad 3 \Longleftarrow \begin{matrix} 1 \\ 2 \\ 3 \end{matrix}$$

We see that the three elements are paired with each of 1, 2, and 3; thus, the number of elements in $S \times S$ is $3^2 = 9$.

Suppose $T = \{1, 2, 3, 4\}$. The elements in $T \times T$ are as follows:

$(1,1), (1,2), (1,3), (1,4)$	the ordered pairs with 1 as first element
$(2,1), (2,2), (2,3), (2,4)$	the ordered pairs with 2 as first element
$(3,1), (3,2), (3,3), (3,4)$	the ordered pairs with 3 as first element
$(4,1), (4,2), (4,3), (4,4)$	the ordered pairs with 4 as first element

Since there are four collections of ordered pairs with four pairs in each, the number of elements in $T \times T$ is $4^2 = 16$. In general, if the number of elements in a set S is m then the number of elements in $S \times S$ is m^2; that is,

$$\text{if } n(S) = m, \qquad \text{then } n(S \times S) = m^2$$

Let $S = \{3, 4, 5, 6, 7, 8\}$. Then $n(S) = 6$ and $n(S \times S) = 6^2 = 36$. Since each possible two-digit number that can be formed from the set is associated with exactly one of the ordered pairs of $S \times S$, the number of two-digit numbers that can be formed from the digits in S where repetition is allowed is 36. Therefore, 36 is the answer to Question 1.

Now, let us turn our attention to Question 2. The problem of selecting a presidential and vice-presidential ticket from a group of six individuals differs from the preceding problem in that no two ordered pairs have the same first and second elements. Since we are dealing with a set of six elements, we can find exactly six ordered pairs which have an element paired with itself. Since such pairs are not permissible slates, the number of permissible slates is six fewer than the number of ordered pairs in $S \times S$. Thus, the number of possible slates of candidates that the given party can present to the voters is $6^2 - 6 = 30$.

In general, if S is a set with m elements, then the number of elements (x, y) in $S \times S$ where $x \neq y$ is $m^2 - m = m(m - 1)$. This leads us to define what is meant by a permutation.

Definition. *An ordered arrangement of r elements selected from a set with m elements where $m \geq r$ and where no two elements in the arrangement are the same is called a* permutation *of m things taken r at a time. The total number of such permutations from the set is denoted by P_r^m, or $(m)_r$.*   *permutation*

Example 1. Let $S = \{a, b, c\}$. Both ab and ba are permutations of three elements taken two at a time from S. The other such permutations are ac, ca, bc, and cb. Hence, $P_2^3 = 6$.

As we have seen, the number of ordered pairs of elements that can be selected from m elements where no two elements in an arrangement are the same is $m(m - 1)$. Thus, $P_2^m = m(m - 1)$ where $m \geq 2$. For example, the number of two-digit numbers in which no digit is repeated that can be obtained from $\{1, 2, 3, 4, 5, 6, 7, 8\}$ is $P_2^8 = (8)(7) = 56$.

Now, consider the set $\{a, b, c, d, e, f\}$. Let us determine P_3^6, the total number of permutations of six things taken three at a time from this set. All of the ordered arrangements of three elements with a as the first element are exhibited on the following page. For example, abc, abd, abe, abf, acb, and acd are the first six indicated. Notice that with a as first element, the number of ordered triples is just the number of permutations of 5 things $\{b, c, d, e, f\}$ taken 2 at a time; that is, $5 \times 4 = 20$. Since we can obtain this many ordered triples with each of the 6 elements in S, the total number of ordered triples is $6 \times 5 \times 4 = 120$. Hence,

$$P_3^6 = 6 \times 5 \times 4 = 120$$

It should now be clear that the number of permutations of 6 things taken 4 at a time is $6 \times 5 \times 4 \times 3 = 360$.

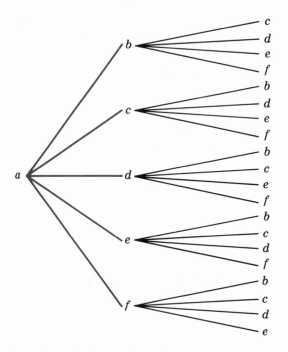

In general, if $m \geq r$, then the total number of permutations of m things taken r at a time is

$$m(m-1)(m-2) \cdots (m-r+1)$$

If m is a positive integer, then $m!$ (read "m factorial") is used to represent the product $m(m-1)(m-2) \cdots (3)(2)(1)$. For example,

$$6! = 6 \times 5 \times 4 \times 3 \times 2 \times 1$$

The factorial notation can be used to give a concise formula for P_r^m. For example,

$$P_4^6 = 6 \times 5 \times 4 \times 3$$
$$= \frac{6 \times 5 \times 4 \times 3 \times 2 \times 1}{2 \times 1}$$
$$= \frac{6!}{2!}$$

In general, if $0 < r < m$ then

$$m(m-1)(m-2) \cdots (m-r+1)$$
$$= \frac{m(m-1)(m-2) \cdots (m-r+1)(m-r)(m-r-1) \cdots (3)(2)(1)}{(m-r)(m-r-1) \cdots (3)(2)(1)}$$
$$= \frac{m!}{(m-r)!}$$

Thus,
$$P_r^m = \frac{m!}{(m-r)!} \qquad \text{(I)}$$

Since the number of ordered arrangements of m things taken m at a time is $m!$, $P_m^m = m!$. The usual procedure is to *define* 0! to be 1; thus, formula (I) holds when $r = m$ or $r = 0$.

In the third question asked at the beginning of this chapter, we wanted to know how many pairs could be picked from a set of 6 elements where order was not a factor. For example, if $\{a, b, c, d, e, f\}$ represents the six makes of cars from which a selection of two is to be made, then the pair (a, b) and the pair (b, a) would be the same. Since $\{a, b\} = \{b, a\}$, the question is equivalent to asking how many two-element subsets there are of a set with six elements. This leads us to the following definition.

Definition. Let S be a set with m elements. A subset of S containing r elements is called a combination *of m things taken r at a time. The total number of such combinations (subsets of S with r elements) is denoted by C_r^m, or $\binom{m}{r}$.*   *combination*

Example 2. Let $S = \{a, b, c\}$. One two-element subset of S is $\{a, b\}$. The other two-element subsets of S are $\{a, c\}$ and $\{b, c\}$. Thus, the total number of combinations of three things taken two at a time is three; that is, $C_2^3 = 3$.

If S is a set with 8 elements, we know that the number of permutations of 8 things taken 3 at a time is

$$P_3^8 = \frac{8!}{(8-3)!} = \frac{8!}{5!}$$
$$= 8 \times 7 \times 6$$
$$= 336$$

Any three elements of S account for 3! permutations but only *one combination* of 8 things taken 3 at a time. Consequently,

$$3! \times C_3^8 = P_3^8$$

Therefore,
$$C_3^8 = \frac{P_3^8}{3!}$$

$$C_3^8 = \frac{8!}{3! \, (8-3)!}$$

$$C_3^8 = \frac{8!}{3! \, 5!}$$

The number of combinations of m things taken r at a time can always be calculated from the formula

$$C_r^m = \frac{m!}{r! \, (m-r)!}$$

Example 3. If a club has seven eligible members to serve as president, vice-president, and treasurer, how many different slates of candidates can the nominating committee present to the members?

Solution: The answer is the total number of permutations of 7 things taken 3 at a time. Thus, there are

$$P_3^7 = \frac{7!}{(7-3)!}$$
$$= \frac{7!}{4!}$$
$$= 7 \times 6 \times 5$$
$$= 210 \text{ different possibilities}$$

Example 4. Suppose an ice cream shop decides to sell three flavors of ice cream in addition to vanilla and chocolate. (a) If the supplier has seven flavors in addition to vanilla and chocolate from which to choose, how many different choices can the ice cream shop make? (b) If a customer wishes to buy a cone with two dips, how many different choices does he have?

Solution: (a) The number of choices of three flavors from the seven flavors is the total number of combinations of 7 things taken 3 at a time. Thus, there are

$$C_3^7 = \frac{7!}{3! \, (7-3)!}$$
$$= \frac{7!}{3! \, 4!}$$
$$= \frac{7 \times 6 \times 5}{3 \times 2 \times 1}$$
$$= 7 \times 5$$
$$= 35 \text{ different choices}$$

(b) Since the number of cones the customer can choose, each having two different kinds of ice cream, is the total number of combinations of 5 things taken 2 at a time; this number is

$$C_2^5 = \frac{5!}{2! \, 3!}$$
$$= \frac{5 \times 4}{2 \times 1}$$
$$= 10$$

Since the customer may also select five different cones where both dips are the same, the total number of choices to choose from is 15.

There is no end to the variety of counting problems. But, fortunately, after careful analysis many can be solved with the principles exhibited in this section.

EXERCISES

1. How many three-digit numbers can be formed from the set {1, 2, 3, 4, 5, 6, 7} provided:
    (a) The digits may be repeated.
    (b) No digit is repeated.

2. A father wishes to have a picture taken with his four sons where two sons stand on each side of him. How many different ways can they line up for the picture?

3. There are nine persons on the board of trustees of a given company. If a committee consisting of five trustees is to be selected to decide on the design of a new building, how many different such committees could be chosen?

4. How many different possible ways can three persons be seated in a row of four chairs?

5. A salesman can take two different routes from town A to town B, and four different routes from town B to town C. How many different routes can he take from town A to town C by going through town B?

6. There are twenty-four letters in the Greek alphabet. How many different Greek-letter fraternity names containing three letters each can be chosen if there is no restriction on repeated letters?

7. Show for a positive integer n that $(n + 1)! - n! = n(n!)$.

8. Prove that if $m > r$, then $C_r^m + C_{r-1}^m = C_r^{m+1}$

9. How many four-digit numbers can be made from the set {1, 2, 3, 4, 5, 6} provided:
    (a) No digit is repeated.
    (b) The digits may be repeated.
    (c) The digits may be repeated but the number is greater than 3,655.
    (d) No digit is repeated and the number is even.
    (e) No digit is repeated and the number is odd.

10. How many four-digit numbers can be made from the set {1, 2, 3, 4, 5, 6, 7} provided:
    (a) No digit is repeated.
    (b) The digits may be repeated but the number is greater than 3,767.
    (c) No digit is repeated and the number is even.
    (d) No digit is repeated and the number is divisible by 5.

11. (a) Compute $C_0^5 + C_1^5 + C_2^5 + C_3^5 + C_4^5 + C_5^5$.
    (b) Interpret your answer to part (a) with reference to subsets of a five element set.

12. (a) By direct multiplication, find the product $(x + y)^4$.
    (b) Is $(x + y)^4 = C_0^4 x^4 + C_1^4 x^3 y + C_2^4 x^2 y^2 + C_3^4 xy^3 + C_4^4 y^4$?
    (c) If $x = y = 1$ in part (b), what does this prove?

13. A small child has a penny, a nickel, a dime, a quarter, and a half-dollar. With these coins, how many different amounts could the child deposit in a savings account? (Assume a deposit is made.)

14. How many four-digit numbers can be formed from the set {1, 2, 3, 4, 5,

165

6, 7, 8} provided:

(a) The digits may be repeated.

(b) No digit is repeated.

15. A man decides to buy three stocks from a collection of seven recommended stocks. How many choices does he have to select from?

16. How many three-digit numbers can be formed from the set {1, 2, 3, 4, 5, 6, 7, 8} provided:

(a) The digits may be repeated.

(b) No digit is repeated.

(c) No digit is repeated and each number is odd.

(d) No digit is repeated and each number is a multiple of 5.

17. A person is asked to select five items from lists A and B where two must be selected from A which contains four items and three must be selected from B which contains seven items. How many possible choices for selection does the person have?

18. Consider an ordered arrangement such as 12345. An *inversion* of the arrangement is an arrangement obtained when exactly two adjacent positions are interchanged. For example, 13245 is an inversion of 12345. Let us list successive inversions of 12345 that will produce the permutation 32154; they are

$$12354$$
$$13254$$
$$31254$$
$$32154$$

For each of the following permutations of 12345, exhibit successive inversions that will produce the given permutation. In each case, state the number of inversions you used.

(a) 15234   (b) 14523   (c) 32541   (d) 45321   (e) 54321

19. Consider the ordered arrangement 1234567. Let us list successive inversions to obtain the permutation 1423675. (See Exercise 18.)

Given:	1234567
(1)	1243567
(2)	1423567
(3)	1423657
(4)	1423675

Since we could interchange 6 and 7 starting in (4) and then interchange 6 and 7 again and be back where we started, we could use 6 inversions as well as 4 to obtain the given permutation; thus, the number of inversions is not unique. However, in both cases the number of inversions is even. It can be proved that the evenness or oddness of the number of inversions of a given permutation is unique. For the ordered arrangement 1234567, state whether the number of inversions in the following permutations is even or odd.

(a) 1234756   (b) 1234765   (c) 1537426

(d) 4327651   (e) 7654321   (f) 2143756

(g) 1726354   (h) 7651234   (i) 7162534

20. A permutation of an ordered arrangement is said to be *odd* or *even* according to whether the number of inversions in the permutation is odd or even. (See Exercises 18 and 19.) Notice for the permutation 1423765 of the ordered arrangement 1234567 that 4 precedes *two* digits which it does not precede in the given arrangement, namely 2 and 3. Similarly, 7 precedes *two* digits (6 and 5) and 6 precedes *one* such digit. It should be obvious by looking at what is involved that $2 + 2 + 1 = 5$ is the number of inversions needed to obtain the given permutation. In general, the indicated technique can be used to determine if a permutation of a given arrangement is even or odd. Use this technique to check your answers in Exercise 19.

21. A puzzle famous for nearly a hundred years is called the "15 Puzzle." In the puzzle, there are 15 squares which are placed into a container resembling a square shallow box having the width and length of four of the given squares. (See Figure 7.1.) The object of the puzzle is to change the given arrangement of the squares in the box to some other given arrangement by moving squares successively into the empty space

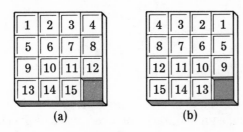

(a)   (b)

FIGURE 7.1

and without removing any from the box. If we associate with Figure 7.1a the ordered arrangement 1, 2, 3, 4, 5, 6, 7, 8, 9, 10, 11, 12, 13, 14, 15 obtained by listing the numbers in successive rows, then the arrangement associated with Figure 7.1b is 4, 3, 2, 1, 8, 7, 6, 5, 12, 11, 10, 9, 15, 14, 13 which is a permutation of the given arrangement. Two American mathematicians proved in the latter part of the last century that if one starts with the normal arrangement in Figure 7.1a then a given arrangement can be obtained if and only if it is an even permutation of the normal arrangement. (See Exercises 18, 19, and 20.)

(a) Starting with the standard arrangement, which of the following arrangements can be obtained in the "15 Puzzle"?

(i)
4	3	2	1
8	7	6	5
12	11	10	9
15	14	13	

(ii)
15	14	13	12
11	10	9	8
7	6	5	4
3	2	1	

167

(iii)

1	3	5	7
2	4	6	8
9	11	13	15
10	12	14	

(iv)

1	5	9	13
2	6	10	14
3	7	11	15
4	8	12	

(v)

1	2	3	4
8	7	6	5
9	10	11	12
15	14	13	

(vi)

1	2	4	7
3	5	8	11
6	9	12	14
10	13	15	

(b) How many different arrangements are possible to obtain from the given arrangement? In other words, how many "15 Puzzles" are solvable?

3. BASIC IDEAS OF PROBABILITY

Let us begin our discussion of the basic ideas of probability by using familiar objects: a coin and a pair of dice. If we toss a coin, a number of things can happen: it can come up heads, it can come up tails, it can land on its edge, it might disintegrate in the air, etc. For our purposes, we reject all but the first two possibilities and assume a tossed coin comes up heads or tails; furthermore, we assume that we have an "ideal" coin so that each outcome is equally likely. We shall make a similar assumption about the roll of a pair of dice; that is, we shall assume that a single die will come up 1, 2, 3, 4, 5, or 6 and that each outcome is equally likely.

Not only do we assume that it is as equally likely that a head comes up as it is that a tail comes up on the toss of a coin, but also we assume the toss is independent of previous tosses. The second basic premise is quite important. Roughly speaking, we assert that a previous toss of the coin has no effect on a successive toss. (We assume the coin has no memory.) Thus, a subsequent tossing of a coin is called an *independent event* from the previous toss.

independent event

To emphasize the meaning of what is meant by independent events, let us consider the story of Mr. Able, Mr. Baker, and Mr. Cain. One day, Mr. Able tossed a coin nine consecutive times and each time a head came up. Both Mr. Baker and Mr. Cain observed the occurrence. Also, Mr. Baker and Mr. Cain knew a little (too little) about probability. Upon observing the toss of nine consecutive heads, Mr. Baker reasoned that since the chances were 1 in 1,024 of tossing ten consecutive heads, it was an exceptionally good bet that a head would not be tossed again. So Mr. Baker made a ten-to-one bet with Mr. Able that the tenth toss would be a tail. Mr. Able took the bet, made the toss, and then collected the bet since a head came up.

Mr. Cain who had observed the ten tosses and the bet, reasoned quite differently from Mr. Baker. He felt that the odds were so small (less than one in a thousand) that heads could come up in ten consecutive tosses, that surely Mr. Able was tossing a two-headed coin. Mr. Cain therefore offered a ten to one bet that a head would come up. Mr. Able took the bet, made the toss, and then collected the bet since a tail came up.

Of course, Mr. Able was "lucky" to win both bets but Mr. Baker and Mr. Cain made very bad bets. Since Mr. Baker must have assumed that the coin was fair and the toss was fair, his bet was very foolish, for he assumed that the preceding outcomes affected the next toss, and that the events were not independent. If the coin is fair, if the toss is fair, and if we reject the fact that the coin might land on its edge, then the chances that a head will come up on a given toss is one out of two. Mr. Cain, to have made his bet, must have thought the chances of an unfair coin were better than the toss of ten consecutive heads. He might have saved money by inspecting the coin before making the bet.

Suppose we toss a single coin twice. The set of all possible outcomes (results) of the trials of such a random experiment is called the *sample space* of the experiment. For example, the sample space for the experiment of tossing a single coin twice consists of the ordered pairs (Heads, Heads), (Heads, Tails), (Tails, Heads), and (Tails, Tails), where the first element in the ordered pair represents the first toss and the second element represents the second toss. Often, we let H represent heads and T represent tails, and describe the sample space S as follows:

sample space

$$S = \{(H, H), (H, T), (T, H), (T, T)\}$$

Each individual outcome is an *element* of the sample space and a subset of a sample space is called an *event*. For example, $\{(H, H), (T, T)\}$ is the event that both tosses are the same. Suppose we toss a coin and then a fair die. The sample space for the experiment would be the following set:

element

event

$$\{(H, 1), (H, 2), (H, 3), (H, 4), (H, 5), (H, 6),$$
$$(T, 1), (T, 2), (T, 3), (T, 4), (T, 5), (T, 6)\}$$

169

The subset $\{(H, 1), (H, 2), (H, 3), (H, 4), (H, 5), (H, 6)\}$ represents the event of tossing a head.

Let S be the sample space associated with the tossing of a coin four consecutive times. A couple of elements in S would be (H, T, H, T) and (T, T, H, T). How many elements are in S? Since the coin can come up 2 ways for each of the four tosses, it follows that $n(S) = 2 \times 2 \times 2 \times 2 = 16$. Let E be a subset (event) of S defined by a specific condition. For example, let E be the event that exactly two heads are tossed and that they are tossed consecutively; thus,

$$E = \{(H, H, T, T), (T, H, H, T), (T, T, H, H)\}$$

It should be clear that there are three elements in E; that is, $n(E) = 3$. We define the ratio $n(E)/n(S) = \frac{3}{16}$ to be the *probability* of the event; in other words, the probability that exactly two heads will be tossed in succession is $\frac{3}{16}$ (three chances in sixteen).

probability   In general, if S is a (nonempty) sample space and if E is some event (subset) of S, then the *probability* of the event E is denoted by $P(E)$ and is defined by

$$P(E) = \frac{n(E)}{n(S)}$$

Since $0 \le n(E) \le n(S)$ and since $n(S) \ne 0$, it follows that

$$0 \le \frac{n(E)}{n(S)} \le 1$$

thus,
$$0 \le P(E) \le 1$$

Recall that if S is a set and E is a subset of S, then E' is the complement of E relative to S; furthermore, $E \cap E' = \varnothing$ and $E \cup E' = S$. Consequently,

$$n(S) = n(E) + n(E')$$

If E is an event for a sample space S, then $P(E')$ is the *probability that the event E will not occur;* furthermore,

$$P(E') = \frac{n(E')}{n(S)}$$
$$= \frac{n(S) - n(E)}{n(S)}$$
$$= 1 - \frac{n(E)}{n(S)}$$
$$= 1 - P(E)$$

The argument shows, as we would expect, that if the probability that an event will occur is $P(E)$, then the probability $P(E')$ that it will not occur is $1 - P(E)$.

Example 1. Let S be the sample space of tossing a coin four consecutive times. Now, let E_2 be the event of tossing *at least two* successive heads. Thus,

$$E_2 = \{(H, H, T, T), (H, H, H, T), (H, H, H, H), (T, H, H, T),$$
$$(T, H, H, H), (T, T, H, H), (H, T, H, H), (H, H, T, H)\}$$

and the probability of tossing at least two heads in succession is

$$P(E_2) = \frac{n(E_2)}{n(S)} = \frac{8}{16} = \frac{1}{2}$$

The probability $P(E_2')$ that no two successive tosses are heads is also $1/2$.

Example 2. Let S be the sample space of tossing a coin four consecutive times. Let E_3 be the event that at least three successive tosses of the coin will be heads. Then,

$$E_3 = \{(H, H, H, T), (T, H, H, H), (H, H, H, H)\}$$

and the probability of tossing at least three heads in a row is

$$P(E_3) = \frac{n(E_3)}{n(S)} = \frac{3}{16}$$

The probability $P(E_3')$ that no three successive tosses will be heads is $13/16$.

There are two ways of determining the probability of tossing four successive heads with one coin. One way is to continue as in Examples 1 and 2 and let $E_4 = \{(H, H, H, H)\}$. Thus, $P(E_4) = 1/16$. Another way is to consider first the probability of tossing a head in one toss of the coin. Here, $S = \{H, T\}$, $E = \{H\}$, and the probability is $P(E) = 1/2$. Since a second toss is independent of the first toss, the probability of the two events is the product of the separate probabilities; thus, the probability of tossing two consecutive heads is $(1/2)^2 = 1/4$. Similarly, the probability of tossing four successive heads is $(1/2)^4 = 1/16$.

Example 3. What is the probability of rolling a seven on a pair of dice?

Solution: Since each die can come up with six different numbers, the sample space S has $6 \times 6 = 36$ different elements. If E is the event that the sum of the numbers on the two faces is seven, then

$$E = \{(6, 1), (5, 2), (4, 3), (3, 4), (2, 5), (1, 6)\}$$

and $n(E) = 6$. Thus, $P(E) = 6/36 = 1/6$.

Example 4. (a) What is the probability of rolling an even number on a pair of dice?
(b) What is the probability of rolling an odd number on a pair of dice?
(c) What is the probability of rolling a number greater than seven on a pair of dice?
(d) What is the probability of rolling either an even number or a number greater than seven on a pair of dice?

Solution: (a) If E_1 is the event of rolling an even number, then

$$E_1 = \{(1, 1),\ (1, 3),\ (3, 1),\ (2, 2),\ (5, 1),\ (1, 5),\ (4, 2),\ (2, 4),\ (3, 3),$$
$$(6, 2),\ (2, 6),\ (5, 3),\ (3, 5),\ (4, 4),\ (6, 4),\ (4, 6),\ (5, 5),\ (6, 6)\}$$

and $n(E_1) = 18$. Thus, $P(E_1) = {}^{18}\!/_{36} = {}^1\!/_2$.
(b) Since E_1 is the event of rolling an even number, E_1' is the event of rolling an odd number. Thus,

$$P(E_1') = 1 - P(E_1)$$
$$= 1 - {}^1\!/_2$$
$$= {}^1\!/_2$$

(c) If E_2 is the event of rolling a number greater than seven, then

$$E_2 = \{(6, 2),\ (2, 6),\ (3, 5),\ (5, 3),\ (4, 4),\ (6, 3),\ (3, 6),\ (5, 4),\ (4, 5),\ (4, 6),$$
$$(6, 4),\ (5, 5),\ (6, 5),\ (5, 6),\ (6, 6)\}$$

and $n(E_2) = 15$. Thus, $P(E_2) = {}^{15}\!/_{36} = {}^5\!/_{12}$.
(d) Since $E_1 \cap E_2 \neq \varnothing$, the two events are not mutually exclusive. Furthermore, since

$$E_1 \cap E_2 = \{(6, 2),\ (2, 6),\ (5, 3),\ (3, 5),\ (4, 4),\ (6, 4),\ (4, 6),\ (5, 5),$$
$$(6, 6)\}$$

we have that $n(E_1 \cap E_2) = 9$. Thus,

$$P(E_1 \cup E_2) = \frac{n(E_1 \cup E_2)}{n(S)}$$
$$= \frac{n(E_1) + n(E_2) - n(E_1 \cap E_2)}{n(S)}$$
$$= \frac{18 + 15 - 9}{36}$$
$$= \frac{2}{3}$$

is the probability that at least one of the two events occur.

Example 5. (a) If a family is to have four children, what is the probability that exactly two of the children will be boys?
(b) What is the probability that exactly three will be the same sex?

Solution: (a) (We make the assumption that the birth of a boy and the birth of a girl are equally likely.) Since each child may be a boy or a girl, the sample space S has $2 \times 2 \times 2 \times 2 = 16$ elements. If E_1 is the event that exactly two children will be boys, then

$$E_1 = \{(B, B, G, G), (B, G, B, G), (B, G, G, B), (G, B, B, G),$$
$$(G, B, G, B), (G, G, B, B)\}$$

(where order of listing indicates order of birth) and $n(E_1) = 6$. (Notice that $n(E_1) = C_2^4$.) Thus, $P(E_1) = 6/16 = 3/8$ is the probability that the number of boys and the number of girls will be the same.

(b) If E_2 is the event that exactly three children will be the same sex, then

$$E_2 = \{(B, B, B, G), (B, B, G, B), (B, G, B, B), (G, B, B, B),$$
$$(G, G, G, B), (G, G, B, G), (G, B, G, G), (B, G, G, G)\}$$

and $n(E_2) = 8$. Since the number of ways to have exactly three boys is $C_3^4 = 4$, the number of ways to have exactly three boys or girls is $2C_3^4 = 8$. Thus, $P(E_2) = 8/16 = 1/2$. (You might find it surprising that a three-one division between the sexes is more likely than a two-two division; the chances are fifty-fifty that a three-one split will occur.)

Example 5 might give some indication that our intuition about the probability of an event may prove unreliable. Before reading the next two examples, test your intuition by guessing an answer to the following two questions. (1) If each of four persons writes down a letter selected at random from the first ten letters of the alphabet, what is the probability that at least two write the same letter? (2) In a class with 23 students, what is the probability that at least two have the same birthday (month and day)?

Example 6. Assume each of four individuals writes down one of the first ten letters of the alphabet. If we assume that the choice of each letter is equally likely, what is the probability that at least two of them will write the same letter?

Solution: Let S be the sample space and let E be the event that at least two persons write the same letter. There will be elements of E representing the following three situations: exactly two letters the same, exactly three letters the same, and exactly four letters the same. A little experience (or effort) will confirm the fact that it is easier to find $n(E')$ than it is to find $n(E)$. Therefore, the problem tends to be easier to solve if we determine the probility $P(E')$ that no two persons write the same letter.

Since one person can write down any one of 10 letters, the number of selections left for the second person so that the two letters will be different is 9. The third person has only 8 selections to make to be different from the first two and the fourth person will have just 7 selections. Thus,

$$n(E') = 10 \times 9 \times 8 \times 7$$

Since each individual has ten choices,

$$n(S) = 10 \times 10 \times 10 \times 10$$

173

Consequently,

$$P(E') = \frac{10 \times 9 \times 8 \times 7}{10 \times 10 \times 10 \times 10}$$

$$= \frac{504}{1,000}$$

$$= 0.504$$

Thus, $P(E) = 1 - P(E') = 0.496$. (It is almost an even bet that at least two individuals will write down the same letter.)

Example 7. (*The Birthday Problem*) How many individuals are required to be attending a party so that the probability is better than $\frac{1}{2}$ that *at least* two persons present will have the same birthday (month and day)?

Solution: (We assume that a year has 365 days and that it is equally likely for a person to be born on each of these days. The solution to this problem is quite similar to the solution to the previous example.) If E is the event that at least two persons have the same birthday, then E' is the event that no two persons have the same birthday. We determine $P(E')$ first.

Two persons can have *different* birthdays in 365×364 ways. Thus, $(365 \times 364)/(365)^2$ is the probability that two persons will have different birthdays. The probability that four persons, for example, will have different birthdays is

$$\frac{365 \times 364 \times 363 \times 362}{(365)^4}$$

Thus, the probability that four persons will not all have different birthdays is

$$1 - \frac{365 \times 364 \times 363 \times 362}{(365)^4} = 0.0163559$$

That is, the probability that at least two of the four persons have the same birthday is 0.0163559. (To find the probability for any number of persons is not difficult, but it is tedious.)

Let N be the number of persons present at a party and let P be the probability that at least two persons will have the same birthday. The table on the facing page exhibits the probabilities where N is greater than 1 and less than 44.

From the table we see the probability that at least two persons will have the same birthday is better than $\frac{1}{2}$ if N is as large as twenty-three! The probability is better than $\frac{9}{10}$ that at least two persons have the same birthday if as many as forty-one persons are present. In fact, if as few as fifty-seven persons are present, the chances are better than 99 out of 100 that at least two of them have the same birthday. (Actually, our assump-

N	P	N	P
2	0.0027397	23	0.5072972
3	0.0082042	24	0.5383443
4	0.0163559	25	0.5686997
5	0.0271356	26	0.5982408
6	0.0404625	27	0.6268593
7	0.0562357	28	0.6544615
8	0.0743353	29	0.6909685
9	0.0946238	30	0.7063162
10	0.1169482	31	0.7304546
11	0.1411414	32	0.7533475
12	0.1670248	33	0.7749719
13	0.1944103	34	0.7953169
14	0.2231025	35	0.8143832
15	0.2529013	36	0.8321821
16	0.2836040	37	0.8487340
17	0.3150077	38	0.8640678
18	0.2469114	39	0.8782197
19	0.3791185	40	0.8912318
20	0.4114384	41	0.9031516
21	0.4436883	42	0.9140305
22	0.4756953	43	0.9239229

tion that each day of the year is equally likely for births is not true. However, it should be obvious that if some days are more likely than others, then it will be even more probable than the table indicates that any group of N people includes two people with the same birthday.)

Example 8. (*Odds*) Let S be the sample space for four successive tosses of a fair coin. Hence, $n(S) = 16$. Let E be the event that at least two heads are tossed *and* that the first toss is a head. Thus,

$$E = \{(H,\ H,\ H,\ H),\ (H,\ H,\ T,\ H),\ (H,\ H,\ H,\ T),\ (H,\ H,\ T,\ T),$$
$$(H, T, H, H),\ (H, T, H, T),\ (H, T, T, H)\}$$

and $n(E) = 7$. Consequently $P(E) = 7/16$ is the probability that at least two heads are tossed and the first toss is a head. We say that the odds are 7 to 9 in favor of E and 9 to 7 against E. In general, if $P(E) = p/(p + q)$, we say that the *odds* are p to q in favor of E and the odds against E are q to p.

In the preceding example, we see that the *odds in favor* of an event is the ratio of the probability that the event will occur to the probability that the event will not occur. The *reciprocal* of this number is the *odds against* the event.

odds in favor

odds against

175

mathematical expectation

Closely associated with *mathematical odds* is *mathematical expectation*. Roughly speaking, mathematical expectation is a number giving the "worth" of a game. For example, mathematical expectation will provide an answer to the following question. Suppose two coins are tossed in a betting game where $5.00 is paid to the bettor if two heads come up; nothing is paid otherwise. What would be a fair price to require a player to spend in order to play? (By "fair price" we mean that in the long run winning or losing will depend only on "luck.")

Let $p_1, p_2, p_3, \ldots, p_n$ be the probabilities of the outcomes of n independent events. If the values of the outcomes are $v_1, v_2, v_3, \ldots, v_n$, respectively, then the *mathematical expectation* (of the game) is

$$p_1 v_1 + p_2 v_2 + p_3 v_3 + \cdots + p_n v_n$$

For the pair of tossed coins in the game described above, the probability of two heads coming up is $p_1 = 1/4$; the probability of a head and a tail being tossed is $p_2 = 1/2$; and the probability of two tails being tossed is $p_3 = 1/4$. If $v_1 = \$5.00$ is the value of the first event and zero is the value of the second and third events, then

$$1/4(\$5.00) + 1/2(0) + 1/4(0) = \$1.25$$

is the mathematical expectation; thus, $1.25 is the amount a person should be required to bet for it to be a fair game.

For a game where a large number of bets are made, we conclude the following: a bet less than the mathematical expectation will ensure that the bettor is a winner; a bet greater than the mathematical expectation will ensure that the bettor is a loser; winning or losing with a bet equal to the mathematical expectation will depend on "luck." Needless to say, roulette and other such games in gambling casinos are of the second category.

Suppose on a single roll of a pair of dice that "the house" is willing to pay off 6 for 1 if a 2 or 12 is thrown, 2 for 1 if a 9 is thrown, and 4 for 1 if a 3 or 11 is thrown. What is the mathematical expectation of the game? (*Note:* 6 *for* 1, for example, is equivalent to a 5 *to* 1 bet.)

Outcome	Probability	Value
2	$p_1 = 1/36$	6 for 1
3	$p_2 = 2/36$	4 for 1
9	$p_3 = 4/36$	2 for 1
11	$p_4 = 2/36$	4 for 1
12	$p_5 = 1/36$	6 for 1

SEC. 3 · Basic Ideas of Probability

If M.E. is the mathematical expectation, then

$$\text{M.E.} = \tfrac{1}{36}(6) + \tfrac{2}{36}(4) + \tfrac{4}{36}(2) + \tfrac{2}{36}(4) + \tfrac{1}{36}(6) = 1$$

Thus, if one dollar is bet on each roll, then the game is fair; in the long run, one will break even.

The type of probability we have been discussing is often called *a priori probability*. With this type of probability we can assign measures to events without carrying out actual experiments. Although *a priori* probability is extremely important in both practical and theoretical work, it would not be very effective for such things as determining life expectancy for insurance purposes. *(a priori probability)*

The type of probability for such things as life expectancy is called *statistical probability*. The probabilities are determined as a result of certain facts obtained from experiments; hence, it is also called *empirical, experimental, or a posteriori probability*. *(statistical probability)* *(a posteriori probability)*

EXERCISES

1. In the roll of a pair of dice, determine the probability of the following events.
   (a) The sum of the numbers on the dice is 12 or 2.
   (b) The sum of the numbers on the dice is 11.
   (c) The sum of the numbers on the dice is 11 or 7.
   (d) The sum of the numbers on the dice is less than 6.

2. Assume a family has six children and assume that having a boy is equally likely as having a girl.
   (a) What is the probability that exactly four are the same sex?
   (b) What is the probability that at least four are the same sex?
   (c) What is the probability that there are three boys and three girls?

3. (a) If six coins are tossed, what is the probability that exactly two heads come up?
   (b) What is the probability that exactly three heads come up?

4. If we toss a coin and roll a fair die, what is the probability that a head and a number greater than four come up?

5. A box contains three black balls and four red balls. If two balls are picked at random (without replacement) from the box, what is the probability that they will both be black?

6. Let $S = \{2, 3, 4, 5, 6\}$. What is the probability that the sum of two different numbers picked at random from the set is an odd number?

7. From a regular bridge deck, what is the probability for selecting five hearts in one draw of five cards?

8. From a regular bridge deck, what is the probability for selecting five cards of the same suit in one draw of five cards?

177

9. Five numbered tags having one and only one of the numbers 1, 5, 10, 25, or 50 on each are placed in a box.
(a) What is the probability that the sum of the numbers on three tags selected from the box will be less than forty?
(b) Equal to forty?
(c) Greater than forty?

10. Suppose a positive integer less than or equal to one hundred is selected at random. What is the probability the number has 3 or 5 as a factor?

11. A box contains four dimes and a nickel. If three coins are picked at random from the box, what is the probability of having change for a quarter?

12. A box contains four dimes and two nickels. If three coins are picked at random from the box, what is the probability of having change for a quarter?

13. (a) In the roll of a pair of dice and the flip of a coin, what is the probability that the sum of the numbers on the dice is even and that the coin comes up heads?
(b) What is the probability that the sum is even or a head comes up?

14. If we toss a coin and roll a fair die, what is the probability that a head and a number greater than three come up?

15. Let $S = \{2, 3, 4, 5, 6, 7, 8\}$. What is the probability that the sum of two different numbers picked at random from this set is an odd number?

16. Assume each of five persons writes down one of the first ten letters of the alphabet. If we assume that the choice of each letter is equally likely, what is the probability that at least two persons will write the same letter?

17. Suppose a number less than one hundred is selected at random. What is the probability that the number has 3, 5, or 7 as a factor?

18. Is the following game a "house" game, fair game, or bettor's game? A bettor is required to pay the house $3.00 on each roll of a pair of dice. If a 2, 5, 8, or 11 comes up, the player is paid the number of dollars on the face of the dice. Otherwise, he receives nothing.

19. Is the following game a "house" game, fair game, or bettor's game? A bettor is required to pay the house $3.25 on each roll of a pair of dice. If a 4, 6, 8, or 10 comes up, the player is paid the number of dollars on the face of the dice. Otherwise, he receives nothing.

20. Is the following a fair game? A player is required to pay $8.50 for the opportunity to select at random two bills from a box containing four one dollar bills, two five dollar bills, and two ten dollar bills.

4. INTRODUCTION TO STATISTICS

We have already mentioned the field of mathematics called statistics. The student is probably familiar with the fact that the theory and techniques of statistics are applicable to science, education, sociology, psychology, insurance, advertising, etc. Major tasks for the statistician are collecting, organizing, analyzing, and interpreting numerical facts. We shall not discuss in detail the collection of data, but it is an important feature of statistical work. Anyone who is familiar with the early predictions of presidential elections should be keenly aware of the importance of how statistical data is collected.

In this section we consider some of the basic ideas and techniques connected with organizing numerical data. In the next section we discuss measures of central tendency (averages) and measures of dispersion. Although ours will not be an in-depth discussion, it will provide a minimal knowledge of statistics that is important to an educated person.

Let us consider the set of grades made by 40 students on a particular test. They are as follows:

21	25	27	27
27	27	19	23
21	21	27	28
26	25	28	27
28	27	28	27
28	26	24	25
28	26	30	30
30	27	26	25
28	24	30	24
28	27	27	23

We have organized the scores into four columns with ten scores in each, but this organization is not very revealing or useful. Let us arrange the scores in order of magnitude.

30	28	27	25
30	28	27	24
30	27	27	24
30	27	26	24
28	27	26	23
28	27	26	23
28	27	26	21
28	27	25	21
28	27	25	21
28	27	25	19

One fact that is easily determined from our second organization of the scores is the *range* of the data. The *difference* between the greatest number and the least number is called the *range;* in our example, the range is $30 - 19 = 11$.   *range*

179

frequency distribution

classes

class limits

Another organization of the data is what is called a *frequency distribution*. This is particularly useful if the number of scores is quite large. To make a frequency distribution, one first determines *classes* into which the data will be organized. The greatest number and least number in a class are called the *class limits*. For example, we shall choose the following classes for our first frequency distribution of the scores: 19–21, 22–24, 25–27, 28–30. We see that 28 and 30 are the class limits for the upper class.

Frequency Distribution I

Class	Frequency
28–30	12
25–27	19
22–24	5
19–21	4

Another frequency distribution for the same data using a different class size would be the following:

Frequency Distribution II

Class	Frequency
29–30	4
27–28	19
25–26	8
23–24	5
21–22	3
19–20	1

histogram

We can make several graphical (pictorial) representations of our data. One is called a *histogram*. We take the arithmetic mean (midpoint) between the upper limit of one class and the lower limit of the next higher class to determine what are called *class boundaries*. For our first frequency distribution the class boundaries are 18.5, 21.5, 24.5, 27.5, and 30.5. For $21.5 < x < 24.5$ we let $f(x)$ be the number of scores in the included class; next, rectangles are constructed as in Figure 7.2.

frequency polygon

In Figure 7.3, we not only construct a histogram for Frequency Distribution II but also draw a frequency polygon. A *frequency polygon* is the graph obtained by connecting with line segments the midpoints of the tops of the adjacent rectangles in the histogram.

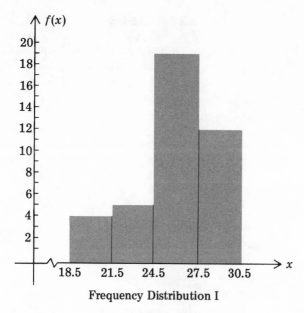

Frequency Distribution I

FIGURE 7.2

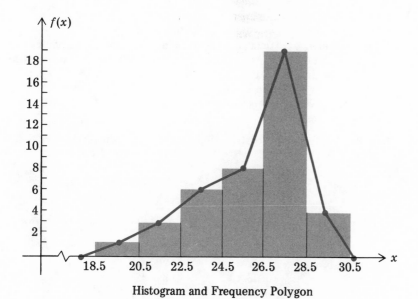

Histogram and Frequency Polygon

Frequency Distribution II

FIGURE 7.3

EXERCISES

1. The following are scores made by 50 students on a placement test.

35	20	27	14	28
22	39	28	40	33
29	23	34	35	41
35	33	30	31	29
31	19	27	37	43
20	11	23	30	43
16	20	25	37	35
29	20	37	18	35
24	36	15	19	12
39	43	16	21	19

Arrange the scores by order of magnitude.

2. What is the range of the scores in Exercise 1?

3. For the data in Exercise 1, make a frequency distribution table using classes 11–13, 14–16, 17–19, etc.

4. Make a histogram and frequency polygon using the results in Exercise 3.

5. For the data in Exercise 1, make a frequency distribution table using classes 10–14, 15–19, 20–24, etc.

6. Make a histogram and frequency polygon using the results in Exercise 5.

7. For the data in Exercise 1, make a frequency distribution table using classes 10–11, 12–13, 14–15, etc.

8. Make a histogram and frequency polygon using the results in Exercise 7.

9. (a) In a frequency distribution, the ratio of the number of elements in a class to the total number of elements in the distribution is called *relative frequency* for the class. Find the relative frequency for each class in the frequency distribution in Exercise 3.

(b) For any given frequency distribution, what is the sum of all the relative frequencies?

Use the following frequency distribution for scores on a mathematics test to work exercises 10 through 13.

Class	Frequency	Class	Frequency
775–799	1	525–549	70
750–774	2	500–524	74
725–749	5	475–499	77
700–724	17	450–474	56
675–699	21	425–449	41
650–674	32	400–424	25
625–649	36	375–399	15
600–624	56	350–374	3
575–599	73	325–349	3
550–574	84	300–324	1

10. How many students took the test?
11. What is the difference between class limits in each frequency class?
12. How many students scored 500 or above on the test?
13. Make a frequency distribution table using the following classes: 300–399, 400–499, 500–599, etc.

5. MEASURES OF CENTRAL TENDENCY AND DISPERSION

There are several measures of central tendency, usually called *averages,* for a collection of numerical data. The most familiar measures of central tendency are the arithmetic mean, mode, and median. Two other averages, which we do not discuss, are the geometric and harmonic means.

Nearly everyone has had occasion to find the arithmetic mean of a set of numbers. Let $x_1, x_2, x_3, \ldots, x_n$ be a set of n numbers; then, the *arithmetic mean m* is defined by *arithmetic mean*

$$m = \frac{x_1 + x_2 + x_3 + \cdots + x_n}{n}$$

For the 40 scores given in the first part of the last section, we can find the arithmetic mean in several ways. Using the definition directly, we find the sum of the 40 scores is 1,045; thus, the arithmetic mean m is

$$m = {}^{1045}\!/_{40} = 26.125$$

If we notice in our 40 scores that 4 students scored 30, 8 scored 28, 11 scored 27, 4 scored 26, 4 scored 25, 3 scored 24, 2 scored 23, 3 scored 21, and 1 scored 19, then the total of all the scores is

$$4(30) + 8(28) + 11(27) + 4(26) + 4(25) + 3(24) + 2(23) + 3(21) + 1(19)$$
$$= 120 + 224 + 297 + 104 + 100 + 72 + 46 + 63 + 19 = 1,045$$

Furthermore, we see that the sum of the frequencies is the total number of students taking the test; that is,

$$4 + 8 + 11 + 4 + 4 + 3 + 2 + 3 + 1 = 40$$

For a set of numbers, if f_k is the frequency of the number x_k then the arithmetic mean for the set is given by

$$m = \frac{x_1 f_1 + x_2 f_2 + x_3 f_3 + \cdots + x_n f_n}{f_1 + f_2 + f_3 + \cdots + f_n}$$

Consider a frequency distribution table with k classes. If $x_1, x_2,$

$x_3, \ldots, x_k$ are the *midpoints* of the k classes and if $f_1, f_2, f_3, \ldots,$ f_k are the frequencies of the k classes, we define the *arithmetic mean* m by

$$m = \frac{x_1f_1 + x_2f_2 + x_3f_3 + \cdots + x_kf_k}{f_1 + f_2 + f_3 + \cdots + f_k}$$

In our Frequency Distribution I in the last section, the number of classes k is 4. Furthermore, $x_1 = 20$, $x_2 = 23$, $x_3 = 26$, $x_4 = 29$ and $f_1 = 4$, $f_2 = 5$, $f_3 = 19$, $f_4 = 12$. Thus, the arithmetic mean m is

$$m = \frac{20(4) + 23(5) + 26(19) + 29(12)}{4 + 5 + 19 + 12}$$

$$= \frac{80 + 115 + 494 + 348}{40}$$

$$= \frac{1,037}{40} = 25.925$$

We should not be surprised by the fact that the arithmetic mean for the grouped data varies slightly from the arithmetic mean for the ungrouped data.

For Frequency Distribution II in the last section, we see that

$x_6 = 29.5$	$f_6 = 4$	$x_6f_6 = 118.0$
$x_5 = 27.5$	$f_5 = 19$	$x_5f_5 = 522.5$
$x_4 = 25.5$	$f_4 = 8$	$x_4f_4 = 204.0$
$x_3 = 23.5$	$f_3 = 5$	$x_3f_3 = 117.5$
$x_2 = 21.5$	$f_2 = 3$	$x_2f_2 = 64.5$
$x_1 = 19.5$	$f_1 = 1$	$x_1f_1 = \underline{19.5}$
		Sum: 1,046.0

The arithmetic mean using this distribution is

$$m = {}^{1046}/_{40} = 26.15$$

median

Let a set of numbers be arranged by order of magnitude. If there is an odd number of numbers, the *median* is the middle number in the ordered array. If there is an even number of numbers in the set, the median is the arithmetic mean of the two middle numbers. For our forty test scores the two middle numbers (20th and 21st) are both 27; thus, the median scored for the set is 27.

mode

For a set of numbers the number that occurs most often, if there is one, is called the *mode*. For our forty test scores the mode is 27. Consider the following three sets of data:

Example A	*Example B*	*Example C*
100	73	100
90	73	72
80	72	71
80	72	70
70	70	70
70	70	70
70	70	70
60	68	70
60	68	69
50	67	68
40	67	40

Arithmetic mean = median = mode = 70

The numbers were "hand-picked" so it would be rather obvious that the arithmetic mean, median, and mode are all 70. However, the sets are quite different. If one considered the numbers as representing weather temperatures on eleven days, it is obvious that an "average temperature" of 70 could be quite misleading. We have talked about the range of a set of numerical data and we see that Example *B* has a different range from Examples *A* and *C*. However, Examples *A* and *C* have the same range in addition to the same arithmetic mean, mode, and median.

What is needed is a better (more revealing) measure for *dispersion* than the range. There are several other measures for dispersion; one is called variance. Let x_1, x_2, x_3, . . . , x_n be a set of numbers with m as arithmetic mean. The *variance* v is defined as follows: *variance*

Variance: $$v = \frac{(x_1 - m)^2 + (x_2 - m)^2 + (x_3 - m)^2 + \cdots + (x_n - m)^2}{n}$$

Roughly speaking, we determine variance by finding out how far each number is from the arithmetic mean and then finding the arithmetic mean of the squares of these distances.

Let us find the variance for each of the examples, *A*, *B*, and *C*.

Example A

$$v_A = \frac{30^2 + 20^2 + 10^2 + 10^2 + 10^2 + 10^2 + 20^2 + 30^2}{11}$$

$$= \frac{3,000}{11} = 272.72\overline{72}. \ . \ .$$

185

Example B

$$v_B = \frac{3^2 + 3^2 + 2^2 + 2^2 + 2^2 + 2^2 + 3^2 + 3^2}{11}$$

$$= \frac{52}{11} = 4.7272. \ . \ .$$

Example C

$$v_C = \frac{30^2 + 2^2 + 1^2 + 1^2 + 2^2 + 30^2}{11}$$

$$= \frac{1{,}810}{11} = 164.54\overline{54}. \ . \ .$$

It is obvious that although Examples A and C have the same arithmetic mean, mode, median, and range, the variances v_A and v_C are quite different. It should be clear that variance gives us a measure of how numbers are scattered with respect to the arithmetic mean. If the numbers are clustered about the arithmetic mean, the variance is small. As the numbers become less clustered about the arithmetic mean, the variance increases.

standard deviation

Another measure of dispersion is called standard deviation. *Standard deviation,* denoted by σ(sigma), is defined to be the (non-negative) square root of the variance; thus,

$$\sigma = \sqrt{v}$$

Obviously, the basic properties of variance also apply to the standard deviation.

For a frequence distribution with k classes, if $x_1, x_2, x_3, \ldots , x_k$ are the *midpoints* of the k classes, if $f_1, f_2, f_3, \ldots , f_k$ are the frequencies for the k classes, and if m is the arithmetic mean, the variance v is defined by

$$v = \frac{f_1(x_1 - m)^2 + f_2(x_2 - m)^2 + f_3(x_3 - m)^2 + \cdots + f_k(x_k - m)^2}{f_1 + f_2 + f_3 + \cdots + f_k}$$

EXERCISES

1. What is the standard deviation for the data in Example A?
2. What is the standard deviation for the data in Example B?
3. What is the standard deviation for the data in Example C?
4. Find the standard deviation for the forty test scores using Frequency Distribution I in the last section.

5. Find the standard deviation for the forty test scores using Frequency Distribution II in the last section.

6. Find the standard deviation for the fifty placement test scores using the frequency distribution in Exercise 3 of the last section.

7. Find the standard deviation for the fifty placement test scores using the frequency distribution in Exercise 5 of the last section.

8. Find the standard deviation for the test scores given in the frequency distribution for Exercise 10 in the last section.

9. Find the standard deviation for the fifty placement test scores using the frequency distribution in Exercise 7 of the last section.

10. Find the standard deviation for the test scores using the frequency distribution in Exercise 13 of the last section.

George Boole (1815–1864)

George Boole, English logician and mathematician, was born on November 2, 1815. He developed logic as an abstract mathematical system. His best known works are the *Mathematical Analysis of Logic* (1847) and *Laws of Thought* (1854). Boole's development of logic paralleled the approach taken in algebra, where problems are translated into algebraic symbols and rules of algebra are applied to the symbols to obtain solutions. Boole created a method to translate problems from logic into logical symbolism and developed appropriate operations on the symbols to represent the rules of the logic. The algebra of logic reduces the ambiguities resulting from the use of language and, in addition, makes important logical relationships more evident. The work of Boole influenced the writing of the twentieth century mathematical masterpiece by Bertrand Russell and Alfred North Whitehead entitled *Principia Mathematica* and the important work on the foundations of geometry by David Hilbert. Boole also made important contributions to the theory of differential equations and the calculus of finite differences. His research publications led to his appointment in 1849 as a professor of mathematics at Queens College in Ireland. There he remained until his death on December 8, 1864, at the age of forty-nine.

8

Logic and the Axiomatic Approach

1. Introduction to Logic
2. Testing the Validity of Arguments
3. Introduction to Axiomatics
4. Venn Diagrams and Lewis Carroll Puzzles

*Mathematics in its widest significance is the development
of all types of familiar, necessary, deductive reasoning.*

ALFRED NORTH WHITEHEAD

1. INTRODUCTION TO LOGIC

All was not well at the Karl Sagus mansion. Mr. Sagus had been found murdered in the study. The famous detective, Mr. Watkins, had been called in to solve the crime.

The suspects were the butler, the maid, the gardener, and an unidentified intruder. Mr. Watkins quickly realized that knowing whether or not the door to the study was locked and what condition the maid's shoes were in would be important clues in the crime. He first concluded that the butler did not murder Mr. Sagus or that the door to the study was locked. He also knew it was not true that if the door to the study were unlocked, then the maid killed Mr. Sagus.

After interrogation of the suspects, Mr. Watkins found that when the crime was committed, everyone except the murderer was outside the house in the rain looking for Mr. Sagus' Chihuahua which had slipped out the kitchen door. Obviously, if the maid did not commit the crime, then she had to have mud on her shoes. But it became clear to Mr. Watkins that if the gardener did not do it, then the butler was guilty or the maid's shoes were clean.

Reviewing all of the facts, Mr. Watkins walked to the telephone and called the police to come and pick up the perpetrator of the dastardly deed.

Questions

1. In your opinion, did Mr. Watkins have enough information to be certain who murdered Mr. Sagus?
2. Who do you think committed the crime?

Obviously, what is involved in attempting to solve our murder mystery is the drawing of logical conclusions from a given set of facts. Before the end of this chapter we shall make a careful analysis of the problem presented. First, let us look carefully at the "rules" of logic and at the relationship of logic to mathematics.

In plane geometry we begin with a set of statements (assumptions called *axioms,* or *postulates*), and then proceed to deduce certain conclusions which are called *theorems.* The initial assumptions are about points and lines; however, there is no attempt made (or should be made) to give a definition of a point or line. Of course, we have intuitive ideas about the concepts but they are not essential to the development of the theory. Since "point" and "line" are undefined terms, it would be difficult to justify classifying the theory of plane geometry as mathematics on the basis of the subject matter. Certainly, the process of using deductive reasoning to draw logical conclusions from a set of given statements is primarily what distinguishes plane geometry as mathematics.

Let us state a few definitions of mathematics given by famous mathematicians. The first American mathematician to gain an international reputation was Benjamin Peirce. In 1870 he wrote in the American Journal of Mathematics:

> Mathematics is the science which draws necessary conclusions.

In *Principles of Mathematics,* Bertrand Russell wrote:

> Pure mathematics is the class of all propositions of the form "p implies q," where p and q are propositions containing one or more variables, the same in the two propositions, and neither p nor q contains any constants other than logical constants.

In the preface of *Universal Algebra,* A. N. Whitehead wrote:

> Mathematics in the widest significance is the development of all types of formal, necessary, deductive reasoning.

As indicated earlier, it is unlikely that all mathematicians would agree on any one definition of mathematics. However, few would deny that logic plays a central role in the subject. Our purpose in this section is to give an informal discussion of the basic ideas of logic; the basic ideas of logic are important in every branch of mathematics. A brief discussion of the "rules of the game" should aid us in our effort to learn *how* conclusions are deduced from a given set of statements.

Technically, "statement" in formal logic is an undefined term, as are "point" and "line" in geometry. However, we take the usual approach of giving an intuitive idea of the concept so that the assumptions (postulates) which we subsequently make seem plausible. *statement* A *statement* is a declarative sentence for which it is meaningful to say whether or not it is true. The following are examples of statements:

1. He has red hair.
2. There is no prime number between 268,344 and 268,400.
3. The moon is made of green cheese.
4. Every odd integer squared is odd.
5. Every even integer greater than four can be expressed as the sum of two odd primes.

truth-value

Whether or not Statement 1 above is true would depend on to whom "he" refers. It might not be an easy task for the reader to determine whether Statement 2 is true or not, but the difficulty in determining the *truth-value* (true or false) does not change its classification as a statement. In fact, it is unknown whether or not Statement 5 is true. Statement 3 is false and Statements 2 and 4 are true.

It should be clear from our definition that the following are not statements:

1. How much is that doggie in the window?
2. Yankee go home!
3. Around the mulberry bush.

connectives

From simple statements we can build compound statements by the use of *connectives*. Some of the standard connectives are *and, not, or,* and *if . . . then.* For example, consider the statements "Triangles *A* and *B* are congruent" and "Triangles *A* and *B* are similar." The following are compound statements formed by using these four connectives:

1. Triangles *A* and *B* are congruent and they are similar.
2. Triangles *A* and *B* are not congruent.
3. Triangles *A* and *B* are congruent or they are similar.
4. If triangles *A* and *B* are congruent, then they are similar.

In ordinary language we use many other connectives but they can be shown to be logically equivalent to some combination of these given four connectives. (Notice in the preceding sentence that "but" was used to connect two statements; it should be clear that "but" is logically equivalent to "and.") Not only can each compound statement be written in terms of these four connectives but, in fact, the list can be shortened to include just "or" and "not." However, since such an approach complicates matters unnecessarily, we shall not consider shortening the list.

In algebra, it is standard practice to use symbols (letters such as *x* and *y*) to represent numbers. Similarly, it is standard practice in the study of logic to use symbols such as *p*, *q*, *r*, etc. to represent statements. If *p* represents "Triangles *A* and *B* are congruent," and *q* represents "Triangles *A* and *B* are similar," then the following are abbreviated forms of the four compound statements given earlier.

1. "*p* and *q*"   This is called the *conjunction* of *p* and *q*.
2. "not *p*"   This is called the *negation* of *p*.
3. "*p* or *q*"   This is called the *disjunction* of *p* and *q*.
4. "*p* implies *q*"   This is called an *implication* or *conditional*
   or   *statement,* with *p* as *antecedent* and *q* as con-
   "if *p* then *q*"   *sequent.*

Let us now state how one determines whether or not a compound statement is true by knowing the truth-values of the statements that make it up.

Rule 1. The conjunction of two statements p and q is true when both   *conjunction*
p and q are true and at no other time.

Example 1. Two is an even number and five is an odd number. (This conjunction is true.)

Example 2. Two is an even number and the moon is made of green cheese. (This conjunction is false.)

Example 3. Two is an odd number and the moon is made of green cheese. (This conjunction is false.)

Let *p* be a statement, let *q* be a statement, and let *T* and *F* represent true and false, respectively. Then, the preceding rule for the truth-values of the conjunction of two statements can be abbreviated rather easily in the following manner:

Conjunction

p	*q*	*p and q*
T	T	T
T	F	F
F	T	F
F	F	F

The above table is called a *truth-table;* it shows all of the combi-   *truth-table*
nations of truth-values for the given statements and indicates when the compound statement is true and when it is false.

The rules for the negation of a simple statement are quite reason-   *negation*
able and easy to accept.

Rule 2. If p represents a true statement then "not p" is false; if p rep-
resents a false statement then "not p" is true.

The following is the truth-table for the negation.

Negation

p	$not\ p$
T	F
F	T

In ordinary language there is some confusion over the use of the connective "or." (This is why in legal documents we often see "and/or" in compound statements.) For example, suppose John says "I am going to England this summer or I am going to France this summer." We would quickly agree that if he does neither, then the compound statement is false. Also, if he goes to one country and not the other, then we would agree that the statement is true. What if he goes to both places this summer? We shall *agree* that in this case the statement is also true; in other words, "or" will be used in the *inclusive* sense. The following is the truth-table for the disjunction of two statements.

Disjunction

p	q	$p\ or\ q$
T	T	T
T	F	T
F	T	T
F	F	F

disjunction **Rule 3.** *The disjunction of two statements is false if and only if both statements are false.*

With our agreement to use "or" only in the inclusive sense, an interesting question arises naturally when we consider the following. Suppose John had said, "I am going to England or France this summer but not to both." This would be equivalent to using "or" in the exclusive sense. How do we construct a compound statement using our four connectives which would be equivalent to this statement? Before attempting to answer this question we should first notice that we have rather casually dropped the word "equivalent" into our discussion. What we mean by saying two compound statements *equivalent* are *equivalent* is that they have the same truth-values, that is, the same truth-tables. The truth-table for the exclusive "or" would be as follows:

Exclusive "Or"

p	q	p *(exclusive) or* q
T	T	F
T	F	T
F	T	T
F	F	F

Notice that "*p* (exclusive) or *q*" is false when both *p* and *q* are true.

Now, consider the truth-values for the statement "*p* and (not *q*)." This conjunction is true only when *p* is true and *q* is false.

p	q	*not q*	p *and (not* q)		p	q	*not p*	*(not* p) *and* q
T	T	F	F		T	T	F	F
T	F	T	T		T	F	F	F
F	T	F	F		F	T	T	T
F	F	T	F		F	F	T	F

Similarly, "(not *p*) and *q*" is true only when *p* is false and *q* is true. Thus, the *disjunction* (inclusive or) of "*p* and (not *q*)" and "(not *p*) and *q*" is true when one is true and the other false; it is false when both are false or when both are true. Therefore,

"*p* (exclusive) or *q*"

is an equivalent statement to

"[*p* and (not *q*)] or [(not *p*) and *q*].

p	q	[p *and (not* q)] *or* [*(not* p) *and* q]
T	T	F
T	F	T
F	T	T
F	F	F

In words, "I am going to England this summer and not to France or I am going to France this summer and not to England." This statement is equivalent to "I am going to England or France this summer but not to both."

The last basic connective we discuss in detail presents some difficulties not encountered with the others. The two most prominent reasons are the following. First, one does not find the statement "John loves Mary and the moon is made out of green cheese," too out of place in ordinary language. In fact, we would quickly conclude that it was false. But, the statement "If John loves Mary, then the moon is made out of green cheese," is so unlikely in ordinary language that there is a built-in resistance to admitting it as a proper compound statement and one worthy of our consideration. But before considering such compound statements, if we insist in an implication that some connection must exist between the antecedent and the consequent then we quickly find ourselves in a hopeless situation; proving or disproving any such connection might be impossible. (Does or does not John's love for Mary have anything to do with the composition of the moon?) In other words, the truth-values of an implication should depend only on the truth-values of the antecedent and the consequent and not on any relationship, or lack of it, between the two statements. The second difficulty is making the truth-table for the implication seem as reasonable as the others. For example, suppose John does not love Mary; shall we consider the implication "If John loves Mary, then the moon is made of green cheese," to be true or false? Without dwelling further on the difficulties or on the purposes for the selection we make for the "rules of the game," let us state the truth-values for a conditional statement and give the truth-table.

implication   **Rule 4.** *The implication "p implies q" is false only when p is true and q is false; it is true in all other cases.*

Implication

p	q	p implies q
T	T	T
T	F	F
F	T	T
F	F	T

Example 4. Write each of the following statements using one or more of the four connectives *and, not, or,* and *if . . . then . . . .*
(a) Mathematics is difficult but it is interesting.
   Answer. Mathematics is difficult and it is interesting.
(b) Jack and Jill went up the hill.
   Answer. Jack went up the hill and Jill went up the hill.
(c) Neither Al nor John is on the team.
   Answer. Al is not on the team and John is not on the team.

In mathematics, the words "necessary" and "sufficient" are often used in making conditional statements. Instead of making the statement "If two triangles are congruent, then they are similar," we might make either of the equivalent statements that follow.

1. Two triangles being congruent is a sufficient condition that they be similar.
2. Similarity of two triangles is necessary for them to be congruent.

In general, if p and q are statements, then

$$p \text{ is sufficient for } q$$
$$q \text{ is necessary for } p$$
$$p \text{ only if } q$$

are all equivalent statements to

$$\text{If } p \text{ then } q$$
$$\text{or}$$
$$p \text{ implies } q$$

Example 5. Write each of the following statements using one or more of the four connectives *and, not, or,* and *if . . . then . . . .*
(a) For Wintergreen to win the election it is necessary for him to carry New York.
   Answer. If Wintergreen wins the election, then he carries New York.
(b) Carrying New York is a sufficient condition for Wintergreen to win the election.
   Answer. If Wintergreen carries New York, then he will win the election.
(c) Two triangles are congruent only if they are similar.
   Answer. If two triangles are congruent, then they are similar.
(d) Today is Saturday if and only if yesterday was Friday.
   Answer. If today is Saturday, then yesterday was Friday, and if yesterday was Friday, then today is Saturday.
(e) I shall buy a car provided I can borrow the money.
   Answer. If I can borrow the money, then I shall buy a car.
   [Note: This answer (as well as the others) is not unique. Two other correct answers (logically equivalent to the preceding) are the following:
   (i) If I do not buy the car, then I could not borrow the money.
   (ii) I cannot borrow the money or I shall buy the car.]

Example 6. Show that "not (p implies q)" is equivalent to "p and (not q)." In other words, show that the negation of the implication "p implies q" is the conjunction "p and (not q)."

Solution: We can consider separately the four different possible combinations of truth-values for p and q and explain (in words) why both compound statements in each case have the same truth values. However, a simpler

197

and more routine approach is to consider the truth-tables for both statements and exhibit that the resulting truth-values for both statements are the same.

p	q	not q	p and (not q)
T	T	F	F
T	F	T	T
F	T	F	F
F	F	T	F

p	q	p implies q	not (p implies q)
T	T	T	F
T	F	F	T
F	T	T	F
F	F	T	F

Example 7. Consider the implication "p implies q." Show that "(not q) implies (not p)" is equivalent to the given implication. The implication "(not q) implies (not p)" is called the *contrapositive* of the given implication.

contrapositive

Solution:

p	q	not q	not p	(not q) implies (not p)	p implies q
T	T	F	F	T	T
T	F	T	F	F	F
F	T	F	T	T	T
F	F	T	T	T	T

The truth-values for the contrapositive are the same as for the implication.

EXERCISES

1. Write each of the following statements using one or more of the connectives *and, not, or,* and *if . . . then . . . .*
(a) Nine is not an even number nor is it a prime.
(b) I shall succeed only if I work hard.
(c) For Smith to win the election it is necessary for him to get the nomination.
(d) Two triangles are similar only if they are congruent.

(e) Being nine feet tall is a sufficient condition to get on the basketball team.

(f) A necessary and sufficient condition that Wintergreen be elected President is that he carry Maine.

2. Let p, q, r, and s be the following statements:

p: Jones wins.
q: He gets the support of labor.
r: He appears on TV.
s: He gets the support of the party.

Translate the following into abbreviated symbolic statements using p, q, r, and s and the four given connectives.

(a) Jones will win only if he gets the support of labor.

(b) If Jones appears on TV but does not get the support of labor, then he will not win.

(c) It is necessary for Jones to appear on TV in order to win.

(d) It is necessary to get the support of the party and the support of labor for Jones to win.

(e) Getting labor's support is sufficient to get the party's support.

3. Make a truth-table for each of the following statements.
   (a) p implies (not q)   (b) p and (not q)

4. Make a truth-table for each of the following statements.
   (a) (not p) or q (b) (p and q) and (not r)

5. Consider the implication "p implies q." The *converse* of this implication is "q implies p" and the *inverse* is "(not p) implies (not q)."

   (a) Is an implication equivalent to its converse? Verify your answer with a truth-table.

   (b) Is an implication equivalent to its inverse? Verify your answer with a truth-table.

   (c) Are the converse and inverse of an implication equivalent statements? Verify your answer with a truth-table.

6. Let p and q be statements. Show that the negation of "p and q" is "(not p) or (not q)." [Prove "not (p and q)" is equivalent to "(not p) or (not q)."]

7. Let p and q be statements. Show that the negation of "p or q" is "(not p) and (not q)."

8. State in words the negation of each of the following statements. (See Example 6, page 197, Exercises 6 and 7 above, and avoid the phrase "it is false that.")

   (a) It is surely false that Smith is older than Brown.

   (b) If two triangles are congruent, then they are similar.

   (c) I shall go to England this summer or I shall go to France.

   (d) Two is a prime number and it is even.

   (e) The statement is false only if I can find a counter-example.

   (f) I shall go to England or France this summer but not to both.

9. Construct a truth-table for each of the following, where p, q, and r are statements:

   (a) (p or q) implies r

(b) p or (q implies r)

(c) (p implies r) or (q implies r)

(d) Are any of the statements in (a), (b), and (c) equivalent? If so, which ones?

(e) If the statement in (a) is false, can you conclude whether or not p is true?

(f) If the statement in (b) is false, can you conclude whether or not p is true?

10. Let p and q be statements and consider the implication "p implies q."

(a) If the implication is false, what, if anything, can you conclude about the truth of p? Of q?

(b) If the implication is true, what, if anything, can you conclude about the truth of p? Of q?

(c) If the implication is true and the consequent is true, can you conclude anything about the antecedent?

(d) If the implication is true and the antecedent is true, can you conclude anything about the consequent?

11. A compound statement involving statements p, q, r, etc., which is true regardless of the truth-values of the separate statements p, q, r, etc., is called a *tautology*. Determine which of the following are tautologies. (*Hint:* Use truth-tables.)

(a) (p or q) implies p

(b) p implies (p or q)

(c) (p and q) or (not q)

(d) p and (not p)

(e) p or (not p)

(f) (p or q) and (q or r)

(g) (p implies q) and (not q and p)

12. Let p, q, r, s, and t be the following statements.

p: The door to the study was locked.

q: The butler committed the murder.

r: The maid committed the murder.

s: The gardener committed the murder.

t: The maid had mud on her shoes.

Write in abbreviated form all of the statements which Mr. Watkins knew to be true in the Karl Sagus murder case. (See page 190).

2. TESTING THE VALIDITY OF ARGUMENTS

By now the student should realize that writing out the connectives in all statements can become rather cumbersome. Since we use letters to represent statements, it should seem reasonable that we "invent" symbols to represent connectives. The following symbols are the ones generally used.

Connective	Symbol
and	$\wedge$
or	$\vee$
not	$\sim$
implies	$\rightarrow$

Consider the following examples:

Statement	Symbolized
p and q	$p \wedge q$
(not p) or q	$\sim p \vee q$
not (p or q)	$\sim(p \vee q)$
(not p) implies (q or r)	$\sim p \rightarrow (q \vee r)$

We know that if "$p \rightarrow q$" is a true statement and if p is true, then we can conclude that q is true. For example, knowing that the statement

> If Wintergreen wins the New Hampshire primary,
> then he will be elected President;

is true and knowing that

> Wintergreen wins the New Hampshire primary

is true are enough to conclude that Wintergreen will be elected President. In classical logic, this type of argument is called *modus ponens*. Similarly, suppose "$p \rightarrow q$" is true and suppose "$\sim q$" is true. Thus, q is false, and since the implication is true with a false consequent it follows that the antecedent p must be false. Therefore, "$\sim p$" is true. In classical logic, this is called *modus tollens*.

modus ponens

modus tollens

Both *modus ponens* and *modus tollens* are called *valid arguments*. When we say that an argument is *valid*, we mean that on the assumption that the premises (given statements) are true it follows that the conclusion is true. In general, an argument with p_1, p_2, p_3, . . . , p_n as premises and Q as conclusion is said to be a valid argument if and only if

$$(p_1 \wedge p_2 \wedge p_3 \wedge \cdots \wedge p_n) \rightarrow Q$$

is a tautology. (As we said in the last section, a tautology is a compound statement which is true regardless of the truth-values of the separate statements which make it up.)

Arguments are often given in the following form.

Modus Ponens

Given: (i) $p \rightarrow q$ is true
(ii) p is true

Conclusion: q is true

Modus Tollens

Given: (i) $p \rightarrow q$ is true
(ii) $\sim q$ is true

Conclusion: $\sim p$ is true

The following are truth-tables to show that *modus ponens* and *modus tollens* are valid arguments.

Modus Ponens

p	q	$p \rightarrow q$	$(p \rightarrow q) \land p$	$[(p \rightarrow q) \land p] \rightarrow q$
T	T	T	T	T
T	F	F	F	T
F	T	T	F	T
F	F	T	F	T

Modus Tollens

p	q	$p \rightarrow q$	$\sim q$	$[(p \rightarrow q) \land \sim q]$	$\sim p$	$[(p \rightarrow q) \land \sim q] \rightarrow \sim p$
T	T	T	F	F	F	T
T	F	F	T	F	F	T
F	T	T	F	F	T	T
F	F	T	T	T	T	T

syllogism

Another valid argument is called the *syllogism,* or *transitive property of the implication.* It is as follows.

Given: (i) $p \rightarrow q$
(ii) $q \rightarrow r$

Conclusion: $p \rightarrow r$

(*Note:* We assume here and in such subsequent arguments that the premises are true.) Let us first verify by an indirect proof that the conclusion in the syllogism is a logical consequence of the two given statements.

Assume $p \rightarrow r$ is false. Then r is false and p is true. If p is true and $p \rightarrow q$ is true, then (by *modus ponens*) q is true. Using Statement (ii), if $q \rightarrow r$ is true and q is true then r is true. But this contradicts our earlier conclusion that r is false. Consequently, our assumption is false and we can conclude that $p \rightarrow r$ is true.

The transitive property of the implication can also be proved to be a valid argument by using a truth-table to show that $[(p \rightarrow q) \land (q \rightarrow r)] \rightarrow (p \rightarrow r)$ is a tautology. Another way is to use the following truth-table.

	p	q	r	$p \rightarrow q$	$q \rightarrow r$	$p \rightarrow r$
1.	T	T	T	T	T	T
2.	T	F	T	F	T	T
3.	F	T	T	T	T	T
4.	F	F	T	T	T	T
5.	T	T	F	T	F	F
6.	T	F	F	F	T	F
7.	F	T	F	T	F	T
8.	F	F	F	T	T	T

Notice that $p \rightarrow q$ is true in and only in lines 1, 3, 4, 5, 7, and 8. Also, $q \rightarrow r$ is true in and only in lines 1, 2, 3, 4, 6, and 8. Hence, both implications are true in exactly lines 1, 3, 4, and 8. We observe that $p \rightarrow r$ is true in lines 1, 3, 4, and 8; thus, when $p \rightarrow q$ and $q \rightarrow r$ are both true, it follows that $p \rightarrow r$ is true.

Let us consider some more examples to see how we can determine if a given argument is valid.

Example 1. Suppose we are given the following argument.

$$\begin{array}{ll} \textit{Given:} & \text{(i) } p \rightarrow q \\ & \underline{\text{(ii) } \sim p \rightarrow r} \\ \textit{Conclusion:} & \sim r \rightarrow q \end{array}$$

Is the argument valid? In other words, does the conclusion follow from the given statements? The answer is "yes" and it can be verified by each of the following three methods.

METHOD I. Since $\sim p \rightarrow r$ is true, we conclude that the contrapositive (see Example 7, page 198) $\sim r \rightarrow p$ is also true. Knowing that

$$\sim r \rightarrow p$$
and
$$p \rightarrow q$$

are true, we conclude from the transitive property of the implication that

$$\sim r \rightarrow q$$

is true. Thus, the argument is valid.

METHOD II. Let us suppose that $\sim r \to q$ is false. Then, we can conclude that $\sim r$ is true and q is false. Therefore, r is false, and since it is given that $\sim p \to r$ is true we can conclude that $\sim p$ is false. Consequently, p is true, and since $p \to q$ is true it follows that q is true.

By assuming that $\sim r \to q$ is false, we have shown that q is false and q is true, a contradiction. Thus, our assumption is false and we conclude that $\sim r \to q$ is true.

This second method can prove unsatisfactory. Suppose we cannot find a contradiction; it does not say one does not exist. Another difficulty is that if an argument is not valid, then it is possible that neither the conclusion nor its negation will follow from what is given (see Example 2 below). In fact, the negation of the conclusion might be a logical consequence of the given statements (see Example 3 below). Obviously, in this case, one could not obtain a contradiction by assuming that the negation of the conclusion is true.

METHOD III. Of course, another way to find whether or not such arguments are valid is to make a truth-table. Since this approach is quite routine, it is basically simpler than the other methods; however, if a large number of statements are involved, it can become an unnecessarily cumbersome approach to the problem. The following is the corresponding truth-table for the given statements and the conclusion.

	p	q	r	$\sim p$	$\sim r$	$p \to q$	$\sim p \to r$	$\sim r \to q$
1.	T	T	T	F	F	T	T	T
2.	T	F	T	F	F	F	T	T
3.	F	T	T	T	F	T	T	T
4.	F	F	T	T	F	T	T	T
5.	T	T	F	F	T	T	T	T
6.	T	F	F	F	T	F	T	F
7.	F	T	F	T	T	T	F	T
8.	F	F	F	T	T	T	F	F

Since $p \to q$ is true, we know that the truth-values given in lines 2 and 6 are not possible. Since $\sim p \to r$ is true, lines 7 and 8 can be deleted. Since $\sim r \to q$ is true for all the remaining possibilities (in lines 1, 3, 4, and 5), the argument is valid.

Example 2. Test the validity of the following argument:

$$\begin{array}{ll} \textit{Given:} & \text{(i) } p \wedge q \\ & \text{(ii) } \sim p \to r \\ \textit{Conclusion:} & \quad\quad r \end{array}$$

Consider a truth-table for the given statements, the conclusion, and the statement $[(p \wedge q) \wedge (\sim p \to r)] \to r$. We wish to show that the latter statement which we denote by S is a tautology.

	p	q	r	$\sim p$	$p \wedge q$	$\sim p \to r$	$(p \wedge q) \wedge (\sim p \to r)$	S
1.	T	T	T	F	T	T	T	T
2.	T	F	T	F	F	T	F	T
3.	F	T	T	T	F	T	F	T
4.	F	F	T	T	F	T	F	T
5.	T	T	F	F	T	T	T	F
6.	T	F	F	F	F	T	F	T
7.	F	T	F	T	F	F	F	T
8.	F	F	F	T	F	F	F	T

Since $[(p \wedge q) \wedge (\sim p \to r)] \to r$ is *not* a tautology (see line 5), the argument is not valid.

Example 3. Test the validity of the following argument:

Given: (i) $p \to q$

(ii) $\sim p \to s$

Conclusion: $\sim q \wedge \sim s$

Let us try to deduce the conclusion directly from the given statements. Since $p \to q$ is true, the contrapositive $\sim q \to \sim p$ is also true. Since $\sim q \to \sim p$ and $\sim p \to s$ are true, by the transitive property of the implication we have that

$$\sim q \to s$$

is true. Since $\sim q \wedge \sim s$ is the negation of $\sim q \to s$ (see Example 6, page 197), we conclude that

$$\sim q \wedge \sim s$$

is false and the argument is not valid. The situation here is different from the last example; we can actually *prove* that the negation of the conclusion is true. Obviously, assuming that the negation of the conclusion is true with the hopes of getting a contradiction would be a useless task. The following is the corresponding truth-table verification that the argument is *not valid.*

	p	q	s	$\sim p$	$\sim q$	$\sim s$	$p \to q$	$\sim p \to s$	$\sim q \wedge \sim s$
1.	T	T	T	F	F	F	T	T	F
2.	T	F	T	F	T	F	F	T	F
3.	F	T	T	T	F	F	T	T	F
4.	F	F	T	T	T	F	T	T	F
5.	T	T	F	F	F	T	T	T	F
6.	T	F	F	F	T	T	F	T	T
7.	F	T	F	T	F	T	T	F	F
8.	F	F	F	T	T	T	T	F	T

Knowing that $p \to q$ is true makes it possible to delete lines 2 and 6. Knowing that $\sim p \to s$ is true makes the combinations in lines 7 and 8 impossible. For the remaining possibilities, $(p \to q) \land (\sim p \to s)$ is true and $\sim q \land \sim s$ is false. Thus,

$$[(p \to q) \land (\sim p \to s)] \to (\sim q \land \sim s)$$

is false in lines 1, 3, 4, and 5, and is not a tautology.

Using a truth-table, as in Example 3, can lead to one difficulty which we should mention. Suppose P_1 and P_2 are two given statements and Q the given conclusion. If $P_1 \land P_2$ were true when Q is false, then

$$[P_1 \land P_2] \to Q$$

would be false; thus, $[P_1 \land P_2] \to Q$ is not a tautology and the argument would be invalid. However, it might be that P_1 and P_2 could never be true at the same time; assuming so does not make it so. In this case,

$$P_1 \land P_2$$

would always be false. Hence,

$$[P_1 \land P_2] \to Q$$

would be a tautology and would represent a valid argument whether Q were true or false. For example, both of the following are valid arguments according to our definition.

Given: (i) p *Given:*   (i) p
      (ii) $\sim p$ (ii) $\sim p$
Conclusion: q *Conclusion:* $\sim q$

The validity of both are easily verified by showing that

$$[p \land \sim p] \to q \quad \text{and} \quad [p \land \sim p] \to \sim q$$

are tautologies. As desired, however, if the assumptions are true and the argument is valid then the conclusion is true; but, from a false assumption, one can prove anything.

Now let us settle the Karl Sagus murder mystery. If we let p, q, r, s, and t be the statements as suggested in Exercise 12, page 200, then the facts that Mr. Watkins ascertained are the following.

1. $\sim q \lor p$

(The butler did not murder Mr. Sagus or the door to the study was locked.)

2. $\sim(\sim p \rightarrow r)$

(It is false that if the door to the study were not locked then the maid killed Mr. Sagus.)

3. $\sim r \rightarrow t$

(If the maid did not commit the crime then she had mud on her shoes.)

4. $\sim s \rightarrow (q \vee \sim t)$

(If the gardener did not do it, then the butler was guilty or the maid's shoes were clean.)

Since Statement 2 is the negation of the implication $\sim p \rightarrow r$, it is equivalent to the conjunction $\sim p \wedge \sim r$. This implies that $\sim p$ is true and $\sim r$ is true; that is, p is false and r *is false*. Since p *is false*, from Statement 1 we conclude that $\sim q$ is true; thus, q *is false*. Also, since $\sim r$ is true, the truth of Statement 3 implies that t must be true. Consequently, $\sim t$ *is false*. Since q is false, it follows that $q \vee \sim t$ in Statement 4 *is false*. Since the implication

$$\sim s \rightarrow (q \vee \sim t)$$

is true with a false consequent, we conclude that the antecedent $\sim s$ is false. Therefore, s *is true* and the gardener committed the murder.

EXERCISES

In Exercises 1 through 10, state the negation symbolically.

1. $(p \vee q) \rightarrow r$ 2. $p \vee (q \rightarrow r)$
3. $(p \wedge \sim q) \vee r$ 4. $p \vee q \vee r$
5. $p \wedge q \wedge r$ 6. $(p \rightarrow q) \rightarrow r$
7. $p \rightarrow (q \rightarrow r)$ 8. $(p \wedge q) \rightarrow (r \vee s)$
9. $(p \wedge q) \rightarrow r$ 10. $p \wedge (q \rightarrow r)$

11. *Implication:* If x is a positive integer, then x^2 is a positive integer.
    (a) State the converse.   (b) State the inverse.
    (c) State the contrapositive.   (d) State the negation.
12. *Implication:* If $y - x$ is a nonnegative number, then x is less than or equal to y.
    (a) State the converse.   (b) State the inverse.
    (c) State the contrapositive.   (d) State the negation.
13. Construct a truth-table for each of the following statements and deter-

mine if it is a tautology.

(a) $(p \to q) \lor (q \to p)$ (b) $(p \land q) \lor (\sim p \lor \sim q)$

14. Construct a truth-table for each of the following statements and determine if it is a tautology.

(a) $(p \to q) \lor (r \to p)$ (b) $(p \lor r \lor q) \to (\sim p \land r)$

15. *Implication:* If x is a real number, then x^2 is a positive real number or x^2 is zero.

(a) State the converse.   (b) State the inverse.

(c) State the contrapositive.   (d) State the negation.

16. *Implication:* If an integer has 4 and 6 as factors, then it has 12 as a factor.

(a) State the converse.   (b) State the inverse.

(c) State the contrapositive.   (d) State the negation.

Test the validity of the arguments in Exercises 17 through 28.

17. *Given:*   (i) $p \lor q$ 18. *Given:*   (i) $p \lor q$
            (ii) q (ii) $\sim q$
Conclusion: p *Conclusion:* p

19. *Given:*   (i) $p \to q$ 20. *Given:*   (i) $p \lor q$
            (ii) $\sim r \to \sim q$ (ii) $r \land \sim q$
Conclusion: $p \to r$ *Conclusion:* p

21. *Given*   (i) $p \land \sim q$ 22. *Given:*   (i) $p \to q$
          (ii) $q \to s$ (ii) $q \to p$
Conclusion: s *Conclusion:* $p \land q$

23. *Given*   (i) $p \lor q$ 24. *Given:*   (i) $p \to q$
         (ii) $q \land r$ (ii) $q \to r$
         (iii) $r \to t$ (iii) p
Conclusion: $p \to t$ *Conclusion:* r

25. *Given:*   (i) $\sim(p \lor q)$ 26. *Given:*   (i) $\sim[p \to (q \land s)]$
          (ii) $p \lor r$ (ii) $q \land t$
          (iii) $r \to s$ (iii) $s \lor u$
Conclusion: s *Conclusion:* u

27. *Given:*   (i) $p \to q$ 28. *Given:*   (i) $p \land (s \lor r)$
          (ii) $q \to r$ (ii) $t \to s$
          (iii) $\sim s \to \sim r$ (iii) $\sim u \to \sim r$
          (iv) p (iv) $u \to q$
Conclusion: s *Conclusion:* q

29. Give a truth-table verification of the validity of the conclusion that the gardener killed Mr. Sagus.

Test the validity of the arguments in Exercises 30 through 35.

30. If Wintergreen did not win the New Hampshire primary, then he did not work or he did not get the support of labor. If he did not work, then he

did not get the support of labor. Hence, if Wintergreen did not win the New Hampshire primary, then he did not get labor's support.

31. If Jones works hard, then he gets a raise. If Green does not get a raise, then Jones does not get a raise. Neither Brown nor Jones fails to work hard. Consequently, Green gets a raise.

32. If taxes are raised, then the budget will be balanced. It is false that the budget will be balanced and inflation will not be checked. If Congress will not meet its obligation, then inflation will not be checked. Taxes will be raised. Therefore, Congress will meet its obligation.

33. If Wintergreen gets elected, he will raise taxes. If Winterbottom gets elected, he will not raise taxes. Hence, if Wintergreen gets elected, it follows that Winterbottom does not get elected.

34. Let x and y be two numbers. If x is less than 10 and y is less than 5, then their sum is less than 15. If their sum is greater than or equal to 15, then x is negative. However, it is not true that if y is less than 5, then x is negative. Thus, x is less than 10.

35. If I go to the dance, then I will meet new people. If I buy new shoes, then I will go to the dance. I will go downtown and eat an eight dollar dinner. If I meet new people, then I enjoy myself. If I do not buy new shoes, then I will not go downtown. Therefore, I know I will enjoy myself.

3. INTRODUCTION TO AXIOMATICS

In 1903, Bertrand Russel gave a formal definition of mathematics in his book entitled *Principles of Mathematics*. This definition (which was quoted in Section 1) is much less well-known than the following which is also credited to Russell:

> Mathematics is that subject in which one never knows what he is talking about or if what he says is true.

As we know, many serious, and perhaps profound, things have been said in jest; the preceding definition of mathematics seems to be an excellent example of such a statement. To understand the serious side of this definition, it is necessary to understand what is meant by an axiomatic development of mathematics.

To better understand the *axiomatic approach* in developing a mathematical system, let us recall our study of euclidean plane geometry. Euclidean geometry deals with lines and points and with plane figures built up from them. The lines and points of geometry are not objects in the physical world; they are, instead, abstractions from our intuitive ideas of straight lines and points. A straight line is an abstraction from a taut string, a ray of light, or the like. Geometry is

axiomatic approach

postulates, axioms

an example of a *deductive* science; by this we mean that lines, points, and geometric figures are proved to have certain properties using logical deductions from a certain set of basic *assumptions* called *postulates,* or *axioms,* of geometry. Although many dictionaries state that the word "axiom" means "self-evident truth" while the word "postulate" means "assumed truth," a mathematician usually uses the words interchangeably for any basic assumption.

theorem

proof

A *theorem* in geometry is a statement that some geometric figure has a certain property or that two or more figures are related in a certain way. A *proof* of a theorem consists of logical deductions made from the basic assumptions to prove that the statement is true. Of course, theorems already proved from the postulates can be used in the proof of any succeeding theorem.

For the purpose of logical reasoning about lines and points, it is immaterial whether we know just what a straight line or point is; the fundamental properties and relations between lines and points expressed in the basic assumptions are all we need to know. Geometric properties which are discovered by experiment or by physical interpretations of point and line are quite welcome but they have no part in the logical deduction, except possibly to motivate the pattern of the deductive argument given to prove a theorem. This is not only a rather sophisticated view of mathematics but also a modern view; it was not until the last century that mathematicians clearly recognized the distinction between an abstract mathematical system and the physical model from which it might have been obtained. (It is hoped that the reader does, or will, appreciate the distinction.)

In the logical development of geometry, for example, there are several questions to be answered concerning the set of postulates chosen.

Questions

> 1. How do we choose, or find, the postulates from which we develop the geometry?
> 2. Is the set of postulates consistent?
> 3. Is there more than one set of postulates that could be used to develop the theory, and, if so, what criteria are used to decide which set of postulates to choose?
> 4. Are the assumptions logically independent?

To answer the first question as it pertains to euclidean geometry is easy: the postulates are indeed abstractions from intuitive ideas about lines and points which seem to be valid in the physical world that surrounds us.

When we ask whether or not a set of postulates is logically consistent, we are asking whether or not some statement and its negation are logical consequences of the given assumptions; in other words, is the set of postulates self-contradictory? Unfortunately, this is a question whose answer often depends on faith and not on the proof of a theorem. (A mathematician is not without faith.) For example, there is no proof that the set of postulates for euclidean plane geometry is consistent. However, it is comforting to know that in two thousand years no theorem and its negation have ever been deduced from the euclidean postulates; thus, it is not unreasonable to believe that this set of postulates is consistent. (Our faith in the consistency of the postulates is not "blind faith.")

More than one set of postulates can be used to develop a particular mathematical theory. If we have five consistent postulates from which five theorems can be proved, we could take the ten statements as basic assumptions since they would be consistent and since any property that could be derived from the five assumptions in the first set could be derived from the ten assumptions in the second set. It is generally considered mathematically more elegant to use as few postulates as possible to develop a particular theory; however, this basis for selection is occasionally ignored. Suppose, for example, that eight basic assumptions are necessary to develop a certain theory in a manner comprehensible for the student where, in fact, only four assumptions are logically necessary; it would then be reasonable to sacrifice some elegance for understanding if the use of only the four assumptions placed the theory out of the student's reach.

Even if we can prove that the postulates in a set are logically independent (that is, no postulate can be derived as a logical consequence of the others) the choice of the postulates is still not necessarily unique. For example, in euclidean geometry we can replace Euclid's fifth postulate* by Playfair's Axiom,† and then prove all the theorems of plane geometry as well as proving Euclid's fifth postulate as a theorem. In fact, this is what is generally done in elementary plane geometry. Any two postulates which can be used interchangeably in this manner are said to be *logically equivalent*. In euclidean plane geometry, we prove that the sum of the three interior angles of a triangle is always equal to two right angles; this state-

logically equivalent

---

* If a straight line falling on two straight lines makes the interior angles on the same side less than two right angles, the two straight lines, if produced indefinitely, meet on that side on which the angles are less than the two right angles.

† Given a line and a point not lying on the line, then there exists, in the plane determined by the line and the point, one and only one line which contains the point but not any point on the line.

ment can also be proved to be logically equivalent to Playfair's Axiom, and, thus, to Euclid's fifth postulate.*

If we suspected that Playfair's Axiom was not logically independent of the other postulates of euclidean geometry (excluding the fifth), we might try to prove it as a theorem from the other assumptions. If we were unable to get a direct proof of Playfair's Axiom from the other assumptions, then it would be natural to attempt an indirect proof. That is, we would use the other assumptions of euclidean geometry and the negation of Playfair's Axiom and then attempt to obtain a contradiction. Assuming it is false that in a plane one and only one line could be drawn parallel to a given line through a point not on the line would involve two cases. First, we would assume that each line drawn through the point intersects the given line; second, we would assume that there was more than one line through the point that is parallel to (does not intersect) the given line. In either case, instead of finding a contradiction we could prove several very interesting theorems. For example, we could prove not only that congruent triangles are similar but that similar triangles are congruent. Basically, assuming that there is no line through a given point parallel to a given line would lead to what is called *elliptic geometry;*† assuming that there is more than one line through a point parallel to a given line would lead to what is called *hyperbolic geometry.*

elliptic geometry

hyperbolic geometry

We do not know if the postulates of elliptic geometry or the postulates of hyperbolic geometry lead to a contradiction. However, we can *prove* that if one set is not consistent then the euclidean postulates are not consistent. In other words, if the euclidean postulates are consistent then so must be the sets of postulates for the other two geometries. Although euclidean geometry might be more useful in physical applications, euclidean geometry is not logically superior to either elliptic or hyperbolic geometry.

When we say that a statement in mathematics, such as *the sum of the three interior angles of a triangle is always two right angles,* is a *true statement,* we mean only that the statement is a *logical consequence* of the postulates for euclidean plane geometry. It is also *true* (in the same sense) that the sum of the three interior angles of a triangle is *more than* two right angles; this is a logical consequence of

---

* Two other statements which are logically equivalent to Euclid's fifth postulate are the following: (1) There exists a circle passing through any three points not lying on a straight line. (2) There can always be drawn through any point within an angle less than two-thirds of a right angle a straight line which meets both sides of the angle. (There are others.)
† Some changes other than denying the fifth postulate would be necessary, but this is the significant change.

the set of postulates for elliptic plane geometry. It can also be proved from the postulates of hyperbolic plane geometry that the sum of the three interior angles of a triangle is *less than* two right angles. Since there is no way to prove, for example, that the euclidean postulates are a description of physical reality, there is no way to be certain that a euclidean theorem is *true* in the physical universe. (We should mention that in fact the elliptic postulates might be a better description of the physical universe than the euclidean postulates.)

In order to complete an explanation of Russell's definition of mathematics, let us restate an idea mentioned earlier. In the study of any mathematical system, we must begin with certain undefined terms. We know that *point, line,* and *between* are examples of some of the undefined terms of geometry. The usual procedure followed is to give an intuitive idea of the meaning of each undefined term by stating familiar synonyms or by giving concrete examples, if they are available. We might say that a straight line is the shortest distance between two points. This is no definition unless "distance" has been defined or is taken as an undefined term. One would be hard pressed to define distance unless he knew what a straight line was. Obviously, attempts to define all terms lead to circular definitions. Thus, if the term "line" is undefined, then the mathematician is in the position of "not knowing what he is talking about."

In the elementary use of numbers, knowing how to derive all the properties of numbers from a set of postulates or axioms is not of great importance. It is only when we try to go more deeply into the nature of mathematics and mathematical reasoning that such knowledge becomes important.

The idea that there should be a logical development of the number system, similar to that for geometry, did not occur to mathematicians until the nineteenth century, and it took many years for the theory to be completely developed. In order to develop the natural numbers (1, 2, 3, 4, 5, etc.) from a set of axioms, one usually begins with the system first devised by the Italian mathematician and logician Giuseppe Peano (1858–1932).

Before listing these postulates from which we can derive all the properties of the set of natural numbers, let us call attention to undefined and primitive notions. We take "natural number" and "successor" as undefined concepts. Of course, natural number refers to "counting number"; 1 is the first counting number, the successor of 1 is the "next" natural number, 2. If we denote the successor of the natural number n by n', then, by definition, $1' = 2$, $2' = 3$, $3' = 4$, $4' = 5$, etc. In other words, "3" is a symbol invented to denote the successor of the successor of 1.

Peano's Postulates

1. 1 is a natural number.
2. For every natural number n, there exists one and only one natural number, denoted by n', called the *successor* of n.
3. If m and n are natural numbers and if $m' = n'$ then $m = n$. (No two different natural numbers have the same successor.)
4. For any natural number m, $m' \neq 1$. (No natural number has 1 as its successor.)
5. Let S be a collection of natural numbers with the following properties. (a) 1 is in S. (b) If the natural number k is in S, then k' is also in S. Then, the set S of natural numbers for which (a) and (b) are true contains all the natural numbers.

Using Peano's postulates we can define addition and multiplication and prove such statements as the following:

1. For every pair of natural numbers m and n, we can uniquely assign to the pair a number called the sum, denoted by $m + n$, and a number called the product, denoted by $m \cdot n$, $m \times n$, or mn.
2. For any natural numbers m, n, and p,

$$(m + n) + p = m + (n + p) \qquad \text{and} \qquad (mn)p = m(np)$$

3. For any pair of natural numbers m and n,

$$m + n = n + m \qquad \text{and} \qquad mn = nm$$

4. For any natural numbers m, n, and p,

$$m(n + p) = (mn) + (mp)$$

5. For any pair of natural numbers m and n, one and only one of the following is true.
   (a) $m = n$.
   (b) There exists a natural number p such that $m + p = n$.
   (c) The exists a natural number q such that $m = n + q$.

In the axiomatic development of our number systems, we use the natural numbers to construct the set of integers, the integers to construct the rationals, the rationals to construct the reals, and the reals to construct the complex numbers. Since an axiomatic development of the number systems is quite sophisticated, it is not attempted in elementary or secondary schools. It is within the grasp of the college student, but it is not within the scope of this text.

Let us conclude the section by considering a relatively simple axiomatic system. We are primarily interested in gaining an understanding of the nature of the axiomatic approach and in gaining some experience in proving theorems.

An Axiomatic System. Let S be a set with four elements and let $S \times S$ denote the set of all ordered pairs (a, b) of elements from S. Let L be any subset of $S \times S$ for which the following are true.

P_1: If $a \in S$, $b \in S$, and $a \neq b$, then $(a, b) \in L$ or $(b, a) \in L$ but not both.

P_2: If $(a, b) \in L$, then $a \neq b$.

P_3: If $(a, b) \in L$ and $(b, c) \in L$, then $(a, c) \in L$.

Let us prove four theorems that follow from these postulates.

Theorem 1. *If $(a, b) \in L$, then $(b, a) \notin L$.*

Proof: (*Indirect Proof*). Assume that $(b, a) \in L$. By P_3, if $(a, b) \in L$ and $(b, a) \in L$, then $(a, a) \in L$; this contradicts P_2. Thus, if $(a, b) \in L$, then $(b, a) \notin L$.

Theorem 2. *If $(a, b) \in L$ and $c \in S$, then either $(a, c) \in L$ or $(c, b) \in L$.*

Proof: If $c = a$, then $(c, b) \in L$ and the theorem is true. Thus, assume that $c \neq a$. Then by P_1, $(a, c) \in L$ or $(c, a) \in L$. If $(a, c) \in L$, then the theorem is true. If $(a, c) \notin L$, then $(c, a) \in L$. Since $(a, b) \in L$ by hypothesis, we conclude by P_3 that $(c, b) \in L$.

Theorem 3. *There exists at least one $u \in S$ such that $(u, x) \notin L$ for every $x \in S$.*

Proof: (*Indirect Proof*). Assume for every $u \in S$ that $(u\ x) \in L$ for *at least one x in S.* Let a_1 be any element of S; thus, there is an $a_2 \in S$ such that $(a_1, a_3) \in L$. It follows by P_2 that $a_1 \neq a_2$. Furthermore, by our assumption it follows that there exists an a_3 in S such that $(a_2, a_3) \in L$. Again, by P_2 we conclude that $a_2 \neq a_3$. Since $(a_1, a_2) \in L$ and $(a_2, a_3) \in L$, $(a_1, a_3) \in L$ by P_3. By P_2, $a_1 \neq a_3$. Consequently, a_1, a_2, and a_3 are different elements of S.

Again by our assumption, we know that there is an $a_4 \in S$ such that $(a_3, a_4) \in L$. By P_2, $a_3 \neq a_4$. Since $(a_1, a_3) \in L$ and $(a_3, a_4) \in L$, we have by P_3 that $(a_1, a_4) \in L$; similarly, $(a_2, a_4) \in L$. Thus, $a_1 \neq a_4$, $a_2 \neq a_4$, and a_1, a_2, a_3, and a_4 are all different.

As above, we can show our assumption implies that there exists an a_5 in S which is different from the other four elements in S. (It is left as an exercise for the student.) This will contradict the fact that S has exactly four elements. Thus, the theorem is proved.

Theorem 4. *There is at most one* $u \in S$ *such that* $(u, x) \notin L$ *for every* $x \in S$.

Proof: (*Indirect Proof*). Let u_1 and u_2 be two different elements of S such that $(u_1, x) \notin L$ and $(u_2, y) \notin L$ for every x and y in S. Since $u_1 \neq u_2$, either $(u_1, u_2) \in L$ or $(u_2, u_1) \in L$ by P_1. Since we assume $(u_1, x) \notin L$ for every x in S, it follows that $(u_1, u_2) \notin L$. Similarly, $(u_2, u_1) \notin L$; thus we have that $u_1 = u_2$, a contradiction. Consequently, there cannot be two different such elements in S.

Let us now show that a model for our system exists. That is, let us produce a set S and a subset L of $S \times S$ such that P_1, P_2, and P_3 are true. Let $S = \{1, 2, 3, 4\}$ and let $(u, v) \in L$ if and only if u is less than v. Hence,

$$L = \{(1, 2), (1, 3), (1, 4), (2, 3), (2, 4), (3, 4)\}$$

The student should stop to verify that P_1, P_2, and P_3 are satisfied; this is indeed a model for our system. Notice that there is one and only one element of S, namely 4, such that $(4, x) \notin L$ for every $x \in S$.

independent

It is not too difficult to prove that P_1, P_2, and P_3 are *independent;* that is, no one of the properties follows from one or both of the others. We do it by actually exhibiting subsets of $S \times S$ where $S = \{1, 2, 3, 4\}$ which have one property and not the other two or which have two of the properties and not the remaining. The following subsets show all combinations, including none of P_1, P_2, P_3.

$$L_1 = \{(1, 1), (1, 2), (2, 1), (2, 3)\}$$
$$L_2 = \{(1, 2), (2, 1), (1, 4), (2, 3)\}$$
$$L_3 = \{(1, 2), (2, 3), (1, 3), (2, 2)\}$$
$$L_4 = \{(1, 2), (1, 3), (1, 4), (2, 3), (2, 4), (3, 4), (2, 2)\}$$
$$L_5 = \{(2, 1), (4, 4), (3, 2), (4, 2), (1, 3), (1, 4), (4, 3)\}$$
$$L_6 = \{(2, 1), (3, 2), (4, 2), (1, 3), (1, 4), (4, 3)\}$$
$$L_7 = \{(1, 3), (3, 4), (1, 4)\}$$

Determining which, if any, of P_1, P_2, and P_3 that each set L_i has where $1 \leq i \leq 7$ is left as an exercise for the student.

EXERCISES

1. Which of the properties P_1, P_2, P_3 does L_1 have?
2. Which of the properties P_1, P_2, P_3 does L_2 have?
3. Which of the properties P_1, P_2, P_3 does L_3 have?
4. Which of the properties P_1, P_2, P_3 does L_4 have?

5. Which of the properties P_1, P_2, P_3 does L_5 have?
6. Which of the properties P_1, P_2, P_3 does L_6 have?
7. Which of the properties P_1, P_2, P_3 does L_7 have?
8. Complete the proof of Theorem 3.
9. How could you show that the finiteness of set S was necessary for Theorem 3 to be true? Do it.
10. Which of the four theorems would be true if S is any infinite set?

4. VENN DIAGRAMS AND LEWIS CARROLL PUZZLES

Let

$A = \{1, 2, 3, 4, 5, 6\}$, $B = \{3, 4, 6, 8\}$, and $C = \{1, 4, 5, 6, 9, 11, 13\}$

Then $\qquad B \cup C = \{1, 3, 4, 5, 6, 8, 9, 11, 13\}$

and $\quad A \cap (B \cup C) = \{1, 2, 3, 4, 5, 6\} \cap \{1, 3, 4, 5, 6, 8, 9, 11, 13\}$
$$= \{1, 3, 4, 5, 6\}$$

Similarly, $A \cap B = \{3, 4, 6\}$ and $A \cap C = \{1, 4, 5, 6\}$; thus,

$$(A \cap B) \cup (A \cap C) = \{1, 3, 4, 5, 6\}$$

Notice that $\quad A \cap (B \cup C) = (A \cap B) \cup (A \cap C)$

This is no accident, as we shall now prove.

Theorem. *If A, B, and C are sets, then $A \cap (B \cup C) = (A \cap B) \cup (A \cap C)$.*

Proof: [Since the union and intersection of two sets is a set, both $A \cap (B \cup C)$ and $(A \cap B) \cup (A \cap C)$ are sets. To prove these sets are equal, we prove that $[A \cap (B \cup C)] \subseteq [(A \cap B) \cup (A \cap C)]$ and $[(A \cap B) \cup (A \cap C)] \subseteq [A \cap (B \cup C)]$.]
PART 1. Let x be any element in $[A \cap (B \cup C)]$.

Statements	*Reasons*
1. $x \in A$ and $x \in (B \cup C)$.	1. Definition of intersection
2. If $x \in (B \cup C)$, then $x \in B$ or $x \in C$.	2. Definition of union
3. Thus, $x \in (A \cap B)$ or $x \in (A \cap C)$.	3. Definition of intersection
4. Hence, $x \in [(A \cap B) \cup (A \cap C)]$.	4. Definition of union
5. $[A \cap (B \cup C)] \subseteq [(A \cap B) \cup (A \cap C)]$.	5. Definition of subset

PART 2. Left as an exercise.

217

universal set

complement

Venn diagrams

Usually, throughout a given discussion only subsets of some given set are considered; the given set is called the *universal set,* or *universe of discourse.* If it is clear that only subsets of some universal set I are to be considered, it is customary to write A' instead of A'_I for the complement of A relative to I; in this case, A' is called the *complement of A.* For example, if the universal set is the set of integers and E is the set of even integers then E' is the set of odd integers.

If I is a universal set, there is a convenient method to picture the operations of union, intersection, and complementation on subsets of I. We draw a rectangle and let the interior of the rectangle represent the universal set. Within the rectangle, we draw circles and let the interiors and exteriors of these circles represent subsets of I. We shade the regions in the rectangle that represent the subsets being considered. For example, if A and B are subsets of I, then we draw circles in the interior of I, and the interior of these circles represent the sets A and B. The subset $A \cap B$ of I is represented by the points in the rectangle that are in the interior of both circle A and circle B. Such pictorial representations of subsets of some universal set are called *Venn diagrams*, named for the English logician John Venn (1834–1923) who first used them. In Figure 8.1, we give six different Venn diagrams with expressions defining the shaded regions.

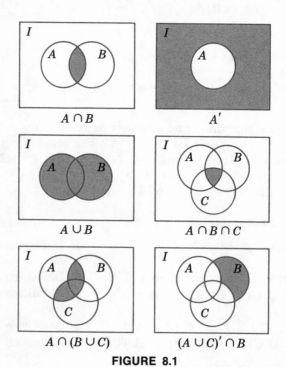

FIGURE 8.1

Venn diagrams are used to work other kinds of problems; consider the following example.

Example 1. In a college poll of fifty students, the following information was obtained.

> 2 were registered for biology, English, and mathematics.
> 8 were registered for biology and mathematics.
> 15 were registered for English and mathematics.
> 12 were registered for biology and English.
> 25 were registered for mathematics.
> 23 were registered for biology.
> 28 were registered for English.

(a) How many were not registered for any of the three courses of biology, English, and mathematics?

(b) How many of those polled were taking mathematics but not biology or English?

(c) How many of those polled were taking only one of the three given courses?

(d) How many of those polled were taking biology and mathematics but not English?

Solution: (See the Venn diagram in Figure 8.2.) We let B, M, and E be the sets of students registered for biology, mathematics, and English, respectively. Since 2 students are registered for all three courses, we write 2 in the intersection of all three sets. Since, for example, 15 are registered for mathematics and English, $15 - 2 = 13$ is the number registered for mathematics and English but not biology. The numbers 6 and 10 are inserted in the Venn diagram for similar reasons. Then, we see in the Venn diagram that there are $10 + 2 + 6 = 18$ students registered for biology and at least one of the other two courses. Since there are 23 students registered for biology, there are $23 - 18 = 5$ registered for biology and not the other two courses. Similarly, we fill in 4 and 3 in the corresponding parts of the other circles. Now adding all of the numbers inside the three circles we get a sum of 43; since 50 students were polled, this leaves $50 - 43 = 7$

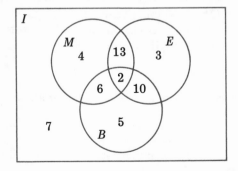

FIGURE 8.2

students who were not registered for any of the three courses. The answers to the given questions may be read directly from the Venn diagram. (a) 7; (b) 4, (c) $5 + 4 + 3 = 12$; (d) 6.

Venn diagrams can be used for sets A, B, and C to show, for example, that $A \cap (B \cup C) = (A \cap B) \cup (A \cap C)$. Venn diagrams are also useful to exhibit other properties of sets. Let A and B be subsets of a universal set I and assume $A \subseteq B$; Figure 8.3a shows this fact. The complement of A is all points outside the inner circle. (See Figure 8.3b.) Similarly, B' is all of the points outside the outer circle. Obviously, all points outside the outer circle are also points outside the inner circle; this is a geometric proof that if $A \subseteq B$ then $B' \subseteq A'$.

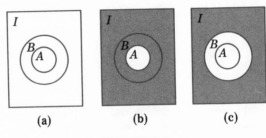

(a)   (b)   (c)

FIGURE 8.3

Two other important properties of sets which can be proved as theorems or exhibited by Venn diagrams are the following. (a) If A, B, and C are sets such that $A \subseteq B$ and $B \subseteq C$ then $A \subseteq C$; this is called the *transitive property* of set inclusion. (b) The complement of the complement of a set A is A; that is, $(A')' = A$.

The solutions of many puzzles can be obtained by using the properties of sets. Let us consider a few such puzzles which appear in *Symbolic Logic*, a book written by the English mathematician Charles Dodgson (1832–1898). These puzzles are generally called Lewis Carroll puzzles since Dodgson, who also wrote *Alice in Wonderland*, is better known by this *nom de plume*.

Puzzle 1.
  Given: (a) The only types of food that my doctor allows me to eat are not very rich.
  (b) Nothing that agrees with me is unsuitable for supper.
  (c) Wedding cake is always very rich.
  (d) My doctor allows me to eat all types of food that are suitable for supper.

Use the given statements to conclude that wedding cake always disagrees with me.

Solution: Consider the following sets:

I: The set of all types of food.
A: The set of types of food my doctor allows me to eat.
B: The set of types of food that agree with me.
C: The set of types of food suitable for supper.
D: The set of very rich types of food.
E: The set consisting of wedding cakes.

STEP 1. Since D' is the set of foods which are not very rich, we conclude from (a) that $A \subseteq D'$.

STEP 2. Part (b) says any food which agrees with me is suitable for supper. Thus, $B \subseteq C$.

STEP 3. Since wedding cakes are a subset of the set of rich foods, we have that $E \subseteq D$.

STEP 4. Part (d) says that $C \subseteq A$.

Since $B \subseteq C$ and $C \subseteq A$, it follows that $B \subseteq A$. Since $A \subseteq D'$, again by the transitive property we conclude $B \subseteq D'$. Using the fact that $E \subseteq D$, we have that $D' \subseteq E'$; thus, $B \subseteq E'$.

From $B \subseteq E'$, we conclude that $(E')' \subseteq B'$; that is, $E \subseteq B'$. In words, E is a subset of B' and we have that wedding cakes are included in the set of foods that do not agree with me.

Puzzle 2.

Given: (a) No kitten that loves fish is unteachable.
(b) No kitten without a tail will play with a gorilla.
(c) Kittens with whiskers always love fish.
(d) No teachable kitten has green eyes.
(e) No kittens have tails unless they have whiskers.

Use the given statements to conclude that no kitten with green eyes will play with a gorilla.

Solution: Consider the following sets:

I: The set of all kittens.
A: The set of kittens that love fish.
B: Kittens that are teachable.
C: Kittens that play with gorillas.
D: Kittens with whiskers.
E: Kittens with green eyes.
F: Kittens with tails.

STEP 1. From (a) we conclude that $A \subseteq B$.

STEP 2. From (b) we conclude that $F' \subseteq C'$.

STEP 3. From (c) we conclude that $D \subseteq A$.

STEP 4. From (d) we conclude that $B \subseteq E'$.

STEP 5. From (e) we condlude that $F \subseteq D$.

221

Obviously, we want a conclusion involving E and C. (This should be kept in mind in determining how the given information should be used.)

From Step 2, $(C')' \subseteq (F')'$, or $C \subseteq F$. Combining this with Step 5, $C \subseteq D$. Combining this result with Step 3, we conclude that $C \subseteq A$. Using the transitive property again with Step 1, we have $C \subseteq B$. Finally, using Step 4, $C \subseteq E'$. This is equivalent to $(E')' \subseteq C'$, or $E \subseteq C'$. Thus the set of kittens with green eyes is a subset of the set of kittens that will not play with gorillas. In other words, no kitten with green eyes will play with a gorilla.

EXERCISES

Use the following sets in Exercises 1 through 4. Let

$$A = \{1, 2, 3, 4, 5, 6, 7, 8\}$$
$$B = \{x \mid x \text{ is a positive factor of } 8\}$$
$$C = \{1, 3, 5, 7, 9, 11, 13\}$$
$$D = \{1, 2, 3, 4, 5, 6, 7, 8, 9, 10, 11, 12, 13, 14, 15\}$$

1. List the elements in each set.
   (a) $A \cup B$ (b) $A \cap B$ (c) $B \cup C$
   (d) $B \cap C$ (e) $A \cup C$ (f) $A \cap C$

2. Let $n(S)$ represent the number of elements in a finite set S.
   (a) Verify that $n(B \cup C) = n(B) + n(C) - n(B \cap C)$.
   (b) Verify that $n(A \cup B) = n(A) + n(B) - n(A \cap B)$.
   (c) Verify that $n(C \cup D) = n(C) + n(D) - n(C \cap D)$.
   (d) Verify that $n(A \cup C) = n(A) + n(C) - n(A \cap C)$.

3. List the elements in each of the following sets.
   (a) A'_D (b) B'_D (c) C'_D
   (d) $(A \cap B)'_D$ (e) $A'_D \cup B'_D$ (f) $(A \cup B)'_D$
   (g) $A'_D \cap B'_D$ (h) $(B \cup C)'_D$ (i) $B'_D \cap C'_D$

4. Which of the following are true?
   (a) $B \subseteq A$
   (b) $A \cup (B \cap C) = (A \cup B) \cap (A \cup C)$
   (c) $A \cap (B \cup C) = (A \cap B) \cup (A \cap C)$
   (d) $\varnothing \subseteq A$
   (e) $9 \in A$
   (f) $2 \notin B$

5. Give expressions that represent each of the following Venn diagrams.

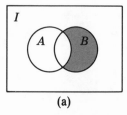

(a)

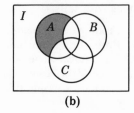

(b)

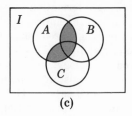

(c)

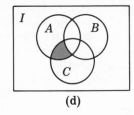

(d)

6. Give expressions that represent each of the following Venn diagrams.

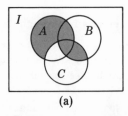

(a)

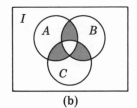

(b)

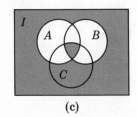

(c)

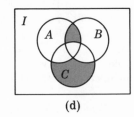

(d)

7. Draw Venn diagrams for each of the following expressions where A, B, and C are subsets of some universal set I.
(a) $(A \cup B) \cap C$ (b) $(A \cap B) \cup (A \cap C)$ (c) $A' \cup B$
(d) $A' \cap B$ (e) $(A' \cap B')'$ (f) $A \cap B' \cap C$

8. Draw Venn diagrams for each of the following expressions where A, B, and C are subsets of some universal set I.
(a) $A \cap (B \cup C)'$ (b) $(A' \cup B')'$ (c) $(A \cap B)' \cap C$
(d) $A' \cap B' \cap C'$ (e) $(A' \cap B' \cap C')'$ (f) $A' \cap (B \cup C)'$

9. Complete the proof on page 217 that $A \cap (B \cup C) = (A \cap B) \cup (A \cap C)$.

10. Use a Venn diagram to verify that $A \cup (B \cap C) = (A \cup B) \cap (A \cup C)$.

11. Let R, S, and T be sets. Show that $n(R \cup S \cup T) = n(R) + n(S) + n(T) - n(R \cap S) - n(R \cap T) - n(S \cap T) + n(R \cap S \cap T)$.

12. (a) Suppose 462 families own at least one of three different makes of automobiles and suppose no family owns as many as two cars of the same make. If 228 families own Make A, 258 own Make B, 332 own Make C, and 310 families own at least two of these makes, how many of these 462 families own all three kinds of automobiles? (See Exercise 11.)
(b) How many own only two makes of automobiles?
(c) How many own only one make?

13. In a college poll of 75 students, the following information was obtained: 4 were registered for biology, English, and mathematics; 7 were registered for biology and mathematics; 16 were registered for English and mathematics; 11 were registered for biology and English; 30 were registered for mathematics; 32 were registered for biology; and 41 were registered for English. (a) How many were not registered for any of the three courses of biology, English and mathematics? (b) How many of those polled were taking mathematics but not biology or English? (c) How many of those polled were taking only one of the three given courses? (d) How many of those polled were taking biology and mathematics but not English?

Solve each of the Lewis Carroll puzzles in Exercises 14 through 22.

14. *Given:* (i) Babies are illogical. (ii) Nobody is despised who can manage a crocodile. (iii) Illogical persons are despised. With the techniques used to solve Puzzles 1 and 2, deduce that babies cannot manage crocodiles.

15. *Given:* (i) Everyone who is sane can do logic. (ii) No lunatics are fit to serve on a jury. (iii) None of your sons can do logic. Deduce that none of your sons is fit to serve on a jury.

16. *Given:* (i) My gardener is well worth listening to on military subjects. (ii) No one can remember the battle of Waterloo, unless he is very old. (iii) Nobody is really worth listening to on military subjects, unless he can remember the battle of Waterloo. Deduce that my gardener is very old.

17. *Given:* (i) When I work a logic example without grumbling, you may be sure it is one that I can understand. (ii) These are not arranged in regular order like the examples I am used to. (iii) No easy example ever makes my head ache. (iv) I cannot understand examples that are not arranged in regular order like those I am used to. (v) I never grumble at an example unless it gives me a headache. Deduce that these logic examples are difficult.

18. *Given:* (i) All my sons are slim. (ii) No child of mine is healthy who takes no exercise. (iii) All gluttons, who are children of mine, are fat. (iv) No daughter of mine takes any exercise. Deduce that all gluttons, who are children of mine, are unhealthy.

19. *Given:* (i) Nobody who really appreciates Beethoven fails to keep silent while the *Moonlight Sonata* is being played. (ii) Guinea pigs are hopelessly ignorant of music. (iii) No one who is hopelessly ignorant of music ever keeps silent while the *Moonlight Sonata* is being played. Deduce that guinea pigs never really appreciate Beethoven.

20. *Given:* (i) No experienced person is incompetent. (ii) Jenkins is always blundering. (iii) No competent person is always blundering. Deduce that Jenkins is inexperienced.

21. *Given:* (i) All the dated letters in this room are written on blue paper. (ii) None of them are in black ink, except those that are written in the

third person. (iii) I have not filed any of them that I can read. (iv) None of them that are written on one sheet are undated. (v) All of them that are not crossed are in black ink. (vi) All of them written by Brown begin with "Dear Sir." (vii) All of them written on blue paper are filed. (viii) None of them written on more than one sheet is crossed. (ix) None of them that begin with "Dear Sir" is written in the third person. Deduce that I cannot read any of Brown's letters.

22. *Given:* (i) No interesting poems are unpopular among people of real taste. (ii) No modern poetry is free from affectation. (iii) All your poems are on the subject of soap bubbles. (iv) No affected poetry is popular among people of real taste. (v) No ancient poem is on the subject of soap bubbles. Question: Can we conclude that all of your poems are uninteresting?

John von Neumann (1903–1957)

John von Neumann was born at Budapest, Hungary, on December 28, 1903. He received a doctorate in mathematics from the University of Budapest at the age of twenty. From 1926 until 1929 he taught at the University of Hamburg. From a professorship in mathematical physics at Princeton University he became a Professor of Mathematics at the Institute for Advanced Study at Princeton, New Jersey, when it was founded in 1933; it was a position he retained until his death.

Like some of his great predecessors in mathematics, von Neumann had a reputation for being able to perform phenomenal computations and solve complicated problems mentally. He directed the development of the first electronic computers at the Institute for Advanced Study; he was one of the founders of game theory; and he made basic contributions to quantum theory, to the development of atomic energy, and to long range weather forecasting. He was both a member of the Atomic Energy Commission and a consultant on the Atomic Bomb Project at Los Alamos. In addition, he was also a consultant to both the Army and Navy during World War II. In 1956, he won the $50,000 Enrico Fermi award for his work on the theory, design, and construction of computers.

Von Neumann spent the last days of his life in Walter Reed Hospital where he died of cancer. Nevertheless, he continued making contributions to the Atomic Energy Commission until his untimely death on Feb. 8, 1957 at the age of 54.

9 The Principles of Computer Programming

1. Simple Computer Programs
2. Programming Repetitive Procedures
3. Applications

It is unworthy of excellent men to lose hours like slaves in the labor of calculations which could safely be relegated to anyone else if machines were used.

GOTTFRIED WILHELM LEIBNIZ

1. SIMPLE COMPUTER PROGRAMS

Introduction. The computer is one of the most significant tools that has been developed to aid the human mind. It frees man from tedious routine tasks and enables him to investigate problems that were impossible with only pencil and paper or desk calculators. The press tends to publicize only extreme cases of computer activities. Some reports might lead one to believe that the computer is a superhuman brain. In other cases, the computer is pictured as a device that makes errors beyond the ability of a human. No human would inadvertently send you 10,000 copies of a magazine or add a million dollars to your bank account. Between the extremes of superhuman and superdisastrous activities lies the typical use of computers. The computer is used to perform routine computations for banks and businesses. It controls the flow of traffic, predicts weather, retrieves information, and even plays checkers or tic-tac-toe.

Although the computer is used on extremely complex problems, the basic principles are rather simple. The instructions to perform a task must be given to the computer with precision and in detail. Furthermore, the instructions must be given in terms of simple arithmetic. The ability to give instructions to a computer requires that the programmer have a complete grasp of the problem and have the experience necessary to combine the basic principles into appropriate instructions. Few people could set down a sufficiently detailed set of instructions for a machine to play checkers, even ignoring questions of how the computer would be made to carry out these instructions.

We hope to show not only how the logic of the computer is self-limiting, but also how inclusive its scope is within those limits. In this way the reader may begin to understand how computers "think." We take our collection of computer instructions from the computer "language" named BASIC, which is used widely for programming

BASIC

computers. The letters of BASIC stand for Beginners All-purpose Symbolic Instruction Code.

Large modern computers can perform a million additions or multiplications per second. They must follow a detailed list of instructions for each task. Unlike desk calculators though, a list of instructions is stored inside the machine and some instructions are repeated hundreds or even millions of times while a single problem is being solved. Though the history of calculating machines is quite old, the concept of storing the instructions inside the machine was suggested by von Neumann in 1945 and built three years later. This idea is essential to our modern computers. The form of instructions have become much simpler to use than forms used by von Neumann's machines. BASIC was developed during the early 1960s and is perhaps the simplest general purpose language available. For very complicated problems, other languages are necessary.

Calculating the Area of a Circle. Though computers can be given long strings of instructions, they must be instructed in great detail. Just as a desk calculator will not "know" how to calculate the circumference or area of a circle having radius 7, neither will a computer. Unlike most desk calculators, computers have storage locations, that is, places for storing or saving a number for later use. For example, if the number π is to be used several times we would have 3.1416 put in one of its storage locations and later just tell the machine to use the number in that location. How do we do that? We choose a name like PI which is convenient for ourselves, (or P or X or any combination of capital letters), and then type onto a card or into a typewriter connected to the computer.

LET PI = 3.1416

Similarly, for the above problem we might put the number 7 in a location we would call RADIUS (or perhaps just RAD or R).

LET RADIUS = 7

A location can contain only one number. We find the circle's circumference in two steps (though there are several other ways). Since the circumference is $2\pi r$ where r is the radius, the first step is to have the computer make this calculation. We tell the computer to name a location, say, CIRCUMF and to put in it the number which is 2 times the number in location PI, times the number in location RADIUS. Multiplication is indicated by "*". The instruction is

LET CIRCUMF = 2 * PI * RADIUS

The second step is to find out what the result is. Perhaps we have been typing our instructions into a typewriter connected directly to the computer. Then we could have the computer type the number in location CIRCUMF on our typewriter by using the instruction

PRINT CIRCUMF

program

The fantastic speed of the computer, thousands and sometimes millions, of calculations per second would be wasted if it carried out only one instruction at a time. Instead it is given an entire *program*, that is, the whole list of instructions. The above program would be

> *Program 1*
> 10   LET PI = 3.1416
> 20   LET RADIUS = 7
> 30   LET CIRCUMF = 2 * PI * RADIUS
> 40   PRINT CIRCUMF
> 100   END

After the entire program was in the computer, it would be told to run the program, and the number 43.9824 would be automatically typed. The last line of a program written in the standard version of BASIC is always the instruction END. Each line of a BASIC program must be numbered to show the order of lines. The designers of the BASIC language decided to allow gaps in the line numbers so that programs would be easy to expand or correct. Extra instruction lines can be fitted into the gaps without our having to remember the previous instructions.

This program could easily be "translated" into any other programming language. Different languages have different rules but their main objectives are similar. One rule of BASIC is not followed in this chapter, and that concerns the *length* of names of locations. Various computer languages have different rules about the names locations are allowed to have. Most versions of BASIC restrict names to be either just one letter, or one letter and one digit. For example, A, R, A9, and Z1 are allowed but AW, RADIUS, A99, and 6Q are not. The designers of BASIC could easily have avoided such restrictions.

Since the program has instructions giving the values of π and the radius, it is simple to add instructions for the calculation of the area of a circle (which is πr^2 when r is the radius). We will have a location named A for area. The following instructions are for making the calculation and then printing the value placed in location A.

> 50   LET A = PI * RADIUS * RADIUS
> 60   PRINT A

The instructions are numbered so as to fit between instructions 40 and 100. To make these calculations for a circle of a different radius, just change the number in instruction 20.

The Vocabulary of Basic. There is a small group of special *command words* and symbols in BASIC which are recognized by computers. They have specific meanings and can be thought of as the vocabulary of BASIC. These words instruct the computer to perform certain tasks. Three of these, LET, PRINT, and END, have already been introduced. The following list gives the command words and instruction symbol used in programs in this chapter.

COMMAND WORDS	SYMBOLS
END	$=$
GO TO	$+$
IF . . . THEN	$-$
INPUT	$*$ (*times*)
LET	/ (*divided by*)
PRINT	( )
	$>$ (*is greater than*)
	$<$ (*is less than*)

Be careful to use these words just as they are in the sample programs. Another special command word STOP, used in conjunction with INPUT, will also be introduced later.

More about LET *Instructions.* Notice that instructions 30 and 50 are just for arithmetic calculations, though they might look like algebra to someone who did not know that the "$=$" sign is only for putting a calculated number in a location. The LET instructions always have a location name between the LET and "$=$" sign and nothing else. On the right of the "$=$" sign is a number (as in instruction lines 10 and 20) to be stored in that location or a formula for the computer to evaluate. Such formulas can be quite complex. They may involve multiplication ($*$), addition ($+$), subtraction ($-$), and division (/). A glance through this chapter's many examples of LET instructions will give an indication of some of the scope allowed. Many mistakes can be avoided by always reading LET statements a specific way. Read "LET A $=$ . . ." as

"Let location A be given the value . . ."

The following "instructions" cannot be read like that because a number of an expression appears where there should be a single location name.

EXAMPLES OF MEANINGLESS INSTRUCTIONS:

LET 2.5 = RADIUS
LET 7 = 7
LET A + B = C + D
LET X * X − 1 = 0

EXAMPLES OF LEGITIMATE INSTRUCTIONS:

LET D = RADIUS + RADIUS
LET DIST = RATE * TIME
LET RATE = DIST/TIME
LET PERIMETER = 2 * LENGTH + 2 * HEIGHT
LET P = 2 * (LENGTH + HEIGHT)

Sometimes it is necessary to change the value in a location by adding 1 to it, or perhaps by doubling it. The following instruction increases the value in location N by 1.

LET N = N+1

The appearance of the same location on both sides of "=" makes no problem for the computer. There are two steps in carrying out a LET instruction. First the expression on the right is calculated. The resulting number is then put in location N. Since a location can only hold one number, the old value is automatically erased. Parentheses are used in BASIC just as in arithmetic. They can always be included in expressions to help make the meaning clear. The rules of arithmetic say that $2(h + w)$ is different from $2h + w$. If there are no parentheses, all the multiplications (like 2 times h) and divisions are carried out first and then the additions and subtractions.

EXERCISES

1. Write two instructions for the above program 1 so it will also have the diameter of the circle calculated and printed when executed by the computer.

2. Describe carefully what each of the following instructions means.
   (a) PRINT A
   (b) LET RAD = 7
   (c) LET N = N+1

(d) LET N = 2*N

(e) LET SUM = A + B + 2*(C + D)

3. What values are printed by the computer in the following program?

Program 2	10	LET NUMBER = 10
	20	LET Q = 317
	30	LET NUMBER = Q
	40	PRINT NUMBER
	100	PRINT Q
	200	END

In other words, does instruction 30 change the value in location NUMBER or does it change the value in Q?

4. What would the answer of Exercise 3 be if instruction 30 was changed to the following?

$$30 \quad \text{LET } Q = \text{NUMBER}$$

5. Tell why the following instructions are not legitimate in BASIC.

(a) LET V+1 = V

(b) LET R = 7 inches

(c) DIVIDE A/B

(d) DIVIDE A BY B

(e) LET R = R/(A+B)

(f) SET R = 7

(g) LET 2*R = 14

6. Write an instruction in BASIC for each of the following procedures.

(a) Put .75 in a location to be named RADIUS.

(b) Put in location INCHES the number which is 12 times the number in location FEET.

(c) Increase the number in location N by 1.

(d) Double the number in location N.

(e) Change the number in location N to O.

(f) Let the area A be the square of the side S. (That is, let the number in location A be the square of the number in S.)

7. What does the computer print when it executes this program?

Program 3	100	LET N = 3/4
	110	LET N = N+1
	120	PRINT N
	999	END

8. Write a program for calculating the volume of a ball whose radius is 7.003. (The formula for the volume is $\frac{4}{3}\pi r^3$ when r is the radius.)

Getting the Computer to Reply. The PRINT instruction has been used here several times already. Computers transmit results in many forms. They may print on a typewriter or printer or punch numbers on punch cards. Computers that automatically control industrial processes send numerical signals directly to the machines they operate. The principle is similar to sending signals to operate a typewriter. The emphasis in this chapter is on describing the way computers are made to manipulate data internally, that is, on the logical rules of computers, and so we only point out a few variations of the PRINT instruction. The instruction

PRINT RADIUS, AREA

will cause both numbers to be printed on the same line. Several locations can be printed on one line. To have *words* printed, we put what we want printed *in quotations*. The instruction

PRINT "RADIUS", "AREA"

causes the computer to print the actual words "radius" and "area" on a single line of the page, skipping several spaces between the words. We can combine the two formats. For example,

PRINT "THE RADIUS IS", RADIUS

If RADIUS had the value 2.5, the computer would print

THE RADIUS IS   2.5

The following program gives examples of what can be printed.

Program 4

```
110    PRINT "THIS PROGRAM ADDS
       TWO NUMBERS"
120    LET X = 3.0
130    LET Y = 4.1
140    LET SUM = X + Y
150    PRINT "THE SUM OF", X,
       "PLUS", Y, "IS", SUM
160    END
```

The computer will now print

```
THIS PROGRAM ADDS TWO NUMBERS
THE SUM OF    3.0    PLUS    4.1    IS    7.1
```

EXERCISE

9. Write a two-line program which will have the computer type "I think; therefore I am."

2. PROGRAMMING REPETITIVE PROCEDURES

Loops and the GO TO *Instruction.* Perhaps the main advantage a computer has over an adding machine is that it can perform operations repeatedly. There would be no point in having a machine that can carry out an addition in perhaps a millionth of a second if it took much longer to get the program and numbers into the computer. So far there has been no indication how we get the computer to do any instruction more than once (other than to just have it run the whole program twice). So far the program lines are executed in order until the END instruction is reached. All computer languages have an instruction for telling the computer to go back or forward to a different line and start executing the instructions there. The instruction GO TO 200 will tell the computer that the next instruction to be performed is on line 200 (and then the line following 200, etc.) unless another GO TO transfers it somewhere else. Notice that so far there is no way to stop the computer once it is sent back to an earlier line because the computer will automatically keep returning to the GO TO instruction. The next program prints the sequence 1, 2, 3, 4, ... We have given no way to stop the computer here and it prints *ad infinitum.* Such unending programs are never used in practice, but this technique is essential to writing complex programs.

Program 5
```
100    LET N = 1
200    PRINT N
300    LET N = N + 1
400    GO TO 200
500    END
```

The order in which the statements are performed is 100, 200, 300, 400 (which says to go back to instruction 200 using the new value in location N), 200, 300, 400 (which says go back to 200), 200, 300, ...

EXERCISES

1. Write a program for printing each of these unending sequences.
    (a) 1973, 1974, 1975, 1976, . . .
    (b) 1, 3, 5, 7, 9, . . .
    (c) 1, 2, 4, 8, 16, . . .
    (d) 0, 1, 1, 2, 3, 5, 8, 13, 21, . . .   Each term (after the first two) is the sum of the preceding two. (*Hint:* One method uses two locations, one for

storing the odd terms called A and the other B for the even terms. If for example, 3 was in A and 5 was in B, then the value in A would be increased to 8. Next increase B, and print A and B. Then change A again, etc.) This sequence is called the Fibonacci series and has applications in genetics, for example.

2. If one grain of wheat is put on the first square of a checkerboard, 2 grains on the second square, 4 on the third square, and the number of grains is doubled on successive squares, then the 64th square would require 9,223,372,036,854,775,808 grains. Write a program (unending) for calculating the number of grains on each square. Use the instruction

    PRINT S, G

    where S is the number of the square and G is the number of grains.

    Remark. The number for square 64 has 19 digits. Locations are not able to hold that many digits. The computer would actually print

    9223E15   *which means* $9,223 \times 10^{15}$

    or some similar approximation—depending on the available version of BASIC. When the number of places to the left of the decimal point becomes too large (usually about 40 digits) the number is just lost. A special message to this effect is usually typed by the computer.

3. Suppose a country had 60 people per square mile of land (which is approximately the average population density of the earth) and the population increased yearly by a factor 1.02. Write a program for printing the number of people per square mile for each succeeding year, year after year, as an unending sequence (ignoring the fact that the population would eventually have to reach a limit).

    Remark. At the above 2% yearly rate of increase the world's population density would reach 1,000,000 people per square mile in 481 years. Manhattan Island now has a population density of 80,000.

Input to the Computer during a Program's Execution. A successful rocket launch requires fast reactions to small deviations from the flight plan. The highspeeds of computers make them ideal monitors and controllers of the ground radars and on board guidance systems using all information sent to the computers by radio. Though these programs are exceedingly complex and though it often seems to the programmer that errors are diabolically hidden and impossible to locate, none the less excruciating precision is necessary. Any error can be disastrous. The first United States rocket launched for Venus went off course during its launch and had to be aborted—by being exploded. The cause of the malfunction? One letter was wrong in one instruction in the program that controlled the rocket during the launch. Fortunately a second "back-up" rocket was ready and was launched just days later—using a corrected program—for the first successful flight past Venus.

This story emphasizes how even in the most advanced applications a program must be completely explicit, leaving nothing to the nonexistent imagination and initiative of a computer. It refers to data being sent out from the computer to control the rocket. This is called "output." The information being received by the computer from the radar and from the rocket itself is called "input." Data can be entered into a computer—into specified locations—while the program is running by using the INPUT instruction. It is an instruction designed so that a programmer using a teletype to instruct the computer can directly change values in locations. For example, if we wanted to calculate the circumferences and areas using several different values for radii, we could write the instruction (using location R for radius)

output

input

20   INPUT R

instead of the old instruction 20 which gave the location a value. When the program is being executed the INPUT instruction will cause the computer to type a question mark on the teletype and then wait until someone types a number into the teletype. That number is automatically placed in location R. If no number is typed in, the computer will not be able to continue. Using the GO TO instruction, we can write a program which will make the calculations for any number of radii. Just insert a GO TO instruction right before the END instruction. When the calculation and printing are finished for one radius, the GO TO statement will transfer the computer to the INPUT statement 20, to receive a new value for location RADIUS from the programmer. The altered program is now given, with some other minor°changes. Line 50 will cause computer to print nothing at all! This instruction is for having a line skipped in the computer printout. The location P is used for storing π.

Program 6
```
          10    LET  P = 3.1416
          20    INPUT  R
          30    LET  A = P * R * R
          40    PRINT  A
          50    PRINT
          90    GO TO 20
         100    END
```

This is the entire program. Notice that there is no indication of the values the computer will be given. Instruction 20 only tells the computer to wait to receive a number which it should put in location

R. We could input any numbers such as 7, 132.9, .6, 0, 7.3, .3, 9. When as many numbers have been used as the programmer wishes, he can end the program execution by typing into the teletype

STOP

instead of a new number. STOP is the *only* command word that can be typed in place of a number. The program execution is then terminated just as if the computer had reached the END instruction. We can now use this program for an unexpected type of problem.

Problem. Find the radius of the circle whose area is 10 by trial and error methods.

The person running the teletype (who we will call "the programmer") makes a guess, say 1, at the correct radius and sees what the area of that circle will be. When he finds the area (3.1416 * 1 * 1) is too small, he makes another guess using a larger radius, say 2, and keeps guessing until he is satisfied he is close enough to area 10. We now demonstrate the way such an interplay might proceed, underlining for clarity what the computer would type on the teletype. Explanatory comments are in italics. The rest is typed by the programmer also on the teletype. It is assumed that the above program has already been typed into the computer. The execution of the program starts when the programmer types RUN or RUNNH.

RUNNH
? 1   *1 is the first guess at the radius.   The resulting area is less*
   3.1416   *than the desired area of 10.*
             Instruction 50 says nothing should be typed on this line.
? 2   *2 is the second guess at the radius but now this area is too*
   12.5664   *large.*
? 1.7   *1.7 gives an area closer to 10 but a larger radius is*
   9.07922   *needed.*
? 1.8   *1.8 is too large so the desired radius is between 1.7*
   10.1788   *and 1.8.*
? 1.78
   9.95385
? 1.781
   9.96503
? 1.783
   9.98743
? 1.786
   10.0211

? 1.785
  10.0098
? 1.784   *So, the desired radius is between 1.784 and 1.785.*
  9.99863
? STOP   *The program execution is now ended by typing STOP.*

PROGRAM STOPPED.
TUNE: 03   *The computer reports it used .03 seconds of calculating time. Only a small fraction of that time was used in doing the arithmetic.*

EXERCISES

4. Write a program for printing the product of any two numbers which the programmer inputs.

5. Add a GO TO instruction so that the procedure in Exercise 4 will be repeated (until the person using the program types STOP).

6. Write a program which will print the square of any number which is fed in via an INPUT instruction. Add a GO TO instruction so that the procedure repeats. Indicate how this program could be used on a teletype to find the square root of a number, say 10, using a trial and error procedure. Can you give a systematic method the person running the teletype might follow?

Simple Decisions and the Conditional Branch. Most programs require the computer to make simple "decisions." If we want it to print only those numbers which are greater than 0, the computer must have a way of "deciding" whether a number is greater than 0. When doing a repetitive procedure 1,000 times, it must be able to "decide" when it has done the procedure that number of times, that is, when it has reached 1,000.

    The GO TO instruction—sometimes called a "transfer"—diverts the computer from executing all the statements in order. The "conditional transfer" may or may not divert the computer. Here the computer is told to compare numbers or location values. For example suppose the computer is fed a sequence of numbers (from the teletype using an INPUT instruction) and we want it to print those numbers which are greater than zero. Hence, if the number in location "N > (is greater than) 0" then we want the computer to print it. Then the next number is checked. The following program executes this procedure by using a "conditional transfer" in instruction 10.

transfer

conditional transfer

239

Program 7   5   INPUT N
                10   IF N > 0 THEN 20
                15   GO TO 5
                20   PRINT N
                25   GO TO 5
                30   END

Instruction 10 is read

"If N is greater than 0, then go to instruction 20; otherwise go to the very next instruction (which is 15).

Suppose the storage location named N has the value 5.3 stored in it. Then, the value in N is greater than 0, so instruction 10 tells the computer to branch to 20. In executing 20, 5.3 is printed. The next instruction 25 tells the computer to go to line 5 and thereby start the procedure again, inputting a new number. If the next number is, say −2.5, then −2.5 is not greater than 0 and so the computer does not branch. Instead it proceeds to the next instruction, 15.

If we instead wanted the computer to print numbers which are less than 5, instruction 10 would be changed to

$$10 \text{ IF } N < 5 \text{ THEN } 20$$

The language permits the use of the following arithmetic comparisons.

SYMBOL	MEANING
>	is greater than
<	is less than
=	equals
>=	is greater than or equal to
<=	is less than or equal to
<>	is not equal to

Study these examples of legitimate IF instructions. Can you write out in English what they mean?

$$\text{IF } A = B \text{ THEN } 10$$
$$\text{IF } A * A > B * B \text{ THEN } 400$$
$$\text{IF VELOCITY} <> 0 \text{ THEN } 20$$

Example. Program 8 "inputs" numbers into three locations, HT (for the height of a right triangle), B (for the base), and HYPOT (for the hypotenuse) and checks to see if the pythagorean triangle rule is satisfied, that is, to see if

$$\text{height}^2 + \text{base}^2 = \text{hypotenuse}^2$$

If it is satisfied, the computer would print "THE FORMULA IS SATIS-FIED". If it is *not* satisfied we will have it print "ERROR, THE FORMULA IS NOT SATISFIED" and then go to END.

Program 8

```
10    INPUT    HT
20    INPUT    B
30    INPUT    HYPOT
100   IF HT * HT + B * B = HYPOT * HYPOT
      THEN 130
110   PRINT "ERROR, THE FORMULA IS
      NOT SATISFIED"
120   GO TO 200
130   PRINT "THE FORMULA IS SATISFIED"
200   END
```

EXERCISES

7. What happens in program 8 if the numbers 3, 4 and 5 are fed in from the teletype? What if 3, 5 and 4 (in that order) are fed in?
8. Program 7 can be shortened by noticing that if "N <=0", then the number in N should not be printed. Show how the program can be made one instruction shorter using this idea.
9. Write a program using two IF instructions for printing only those numbers which are between 0 and 5.

3. APPLICATIONS

The instructions which have been introduced represent the main logical elements of programs for all purposes in large electronic computers. The additional techniques that are available in BASIC and other languages are variations of what can already be done. These principal "tools" of programming are:

Storage locations
Arithmetic capabilities (the LET instruction)
Input from the output to the computer (the INPUT and PRINT instructions)
Transfers of the execution from one instruction to another out of order (the GO TO instruction)
Logic, simple decisions by means of the conditional transfer (the IF . . . THEN instruction)

Some programs are now presented using these features together.

A Repetitive Addition Problem. One of the primary reasons for the importance of computers is their ability to do repetitive procedures. For example, many large businesses use computers for keeping accurate records of accounts, automatically updating them and checking their status. Individual procedures for a single account might be simple but might also have to be repeated for thousands of accounts daily. Another repetitive procedure is used in the following program. Its purpose is to add together all the integers from 1 to 1,000. Of course there is a simple formula from algebra which could be used to find the answer without doing the additions. This program does illustrate however how the machine can be programmed to do the 1,000 additions and *then* stop and print the total.

Adding $1 + 2 + \cdots + 1,000$.

Program 9
```
10    LET S = 0
20    LET I = 1
30    LET S = S + I
40    LET I = I + 1
50    IF I <= 1000 THEN 30
60    PRINT S
70    END
```

The core which causes line 30 to be repeated 1,000 times is the collection of lines 20, 40, and 50, whereas line 30 is the actual operation which we want repeated.

EXERCISES

1. Change the above program so that it adds the *squares* of the integers from 1 to 1,000; that is, write a program to calculate

$$1^2 + 2^2 + 3^2 + \cdots + 1,000^2$$

2. Write a program which will input thirty numbers and print their average.

3. Write a program which will input thirty numbers and then print (only) the largest one of these.

4. Write a program for printing the first thirty numbers of any of the sequences in Exercise 1 of the previous section.

Games and Tic-Tac-Toe. Programs have been written for playing many different kinds of games. Usually the more complicated the game, the worse the computer is at playing the game. The best programs enable powerful computers to play chess about as well as a good tournament player. Really good players would have no difficulty beating the machine. Scientists develop chess playing programs in order to study and better understand how to develop greater logical capabilities in programs. There are far too many possibilities for a computer to check all possible combinations of chess moves; hence it cannot play perfectly. The programmer must provide the program with substantial "guidelines" which he has found useful in his own playing of the game. Tic-tac-toe is simple enough that a complete set of guidelines can be provided so that the computer never loses, but if the opponent plays well, the computer can only draw. Notice that this program does not have a single LET instruction. No computations are made.

To keep the number of possibilities as small as possible our program is written so that the computer has the "first turn." Actually, the computer always makes the same first move. The nine tic-tac-toe points are numbered.

1	2	3
4	5	6
7	8	9

The program indicates its move by giving the number where it plays. The opponent inputs the number of the point where he wishes to move. In this program the computer does no figuring or calculating. All the moves were provided in advance by the programmer.

A tic-tac-toe game can be played against this program without using a computer. Just follow the program line by line as the computer would. Choose specific moves when you reach INPUT instructions. Notice the human opponent's first move is stored in location A, his second in B, then C and D for the third and fourth. To make it easier to follow, comments have been inserted (in italics) which are not parts of the actual program.

Tic-Tac-Toe.

Program 10

```
10     PRINT "I MOVE FIRST AND I PUT MY X AT 9."
20     PRINT "WHERE IS YOUR FIRST MOVE?  GIVE ME THE
       NUMBER."
30     INPUT A
110    IF A=5 THEN 500
120    IF A>6 THEN 700
130    PRINT "MY SECOND MOVE IS AT
       7.  GIVE ME YOURS."          when A<5 or = 6
```

243

```
140    INPUT B
150    IF B< >8 THEN 260
160    IF A=1 THEN 300
170    IF A=3 THEN 400
190    PRINT "MY THIRD MOVE IS AT 5.
       GIVE YOUR MOVE."                          for A=2, 4, or 6
200    INPUT C
210    IF C>1 THEN 240
220    PRINT "SINCE YOU PLAYED AT 1, I PLAY AT 3 AND WIN."
230    GO TO 900
240    PRINT "I WIN BY MOVING TO 1."             transfer from 210
250    GO TO 900
260    PRINT "I WIN BY PLAYING AT 8."            transfer from 150
270    GO TO 900
300    PRINT "I PLAY AT 3.  YOUR PLAY."          from 160
310    INPUT C
320    IF C=5 THEN 350
330    PRINT "I PLAY AT 5 AND WIN."
340    GO TO 900
350    PRINT "SINCE YOU PLAYED AT 5, I PLAY AT 6 AND WIN."
360    GO TO 900
400    PRINT "I PLAY AT 1, YOUR PLAY."           from 170
410    INPUT C
420    IF C=5 THEN 450
430    PRINT "I PLAY AT 5 AND WIN."
440    GO TO 900
450    PRINT "SINCE YOU PLAYED AT 5, I PLAY AT
       4 AND WIN."                               from 420
460    GO TO 900
500    PRINT "MY SECOND MOVE IS AT 6.  GIVE
       ME YOURS."                                from 110
510    INPUT B
520    IF B<>3 THEN 610
530    PRINT "I PLAY AT 7 SINCE I DO NOT WANT TO LOSE."
540    PRINT "YOUR TURN"
550    INPUT C
560    IF C<>8 THEN 630
570    PRINT "I AM FORCED TO PLAY AT 2."
580    PRINT "THE GAME IS CLEARLY DRAWN."
590    PRINT "YOU PLAYED A GOOD GAME."
600    GO TO 900
610    PRINT "I WIN NOW BY PLAYING AT 3."        from 520
620    GO TO 900
630    PRINT "I WIN NOW BY PLAYING AT 8."        from 560
```

```
640      GO TO 900
700      PRINT "MY SECOND PLAY IS AT 3.  YOUR TURN."    from 120
710      INPUT B
730      IF B<>6 THEN 810
740      PRINT "MY THIRD PLAY IS AT 1.  YOUR TURN."
750      INPUT C
760      IF C=2 THEN 790
770      PRINT "I NOW WIN BY PLAYING AT 2."
780      GO TO 900
790      PRINT "I NOW WIN BY PLAYING AT 5."             from 760
800      GO TO 900
810      PRINT "I NOW WIN BY PLAYING AT 6."             from 810
900      END
```

EXERCISES

5. Find as many different ways as possible for a player to get a draw against the computer. Such a "game" may be written as a sequence of the numbers of the points chosen by the computer and its opponent.

6. Write a tic-tac-toe program for which the computer moves second. The more skill incorporated into the program, the better the program is!

7. There is a simple game for two players with thirteen matchsticks lying on a table. The two take turns, each time removing either one, two, or three matches. The player who picks up the last one loses. Figure out a good strategy for the player who goes second. Then write a program using the strategy that will tell the computer how many to "pick up," inputting after each round how many his opponent picked up.

8. Write a program for calculating how many numbers of the sequence 1, 2, 4, 8, 16, . . . are less than 150,000,000.

9. Discuss the differences and similarities between the language BASIC and human language.

10. Interview someone who knows how to program and uses programming as an essential part of his/her work, and write up some *specific* problem that he or she worked on.

11. Discuss the intellectual impact of computers on our civilization. Find articles on this topic on which to base the discussion. A possible emphasis: unified federal data banks for surveillance of the population.

12. Investigate the role and limitations of computers (and possibly intelligent robots) in science fiction.

13. Can computers think? Of course the justification of the answer and interpretation of the question are of utmost importance to "your answer."

14. Do you believe the first sentence of this chapter? What are some of the "most significant tools developed to aid the human mind?"

Leonhard Euler (1707–1783)

Leonhard Euler was born at Basel, Switzerland, in 1707. He went to the St. Petersburg Academy, where his friends Nicolaus and Daniel Bernoulli had previously gone as professors of mathematics. At the age of thirty-four, he left St. Petersburg and became head of the Prussian Academy in Berlin; twenty-five years later he returned to St. Petersburg and remained there until his death.

Euler was one of the great universalists. He proved many original and difficult theorems and solved many equally difficult problems in nearly every branch of mathematics. He was the first to prove that no positive integers x, y, and z exist such that $x^3 + y^3 = z^3$; he synthesized trigonometry into its modern form; and he was the first to solve the Bridges of Königsburg problem. (A complete list of his accomplishments would be extensive; most would be difficult to explain here because of their technical nature.) Besides his contributions to mathematics, he also wrote books on astronomy, ship building, and hydraulics. Euler was particularly interested in number theory, and his contributions to that field alone would have immortalized his name. He was a "lightning calculator"; this trait helped him to accomplish such feats as proving false the famous conjecture of Fermat that $2^{2^n} + 1$ was a prime for each natural number n. (If $n = 5$, then the number was shown by Euler to have 641 as a factor.)

Euler holds the distinction of being one of the most productive mathematicians and prolific mathematical writers of all time. Although he lost his sight in one eye in 1735 and then became totally blind shortly after he returned to Russia, he wrote and dictated over 500 books and papers in his lifetime and left enough unpublished manuscripts when he died that the St. Petersburg Academy did not finish publishing all of them until more than forty years after his death.

10 Number Theory

1. Number Congruence
2. Pythagorean Numbers
3. Mathematical Induction
4. Fundamental Theorem of Arithmetic
5. Euclidean Algorithm

God made the whole numbers; all else is made by man.

LEOPOLD KRONECKER

1. NUMBER CONGRUENCE

Suppose it is three o'clock. What time would the clock read 138 hours from now? In 12 hours it would be three o'clock. In 24 hours, it would again be three o'clock; in fact, in $12x$ hours where x is a positive integer, the time would be three o'clock. After some reflection, it should be obvious that we are first interested in finding the largest multiple of 12 which is less than or equal to 138. This can be done by the long division algorithm.

$$
\begin{array}{r}
11 \\
12\overline{)138} \\
\underline{12} \\
18 \\
\underline{12} \\
6
\end{array}
$$

Therefore, $138 = (12)(11) + 6$ where 11 is the quotient and 6 is the remainder. Since $138 - (12)(11) = 6$, $(12)(11) = 132$ is the largest multiple of 12 less than or equal to 138. Thus, the clock would read six hours later than three o'clock; that is, nine o'clock.

Question

> If it is now five o'clock, what time would the clock read in each of the following cases?
>
> 1. 37 hours from now
> 2. 273 hours from now
> 3. 3,586 hours from now
> 4. 526 hours from now

From $138 = (12)(11) + 6$ which we obtained above, we see that $138 - 6 = (12)(11)$. Thus, the difference $138 - 6$ has 12 as a factor. For numbers such as 138 and 6 whose difference has 12 as a factor we

248

say that 138 is *congruent* to 6, *modulo* 12. Symbolically, $138 \equiv 6$, mod 12. Congruence for integers is obviously quite different from congruence for plane figures in geometry. The general definition of number congruence follows.

Definition. *An integer a is said to be congruent to an integer b,* *congruent*
modulo m, where m is a positive integer, if and only if there is an in-
teger x such that $a - b = mx$. In other words, $a \equiv b$, mod m, if and
only if m is a factor of $a - b$. (Note that a and b are not necessarily
positive integers.)

Examples
  1. $13 \equiv 5$, mod 8, since $8(1) = 13 - 5$
  2. $16 \equiv 2$, mod 7, since $7(2) = 16 - 2$
  3. $26 \equiv 38$, mod 3, since $3(-4) = 26 - 38$
  4. $18 \equiv 0$, mod 6, since $6(3) = 18 - 0$
  5. $11 \equiv 11$, mod 17, since $17(0) = 11 - 11$
  6. $18 \equiv 3$, mod 5
  7. $28 \equiv 36$, mod 4
  8. $15 \equiv 0$, mod 3
  9. $3 \equiv 18$, mod 5
10. $14 \equiv -4$, mod 9
11. $-8 \equiv -11$, mod 3
12. $28 \equiv 28$, mod 3
13. $28 \equiv 28$, mod 8

The congruence relation has the same basic properties as the equals relation. (See Theorem 1 below.) In fact we shall prove several theorems concerning addition and multiplication for congruences which should look familiar.

Theorem 1. *Let m be a positive integer.*
  (i) For any integer a, $a \equiv a$, mod m. (Reflexive property.)
  (ii) If a and b are integers such that $a \equiv b$, mod m, then $b \equiv a$,
mod m. (Symmetric property)
  (iii) If a, b, and c are integers such that $a \equiv b$, mod m, and $b \equiv c$,
mod m, then $a \equiv c$, mod m. (Transitive property.)

Proof: (i) For any integer a, m is a factor of $a - a$. (Any positive integer m is a factor of 0 by the definition of factor.) Thus, $a \equiv a$, mod m.

  (ii) If $a \equiv b$, mod m, then it follows from the definition of the congruence relation that m is a factor of $a - b$. Since m is also a factor of $b - a$, $b \equiv a$, mod m.

  (iii) If $a \equiv b$, mod m, then m is a factor of $a - b$. If $b \equiv c$, mod

249

m, then m is a factor of $b - c$. Therefore, m is a factor of the sum $(a - b) + (b - c) = a - c$. By the definition of the congruence relation, $a \equiv c$, mod m.

Theorem 2. *Let m be a positive integer. If a, b, and c are integers such that $a \equiv b$, mod m, then $a + c \equiv b + c$, mod m.*

Proof: If $a \equiv b$, mod m, then m is a factor of $a - b$; that is, there is an integer x such that

$$mx = a - b$$

Thus, $mx = (a + c) - (b + c)$ (Add and subtract c)

Therefore, m is a factor of the difference $(a + c) - (b + c)$ and by the definition of the congruence relation

$$a + c \equiv b + c,\ \text{mod}\ m$$

Theorem 3. *Let m be a positive integer. If a, b, and c are integers such that $a \equiv b, \text{mod}\ m$, then $ac \equiv bc, \text{mod}\ m$. (Note: If $ac \equiv bc$, mod m, then $ca \equiv cb$, mod m.)*

Proof: Left as an exercise.

Theorem 4. *Let m be a positive integer. If $a \equiv b$, mod m, and $c \equiv d$, mod m, then $a + c \equiv b + d$, mod m.*

Proof: Since $a \equiv b$, mod m, we conclude from Theorem 2 that $a + c \equiv b + c$, mod m. Similarly, $c \equiv d$, mod m, implies that $b + c \equiv b + d$, mod m. By the transitive property of the congruence relation, $a + c \equiv b + d$, mod m.

Theorem 5. *Let m be a positive integer. If $a \equiv b$, mod m, and $c \equiv d$, mod m, then $ac \equiv bd$, mod m.*

Proof: Left as an exercise.

Corollary. *If $a \equiv b$, mod m, then $a^2 \equiv b^2$, mod m.*

Proof: Left as an exercise.

Although $a \equiv b$, mod m, implies that $ac \equiv bc$, mod m, the converse of this theorem is not true. For example, since $24 - 12$ has 6 as a factor, $8 \times 3 \equiv 4 \times 3$, mod 6; however, it is *not* true that $8 \equiv 4$, mod 6. We do have the following theorem which is a restricted cancellation property for multiplication.

Theorem 6. *If ac ≡ bc, mod m, and if m and c have no positive factors in common except 1 (m and c are relatively prime), then a ≡ b, mod m.*

Proof: $ac \equiv bc$, mod m, implies that there is an integer x such that

$$mx = ac - bc$$

Thus $$mx = c(a - b)$$

Since m is a factor of the product $c(a - b)$ and since m and c have no positive factors in common except 1, m is a factor of $(a - b)$. (This familiar fact is a consequence of the Fundamental Theorem of Arithmetic which is proved in Section 4.) Hence,

$$a \equiv b, \text{mod } m$$

The concept of number congruence can also be used to prove some of the previously stated divisibility tests for integers. For example, let us prove that the six-digit number abc,def is divisible by 11 if and only if

$$(b + d + f) - (a + c + e)$$

is divisible by 11. First, recall from our positional notation for integers that

$$abc,def = 10^5 a + 10^4 b + 10^3 c + 10^2 d + 10e + f$$

It is easy to verify (use the corollary of Theorem 5) that

$$10 \equiv -1, \text{mod } 11$$
$$10^2 \equiv 1, \text{mod } 11$$
$$10^3 \equiv -1, \text{mod } 11$$
$$10^4 \equiv 1, \text{mod } 11$$
and $$10^5 \equiv -1, \text{mod } 11$$

Thus, using Theorem 3, we conclude that

$$10^5 a \equiv -a, \text{mod } 11$$
$$10^4 b \equiv b, \text{mod } 11$$
$$10^3 c \equiv -c, \text{mod } 11$$
$$10^2 d \equiv d, \text{mod } 11$$
$$10e \equiv -e, \text{mod } 11$$
and $$f \equiv f, \text{mod } 11$$

Adding the congruences,

$$abc,def \equiv (b + d + f) - (a + c + e), \text{mod } 11$$

251

Therefore, *abc,def* is divisible by 11 if and only if $(b + d + f) - (a + c + e)$ is divisible by 11.

The following theorem exhibits the important relationship implied at the beginning of this chapter between the long division algorithm and the congruence relation. Recall that the long division algorithm is used on two positive integers a and m to find two nonnegative integers q and r such that $a = mq + r$ where $0 \leq r < m$; m is the divisor, q is the incomplete quotient, and r is the remainder. If $r = 0$, then m is a factor of a.

Theorem 7. *Let a, b, and m be positive integers.* $a \equiv b$, *mod m, if and only if a and b have the same remainder in the long division of each by m.*

Proof: PART 1. Assume $a \equiv b$, mod m, and assume $a \geq b$. Thus $a - b = q_1 m$ where q_1 is a nonnegative integer. In the long division of b by m, we have

$$b = q_2 m + r \qquad \text{where } 0 \leq r < m$$

Then, since $\qquad a = b + q_1 m$

we have
$$a = (q_2 m + r) + q_1 m$$
$$a = (q_1 m + q_2 m) + r$$
$$a = m(q_1 + q_2) + r \qquad \text{where } 0 \leq r < m$$

Hence, r is also the remainder in the long division of a by m.

PART 2. Assume that the remainders in the long division of each a and b by m is r. Thus,

$$a = q_1 m + r \qquad \text{where } 0 \leq r < m$$
and $\qquad b = q_2 m + r \qquad \text{where } 0 \leq r < m$

Subtracting the last two equalities,

$$a - b = q_1 m - q_2 m$$
and $\qquad a - b = m(q_1 - q_2)$

Since $q_1 - q_2$ is an integer, m is a factor of $a - b$ and $a \equiv b$, mod m

EXERCISES

1. Prove Theorem 3.
2. Prove Theorem 5.
3. Prove the corollary to Theorem 5.

4. In Theorem 7, explain why there is no loss in generality in assuming $a \geq b$.

5. Let m be a positive integer. Prove that m is a factor of an integer a if and only if $a \equiv 0$, mod m.

6. Prove if $a \equiv b$, mod m, and if n is a positive factor of m, then $a \equiv b$, mod n.

7. Let x be an odd positive integer. Prove that x^2 is congruent to 0, 1, or 4, mod 8.

8. Let $S = \{1, 2, 3, 4, 5, 6\}$. If x is a variable on the set S, which of the following congruences has a solution? (That is, for which congruences is there an element in S which makes the congruence a true statement?) $1x \equiv 1$, mod 7; $2x \equiv 1$, mod 7; $3x \equiv 1$, mod 7; $4x \equiv 1$, mod 7; $5x \equiv 1$, mod 7; $6x \equiv 1$, mod 7.

9. Let $T = \{1, 2, 3, 4, 5, 6, 7\}$. If x is a variable on the set T, which of the following congruences has a solution? $1x \equiv 1$, mod 8; $2x \equiv 1$, mod 8; $3x \equiv 1$, mod 8; $4x \equiv 1$, mod 8; $5x \equiv 1$, mod 8; $6x \equiv 1$, mod 8; $7x \equiv 1$, mod 8. (See Exercise 8.)

10. Solve each of the following for x where x is in $\{0, 1, 2, 3, 4, 5, 6\}$.
(a) $2x + 3 \equiv 0$, mod 7
(b) $5x + 4 \equiv 6$, mod 7
(c) $4x + 2 \equiv 5$, mod 7
(d) $5x + 3 \equiv 4$, mod 7

11. Find the simultaneous solutions for each set of equations where x and y are elements in $\{0, 1, 2, 3, 4, 5, 6\}$.
(a) $2x + 3y \equiv 2$, mod 7
    $4x + y \equiv 4$, mod 7
(b) $3x + 4y \equiv 5$, mod 7
    $4x + 5y \equiv 3$, mod 7

*12. Let $S = \{1, 2, 3, 4, \ldots, p-1\}$ where p is a prime number.
(a) Does $ax \equiv 1$, mod p, have a solution for each a in S? (See Exercise 8.)
(b) Are the solutions to the $p-1$ congruences in part (a) all different?

2. PYTHAGOREAN NUMBERS

One of the early mathematical geniuses was Pythagoras. Since he lived nearly 2,500 years ago, only a few details are known concerning the life of this man. We do know that Pythagoras was born on the island of Samos, near Greece, and later lived in Crotona, in Southern Italy. As a result of his great intellectual ability and his insatiable curiosity, he made many contributions not only to mathematics but also to other fields. Music was among his many and varied interests. While pursuing this interest, he discovered that the tone of a stretched string varies as the length of the string varies; as the string is lengthened, such as on a harp, the tone becomes lower. He also noticed that certain lengths of stretched strings make pleasing sounds when played together. Since numbers represented the lengths of these strings, this aided and abetted his theory that numbers were not only the underlying foundation of music but of everything else. For example, Pythagoras associated certain numbers with love, justice, etc. An attachment of mystic properties to numbers permeated the religion which he and his followers practiced. They are generally referred to as the Pythagoreans.

Let us now discuss the pythagorean theorem and some related ideas. The theorem states that the sum of the squares of the lengths of two sides of a right triangle is equal to the square of the length of the hypotenuse. If x and y are the lengths of the two sides of a given right triangle and if z is the length of the hypotenuse, then the theorem states that $x^2 + y^2 = z^2$. Although we often consider the theorem algebraically in terms of the above equation, it was most likely first discovered and proved as a geometric theorem related to area. The pythagorean theorem is equivalent to asserting that the area of the square having one leg of a given right triangle as one of its sides plus the area of the square having the other leg as one of its sides is equal to the area of the square having the hypotenuse as one of its sides. (See Figure 10.1.)

Let us give a proof of the pythagorean theorem by considering

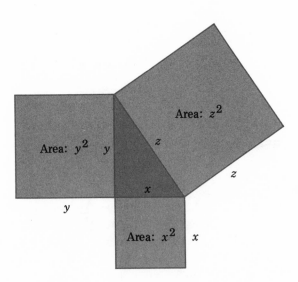

Pythagorean Theorem: $x^2 + y^2 = z^2$

FIGURE 10.1

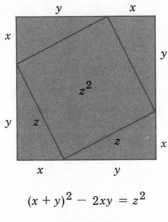

$$(x + y)^2 - 2xy = z^2$$

FIGURE 10.2

Figure 10.2. On a right triangle with x and y as lengths of the legs and z the length of the hypotenuse, construct a square on the hypotenuse with area z^2. Now construct triangles congruent to the original on the other sides of the square. Notice that a square will be formed such that the length of each side is $x + y$. The area of each of the congruent right triangles is $(\frac{1}{2})xy$. Subtracting the area of the four triangles $2xy$ from the area of the square with area $(x + y)^2$ leaves the area z^2 of the interior square; that is,

$$(x + y)^2 - 2xy = z^2$$

Thus, $$x^2 + 2xy + y^2 - 2xy = z^2$$

and $$x^2 + y^2 = z^2$$

Any set of three positive integers x, y, z satisfying $x^2 + y^2 = z^2$ is called a *pythagorean number triple*. How many such triples are there? We are familiar with the pythagorean triple 3, 4, 5. Since $3^2 + 4^2 = 5^2$, it is obvious that any set of integral multiples of 3, 4, 5, such as 6, 8, 10, will also be a pythagorean number triple. Thus, the number of such triples in infinite. However, although {3, 4, 5} and {6, 8, 10} are different sets, we would not normally distinguish between them when trying to find integral solutions to the equation $x^2 + y^2 = z^2$. Therefore, we define a *primitive pythagorean triple* to be a set of three positive integers x, y, z which have 1 as their greatest common factor and such that $x^2 + y^2 = z^2$.

Is the set S of primitive pythagorean triples an infinite set? If we recall the "tile floor" in Figure 5.1 or the fact that the sum of the first n odd integers is n^2, we can readily determine that the set of

pythagorean number triple

primitive pythagorean triple

255

primitive triples is an infinite set. For example, if n is any integer then the difference of the two consecutive squares n^2 and $(n+1)^2$ is the odd integer $2n+1$; thus,

$$n^2 + (2n+1) = (n+1)^2$$

If $2n + 1$ is the square of an odd integer m, then

$$2n + 1 = m^2$$

$$n = \frac{m^2 - 1}{2}$$

and

$$n + 1 = \frac{m^2 + 1}{2}$$

Since m is an odd integer, $m^2 - 1$ and $m^2 + 1$ are even integers and each of n and $n + 1$ are integers. Furthermore, by substituting in $n^2 + (2n + 1) = (n + 1)^2$,

$$\left(\frac{m^2 - 1}{2}\right)^2 + m^2 = \left(\frac{m^2 + 1}{2}\right)^2 \qquad \text{(Formula 1)}$$

If, for example, $m = 3$ then $\dfrac{m^2 - 1}{2} = 4$ and $\dfrac{m^2 + 1}{2} = 5$. Letting $m = 5$, we obtain the primitive triple $\{5, 12, 13\}$. If we let m be any odd prime, we not only get a pythagorean triple but it is also a primitive triple. Hence, we see that the set of primitive triples is infinite.

We should wonder if Formula 1 provides us with *all* the primitive pythagorean triples. To show that it does not, we need only find one primitive triple which is not of the form

$$\frac{m^2 - 1}{2}, \ m, \ \frac{m^2 + 1}{2}$$

Consider the set of integers $\{20, 21, 29\}$ which have 1 as their greatest common factor. Since

$$20^2 + 21^2 = 400 + 441 = 841 = 29^2$$

the set is a primitive pythagorean triple. However, letting $m = 21$ we obtain the triple $\{220, 21, 221\}$. The triple $\{20, 21, 29\}$ cannot be obtained by Formula 1.

We might wonder if a general formula exists which will give all the primitive pythagorean triples. In fact, one does. Developing the formula does not require any great amount of mathematical knowledge but it does require some mathematical sophistication. Let us see what is involved.

Suppose we have three positive integers x, y, and z whose greatest common factor is 1 such that $x^2 + y^2 = z^2$. First, let us show that both x and y cannot be even. If x and y are even, then their squares x^2 and y^2 and, in turn, the sum $x^2 + y^2$ would be even. Thus, z^2 is even and z is even. But this contradicts the assumption that all three numbers do not have a common factor greater than 1. Therefore, both x and y cannot be even.

Let us now prove that x and y cannot both be odd integers. If x is odd, then $x = 2n + 1$ for some integer n and

$$
\begin{aligned}
x^2 &= 4n^2 + 4n + 1 \\
&= 4(n^2 + n) + 1 \\
&= 4n(n + 1) + 1
\end{aligned}
$$

Since either n or $n + 1$ is an even integer, the product $4n(n + 1)$ has 8 as a factor. Therefore, we (again)* conclude that there is an integer p such that

$$x^2 = 8p + 1$$

If y is an odd integer, then there exists an integer q such that

$$y^2 = 8q + 1$$

Consequently, $x^2 + y^2 = 2(4p + 4q + 1) = z^2$. Since z^2 is even, z is even and z^2 has 4 as a factor; but $2(4p + 4q + 1)$ does not have 4 as a factor. Therefore, we can conclude that one of the integers x and y is even and one is odd which, of course, implies that z is odd.

There is no loss in generality to assume that x is odd and y is even. Since y is even, y^2 has 4 as a factor. Since $x^2 + y^2 = z^2$, we conclude that $z^2 - x^2 = y^2$ and

$$\frac{z^2 - x^2}{4} = \frac{y^2}{4}$$

$$\left(\frac{z + x}{2}\right)\left(\frac{z - x}{2}\right) = \frac{y^2}{4} \qquad \text{(an integer)}$$

Since $\dfrac{z + x}{2} + \dfrac{z - x}{2} = z$ and $\dfrac{z + x}{2} - \dfrac{z - x}{2} = x$, the integers $\dfrac{z + x}{2}$ and $\dfrac{z - x}{2}$ have no factors in common except 1 and -1. (If they had a positive common factor different from 1, then so would their sum z and their difference x; in turn, y would have the same common factor, a contradiction.) Finally, since the product of two relatively prime numbers is a perfect square, each of the numbers is a perfect square.

---

* The square of an odd integer is congruent to 1, mod 8.

Thus,

$$\frac{z+x}{2} = u^2, \quad \frac{z-x}{2} = v^2, \quad \frac{y}{2} = uv$$

$$x = u^2 - v^2, \quad y = 2uv, \quad z = u^2 + v^2$$

where u and v are relatively prime positive integers, $u > v$, and one of u and v is even and one is odd.

We have proved that every primitive solution is of the given form. Conversely, if $x = u^2 - v^2$, $y = 2uv$, $z = u^2 + v^2$, u and v are relatively prime positive integers, and $u > v$, then one is even and the other odd $x^2 + y^2 = z^2$. Furthermore, we can prove that x, y, z are relatively prime. Hence, it follows that all primitive solutions of the pythagorean equation are obtained by

$$x = u^2 - v^2, \quad y = 2uv, \quad z = u^2 + v^2 \qquad \text{(Formula 2)}$$

where u and v are relatively prime positive integers, $u > v$, and one of u and v is even and the other is odd.

Once a formula for all integral solutions for $x^2 + y^2 = z^2$ has been obtained, we might wonder if there are any positive integral solutions for the equation $x^3 + y^3 = z^3$. More generally, if n is an integer greater than 2, are there any integral solutions for $x^n + y^n = z^n$? Fermat stated that the answer is "no" and that he had a proof of the theorem. It appears that Fermat was mistaken about having a proof since a proof of the theorem has eluded mathematicians since the mid-seventeenth century. This famous unsolved problem is called *Fermat's Last Theorem*.

It is tedious but not too difficult to prove that $x^3 + y^3 = z^3$ has no integral solutions. In fact, Euler proved that $x^n + y^n = z^n$ has no integral solutions for $n = 3$ and $n = 4$; Dirichlet proved Fermat's theorem for $n = 5$. Today, the theorem has been proved to be true for more than the first two hundred positive integers greater than 2, but a proof of the general theorem remains to immortalize some mathematician.

Euler, Kummer, Lagrange, and Riemann all attempted to prove Fermat's Last Theorem. Gauss is reported to have stated that he thought he could prove it if he took two years out and devoted his full time efforts to the theorem; but he had the (apparent) good judgment not to try. Lindemann, whom we mentioned earlier as the first to settle the famous problem concerning the fact that π was a transcendental number, must have spent the greater part of a decade working on Fermat's Last Theorem. Lindemann even managed to publish two "proofs" which were later shown to contain errors. (Some might question the statement that number theory is the most difficult branch of mathematics, but few would question the statement that it contains some of the most baffling problems.)

With the available tools of modern mathematics and an awareness of the number of famous mathematicians who have either failed to prove Fermat's Last Theorem or assiduously avoided trying, one might ask the following rather shattering question: How do we know for each (true) theorem in mathematics that a proof actually exists? Even if one assumes that Fermat's unsolved problem will be settled, and it probably will, the haunting question still does not go away.

EXERCISES

1. Use Formula 1 to find the pythagorean triple where $m = 7$.
2. Use Formula 1 to find the pythagorean triple where $m = 9$.
3. Use Formula 1 to find the pythagorean triple where $m = 11$.
4. Use Formula 2 to find the pythagorean triple where $u = 2$ and $v = 1$.
5. Use Formula 2 to find the pythagorean triple where $u = 3$ and $v = 2$.
6. Use Formula 2 to find the pythagorean triple where $u = 4$ and $v = 3$.
7. Use Formula 2 to find the pythagorean triple where $u = 5$ and $v = 4$.
8. Use Formula 2 to find u and v for the pythagorean triple $\{105, 88, 137\}$.
9. Use Formula 2 to find u and v for the pythagorean triple $\{69, 260, 269\}$.
10. Bhāskara (1114–1158) is reputed to have given a one word proof of the pythagorean theorem. He exhibited the following figure with the one word "Behold!" Show how the pythagorean theorem can be proved by the use of the figure.

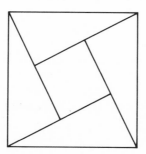

3. MATHEMATICAL INDUCTION

The Greeks were responsible for making proof by deduction an integral part of mathematics. Since that time, *deduction* and *abstraction* have been the hallmarks of mathematics. By now, we should be quite familiar with the essence of deductive reasoning; it is the process of using valid arguments to arrive at conclusions from a given set of hypotheses.

Inductive reasoning is the process of making general conclusions on the basis of a collection of specific observations. Earlier we saw that although $n^2 - n + 41$ is a prime number for the first forty natural numbers we cannot conclude that the formula always yields a prime. ($n^2 - n + 41$ is not a prime for $n = 41$.) We do use, however, inductive reasoning, reasoning by analogy, guessing, etc. to arrive at conjectures of possible theorems, but a theorem must stand on a deductive proof.

Let us consider the conjecture made by Fermat that $2^{2^n} + 1$ is a prime for each positive integer n. For $n = 1$, we obtain

$$2^{2^1} + 1 = 4 + 1 = 5 \qquad \text{a prime}$$

For $n = 2$,

$$2^{2^2} + 1 = 16 + 1 = 17 \qquad \text{a prime}$$

For $n = 3$,

$$2^{2^3} + 1 = 256 + 1 = 257 \qquad \text{a prime}$$

For $n = 4$,

$$2^{2^4} + 1 = 65{,}536 + 1 = 65{,}537 \qquad \text{a prime}$$

It is no small task showing that 65,537 is a prime without a table of primes, but Fermat must have had the necessary determination. From these specific cases, we might conjecture, as did Fermat, that $2^{2^n} + 1$ is always a prime. This type of inductive reasoning has yielded many handsome rewards in number theory but, as might be expected, it has also created its share of havoc.

In every field of mathematics and especially in number theory, many theorems are of the following form: "For every positive integer n, ..." How do we prove such a statement *if* it is true? How do we disprove such a statement if it is false? One important method to *prove* such a statement is the topic of this section. Disproving such a statement can be accomplished by exhibiting one counterexample, one positive integer for which the statement is false.

For a statement such as — For each positive integer n, $2^{2^n} + 1$ is a prime — for which we are not certain of its validity, do we try to prove it or try to find a counterexample? Neither course may be easy or even fruitful as our discussion of Fermat's Last Theorem indicates. Fortunately, Euler has relieved us of any quandary with regard to Fermat's numbers all being primes. Euler showed that

$$2^{2^5} + 1 = 4{,}294{,}967{,}297$$
$$= (641)(6{,}700{,}417) \qquad \text{is not a prime.}$$

Let us state a property of subsets of the set of positive integers. Then we shall show why it is important enough to deserve a distinguishing name in mathematics.

Well-ordering Property. Every nonempty subset of the set of positive integers contains a least positive integer.

The well-ordering property provides us with the basis to prove many theorems concerning the set of positive integers. For example, suppose we wish to prove that for each positive integer n, $\left(\dfrac{n^5}{5} + \dfrac{n^3}{3} + \dfrac{7n}{15}\right)$ is an integer. If we let N be the set of positive integers, then we want to prove that for each $n \in N$,

$$\left(\frac{n^5}{5} + \frac{n^3}{3} + \frac{7n}{15}\right) \in N$$

is a true statement. This can be done as follows using the well-ordering property.

Let $S = \left\{ n \in N \mid \dfrac{n^5}{5} + \dfrac{n^3}{3} + \dfrac{7n}{15} \in N \right\}$. Obviously, $S \subseteq N$, but we wish to prove that $S = N$. To prove $S = N$, we assume $S \neq N$ and obtain a contradiction. (Indirect proof.) If $S \neq N$, then S'_N is not empty, and, by the well-ordering property, it contains a least positive integer; call it t. Let us observe several facts.

1. $\left(\dfrac{t^5}{5} + \dfrac{t^3}{3} + \dfrac{7t}{15}\right) \notin N$ since $t \notin S$.
2. Since for $n = 1$ we have that

$$\frac{1}{5} + \frac{1}{3} + \frac{7}{15} = \frac{3}{15} + \frac{5}{15} + \frac{7}{15} = 1$$

   is an integer, we conclude that $1 \in S$.
3. Therefore, since $1 \in S$, $t \neq 1$. Furthermore, $(t - 1)$ is a positive integer. (Notice it is important to know that $t \neq 1$ for $t - 1$ to be a *positive* integer.)
4. Since $(t - 1)$ is a positive integer less than t, $(t - 1) \notin S'_N$; thus, $(t - 1) \in S$.
5. Hence,

$$\left[\frac{(t-1)^5}{5} + \frac{(t-1)^3}{3} + \frac{7(t-1)}{15}\right] \in N;$$

   that is, by multiplying and collecting terms,

$$\left(\frac{t^5}{5} + \frac{t^3}{3} + \frac{7t}{15}\right) + (-t^4 - 2t^3 - 3t^2 + 2t - 1)$$

is a positive integer.

Since the sum, or difference, of two integers is an integer, and since $\left(\frac{t^5}{5} + \frac{t^3}{3} + \frac{7t}{15}\right)$ is an integer, we conclude that $t \in S$. This is a contradiction since we concluded previously that $t \in S'_N$. Consequently, the assumption that S'_N is nonempty is false; thus, $S'_N = \varnothing$ and $S = N$.

The technique just used is not the usual procedure to prove such a theorem. We generally use the following theorem whose proof parallels the proof in the example.

Theorem. *Let S be a set of positive integers such that each of the following is true.* (a) *$1 \in S$.* (b) *If $k \in S$, then $(k + 1) \in S$.*

Conclusion: S is the set of all positive integers.

Proof: Left as an exercise for the student. (*Hint:* Use the preceding proof as a model.)

Let us use the preceding theorem to prove the following statement is true. For each positive integer n, 43 is a factor of $6^{n+2} + 7^{2n+1}$.

Proof: Let $S = \{n \in N \mid 43 \text{ is a factor of } 6^{n+2} + 7^{2n+1}\}$.
PART 1. (Show that $1 \in S$.) Since $6^3 + 7^3 = 559 = (43)(13)$, we conclude that 1 is an element in S.
PART 2. *Assume $k \in S$; that is, assume $6^{k+2} + 7^{2k+1}$ has 43 as a factor.* [We need to show that $(k + 1) \in S$; that is, we need to prove $6^{k+3} + 7^{2k+3}$ has 43 as a factor.] Now,

$$6^{k+3} + 7^{2k+3} = 6^{k+3} + 6 \cdot 7^{2k+1} + 7^{2k+3} - 6 \cdot 7^{2k+1}$$

Hence, $\quad 6^{k+3} + 7^{2k+3} = 6(6^{k+2} + 7^{2k+1}) + 7^{2k+1}(49 - 6)$
$$= 6(6^{k+2} + 7^{2k+1}) + 7^{2k+1}(43)$$

The second term in the sum of the right-hand side of the equality obviously has 43 as a factor. The first term in the sum has 43 as a factor by assumption; hence, the sum has 43 as a factor. Therefore, $(k + 1) \in S$, and $S = N$ by the preceding theorem.

mathematical induction

The *deductive* method of proof we have just used is called *mathematical induction*. The theorem we stated which is the basis for this type of proof is generally called the *first principle of mathematical induction.* Some other "induction" theorems will be stated in the exercises.

EXERCISES

Prove each of the statements in Exercises 1 through 10.

1. For each positive integer n,

$$1 \cdot 2 + 2 \cdot 3 + 3 \cdot 4 + \cdots + n(n+1) = \frac{n(n+1)(n+2)}{3}$$

2. For each positive integer n,

$$\frac{1}{1 \cdot 4} + \frac{1}{4 \cdot 7} + \frac{1}{7 \cdot 11} + \cdots + \frac{1}{(3n-2)(3n+1)} = \frac{n}{3n+1}$$

3. For each positive integer n,

$$1^3 + 3^3 + 5^3 + \cdots + (2n-1)^3 = n^2(2n^2-1)$$

4. For each positive integer n, $n^5 - 5n^3 + 4n$ has 120 as a factor.
5. For each positive integer n, $n^5 - n$ has 5 as a factor.
6. For each positive integer n, $2^{2n+1} + 1$ has 3 as a factor.
7. For each positive integer n, $4^{n+1} + 5^{2n-1}$ has 21 as a factor.
8. For each positive integer n, $n^3 + (n+1)^3 + (n+2)^3$ has 9 as a factor.
9. For each positive integer n, $\dfrac{n^7}{7} + \dfrac{n^3}{3} + \dfrac{11n}{21}$ is an integer.
10. For each positive integer n,

$$(1)(1!) + (2)(2!) + (3)(3!) + \cdots + (n)(n!) = (n+1)! - 1$$

*11. Prove the following theorem which is often called the *second principle of mathematical induction.* Let S be a set of positive integers for which the following are true. (a) $1 \in S$. (b) S contains the positive integer k whenever S contains each positive integer $n < k$. *Conclusion:* S is the set of all positive integers.

12. Consider the following game called "The Tower of Hanoi." Suppose three pegs are inserted in a board as in Figure 10.3. Construct a "tower" with any given number of disks of different sizes with holes in their centers by placing them on one of the pegs. The diameters of the disks should increase in size from top to bottom. The object of the game is to move the tower to one of the other pegs by moving only one disk at a time, placing it on either of the other pegs, and never placing a disk on top of a smaller disk.

(a) Determine the minimum number of steps to move a tower of three disks from one peg to another peg.

(b) Determine the minimum number of steps to move a tower of four disks from one peg to another peg.

(c) Prove by mathematical induction that the minimum number of moves required to move n disks by the rules from one peg to another is $2^n - 1$.

(d) If one disk is moved each second, approximately how long should it take to complete the game using thirty disks?

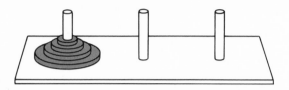

Tower of Hanoi

FIGURE 10.3

4. FUNDAMENTAL THEOREM OF ARITHMETIC

Recall that any integer a is a factor of an integer b if and only if there exists an integer x such that $ax = b$. If a is a factor of b, we often say that a *divides* b and denote this fact by $a \mid b$. We have stated and used the fact that if an integer a is a factor of two integers b and c, then a is a factor of their sum. Let us prove this.

Theorem. *If $a \mid b$ and $a \mid c$ then $a \mid (b + c)$.*

Proof: Since $a \mid b$, there exists an integer x such that $ax = b$. Since $a \mid c$, there exists an integer y such that $ay = c$. (Although x and y might be the same number, this need not be the case. Hence, it is essential to use different letters.)

From $ax = b$ and $ay = c$ we conclude that

$$ax + ay = b + c$$

Thus, $$a(x + y) = b + c$$

Since the sum of two integers is an integer, $(x + y)$ is an integer. By definition of factor, it follows that $a \mid (b + c)$.

Let us now state some similar elementary theorems. The proofs will be left as exercises.

1. If $a \mid b$ and $a \mid c$, then $a \mid (b - c)$.
2. If $a \mid b$ and $b \mid c$, then $a \mid c$.
3. If $a \mid b$ or $a \mid c$, then $a \mid bc$. (Show by counter-example that the converse of this theorem is not true.)
4. If $a \mid b$, then $a^2 \mid b^2$.
5. If $a^2 \mid b^2$, then $a \mid b$.

In Chapter 5 we proved that the set of prime numbers is an infinite set. At that time, we tacitly assumed that every composite number could be expressed as the product of prime numbers. Now, we shall prove this important fact.

Theorem. *Every positive integer n greater than 1 is either a prime or it is expressible as the product of prime numbers.*

Proof: Let S be the set of positive integers which are primes or which can be expressed as the product of primes. Obviously, all of the primes greater than or equal to 2 are in S. If every composite number is in S, then the theorem is true. (We shall prove that this is the case by showing the assumption that there is a composite number not in S leads to a contradiction.) Let T be the set of composite numbers not in S. If T is not empty, there exists a least positive integer $k \in T$ by the well-ordering property. Since k is a composite number, there exist at least two factors a and b of k neither of which is 1 such that

$$k = ab$$

Thus, $a < k$ and $b < k$. Since k is the least element in T and since $a \neq 1$ and $b \neq 1$, it follows that $a \in S$ and $b \in S$. Consequently, either a is a prime or is expressible as the product of primes; similarly, the same is true for b. Therefore, k being the product of a and b can be expressed as the product of primes. Thus, T is empty.

The preceding theorem proves that a composite number such as 1,680 can be expressed as the product of primes. Notice that

$$1,680 = 2 \times 2 \times 2 \times 2 \times 3 \times 5 \times 7$$

If several persons expressed 1,680 as the product of primes, it is not obvious that each would have the "same answer." In other words, it is not obvious that factorization of a composite number into the product of primes is unique, except for the order in which the primes are written. The fact that a composite number is expressible as the product of primes *in one and only one way* is called the Fundamental Theorem of Arithmetic. Let us prove this famous theorem.

Theorem. (Fundamental Theorem of Arithmetic.) *A composite number is expressible as the product of primes in one and only one way.*

Proof: PART 1. The preceding theorem proved that a composite number is expressible as the product of primes in at least one way.

PART 2. Let T be the set of composite numbers which can be expressed as the product of primes in *more than* one way. (We would like to prove that $T = \varnothing$; this will be done by contradiction.) Assume $T \neq \varnothing$. Then, there exists a least composite k in T. Thus,

$$k = xzy \ldots = abc \ldots$$

where x, y, z, ..., a, b, c, ... are primes. Let us first show that since the two sets of prime factors are different, no *two* elements in each set of factors can be the same. If for example, $x = a$ then

$$yz \ldots = bc \ldots$$

are two different factorizations into primes of a composite less than k; this is contrary to the assumption that k was the least such composite.

Now, let us assume for

$$k = xyz \ldots = abc \ldots$$

that x is the least prime in the product $xyz \ldots$; hence, $x^2 \leq xy \leq k$. Similarly, $a^2 \leq k$ if a is the least prime in the product $abc \ldots$. Since $a \neq x$, $ax < k$, and $k - ax$ is a positive integer less than k and is expressible as the product of primes in only one way. Thus, since a and x are factors of k and since $a \neq x$, it follows that

$$k - ax = axuvw \ldots$$

where u, v, and w are primes. Thus

$$k = ax(1 + uvw \ldots)$$

and ax is a factor of k; this implies that

$$abc \ldots = ax(1 + uvw \ldots)$$

Hence, $$bc \ldots = x(1 + uvw \ldots)$$

and x is a factor of $bc \ldots$. Now, $bc \ldots$ is the unique prime factorization of a composite number less than k for which no factor is equal to x; this is impossible since x is a factor of the number. The assumption that T was not empty leads to a contradiction; thus, $T = \varnothing$ and each composite number can be expressed as the product of primes in only one way.

From a logical point of view, Parts 1 and 2 of the preceding theorem have an interesting difference. Although the proof of Part 1 is based on the definition of prime number, the well-ordering property, and the multiplicative properties for integers, Part 2 cannot be proved solely with these properties.

Consider the sequence 1, 4, 7, 10, 13, 16, 19, 22, 25, . . . where the general term is given by $3n - 2$, n a positive integer. Since

$$(3n - 2)^2 = 9n^2 - 12n + 4$$
$$= 9n^2 - 12n + 6 - 2$$
$$= 3(3n^2 - 4n + 2) - 2$$

the square of any number in this sequence is of the form $3N - 2$ where N is an integer and, therefore, is also a number in the sequence. In fact, let $3n - 2$ and $3m - 2$ be any two numbers in the sequence; then

$$(3n - 2)(3m - 2) = 9mn - 6m - 6n + 4$$
$$= 9mn - 6m - 6n + 6 - 2$$
$$= 3(3mn - 2m - 2n + 2) - 2$$

Hence, the product of any two numbers in the sequence is in the sequence. Let us define a *pseudo-prime* as any number in the sequence having only two distinct factors is the sequence; for example, 4, 7, 10, 13, 19, 22, 25, 31, etc., are pseudoprimes. Any other number in the sequence, except 1, is called *T-composite*. It is true that T-composites such as 16, 28, 40 in the sequence are expressible as the product of pseudo-primes. However, the decomposition (factorization) into pseudo-primes is not unique as observed by the pseudo-prime decompositions of 100:

$$100 = 4 \times 25 = 10 \times 10$$

EXERCISES

1. Express each of the following numbers as the product of primes:
   (a) 3,124   (b) 1,240   (c) 4,386
2. Is it true that if $a \mid bc$ then $a \mid b$ or $a \mid c$?
3. Is the theorem in Exercise 2 true if a is prime (no proof needed)?

4. Let $S_1 = \{5n - 1 \mid n$ is any positive integer$\}$
   $S_2 = \{5n - 2 \mid n$ is any positive integer$\}$
   $S_3 = \{5n - 3 \mid n$ is any positive integer$\}$
   $S_4 = \{5n - 4 \mid n$ is any positive integer$\}$
   $S_5 = \{5n \mid n$ is any positive integer$\}$
   (a) Is each set S_1, S_2, S_3, S_4, S_5 an arithmetic sequence?
   (b) Is $S_1 \cup S_2 \cup S_3 \cup S_4 \cup S_5$ the set of positive integers?

5. In Exercise 4, which sets, if any, do not contain any perfect squares?

6. Suppose a and b are integers and $a \mid b$ and $b \mid a$. What can you conclude about a and b?

7. Let $v = p_1 p_2 p_3 \, \ldots \, p_n$ be the product of any finite number of primes all of which are different from 3. Let $N = 4v + 3$. (a) Does N have 3 as a factor? (b) Does N have any of the primes $p_1, p_2, p_3, \ldots, p_n$ as a factor?

8. If x is a prime, why must $x = 2$ or be of the form $4k + 1$ or $4k + 3$ where k is a nonnegative integer?

9. Let $S = \{4k + 1 \mid k$ is a nonnegative integer$\}$. Is this set closed with respect to multiplication?

*10. Prove that there are infinitely many primes of the form $4k + 3$ where k is a nonnegative integer. *Hint:* See Exercises 7, 8, and 9 above. Assume there is a finite number of such primes and let them be denoted by $p_0, p_1, p_2, p_3, \ldots, p_n$. Since 3 is of the given form let $p_0 = 3$ and let $v = p_1 p_2 p_3 \, \ldots \, p_n$. Then, let $N = 4v + 3$. Now, N must have a prime factor. But none of 2, 3, $p_1, p_2, p_3, \ldots p_n$ are factors of N. But since neither 2 nor a number of the form $4k + 3$ is a prime factor of N then the prime factors must be of the form $4k + 1$. But the product of such primes would be of the form $4k + 1$ and not $4k + 3$.

11. Prove if $a \mid b$ and $a \mid c$, then $a \mid (b - c)$.

12. Prove if $a \mid b$ and $b \mid c$, then $a \mid c$.

13. Prove if $a \mid b$ or $a \mid c$, then $a \mid bc$.

14. Prove if $a \mid b$, then $a^2 \mid b^2$.

15. Prove if $a^2 \mid b^2$, then $a \mid b$.

16. Would the Fundamental Theorem of Arithmetic, as stated, be true if 1 were a prime?

17. Would the Fundamental Theorem of Arithmetic, as stated, be true if 1 were a composite number?

18. Show that the sequence $3n - 1$ where n is any positive integer contains no perfect squares. *Hint:*

   Let $\qquad S_1 = \{t \mid t = 3n$ where n is a positive integer$\}$

   let $\qquad S_2 = \{t \mid t = 3n - 1$ where n is a positive integer$\}$

   and let $\quad S_3 = \{t \mid t = 3n - 2$ where n is a positive integer$\}$

   Now, $S_1 \cup S_2 \cup S_3$ is the set of all positive integers. Prove if $x \in S_1$ then $x^2 \in S_1$, if $x \in S_2$ then $x^2 \in S_3$, and if $x \in S_3$ then $x^2 \in S_3$.

19. Prove that the arithmetic sequence 3, 7, 11, 15, 19, 23, . . . has no perfect squares. *Hint:* See Exercise 18.

*20. Prove that every *T*-composite in the sequence 4, 7, 10, 13, . . . is expressible as the product of pseudo-primes.

*21. Using the proof of Part 2 of the Fundamental Theorem of Arithmetic as a model, where would the proof "break down" in trying to prove that every *T*-composite in the sequence 4, 7, 10, 13, . . . could be expressed as the product of primes in only one way?

5. EUCLIDEAN ALGORITHM

In elementary school a student often considers a set with 25 objects and asks two questions such as the following.

1. How many sets with 4 objects each can be removed from the set?
2. How many objects are left after all sets with four objects have been removed?

Questions

These questions are equivalent to asking what is the largest multiple of 4 less than or equal to 25 and what is the difference between 25 and this multiple of 4. The student learns that these questions can be answered by repeated subtraction or by an algorithm called long division, or the division algorithm.

LONG DIVISION		REPEATED SUBTRACTIONS						
		1	2	3	4	5	6	$= q$
$6 = q$								
$4\,\overline{)\,25}$		25	21	17	13	9	5	
24		4	4	4	4	4	4	
$1 = r$		21	17	13	9	5	1	$= r$

If a and b are positive integers and $a > b$ then we can prove there exist unique integers q and r where $0 < q$ and $0 \le r < b$ such that

$$a = qb + r$$

The integer q is called the (incomplete) *quotient* in the long division of a by b and r is called the *remainder*. For example, in the long division of 25 by 4 the quotient is 6 and the remainder is 1. It is intuitively obvious that such integers q and r do exist and are unique. However, it is worthwhile to give proofs of these two facts since it is

quotient

remainder

another good opportunity to gain a better understanding of what constitutes a proof in mathematics.

Theorem. *If a and b are positive integers and $a > b$, then (1) there exist integers q and r where $0 < q$ and $0 \leq r < b$ such that $a = bq + r$ and (2) the integers q and r are unique.*

Proof: PART 1. Let S be the set of all multiples of b which are greater than a. Since

$$(a + 1)b = ab + b > ab \geq a$$

the multiple $(a + 1)b$ of b is greater than a and the set S is not empty. As a consequence of the important well-ordering property, we know that S contains a least element which is a multiple of b. Let tb be the least integer in S. Since tb is the least integer in S, $tb > a$ and $(t - 1)b \leq a$. Since $a > b$, we know that $t \neq 1$; for if $t = 1$ then $tb = b$ and $b > a$, a contradiction. Thus, $t > 1$ and $t - 1 > 0$; furthermore, $0 \leq a - (t - 1)b \leq b$. (In our example where $a = 25$, and $b = 4$, $S = \{28, 32, 36, 40, \ldots\}$ and $tb = 28$; furthermore, $t = 7$, $t - 1 = 6$, and $0 \leq 25 - 6(4) < 6$.)

Since $a = (t - 1)b + a - (t - 1)b$, by letting $q = t - 1$ and $r = a - (t - 1)b$ we have integers q and r where $q > 0$, $0 \leq r < b$, and $a = bq + r$.

PART 2. (Now that we have proved such integers q and r exist, let us prove that they are unique.) Assume integers q_1, q_2, r_1, and r_2 exist such that

$$a = q_1 b + r_1 \qquad \text{where } q_1 > 0 \text{ and } 0 \leq r_1 < b$$

and $\qquad a = q_2 b + r_2 \qquad \text{where } q_2 > 0 \text{ and } 0 \leq r_2 < b$

Thus,

$$a - r_1 = bq_1 \tag{1}$$

and $\qquad\qquad\qquad a - r_2 = bq_2 \tag{2}$

If $r_1 \neq r_2$, we may assume that $r_1 < r_2$ without loss of generality; hence, $0 < r_2 - r_1 < b$. Why? Subtracting Equation (2) from (1), we get

$$r_2 - r_1 = b(q_1 - q_2)$$

Since $r_2 - r_1$ is positive, $b(q_1 - q_2)$ is a positive multiple of b; that is, $b(q_1 - q_2) \geq b$. However, since $r_2 - r_1 < b$, this implies that $b(q_1 - q_2) < b$, a contradiction. Hence, $r_1 = r_2$.

If $r_1 = r_2$, then $b(q_1 - q_2) = 0$. Thus, since $b \neq 0$ we have that $q_1 - q_2 = 0$ and $q_1 = q_2$.

Let us now turn our attention to how the long division algorithm can be used to solve a rather important elementary problem. Let S be the set of factors of 426 and T be the set of factors of 768. We are interested in a routine method to find the greatest number in the set $S \cap T$; this number is the *greatest common factor* of 426 and 768 and is often denoted by g.c.f. In general, if a and b are any two positive integers and if S is the set of factors of a and T is the set of factors of b, then the greatest integer in $S \cap T$ is the greatest common factor of a and b. Since any positive integer has 1 as a factor, we know that $S \cap T$ is not empty; furthermore, since S and T are finite sets, $S \cap T$ is a finite set and has a greatest element. One way the g.c.f. can be obtained is by listing all of the elements in $S \cap T$ and then picking out the greatest number in the set; however, for a pair of numbers such as 27,868,484 and 33,164 this method is rather impractical. We now exhibit a routine method for finding the g.c.f. of 768 and 426 without the necessity of first finding all of the factors of each number.

$$
\begin{array}{r}
1 \\
426 \overline{)\,768} \\
426 \qquad 1 \\
\overline{342 \overline{)\,426}} \\
342 \qquad 4 \\
\overline{84 \overline{)\,342}} \\
336 \quad 14 \\
\text{g.c.f} = \quad 6 \overline{)\,84} \\
84 \\
\overline{0}
\end{array}
$$

We began by finding the quotient and remainder in the long division of 768 by 426. Thereafter, we divided each divisor by the corresponding remainder until we got a remainder of zero. We assert that the next to last remainder 6 is the greatest common factor of 426 and 768. We shall prove that this method can be used to find the g.c.f. of any given pair of positive integers a and b; the process is called the *euclidean algorithm*.

euclidean algorithm

Let a and b be positive integers where $a > b$. Since the remainder is always less than the divisor in each step of the euclidean algorithm, we know that the number of required divisions is finite.

The steps (divisions) in the euclidean algorithm are exhibited as follows.

STEP 1. $\quad\quad\quad a = bq_1 + r_1 \quad\quad\quad$ where $0 < r_1 < b$

STEP 2. $\quad\quad\quad b = r_1q_2 + r_2 \quad\quad\quad$ where $0 < r_2 < r_1$

STEP 3. $\quad\quad\quad r_1 = r_2q_3 + r_3 \quad\quad\quad$ where $0 < r_3 < r_2$

. . . .

STEP $(n-1)$. $\quad r_{n-3} = r_{n-2}q_{n-1} + r_{n-1} \quad$ where $0 < r_{n-1} < r_{n-2}$

STEP n. $\quad\quad\quad r_{n-2} = r_{n-1}q_n \quad\quad\quad$ where $r_n = 0$

We have assumed that in Step n that the remainder is zero. Let us prove that the greatest common factor of a and b is indeed r_{n-1}. Consider Step 1 where $a = bq_1 + r_1$. If G is any factor of a and b, then G is a factor of bq_1 and also the difference $a - bq_1$; that is, G is also a factor of r_1. Conversely, since any factor of b and r_1 is a factor of $bq_1 + r_1$, it follows that any factor of b and r_1 is a factor of a. Consequently, G is the *greatest* common factor of a and b if and only if it is the greatest common factor of b and r_1.

Similarly, we conclude from Step 2 that G is the greatest common factor of b and r_1 if and only if G is the greatest common factor of r_1 and r_2. Thus, the greatest common factor of a and b is the g.c.f. of r_1 and r_2, and conversely.

By Step 3, G is the g.c.f. of a and b if and only if G is the g.c.f. of r_2 and r_3. Continuing, we conclude that G is the greatest common factor of a and b if and only if it is the g.c.f. of r_{n-2} and r_{n-1}. Since $r_{n-2} = r_{n-1}q_n$, we have r_{n-1} is a factor of r_{n-2}; thus the greatest common factor G of r_{n-2} and r_{n-1} is r_{n-1}. Therefore, the g.c.f. of a and b is r_{n-1}.

If we want to find the g.c.f. of three given positive integers a, b, and c, then we could find the greatest common factor g of, say, a and b. Then, the greatest common factor of g and c is the g.c.f. of a, b, and c.

Now that the problem has been solved of finding a routine method to obtain the g.c.f. of a finite set of numbers without first finding all of the factors of each number, it is of interest to consider the number of steps required in the euclidean algorithm to find the g.c.f. of two given numbers. Since the remainder is always less than the divisor it is obvious that the number of steps is at most one less than the smaller of the two given numbers. If no better upper limit on the number of required divisions to find the g.c.f. could be obtained, then the euclidean algorithm, though having mathematical interest, might have to be disregarded as having much practical use. Fortunately, this is not the case and we are able to prove that for any pair of numbers not "unreasonably" large, the number of steps to find the g.c.f. is not prohibitive. In fact, we can prove that the number of divisions required cannot be more than five times the number of digits in the smaller of the two numbers. The proof of this fact, though not technically difficult, does require an ability to follow a deductive proof consisting of several steps and also requires some elementary knowledge of logarithms. (See Appendix B.)

For the positive integers 768 and 426, can we find two integers u and v (not necessarily positive) such that the sum $768u + 426v$ is the greatest common factor 6? The answer is "yes" and the euclidean algorithm gives us a routine method to find such integers. Notice that the steps on page 271 are equivalent to the following.

STEP 1. $\qquad\qquad 768 = (426)1 + 342$

STEP 2. $\qquad\qquad 426 = (342)1 + 84$

STEP 3. $\qquad\qquad 342 = (84)4 + 6$

STEP 4. $\qquad\qquad 84 = (6)14$

From Step 3, $6 = 342 - (84)4$; from Step 2, $84 = 426 - (342)1$. Substituting the second equality in the first, we get

$$6 = 342 - [426 - (342)1]4$$
$$6 = 342 - (426)4 + (342)4$$
$$6 = (342)5 - (426)4$$

From Step 1, $342 = 768 - (426)1$; substituting this in the last equality we get

$$6 = [768 - (426)1]5 - (426)4$$
$$6 = (768)5 - (426)5 - (426)4$$
$$6 = (768)5 + (426)(-9)$$

Obviously, if we let $u = 5$ and $v = -9$, then we have two integers u and v such that $768u + 426v$ is the greatest common factor of the two numbers.

The euclidean algorithm can be used to prove for any pair of positive integers a and b with G as their greatest common factor that there do exist integers u and v such that

$$G = au + bv$$

Let us prove that if $a > b$ and $r_4 = 0$ in the euclidean algorithm, such integers do exist. Since the number of steps in the euclidean algorithm is finite, it should be clear that the proof (though tedious) can be generalized to any number of steps. If $r_4 = 0$, recall that

STEP 1. $a = bq_1 + r_1$ where $0 < r_1 < b$

STEP 2. $b = r_1q_2 + r_2$ where $0 < r_2 < r_1$

STEP 3. $r_1 = r_2q_3 + r_3$ where $0 < r_3 < r_2$

STEP 4. $r_2 = r_3q_4$ where $r_4 = 0$

Since $G = r_3$ we have from Step 3 that

$$G = r_1 - r_2q_3$$

Solving the equality in Step 2 for r_2 and substituting in the last equality, we get

$$G = r_1 - [b - r_1q_2]q_3$$
$$G = r_1 - bq_3 + r_1q_2q_3$$

Solving the equality in Step 1 for r_1 and substituting in the last equality, we get

$$G = (a - bq_1) - bq_3 + (a - bq_1)q_2q_3$$
$$G = a - bq_1 - bq_3 + aq_2q_3 - bq_1q_2q_3$$
$$G = a(1 + q_2q_3) + b(-q_1 - q_3 - q_1q_2q_3)$$

Thus, $u = 1 + q_2q_3$ and $v = -q_1 - q_3 - q_1q_2q_3$ are two integers such that

$$G = au + bv$$

In our numerical example, $q_1 = 1$, $q_2 = 1$, $q_3 = 4$, and $q_4 = 14$. Notice that $1 + q_1q_3 = 1 + 4 = 5$ and $-q_1 - q_3 - q_1q_2q_3 = -1 - 4 - 4 = -9$ and the previous solution is obtained.

We saw in the last chapter that it need not be true that if $a \mid bc$ then $a \mid b$ or $a \mid c$. However, we can prove a similar theorem which is quite important and is a result of our last discovery.

Theorem. If p is a prime number and if $p \mid bc$, then $p \mid b$ or $p \mid c$.

Proof: The prime p is a factor of b or it is not. If it is a factor of b, then the theorem is true. Thus, suppose p is not a factor of b. Since p is a prime and is not a factor of b, the greatest common factor of the two numbers is 1. Therefore, there exist integers u and v such that

$$1 = pu + bv$$

Multiplying both sides by c,

$$c = pcu + bcv$$

By assumption $p \mid bc$ so $p \mid bcv$. Obviously, $p \mid pcu$. Consequently,

$$p \mid (pcu + bcv)$$

that is, $p \mid c$.

EXERCISES

In Exercises 1 through 6, find the g.c.f. of the given set of numbers by using the euclidean algorithm.

1. $\{2,096; 22,225\}$
2. $\{11,104; 12,145\}$
3. $\{1,712; 4,815\}$
4. $\{3,133; 4,097\}$
5. $\{17,186; 33,711\}$
6. $\{18,929; 28,805\}$

7. Find the greatest common factor of 168 and 889 and then find integers u and v such that $G = 889u + 168v$.

8. Find the greatest common factor G of 84 and 194 and then find integers u and v such that $G = 194u + 84v$.

9. Assume $a \mid bc$ and that a and b have no common factor other than 1 and -1. Prove that $a \mid c$.

10. (a) Assume that $r_5 = 0$ in the euclidean algorithm and find integers u and v in terms of the successive quotients q_1, q_2, q_3, and q_4 such that $G = au + bv$.

    (b) Show that part (a) applies in finding the greatest common factor G of 889 and 1946, and determine a pair of integers u and v such that $G = 1,946u + 889v$.

11. (a) Let $a = b$ and show that there exist integers u and v such that $G = au + bv$ where G is the greatest common factor of a and b.

    (b) Can we now conclude that if a and b are any positive integers that there exist integers u and v such that $G = au + bv$ where G is the g.c.f. of a and b?

12. Find integers u and v such that $G = 10,731u + 3,285v$ where G is the greatest common factor of 3,285 and 10,731.

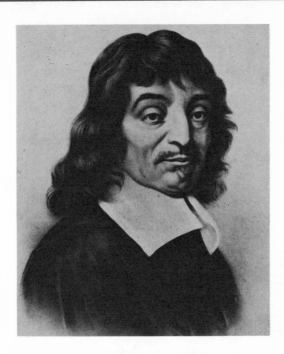

René Descartes (1596–1650)

René Descartes was born on March 31, 1596 near Tours, France. Along with Fermat and Pascal, he is ranked as one of the foremost French mathematicians of the seventeenth century; the century when other men such as Galileo, Newton, Kepler, Shakespeare, and Milton were achieving fame in the arts and sciences. Besides his contributions to mathematics, Descartes wrote a text on physiology, studied psychology, and greatly influenced the development of modern philosophy.

In mathematics Descartes is most widely known for establishing the field of analytic geometry. His treatise, *La Géométrie,* published in 1637, made known his important results in this field. The development of analytic geometry brought about a unification of algebra and geometry, and from this foundation the important ideas of calculus would later follow.

Although he was neither very healthy nor physically strong, he did indulge in an active life for many years. Besides spending some rakish years in Paris, he chose on several occasions to get involved in the wars of the period. The 19 year old Queen Christina of Sweden tried for a year, after hearing of the famous Descartes, to get him to join her retinue of intellectuals. He managed to ignore the invitation until she flattered him by sending a battleship for him to make the journey. Just eleven weeks after arriving in Sweden and confronting the bitter weather, he contracted influenza and died. He was 54.

11

Analytic Geometry

1. Introduction
2. The Coordinate Plane
3. Lines and Circles
4. Relations and Functions
5. Linear Programming (Optional)

Analytic geometry, far more than any of his metaphysical speculations, immortalized the name of Descartes, and constitutes the greatest single step ever made in the progress of the exact sciences.

JOHN STUART MILL

1. INTRODUCTION

The development of analytic geometry contributed greatly to the mathematical revolution that took place in the seventeenth and eighteenth centuries; in turn, the developments of the seventeenth and eighteenth centuries helped to initiate the Golden Age of mathematics, the nineteenth century. John Stuart Mill's statement that "analytic geometry constitutes the greatest single step ever made in the progress of the exact sciences" might be an overstatement, but he was certainly correct when he said that analytic geometry "immortalized the name of Descartes."

By now, the student should have sufficient insight into how mathematics is developed to prompt a healthy suspicion of crediting one mathematician with being the sole inventor of a new subject field. The beginnings of analytic geometry can be traced back to the Greeks, Romans, and to Arab mathematicians such as Omar Khayyam. Most likely, Pierre Fermat did as much original work in analytic geometry as did Descartes, but Fermat published few of his results. In 1637, Descartes published his treatise entitled *La Géométrie;* it achieved for him most of the credit for being the "father" of analytic geometry. Analytic geometry is also referred to as *coordinate geometry,* or *cartesian geometry* in honor of Descartes.

cartesian geometry

Generally speaking, until the time of Descartes, no one regarded algebra and geometry as related fields of mathematics. Today, many familiar theorems can be considered in either setting. For example, the famous pythagorean theorem can be considered in a purely geometric setting or it can be associated with the familiar algebraic expression $x^2 + y^2 = z^2$. The merging of algebra and geometry into analytic geometry provides an enormous enrichment of both subjects and opens many new mathematical vistas to pursue. In fact, the development of calculus flows naturally from the reservoir of mathematical knowledge created by the advent of analytic geometry.

278

2. THE COORDINATE PLANE

As we know, the set of real numbers are paired in a one-to-one fashion with the points on the number line. The set of all *ordered pairs* of real numbers (x, y) can be put into one-to-one correspondence with the points in a plane in the following manner.

In the plane, draw two number lines, one horizontal and one vertical, intersecting at right angles at their origins. (See Figure 11.1.) *coordinate axes* The usual orientation is to have the positive numbers associated with points to the right of the origin on the horizontal number line and with points above the origin on the vertical number line. The two *x axis* number lines are called *coordinate axes*. The horizontal coordinate axis is called the *x axis,* or *first coordinate axis,* and the vertical coordinate axis is called the *y axis,* or *second coordinate axis.* *y axis*

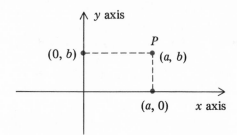

Cartesian Coordinate System in the Plane

FIGURE 11.1

With a point on the *x* axis whose coordinate is *a*, we associate the ordered pair $(a, 0)$. With a point on the *y* axis whose coordinate is *b*, we associate the ordered pair $(0, b)$. If *P* is any point in the plane not on either coordinate axis, if $(a, 0)$ represents the point at the foot of the perpendicular from *P* to the *x* axis, and if $(0, b)$ represents the point at the foot of the perpendicular drawn from *P* to the *y* axis, then the ordered pair (a, b) is paired with the point *P*. This gives us a method to associate a unique point with any ordered pair of real numbers. Similarly, given any ordered pair (a, b) of real numbers we use the technique in reverse to find a unique point in the coordinate plane associated with it. Hence, one and only one point in the coordinate plane is associated with an ordered pair of real numbers. The *cartesian* coordinate system is called the *rectangular coordinate system,* or *car-* *coordinate* *tesian coordinate system.* *system*

If (a, b) and (c, d) are two points in the coordinate plane, then it is easy to use Figure 11.2 and the pythagorean theorem to prove that the distance *D* between the two points is given by

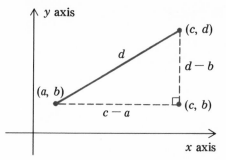

Distance Formula: $D = \sqrt{(c-a)^2 + (d-b)^2}$

FIGURE 11.2

$$D = \sqrt{(c-a)^2 + (d-b)^2}$$

Let (a, b) and (c, d) be two distinct points in the coordinate plane and let (x, y) be the ordered pair associated with the midpoint of the line segment joining the two given points. We can use the distance formula and techniques of algebra to find x and y in terms of a, b, c, and d, but it is much easier to consider Figure 11.3 and recall the fact from plane geometry that if parallel lines cut off equal segments on one transversal then they cut off equal segments on any other transversal. Then, using the fact that the midpoint between two points on the real number line is the arithmetic mean of the two numbers, we

midpoint   see that the *midpoint* of the line segment is

$$\left(\frac{a+c}{2}, \frac{b+d}{2} \right)$$

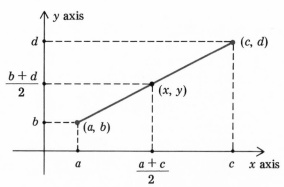

Midpoint: $\left(\dfrac{a+c}{2}, \dfrac{b+d}{2} \right)$

FIGURE 11.3

If (a, b) and (c, d) are two points in the plane such that $a \neq c$ (that is, a line containing the two points is not parallel to the y axis), then we define the *slope* of the line containing (a, b) and (c, d) to be $\quad$ *slope*

$$\frac{d - b}{c - a}$$

The slope, generally denoted by m, corresponds roughly to the *grade* of a highway; it gives the ratio of vertical rise to horizontal distance traversed. However, it is easy to see that although lines "leaning to the right" have positive slope, lines "leaning to the left" have negative slope. (See Figure 11.4.) As a result of the slope definition, a line parallel to the x axis has zero slope; for a line parallel to the y axis, slope is not defined (the denominator in the slope formula would be zero).

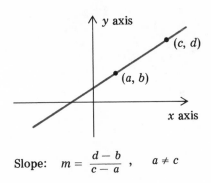

Slope: $\quad m = \dfrac{d - b}{c - a}, \quad a \neq c$

FIGURE 11.4

By using elementary properties of plane geometry, it is not difficult to prove that two different nonvertical lines are parallel if and only if they have the same slope.

With just the few tools at hand from analytic geometry, we can readily prove theorems from plane geometry whose purely geometric (synthetic) proofs are not so easy.

Example 1. Prove that the segments joining the midpoints of successive sides of any quadrilateral is a parallelogram. (A synthetic proof of this theorem is not very difficult, but an analytic proof is quite instructive.) Given any quadrilateral in a plane, let us introduce a coordinate system into the plane. Generally, the way the coordinate system is introduced can simplify a proof. In this case, the best approach is to choose one vertex at the origin of the coordinate system in such a way that one side coincides with the positive x axis. (See Figure 11.5.) With this orientation, the vertices of any quadrilateral will have coordinates of the form $(0, 0)$, $(a, 0)$,

(b, c), and (d, e). The midpoint A of side PQ has coordinates $(a/2, 0)$; the midpoint B of QR is $\left(\dfrac{a+b}{2}, \dfrac{c}{2}\right)$; the midpoint C of RS is $\left(\dfrac{b+d}{2}, \dfrac{c+e}{2}\right)$; and the midpoint D of SP is $(d/2, e/2)$. The line containing points A and B has slope

$$\frac{c/2 - 0}{(a+b)/2 - a/2} = \frac{c}{b}$$

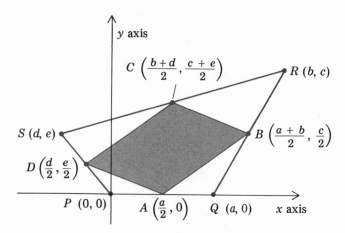

Quadrilateral $PQRS$; Parallelogram $ABCD$

FIGURE 11.5

Similarly, the line containing points C and D has slope c/b. Since the slopes of the two lines are equal, the lines are parallel. In exactly the same way, we can prove that the line containing A and D is parallel to the line containing B and C. Thus, the quadrilateral $ABCD$ is a parallelogram. After having shown that AB and CD are parallel, another way to prove that $ABCD$ is a parallelogram is to prove that the lengths of the line segments AB and CD are equal. (We leave this as an exercise for the student.)

Example 2. For any triangle, prove that the sum of the squares of the lengths of the medians is equal to three-fourths the sum of the squares of the lengths of the sides. (The analytic proof is basically quite easy, but not short; in addition to the ideas of this section, it requires only elementary techniques of algebra. The student would probably find a purely geometric proof rather difficult.)

Solution: We can introduce a coordinate system in such a way that the coordinates of the vertices of any triangle are of the form $(0, 0)$, $(a, 0)$, and (b, c) where a, b, and c are real numbers. (See Figure 11.6.) The mid-

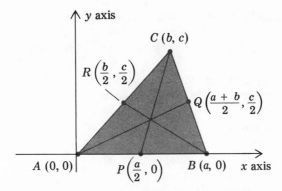

Triangle ABC

FIGURE 11.6

points of the sides of triangle ABC are P, Q, and R with coordinates $\left(\dfrac{a}{2}, 0\right)$, $\left(\dfrac{a+b}{2}, \dfrac{c}{2}\right)$, and $\left(\dfrac{b}{2}, \dfrac{c}{2}\right)$, respectively. Using the distance formula, we obtain

$$|AB|^2 = a^2$$
$$|BC|^2 = (b-a)^2 + c^2 = b^2 - 2ab + a^2 + c^2$$
$$|AC|^2 = b^2 + c^2$$

Thus, $\quad \frac{3}{4}(|AB|^2 + |BC|^2 + |AC|^2) = \frac{3}{2}(a^2 + b^2 + c^2 - ab)$
Similarly,

$$|PC|^2 = \left(b - \frac{a}{2}\right)^2 + c^2 = \frac{4b^2 - 4ab + a^2 + 4c^2}{4}$$

$$|QA|^2 = \left(\frac{a+b}{2}\right)^2 + \left(\frac{c}{2}\right)^2 = \frac{a^2 + 2ab + b^2 + c^2}{4}$$

$$|RB|^2 = \left(\frac{b}{2} - a\right)^2 + c^2 = \frac{b^2 - 4ab + 4a^2 + c^2}{4}$$

Thus, $\quad |PC|^2 + |QA|^2 + |RB|^2 = \dfrac{6b^2 - 6ab + 6a^2 + 6c^2}{4}$

$$= \frac{3}{2}(a^2 + b^2 + c^2 - ab)$$

EXERCISES

1. In Example 1, show that the line containing A and D is parallel to the line containing B and C.

2. In Example 1, show that the lengths of line segments AB and CD are equal.

3. Use the pythagorean theorem to prove that the points $(-3, -1)$, $(2, 5)$, and $(5, \frac{5}{2})$ are vertices of a right triangle.

4. Determine if the points $(1, 1)$, $(3, 4)$, and $(2, 5)$ are vertices of a right triangle.

5. Use the pythagorean theorem to prove that the points $(-4, 10)$, $(18, 6)$, and $(2, -2)$ are vertices of a right triangle.

6. Determine if the points $(1, 1)$, $(5, 7)$, and $(-6, 10)$ are vertices of an isosceles triangle.

7. Determine if the points $(2, 3)$, $(6, 7)$, and $(3, 6)$ are vertices of an isosceles triangle.

8. Determine if the points $(3, 3)$, $(3, 7)$, and $(3 + 2\sqrt{3}, 5)$ are vertices of an equilateral triangle.

9. Suppose A, B, and C are points in the coordinate plane with coordinates $(-3, -4)$, $(3, 0)$, and $(12, 6)$, respectively. Prove that the sum of the distances from A to B and B to C is the distance from A to C. Interpret geometrically.

10. Determine if $(1, 3)$, $(6, 13)$, and $(2, 3)$ are collinear points in the coordinate plane.

11. Determine if $(2, -1)$, $(4, 5)$, and $(-1, -10)$ are collinear points in the coordinate plane.

12. Use the distance formula to prove that the point $(-3, 10)$ is on the perpendicular bisector of the line segment joining $(1, -3)$ and $(8, 2)$.

13. (a) For any parallelogram, show that a coordinate system can be introduced in the plane so that the coordinates of the vertices are $(0, 0)$, $(a, 0)$, (b, c), and $(a + b, c)$.

    (b) Prove that the diagonals of a parallelogram bisect each other by finding the coordinates of the midpoint of each diagonal.

14. Using slopes and the distance formula, *derive* the formula for the coordinates of the midpoint of the line segment joining two distinct points (a, b) and (c, d).

15. Let (a, b) and (c, d) be the coordinates of two different points in the coordinate plane. Find the coordinates of the point two-thirds of the distance from (a, b) to (c, d) on the segment joining the two points.

*16. Prove that the medians of a triangle meet in a point that is two-thirds the distance from each vertex to the midpoint of the opposite side. (See Exercise 15.)

3. LINES AND CIRCLES

graph

Let S be any set of ordered pairs of real numbers. The collection of points in the coordinate plane corresponding to the ordered pairs is called the *graph* of the set. Often, a set of ordered pairs is defined by an equation. For example, let S be the set of all ordered pairs of real numbers satisfying $3x + 5y = 15$; that is, let $S = \{(x, y) \mid 3x + 5y = 15\}$. The graph of S is called the *graph of the equation*. By plotting several points from S, it will appear that the graph is a straight line. In fact, we can prove that the graph in the plane of any linear equation $Ax + By = C$ where A and B are not both zero is a straight line. Knowing that the graph of a linear equation is a straight line makes it possible for us to determine the graph of $3x + 5y = 15$ by finding just two ordered pairs of real numbers satisfying the equation. (See Figure 11.7.)

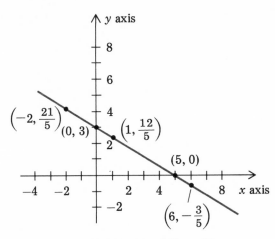

Graph of $3x + 5y = 15$

FIGURE 11.7

Given a set of points T in the coordinate plane, if we can find an equation in x and y such that $(x, y) \in T$ if and only if the ordered pair (x, y) satisfies the equation, then the equation is called the *equation of the graph*. Given an arbitrary graph in the coordinate plane, two things should be obvious: (1) It might be that no equation for the graph exists. (2) Finding an equation, if it does exist, could be a difficult task. Fortunately, equations for many basic plane curves can be determined in a simple and routine manner.

equation of the graph

Let (a, b) and (c, d) be any two points in the coordinate plane where $b \neq d$ and let S be the set of points on the line containing the two points. Let (x, y) be any point on S different from (a, b). (See Figure 11.8.) Since the line containing (a, b) and (c, d) is coincident with the line containing (a, b) and (x, y), the slopes $\dfrac{d - b}{c - a}$ and $\dfrac{y - b}{x - a}$

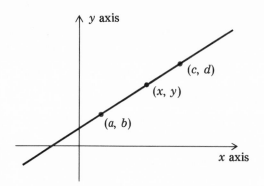

Equation of line containing (a, b) and (c, d):

$$y = \frac{d-b}{c-a}(x-a) + b, \quad a \neq c$$

FIGURE 11.8

are the same. Hence,

$$\frac{y-b}{x-a} = \frac{d-b}{c-a}$$

and
$$y = \frac{d-b}{c-a}(x-a) + b$$

We can show that a point (x, y) not on the line containing (a, b) and (c, d) does not satisfy the above equation. Hence, $y = m(x-a) + b$ is an equation of the line containing the points (a, b) and (c, d) where m represents the slope of the line.

Example 1. Find the equation of the line containing $(2, 3)$ and $(5, 7)$.

Solution: The slope of the line is $(7-3)/(5-2) = \frac{4}{3}$. Using the point $(2, 3)$, we obtain $y = \frac{4}{3}(x-2) + 3$, or $4x - 3y = -1$. [*Note:* If we had used the point $(5, 7)$ in the formula, we would have obtained $y = \frac{4}{3}(x-5) + 7$, or $4x - 3y = -1$ which is, of course, the same result.]

We can use $y = m(x-a) + b$ to determine the equation of a line whether we are given two points or a point and the slope of the line. If we are given a slope and the point where the line intersects the y axis (that is, the y intercept), then $a = 0$ and we obtain $y = mx + b$ which is called the *slope-intercept form* for the equation of a line. From $y = m(x-a) + b$, we obtain $(-m)x + y = b - ma$. Thus, an equation of a line not parallel to the y axis has the form $Ax + By = C$. If $B \neq 0$, it is not difficult to prove that the points in the plane whose coordinates satisfy an equation $Ax + By = C$ lie on a line

$y = mx + b$

286

not parallel to the y axis.

Now let us turn our attention to circles in the plane. If (h, k) is any point in the coordinate plane, then the collection of all points (x, y) in the plane at distance r from (h, k) is a circle with radius r. Therefore, using the distance formula we obtain

$$\sqrt{(x-h)^2 + (y-k)^2} = r$$

or $$(x-h)^2 + (y-k)^2 = r^2$$

Thus, the ordered pair of real numbers representing any point on the circle satisfies the equation; it is not difficult to show that the coordinates of points not on the circle do not satisfy the equation. Hence, an equation of the circle with center at (h, k) and radius r is

$$(x-h)^2 + (y-k)^2 = r^2$$

Since $(x-h)^2 + (y-k)^2 = r^2$ is an equivalent equation to $x^2 - 2hx + h^2 + y^2 - 2ky + k^2 = r^2$, we see that the equation of a circle has the form

$$x^2 + y^2 + Dx + Ey = F$$

Notice we did not say that every equation of this form represents a circle. There are some restrictions on the constants D, E, and F. For example, if $D = 0$, $E = 0$ then no ordered pair of *real* numbers would satisfy the equation $x^2 + y^2 = F$ if F is negative; if $F = 0$, then the point $(0, 0)$ is the graph of the equation.

Let us again bridge the gap between algebra and geometry and show how ideas of geometry complement the concepts of algebra. Consider a line and a circle in the coordinate plane. (See Figure 11.9.) Corresponding to the graphs are a linear equation $Ax + By = C$ and a quadratic equation $x^2 + y^2 + Dx + Ey = F$. Geometri-

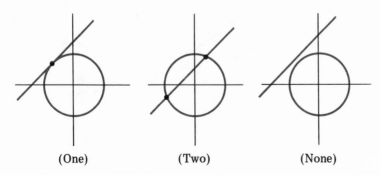

(One)   (Two)   (None)

Real Solutions

FIGURE 11.9

cally, it is easy to see that the line may not intersect the circle, it may intersect the circle in one point (when it is a tangent line), or it may intersect the circle in two points. Algebraically, this would be equivalent to stating that the simultaneous solution of the two equations might have no *real* roots, one pair of real roots, or two pairs of real roots. Furthermore, the system could have at most two pairs of real roots since the line can intersect the circle in at most two points.

We know that nonvertical parallel lines have the same slope. Let us prove that perpendicular lines have negative reciprocal slopes if neither line is vertical. Let L_1 and L_2 be two perpendicular lines in the coordinate plane such that neither is parallel to the y axis. Thus, the equations of L_1 and L_2 have the form $y = m_1 x + b_1$ and $y = m_2 x + b_2$ where m_1 is the slope of L_1 and m_2 is the slope of L_2. Since the lines are not parallel, $m_1 \neq m_2$; furthermore, since neither is parallel to the x axis (or the line perpendicular to it would be parallel to the y axis), $m_1 m_2 \neq 0$. Let the intersection point P of the two lines have coordinates (s, t). (See Figure 11.10.) Since $t = m_1 s + b_1$ and $t = m_2 s + b_2$, it follows that $b_1 - b_2 = s(m_2 - m_1)$. The points Q and R, where the graphs of L_1 and L_2 intersect the y axis, have coordinates $(0, b_1)$ and $(0, b_2)$, respectively. Triangle PQR is a right triangle if and only if

$$|PR|^2 + |PQ|^2 = |QR|^2$$

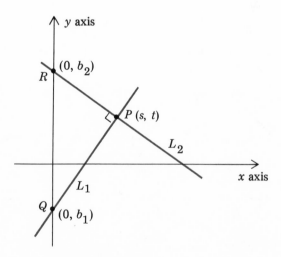

L_1 perpendicular to L_2: $m_1 m_2 = -1$

FIGURE 11.10

Using the distance formula,

$$|PR|^2 = (s - 0)^2 + (m_2 s + b_2 - b_2)^2 = s^2 + m_2^2 s^2$$
$$|PQ|^2 = (s - 0)^2 + (m_1 s + b_1 - b_1)^2 = s^2 + m_1^2 s^2$$

and $\quad |QR|^2 = (b_1 - b_2)^2$

Since $b_1 - b_2 = s(m_2 - m_1)$, $|QR|^2 = s^2(m_2 - m_1)^2$. Hence, PQR is a right triangle if and only if

$$s^2 + m_2^2 s^2 + s^2 + m_1^2 s^2 = s^2 (m_2 - m_1)^2$$

Assuming that $s \neq 0$, $1 + m_2^2 + 1 + m_1^2 = m_2^2 - 2m_1 m_2 + m_1^2$

thus, $\qquad\qquad\qquad 2m_1 m_2 = -2$

and $\qquad\qquad\qquad m_1 = -\dfrac{1}{m_2}$

(We leave as an exercise for the student to prove the theorem when $s = 0$.)

Let us use the available tools to find the equation of the tangent to the circle $x^2 + y^2 = 25$ at the point $(3, 4)$ on the circle. Recall from plane geometry, that a tangent line to a circle is perpendicular to a radius drawn to the point of tangency. The line containing the radius from $(0, 0)$ to $(3, 4)$ has slope $\frac{4}{3}$; hence, the tangent line has slope $-\frac{3}{4}$. Since the tangent line contains the point $(3, 4)$, the equation is

$$y = -\tfrac{3}{4}(x - 3) + 4$$

or $\qquad\qquad\qquad 3x + 4y = 25$

EXERCISES

1. Graph each of the following equations:
   (a) $4x + 3y = 24$ $\qquad\qquad$ (b) $x - 2y = 8$
2. Graph each of the following equations:
   (a) $8x - y = 8$ $\qquad\qquad$ (b) $2x + 3y = 9$
3. What is an equation of the line containing $(5, 3)$ and $(8, 5)$?
4. What is an equation of the line containing $(-3, 2)$ and $(4, 9)$?
5. What is an equation of the line with slope $\frac{2}{3}$ and containing the point $(-3, 7)$?
6. What is an equation of the line with slope $-\frac{9}{5}$ and containing the point $(4, 7)$?

7. What is an equation of the line with slope $5/7$ and containing the origin of the coordinate plane?

8. (a) Graph $3x + 5y = 8$ and $x - 2y = -1$ in the same coordinate plane.
(b) Determine algebraically the pair of real numbers which satisfy both equations.

9. (a) Graph $4x - y = 5$ and $2x + 5y = 9$ in the same coordinate plane.
(b) Determine algebraically the pair of real numbers which satisfy both equations.

10. Use slopes to determine if the points $(1, 1)$, $(3, 4)$, and $(2, 5)$ are vertices of a right triangle.

11. Use slopes to prove that the points $(-4, 10)$, $(18, 6)$, and $(2, -2)$ are vertices of a right triangle.

12. What is an equation of the line parallel to $2x - 3y = 7$ and containing the point $(5, -4)$?

13. What is an equation of the line parallel to $5x + 6y = 11$ and containing the point $(3, 9)$?

14. What is an equation of the line perpendicular to $3x + 4y = 12$ and containing the point $(2, -1)$?

15. What is an equation of the line perpendicular to $5x - 12y = 4$ and containing the point $(7, 3)$?

16. Find an equation of the perpendicular bisector of the line segment joining $(3, 5)$ and $(9, 8)$ by the following two methods.
(a) Use the fact that any point (x, y) is on the perpendicular bisector if and only if the distances to the given points are equal.
(b) Find the midpoint of the segment, determine the slope of the perpendicular bisector and use the point slope formula.

17. Find an equation of the perpendicular bisector of the line segment joining $(-2, 7)$ and $(1, 4)$ by two methods. (See Exercise 16.)

18. Let L_1 be the graph of $3x + 4y = 10$ and let L_2 be the graph of $3x - y = 5$.
(a) Graph L_1 and L_2 in the same coordinate plane.
(b) Graph with L_1 and L_2 each of the five lines obtained from $(3x + 4y - 10) + k(3x - y - 5) = 0$ by letting $k = -2, -1, 1, 3,$ and 5.

19. Determine an equation of the line containing the point $(1, 2)$ and the intersection of $3x + 5y = 11$ and $2x - 3y = 3$.

20. Give an equation of the circle with center at $(-2, 3)$ and radius 6.

21. Give an equation of the circle with center at $(3, -4)$ and radius 4.

22. Give an equation of the circle with center at $(2, 1)$ and containing the point $(5, 7)$.

23. Give an equation of the circle with center at $(-3, 7)$ and containing the point $(5, 8)$.

*24. Determine an equation of the circle containing the three points $(3, 4)$, $(9, 12)$, and $(10, 5)$ by each of the following methods.
(a) Use the fact that all three points must satisfy an equation of the form $x^2 + y^2 + Dx + Ey = F$.

(b) Use the fact that the center is at the intersection of the perpendicular bisectors of the sides of the triangle formed.

*25. Determine an equation of the circle containing the three points $(-5, 5)$, $(2, 6)$, and $(3, -1)$ by two methods. (See Exercise 24.)

4. RELATIONS AND FUNCTIONS

In the last section, our attention was focused on sets of ordered pairs of real numbers which satisfied equations of the form $Ax + By = C$ and $x^2 + y^2 + Dx + Ey = F$; their graphs were lines and circles.

Although sets of ordered pairs of real numbers defined by equations are extremely important in mathematics, sets of ordered pairs defined in other ways also deserve our attention. Consider the following sets.

$f_1 = \{(1, 3), (2, 5), (3, 6), (6, -2)\}$
$f_2 = \{(1, 3), (2, 3), (8, 3), (-3, 3)\}$
$f_3 = \{(1, 4), (1, 5), (2, 0), (0, 6)\}$
$f_4 = \{(x, y) \mid x \text{ and } y \text{ are real numbers and } 2x + 3y = 7\}$
$f_5 = \{(x, y) \mid x \text{ and } y \text{ are real numbers and } y = x^3\}$
$f_6 = \{(x, y) \mid x \text{ and } y \text{ are real numbers and } y^2 = x\}$
$f_7 = \{(x, y) \mid y = 1 \text{ for rational } x \text{ and } y = -1 \text{ for irrational } x\}$

We see that the graphs of each of f_1, f_2, and f_3 consist of exactly four points in the plane. The graph of f_4 is a straight line. The graph of f_7 is "two parallel lines full of holes"; for example, $(3, 1) \in f_7$, $(5/7, 1) \in f_7$, $(-2/3, 1) \in f_7$, $(\sqrt{2}, -1) \in f_7$, $(\pi, -1) \in f_7$, and $(-\sqrt{3}, -1) \in f_7$. The graphs of f_5 and f_6 are given in Figure 11.11.

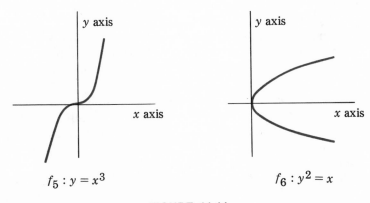

$f_5 : y = x^3$ $f_6 : y^2 = x$

FIGURE 11.11

relation

domain

range

function

Any set of ordered pairs (of real numbers) is called a (real) *relation*. The set of all first elements in a relation is called the *domain* of the relation; the set of all second elements is called the *range*. We can consider the set of orthogonal (perpendicular) projections onto the x axis of all points on the graph of a relation as the domain of the relation; similarly, we can consider the set of orthogonal projections onto the y axis of all points on the graph of a relation as the range. Sometimes, we refer to the x axis as the *domain axis* and the y axis as the *range axis*.

Let D_i and R_i denote the domain and range, respectively, of the relation f_i where $i = 1, 2, 3, 4, 5, 6, 7$. The following is a list of the domain and range of each given relation.

$D_1 = \{1, 2, 3, 6\}$ $R_1 = \{3, 5, 6, -2\}$
$D_2 = \{1, 2, 8, -3\}$ $R_2 = \{3\}$
$D_3 = \{1, 2, 0\}$ $R_3 = \{4, 5, 0, 6\}$
$D_4 = \{\text{All real numbers}\}$ $R_4 = \{\text{All real numbers}\}$
$D_5 = \{\text{All real numbers}\}$ $R_5 = \{\text{All real numbers}\}$
$D_6 = \{\text{All nonnegative reals}\}$ $R_6 = \{\text{All real numbers}\}$
$D_7 = \{\text{All real numbers}\}$ $R_7 = \{-1, 1\}$

Our examples clearly show that the domain and range of a relation need not have the same number of elements. In fact, one set may be infinite and the other finite.

Making a study of relations by investigating various types is not only worthwhile but nearly essential since the number of all possible relations (in the plane) is not finite. One of the most important types of relations is a function. A *function* is a relation such that no two pairs have the same first elements. Geometrically, a function is a relation in the plane such that each line parallel to the y axis intersects the graph in *at most* one point. Of our seven examples of relations, f_1, f_2, f_4, f_5, and f_7 are functions.

For a function f, we use "$f(x)$" (read "f of x," or "the value of f at x") to denote the number in the range of f which is paired with x in the domain. For example, $f_1(1) = 3$, $f_1(2) = 5$, $f_1(3) = 6$, and $f_1(6) = -2$.

We define the *square root function*, for example, by the equation $f(x) = \sqrt{x}$ with the understanding that the domain is any real number for which $\sqrt{x}$ is a real number. Thus, the domain of f contains any nonnegative real number; the range is also the set of nonnegative real numbers.

In elementary algebra, a study is made of such functions as the polynomial functions $[f(x) = 3x^4 - 5x^3 + 7x^2 + 3x - 2]$, the rational functions $\left[g(x) = \dfrac{3x^2 + 1}{2x + 5}\right]$, the algebraic functions $[h(x) =$

$\sqrt{x^2 + 1} + 3x]$, the exponential functions $[F(x) = 10^x]$, and the logarithm functions $[G(x) = \log_{10} x]$. Trigonometry is devoted to a study of the trigonometric functions: sine, cosine, tangent, secant, cosecant, cotangent. As the set of all relations is separated into various types (subsets) for a systematic study, so is the set of all functions.

For the purpose of introducing the basic concepts of calculus, we need little more than the basic ideas normally obtained in high school concerning the algebraic functions. One idea we do need that may be unfamiliar to the student is that of maximum (or minimum) value of a function.

A function f is said to have a *maximum value* if and only if there is a real number v in the domain such that $f(v) \geq f(x)$ for each x in the domain. We say the maximum value is *at v* and the maximum value *is $f(v)$*. In our examples of *functions*,

maximum value

f_1 has a maximum value at 3; the maximum value is 6.
f_2 has a maximum value at each point in its domain; the maximum value is 3.
f_4 has no maximum value.
f_5 has no maximum value.
f_7 has a maximum value at each rational number; the maximum value is 1.

Although the maximum value of a function is unique, the point in the domain which makes the function a maximum need not be unique.

Similarly, a function f is said to have a *minimum value* if and only if there is a real number u in the domain such that $f(u) \leq f(x)$ for each x in the domain. We say the minimum value is *at u* and the minimum value *is $f(u)$*. In our examples of functions,

minimum value

f_1 has a minimum value at 6; the minimum value is -2.
f_2 has a minimum value at each point in its domain; the minimum value is 3.
f_4 has no minimum value.
f_5 has no minimum value.
f_7 has a minimum value at each irrational number; the minimum value is -1.

Obviously, our examples of functions were carefully selected. In general, it is not so easy to determine by inspection the maximum (or minimum) value of a function, if it exists. Occasionally, when the maximum (or minimum) value of a function cannot be determined immediately by inspection, it can be found by elementary techniques from algebra. For example, let us determine the maximum and minimum values, if they exist, of the function f defined by $f(x) = x^2 + 9x + 17$. Our past experiences should tell us that the function has no maximum value since $f(x)$ can be made arbitrarily "large" by choosing x "large." But the function does have minimum value and it can be found by the algebraic technique of "completing the square."

$$f(x) = x^2 + 9x + 17$$
$$= x^2 + 9x + {}^{81}/_4 + 17 - {}^{81}/_4$$
$$= (x + {}^9/_2)^2 - {}^{13}/_4$$

Since $(x + {}^9/_2)^2$ is nonnegative for each real number x, $f(x) \geq -{}^{13}/_4$. Since $f(-{}^9/_2) = -{}^{13}/_4$, the function has $-{}^{13}/_4$ as its minimum value at $-{}^9/_2$. (See Figure 11.12.)

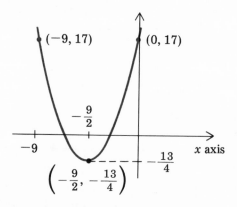

Graph of $f(x) = x^2 + 9x + 17$

FIGURE 11.12

Considering the previous example, the mathematical approach would be to solve, if possible, the associated general problem. For example, let f be the function defined by

$$f(x) = ax^2 + bx + c \qquad \text{where } a > 0$$

Then,
$$f(x) = a\left(x^2 + \frac{b}{a}x\right) + c$$

$$= a\left(x^2 + \frac{b}{a}x + \frac{b^2}{4a^2}\right) + c - \frac{b^2}{4a}$$

$$= a\left(x + \frac{b}{2a}\right)^2 + \frac{4ac - b^2}{4a}$$

With an analysis similar to the one given in the example, we conclude that f has a minimum value at $-\dfrac{b}{2a}$; the minimum value is $\dfrac{4ac - b^2}{4a}$. The function has no maximum value.

To complete the analysis for quadratic polynomial functions, we need to consider the function defined by $F(x) = ax^2 + bx + c$ where $a < 0$. We leave as an exercise for the student to prove that F has no minimum, but it does have a maximum value. The maximum value is $\dfrac{4ac - b^2}{4a}$ at $x = -\dfrac{b}{2a}$. Let us consider an application.

Example 1. Suppose we wish to use an existing wall and 100 feet of fence to enclose a rectangular area by using the fence on three sides. What is the maximum possible area we can obtain?

Solution: We first derive the area function f. (See Figure 11.13.) If we let

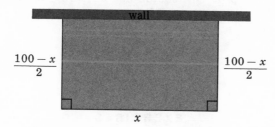

Area function: $f(x) = x\left(\dfrac{100 - x}{2}\right)$

FIGURE 11.13

x be the length of the rectangular region, then $100 - x$ is the amount of fence left for both ends and $(100 - x)/2$ is the length of one end. Thus, the area for each x is given by

$$f(x) = x\left(\frac{100 - x}{2}\right)$$

or
$$f(x) = -\tfrac{1}{2}x^2 + 50x$$

Using the formula or by "completing the square," we find that the function f has a maximum value at $-b/2a = 50$. The maximum area is $f(50) = 1{,}250$ square feet. [The domain of the area function is all positive real numbers less than 100. Obviously, $f(0) = f(100) = 0$. The function will not have a minimum value if we insist on constructing a rectangular enclosure. If the attitude is to allow 0 or 100 in the domain to represent no rectangular construction, then zero would be the minimum (area).]

Example 2. Find the two numbers whose sum is 18 and whose product is as great as possible.

Solution 1: Let x be one number. Thus, $18 - x$ is the other number and the product is

$$p(x) = x(18 - x)$$

Therefore,
$$\begin{aligned} p(x) &= -(x^2 - 18x) \\ &= -(x^2 - 18x + 81) + 81 \\ &= -(x - 9)^2 + 81 \\ &= 81 - (x - 9)^2 \end{aligned}$$

Since $(x - 9)^2$ is nonnegative for each real number and since $p(9) = 81$, the product is greatest when both numbers are 9.

Solution 2: Notice that if $p(x) = 18x - x^2 = ax^2 + bx + c$ then $a = -1$, $b = 18$, and $c = 0$. Thus, $x = -b/2a = -18/2(-1) = 9$ makes the product function a maximum. (Here we use the formula.)

The following problems should not only prove of interest but also pave the way for discovering in the next chapter the main ideas of differential calculus.

EXERCISES

For each of the relations in Exercises 1 through 15 answer the following questions. (a) Is the relation a function? (b) What is the maximum value if it is a function? (c) What is the minimum value if it is a function? (d) What is the domain of the relation? (e) What is the range of the relation?

1. $\{(1, 3), (0, 0), (-1, 7), (3, -8)\}$
2. $\{(\sqrt{3}, \frac{2}{3}), (-\frac{1}{3}, 7), (4, 11)\}$
3. $\{(-1, 2), (3, 2), (17, 2)\}$
4. $\{(2, 1), (3, -1), (4, 1), (7, -1)\}$
5. $\{(x, x^2) \,|\, x \text{ is a real number}\}$
6. $\{(x, x^2 + 4) \,|\, x \text{ is a real number}\}$
7. $\{(x, x^2 - 8) \,|\, x \text{ is a real number}\}$
8. $\{(x, y) \,|\, y = 3x + 6 \text{ where } x \text{ is a real number}\}$
9. $\{(n, (-1)^n) \,|\, n \text{ is a positive integer}\}$
10. $\{(n, 1 - 1/n) \,|\, n \text{ is a positive integer}\}$
11. $\{(x, y) \,|\, y = x^2 + 5x - 3 \text{ where } x \text{ is a real number}\}$
12. $\{(x, y) \,|\, y = 6 + 7x - x^2 \text{ where } x \text{ is a real number}\}$
13. $\{(x, y) \,|\, y = 3x^2 + 5x - 7 \text{ where } x \text{ is a real number}\}$
14. $\{(x, y) \,|\, y = 7x^2 - x \text{ where } x \text{ is a real number}\}$
15. $\{(x, y) \,|\, y = -4x^2 + 2x - 3 \text{ where } x \text{ is a real number}\}$
16. Find the two real numbers whose sum is 15 and whose product is as great as possible.

17. Find the two real numbers whose difference is 20 and whose product is as small as possible.

18. Find the two real numbers whose sum is 16 and the sum of whose squares is a minimum.

19. Find the real number which exceeds its square by the greatest amount.

20. A piece of wire 100 inches long is to be cut into two pieces. One piece of wire is to be bent into a square and the other piece into a circle. How should the wire be cut to get a minimum total area?

5. LINEAR PROGRAMMING (OPTIONAL)

Consider the line in the cartesian coordinate plane whose equation is $2x - 3y = 4$. (See Figure 11.14.) We can prove that all points in the

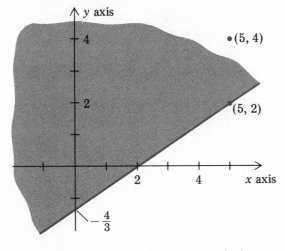

$$S_1 = \{(x, y) \mid 2x - 3y \leq 4\}$$

FIGURE 11.14

coordinate plane satisfying $2x - 3y < 4$ are on one side of the line and all points satisfying $2x - 3y > 4$ are on the other side of the line. Notice, for example, that the point $(5, 4)$ is *above* the line and that $2(5) - 3(4) = 2 < 4$; therefore,

$$S_1 = \{(x, y) \mid 2x - 3y \leq 4\}$$

is the region containing the points on or above the line.

Now, consider the region defined by

$$S_2 = \{(x, y) \mid 5x + 2y \le 48\}$$

Since $5(0) + 2(0) = 0 < 48$, the origin $(0, 0)$ is in the half-plane where $5x + 2y \le 48$. Since the two lines intersect at $(8, 4)$, a fact that can be obtained by solving for the simultaneous solution of $2x - 3y = 4$ and $5x + 2y = 48$, it follows that $S_1 \cap S_2$ is the region indicated in Figure 11.15. If

$$S_3 = \{(x, y) \mid x \ge 0\}$$

then $S_1 \cap S_2 \cap S_3$ is the shaded region indicated in Figure 11.15.

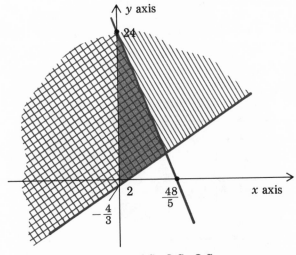

$S_1 \cap S_2$ and $S_1 \cap S_2 \cap S_3$

FIGURE 11.15

Finally, if

$$S_4 = \{(x, y) \mid y \le 6\}$$

and if

$$S_5 = \{(x, y) \mid y \ge 2\}$$

then $S_1 \cap S_2 \cap S_3 \cap S_4 \cap S_5$ is the region indicated in Figure 11.16. If

$$D = S_1 \cap S_2 \cap S_3 \cap S_4 \cap S_5$$

convex polygonal set

then D is called a *convex polygonal set*. The convex polygonal set consists of all ordered pairs of real numbers satisfying the following five inequalities.

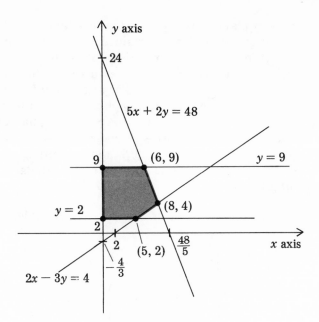

$$S_1 \cap S_2 \cap S_3 \cap S_4 \cap S_5$$

FIGURE 11.16

(1) $$2x - 3y \leq 4$$

(2) $$5x + 2y \leq 48$$

(3) $$x \geq 0$$

(4) $$y \leq 6$$

(5) $$y \geq 2$$

Geometrically, the convex polygonal set consists of all points on the boundary of the polygon and in its interior.

Suppose for each ordered pair of real numbers (x, y) in D we would like to determine the maximum value of the sum $x + y$. Basically, we wish to maximize what is called a (linear) function of two variables. If f represents the function, the domain of f is the set of ordered pairs in D and the range consists of the real numbers $x + y$ where (x, y) is in D. The range value associated with each (x, y) in D is denoted by $f(x, y)$ and is given by

$$f(x, y) = x + y$$

For example, $(3, 3)$ is in D and $f(3, 3) = 3 + 3 = 6$. Similarly, $(\sqrt{3}, 4)$ is in D and $f(\sqrt{3}, 4) = \sqrt{3} + 4 \approx 5.7321$.

299

Consider the xy plane as being placed horizontal (on the floor). A three-dimensional graph of f is determined as follows: For a point (x, y) in D if the function value $f(x, y)$ is positive, then the point on the graph of f associated with (x, y) is at distance $f(x, y)$ directly above the point (x, y) in the xy plane. For negative function values, the corresponding points are below the xy plane. We can prove that a linear function in two variables, such as $f(x, y) = x + y$, has a plane as its graph. Since $f(0, 2) = 2$, $f(8, 4) = 12$ and $f(6, 9) = 15$, we quickly determine three points on the graph of f. (See Figure 11.17.) Since the three points do not lie on a line, they determine the graph of the plane containing the points.

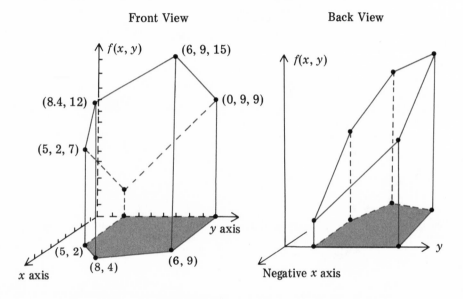

Graph of $f(x, y) = x + y$

$$D = S_1 \cap S_2 \cap S_3 \cap S_4 \cap S_5$$

FIGURE 11.17

From looking at the shaded region in Figure 11.17, it is geometrically obvious that the high point of the graph of f is at $(6, 9)$; that is, $f(6, 9) = 15$ is the maximum value of f for the given domain D. In other words, 15 is the greatest sum that can be obtained by adding pairs of numbers in D.

The problem just discussed is called a linear programming problem. In general, if we have a convex polygonal set in the xy plane for the domain of a linear function f, finding the values that maximize, or minimize, the function is called a *linear programming problem*. Such problems have considerable applications in business, economics, etc. [Eventually, one would want to consider the problem of optimizing such functions as $g(x, y) = x^2 + 4y^3$ for (x, y) in D, but we restrict our study to linear functions.]

linear programming

If f is a linear function in two variables whose domain D is a convex polygonal set in the xy plane, then it can be proved that the maximum, or minimum, value of f must be obtained at a point on the boundary of the polygon. In fact, the maximum (and minimum) value must be obtained at one of the vertices of the polygon. Geometrically, the result is rather obvious. Also, it is geometrically clear that the maximum value may occur at other points on the polygon; for example, the maximum value could be obtained at two vertices and at each point on the line segment joining the two points.

Example 1. Find the maximum and minimum values of f defined by $f(x, y) = 3x + y$ where the domain is that given in Figure 11.17.

Solution: Consider the values of f at each vertex of the convex polygonal set.

$$f(0, 6) = 6$$
$$f(6, 9) = 27$$
$$f(8, 4) = 28$$
$$f(5, 2) = 17$$
$$f(0, 2) = 2$$

Thus, the maximum value is 28 and it is obtained at (8, 4); the minimum value is 2 and it is obtained at (0, 2).

Example 2. Let D be the convex polygonal set given in Figure 11.17. If g is the linear function having D as domain and defined by $g(x, y) = 2x - 5y$, then determine the maximum and minimum values of g.

Solution: Consider the values of g at each vertex of the convex polygonal set D.

$$g(0, 6) = -30$$
$$g(6, 9) = -33$$
$$g(8, 4) = -4$$
$$g(5, 2) = 0$$
$$g(0, 2) = -10$$

Thus, the maximum value of g in D is 0 and it is obtained at (5, 2); the minimum value of g in D is -33 and it is obtained at (6, 9).

Example 3. A manufacturer produces not less than 250 units of product A and not less than 650 units of product B per week. Suppose 5 hours are required to produce one unit of product A and 7 hours are required to make one unit of product B. If the profit per unit on product A is \$50, if the profit per unit on product B is \$30, and if only 7,550 man-hours are available each week to produce the two products, what is the maximum possible profit that the manufacturer can make per week? How many units of each product should be manufactured to maximize profit?

Solution: Let x be the number of units of product A produced and let y be the number of units of product B produced. Thus,

(1) $x \geq 250$

and

(2) $y \geq 650$

Since it takes 5 hours to produce one unit of product A, $5x$ is the total number of man-hours required to make x units of product A; similarly, $7y$ hours are required to make y units of product B. Therefore,

(3) $5x + 7y \leq 7,550$

The profit function P is given by

$$P(x, y) = 50x + 30y$$

The domain of P is the convex polygonal region given in Figure 11.18. The values of P at each vertex of the domain of P is as follows:

$$P(250, 650) = 32,000$$
$$P(600, 650) = 49,500$$
$$P(250, 900) = 39,500$$

Therefore, the maximum weekly profit is \$49,500 and it is obtained by manufacturing 600 units of product A and 650 units of product B.

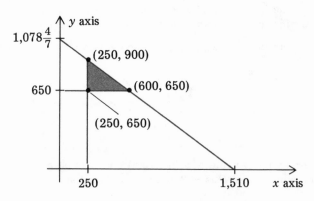

FIGURE 11.18

Example 4. Consider the following sets in the xy plane.

$$S_1 = \{(x, y) \mid y \le 18\}$$
$$S_2 = \{(x, y) \mid x \ge 4\}$$
$$S_3 = \{(x, y) \mid x + y \ge 20\}$$
$$S_4 = \{(x, y) \mid x \quad 20\}$$
$$S_5 = \{(x, y) \mid 3x + 6y \le 132\}$$
$$S_6 = \{(x, y) \mid y \ge 8\}$$
$$D = S_1 \cap S_2 \cap S_3 \cap S_4 \cap S_5 \cap S_6$$

(a) Show D is a convex polygonal set by making a graph.
(b) Find the maximum and minimum values of the function F with D as domain where $F(x, y) = 5x + 15y$.

Solution: (a) See Figure 11.19.
(b) Consider the function values of F at each vertex of the convex polygonal set.

$$F(4, 16) = 260$$
$$F(4, 18) = 290$$
$$F(12, 18) = 330$$
$$F(20, 12) = 280$$
$$F(20, 8) = 220$$
$$F(12, 8) = 180$$

The maximum value of F in D is 330; it is at (12, 18). The minimum value of F in D is 180; it is at (12, 8).

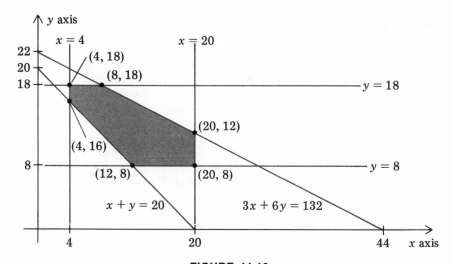

FIGURE 11.19

EXERCISES

Make a graph of each convex polygonal set D given in Exercises 1 through 8.

1. $S_1 = \{(x, y) \mid x \geq 4\}$
   $S_2 = \{(x, y) \mid y \geq 6\}$
   $S_3 = \{(x, y) \mid x + y \leq 12\}$
   $D = S_1 \cap S_2 \cap S_3$

2. $S_1 = \{(x, y) \mid x \leq 12\}$
   $S_2 = \{(x, y) \mid y \leq 7\}$
   $S_3 = \{(x, y) \mid 2x + y \leq 8\}$
   $D = S_1 \cap S_2 \cap S_3$

3. $S_1 = \{(x, y) \mid |x \leq 8\}$
   $S_2 = \{(x, y) \mid x \geq 2\}$
   $S_3 = \{(x, y) \mid y \leq 7\}$
   $S_4 = \{(x, y) \mid y \geq 1\}$
   $D = S_1 \cap S_2 \cap S_3 \cap S_4$

4. $S_1 = \{(x, y) \mid 3x + 2y \leq 32\}$
   $S_2 = \{(x, y) \mid 3x - y \geq 2\}$
   $S_3 = \{(x, y) \mid y \geq 4\}$
   $D = S_1 \cap S_2 \cap S_3$

5. $S_1 = \{(x, y) \mid 3x + 2y \leq 8\}$
   $S_2 = \{(x, y) \mid 3x + 2y \geq 2\}$
   $S_3 = \{(x, y) \mid 4x - y \leq -12\}$
   $S_4 = \{(x, y) \mid 4x - y \geq -6\}$
   $D = S_1 \cap S_2 \cap S_3 \cap S_4$

6. $S_1 = \{(x, y) \mid 3x + y \leq 20\}$
   $S_2 = \{(x, y) \mid 5x - 4y \leq 22\}$
   $S_3 = \{(x, y) \mid 11x - 2y \geq 28\}$
   $D = S_1 \cap S_2 \cap S_3$

7. $S_1 = \{(x, y) \mid 8x + 7y \leq 48\}$
   $S_2 = \{(x, y) \mid 3x - y \geq -11\}$
   $S_3 = \{(x, y) \mid x - 10y \leq 6\}$
   $D = S_1 \cap S_2 \cap S_3$

8. $S_1 = \{(x, y) \mid y \leq 8\}$
   $S_2 = \{(x, y) \mid 2x + y \leq 24\}$
   $S_3 = \{(x, y) \mid y \geq 4\}$
   $S_4 = \{(x, y) \mid x + 2y \geq 12\}$
   $S_5 = \{(x, y) \mid x - y \leq -2\}$
   $D = S_1 \cap S_2 \cap S_3 \cap S_4 \cap S_5$

9. Let F be the function defined by $F(x, y) = 3x + 4y$.
   (a) Find the maximum of F in D for the D given in Exercise 1.
   (b) Find the maximum of F in D for the D given in Exercise 3.
   (c) Find the maximum of F in D for the D given in Exercise 5.
   (d) Find the maximum of F in D for the D given in Exercise 7.

10. Let F be the function defined by $F(x, y) = 3x + 4y$.
    (a) Find the maximum of F in D for the D given in Exercise 2.
    (b) Find the maximum of F in D for the D given in Exercise 4.
    (c) Find the maximum of F in D for the D given in Exercise 6.
    (d) Find the maximum of F in D for the D given in Exercise 8.

11. Let G be the function defined by $G(x, y) = 2x - 7y$.
    (a) Find the maximum of G in D for the D given in Exercise 1.
    (b) Find the maximum of G in D for the D given in Exercise 3.
    (c) Find the maximum of G in D for the D given in Exercise 5.
    (d) Find the maximum of G in D for the D given in Exercise 7.

12. Let G be the function defined by $G(x, y) = 2x - 7y$.
    (a) Find the maximum of G in D for the D given in Exercise 2.
    (b) Find the maximum of G in D for the D given in Exercise 4.
    (c) Find the maximum of G in D for the D given in Exercise 6.
    (d) Find the maximum of G in D for the D given in Exercise 8.

13. Let g be the function defined by $g(x, y) = 5x + 2y$.
    (a) Find the minimum of g in D for the D given in Exercise 1.

(b) Find the minimum of g in D for the D given in Exercise 3.
(c) Find the minimum of g in D for the D given in Exercise 5.
(d) Find the minimum of g in D for the D given in Exercise 7.

14. Let g be the function defined by $g(x, y) = 5x + 2y$.
(a) Find the minimum of g in D for the D given in Exercise 2.
(b) Find the minimum of g in D for the D given in Exercise 4.
(c) Find the minimum of g in D for the D given in Exercise 6.
(d) Find the minimum of g in D for the D given in Exercise 8.

15. Let f be the function defined by $f(x, y) = -4x + 9y$.
(a) Find the minimum of f in D for the D given in Exercise 1.
(b) Find the minimum of f in D for the D given in Exercise 3.
(c) Find the minimum of f in D for the D given in Exercise 5.
(d) Find the minimum of f in D for the D given in Exercise 7.

16. Let f be the function defined by $f(x, y) = -4x + 9y$.
(a) Find the minimum of f in D for the D given in Exercise 2.
(b) Find the minimum of f in D for the D given in Exercise 4.
(c) Find the minimum of f in D for the D given in Exercise 6.
(d) Find the minimum of f in D for the D given in Exercise 8.

17. A manufacturer produces not less than 400 units of product A and not less than 700 units of product B per week. Suppose 8 man-hours are required to produce one unit of product A and 5 man-hours are required to make one unit of product B. If the profit per unit on product A is $40, if the profit per unit on product B is $60, and if only 8,000 man-hours are available each week to produce the two products, what is the maximum possible profit that the manufacturer can make per week? How many units of each product should be manufactured to maximize profit?

18. A student may select a problem from two problem sets to work and hand in. Set I consists of 30 problems which the student estimates will require 4 minutes each to work. Set II consists of 50 problems which the student estimates will require 2 minutes each to work. Each correctly worked problem in Set I receives 5 points and each correctly worked problem in Set II receives 3 points.
(a) If the student has a maximum of $2\frac{1}{2}$ hours to work the assignment, how many problems should be chosen from each set in order to maximize the greatest number of points possible on the assignment?
(b) What is the maximum number of points that he can make on the assignment?

Isaac Newton (1642–1727)

Isaac Newton was born at Woolsthorpe, England, on Christmas day in 1642, the year Galileo died. During his early education, he was not considered a child prodigy; in fact, his school years were not very unusual until he went to Cambridge in 1661. Isaac Barrow, his teacher at Cambridge, was the first to recognize Newton's genius. Barrow had a great influence on Newton's academic growth, and in 1669 resigned the Lucasian chair of mathematics to Newton, quite a rare and magnanimous act in those days.

Newton's discovery of the universal law of gravitation and his invention of differential calculus were made during the two years 1664–1665. It was during these two years, before he was twenty-five and when the University was closed due to the Great Plague, that he exhibited his great creative ability. Newton often waited an inordinate amount of time to publish his discoveries; for example, he waited twenty years to publish his universal law of gravitation; he waited even longer to publish the results on calculus that he had obtained at the age of twenty-three.

As Leibniz did in his development of calculus, Newton relied heavily on his remarkable intuition. He was more interested in the fact that his theories and techniques of calculus worked and produced correct results than in a rigorous verification of the theories and techniques. It remained for the great French mathematician Augustin-Louis Cauchy (1789–1857) to put calculus on a sound theoretical foundation. Newton did establish mechanics on an axiomatic foundation, made contributions to chemistry, and was also a student of theology and philosophy. Although he suffered from poor health as a child, he did not have to contend with the poverty that confronted many of the other great mathematicians in the seventeenth, eighteenth, and nineteenth centuries.

12 Differential Calculus

1. Introduction
2. The Derivative
3. Maxima and Minima
4. Antiderivatives

Taking mathematics from the beginning of the world to the time of Newton, what he has done is much the better half.

GOTTFRIED WILHELM LEIBNIZ

1. INTRODUCTION

Although the foundations of calculus were established as far back as the time of Archimedes (287–213 B.C.), its development as a separate branch of mathematics did not take place until the seventeenth century. The Englishman, Sir Isaac Newton (1642–1727), and the German, Gottfried Wilhelm Leibniz (1646–1716), are both credited with the initial development of the subject. Although an unfortunate controversy raged for years over which of the two created the subject first, it is clear now that each developed calculus independently. There are many similar instances in the history of mathematics where new avenues of study were pursued independently by different mathematicians at about the same time. This should not be surprising since inventing new mathematics is not unlike inventing in other fields; when the proper "tools" are available, a fertile and imaginative mind seizes on the opportunity to create new things and discover new truths.

It will become clear that calculus evolves rather naturally from concepts in analytic geometry. Let us consider several interesting and important problems to indicate the role of analytic geometry as the forerunner of calculus.

Example 1. Find the two nonnegative real numbers with a maximum product such that the square of the first number added to the second number has 24 as the sum.

Discussion and Solution: If we let x be the first number and let y be the second number, then we know that $x \geq 0$, $y \geq 0$, and $x^2 + y = 24$. Thus, $y = 24 - x^2$, and the product we wish to maximize is $x(24 - x^2)$.

Since both x and $(24 - x^2)$ are nonnegative,

$$x^2 \leq 24 \qquad \text{and} \qquad 0 \leq x \leq \sqrt{24} = 2\sqrt{6}$$

Furthermore, the product function p is the cubic polynomial defined by

$$p(x) = x(24 - x^2) \qquad \text{where } 0 \le x \le 2\sqrt{6}$$

The graph of $p(x) = 24x - x^3$ is given in Figure 12.1.

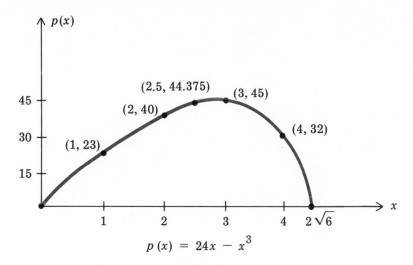

$$p(x) = 24x - x^3$$

FIGURE 12.1

There is a simple algebraic technique (completing the square) to determine the maximum (or minimum) of a quadratic polynomial. Even if such a simple algebraic technique were available for cubic polynomials, we should still be interested in a method of maximizing p that might apply to a more general class of functions. Indeed, such a technique exists and it should be noted in the solution of our problem that we do not rely on the fact that the product function is a cubic polynomial.

We see from the graph of the product function and from the following table of values that the maximum product is obtained when x is close to 3. Thus, 3 and $24 - 3^2 = 15$ are first approximations of the two numbers with the given properties. Unless the problem is "hand-picked", it should not be

x	0	1	2	2.5	2.6	2.7	2.8	2.9	3	4	$2\sqrt{6}$
$p(x)$	0	23	40	44.375	44.824	45.117	45.248	45.211	45	32	0

expected that either the numbers or their product are rational numbers. Therefore, it should be unlikely that we could guess the correct answer. Even if the right answer were guessed, how do we *prove* that the solution is correct?

If the graph of the function has a nonvertical tangent line at each point of the graph (and any polynomial does), then it is geometrically obvious that the high point of the graph (maximum) is where the tangent line to the graph is parallel to the x axis, that is, where the tangent line has slope zero. Thus, if we could derive a formula (function) which gives the slope of the tangent line at each point in the domain of the function, then the solution could be obtained by finding the number between 0 and $2\sqrt{6}$ that makes the slope zero.

Let $(t, p(t))$ be any given point on the graph of the product function. (See Figure 12.2.) If $(x, p(x))$ is any other point on the graph of p, then $x \neq t$ and

$$\frac{p(x) - p(t)}{x - t}$$

is the slope of the line containing the two points. Thus,

$$\frac{p(x) - p(t)}{x - t} = \frac{(24x - x^3) - (24t - t^3)}{x - t}$$

$$= \frac{24(x - t) - (x^3 - t^3)}{x - t}$$

Recall that $x^3 - t^3 = (x - t)(x^2 + xt + t^2)$. Consequently,

$$\frac{p(x) - p(t)}{x - t} = \frac{24(x - t) - (x - t)(x^2 + xt + t^2)}{x - t}$$

$$= 24 - (x^2 + xt + t^2) \qquad \text{for each } x \neq t$$

As x gets nearer to t, the slope of the line containing the two points approaches the slope of the tangent line at t. For $x \approx t$ (x almost equal to t), we see that

$$24 - (x^2 + xt + t^2) \approx 24 - (t^2 + t^2 + t^2) = 24 - 3t^2$$

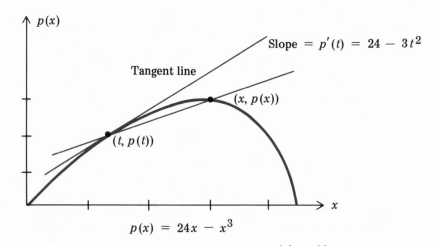

Slope $= p'(t) = 24 - 3t^2$

Tangent line

$(x, p(x))$

$(t, p(t))$

$$p(x) = 24x - x^3$$

Slope containing $(x, p(x))$ and $(t, p(t))$: $\dfrac{p(x) - p(t)}{x - t}$

FIGURE 12.2

Thus, the slope function, which we denote by p', is defined by $p'(t) = 24 - 3t^2$; this is a formula giving the slope of the tangent line to the graph of the polynomial at any point $(t, p(t))$. Notice that if $t = 3$ then $p'(t) = 24 - 3(3^2) = -3$.

Since the slope of the tangent is negative where $t = 3$, the tangent line at $(3, 45)$ leans to the left. Therefore, we conclude that the maximum point on the graph is to the left of the point where $t = 3$. Furthermore, since $24 - 3t^2 = 0$ where $3t^2 = 24$, the slope of the tangent is zero where $t^2 = 8$, or $t = 2\sqrt{2}$; thus, the curve has a horizontal tangent at $x = 2\sqrt{2}$. Consequently, the two nonnegative real numbers that maximize the product are $2\sqrt{2}$ and $24 - (2\sqrt{2})^2 = 24 - 8 = 16$, and the maximum product *is* $32\sqrt{2}$. Be particularly careful to distinguish between *where* the maximum is (domain value making the function a maximum) and *what* the maximum is (maximum range value).

Example 2. Assume a rectangular box open at the top is to be made from a rectangular piece of metal that measures 12 inches by 16 inches by cutting squares out of the corners and then "turning up the sides." (See Figure 12.3.) Find the length of each side of the squares to be cut out in order to make the volume a maximum.

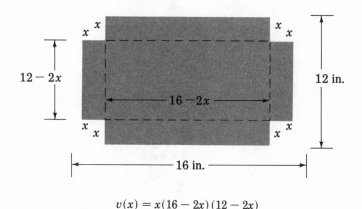

$$v(x) = x(16 - 2x)(12 - 2x)$$

FIGURE 12.3

Solution: Let x be the length of one side of each square. If a box is to be constructed, then $x > 0$ and $x < 6$. The length of the box is $(16 - 2x)$, the width is $(12 - 2x)$, and the height is x; thus, the volume is given by

$$v(x) = x(16 - 2x)(12 - 2x) \qquad \text{where } 0 < x < 6$$

Using the following table of values and a sketch of the graph of the function v, it appears that the maximum value is obtained when x is close to 2.3. (See Figure 12.4.)

311

x	1	2	2.1	2.2	2.3	2.4	2.5	3	4	5
$v(x)$	140	192	193.284	193.952	194.028	193.536	192.5	180	128	60

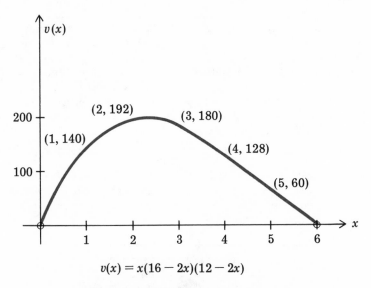

$$v(x) = x(16 - 2x)(12 - 2x)$$

FIGURE 12.4

Now, we use the same approach exhibited in Example 1. Given a number t in the domain of the function v, the slope of the line containing $(t, v(t))$ and $(x, v(x))$ on the graph of v where $x \neq t$ is given by

$$\frac{v(x) - v(t)}{x - t} = \frac{x(12 - 2x)(16 - 2x) - t(12 - 2t)(16 - 2t)}{x - t}$$

$$= \frac{192x - 56x^2 + 4x^3 - 192t + 56t^2 - 4t^3}{x - t}$$

$$= \frac{192(x - t) - 56(x^2 - t^2) + 4(x^3 - t^3)}{x - t}$$

$$= \frac{192(x - t) - 56(x - t)(x + t) + 4(x - t)(x^2 + xt + t^2)}{x - t}$$

Thus, if $x \neq t$, then

$$\frac{v(x) - v(t)}{x - t} = 192 - 56(x + t) + 4(x^2 + xt + t^2)$$

As x approaches t, the slope of the line containing the two points approaches the slope of the tangent line at t. If $v'(t)$ denotes the slope of the tangent line to the graph of v at t, then we say that the *limit* of

$\dfrac{v(x) - v(t)}{x - t}$ as x approaches t is $v'(t)$; symbolically,

$$v'(t) = \lim_{x \to t} \frac{v(x) - v(t)}{x - t}$$

We see that $\quad v'(t) = \lim_{x \to t} [192 - 56(x + t) + 4(x^2 + xt + t^2)]$

$$= 192 - 112t + 12t^2$$

Now, we wish to know the value for t between 0 and 6 that makes the slope $v'(t) = 0$. We set the slope formula equal to zero and solve the resulting equation using the quadratic formula.

$$12t^2 - 112t + 192 = 0$$
$$3t^2 - 28t + 48 = 0$$
$$t = \frac{28 \pm \sqrt{784 - 576}}{6}$$
$$t = \frac{14 \pm 2\sqrt{13}}{3}$$

The only solution between 0 and 6 is given by

$$t = \frac{14 - 2\sqrt{13}}{3}$$
$$t \approx 2.26296$$

Therefore, we should cut squares out of the corners with each side approximately 2.26296 inches in length in order to maximize the volume.

Example 3. Suppose the distance a free-falling body falls in t seconds is given by $s(t) = 16t^2$. What is the velocity of the body at the end of 3 seconds?

Solution: The distance the body falls in 3 seconds is $s(3) = 16(9) = 144$ feet. The distance the body falls in 3.1 seconds is $s(3.1) = 16(3.1)^2 = 153.76$ feet. Thus, the distance the body falls during the interval of one-tenth of a second from 3 seconds to 3.1 seconds is

$$s(3.1) - s(3) = 153.76 - 144 = 9.76 \text{ ft}$$

Since *average velocity* for a body travelling in rectilinear motion (in a straight line) is defined to be distance traversed divided by the time required,

$$\text{average velocity} = \frac{s(3.1) - s(3)}{3.1 - 3}$$
$$= \frac{9.76}{0.1}$$
$$= 97.6 \text{ ft/sec}$$

We would quickly guess, since the velocity is increasing, that the velocity at the end of 3 seconds should be less than 97.6 feet per second. One way to obtain a better approximation of the velocity at the end of 3 seconds is to shorten the time interval. The average velocity in the time interval from 3 to 3.01 seconds is determined as follows.

$$\frac{s(3.01) - s(3)}{3.01 - 3} = \frac{16(3.01)^2 - 16(3)^2}{0.01}$$

$$= \frac{16(3.01^2 - 3^2)}{0.01}$$

$$= 96.96 \text{ ft/sec}$$

Now let us find the average velocity in the time interval from 3 to x seconds where $x > 3$.

$$\frac{s(x) - s(3)}{x - 3} = \frac{16x^2 - 16(3)^2}{x - 3}$$

$$= \frac{16(x^2 - 3^2)}{x - 3}$$

$$= 16(x + 3) \qquad \text{for any } x > 3$$

(The student should stop and verify that the previous solutions are obtained when we let $x = 3.1$ or $x = 3.01$.)

Obviously, as x approaches 3, $16(x + 3)$ approaches 96. Hence, we *define* the *instantaneous velocity* at the end of 3 seconds to be 96 ft/sec and denote it by $s'(3)$; thus,

$$s'(3) = \lim_{x \to 3} \frac{s(x) - s(3)}{x - 3} = 96 \text{ ft/sec}$$

Example 4. Suppose the distance a free-falling body falls in t seconds is given by $s(t) = 16t^2$. What is its velocity at the end of t seconds?

Solution: [The problem is motivated by the previous example. It is natural to generalize from time 3 seconds to time t seconds and derive a formula (function) giving the velocity at the end of t seconds. The solution is completely analogous to what we did for 3 seconds.] If $x > t$, then the average velocity during the time interval from t seconds to x seconds is given by

$$\frac{s(x) - s(t)}{x - t} = \frac{16x^2 - 16t^2}{x - t}$$

$$= \frac{16(x - t)(x + t)}{x - t}$$

$$= 16(x + t) \qquad \text{where } x > t$$

As x approaches t, $16(x + t)$ approaches $32t$. Thus, we define the velocity at the end of t seconds to be $32t$ ft/sec. Notice that we have defined a velocity function v for a free-falling body whose function values are given by $v(t) = 32t$. Therefore,

$$v(t) = s'(t) = \lim_{x \to t} \frac{s(x) - s(t)}{x - t}$$

When finding (guessing) limits of functions, we use several theorems that are intuitively obvious but difficult to prove. For example, we use that if $\lim_{x \to t} f(x) = A$ and $\lim_{x \to t} g(x) = B$ then

$$\lim_{x \to t} [f(x) + g(x)] = A + B$$

$$\lim_{x \to t} [f(x) - g(x)] = A - B$$

$$\lim_{x \to t} [f(x)g(x)] = AB$$

and $\qquad \lim_{x \to t} \dfrac{f(x)}{g(x)} = \dfrac{A}{B} \qquad$ provided $B \neq 0$

To prove these statements would entail the added burden of gaining a complete understanding of a rigorous definition of the limit of a function.

EXERCISES

In Exercises 1 through 10, do each of the following for the given functions. (a) Find the slope of the line containing $(x, f(x))$ and $(2, f(2))$ on the graph of f where $x \neq 2$. (b) Find the slope of the tangent line to the graph of f at 2. (c) At any point $(t, f(t))$ on the graph of f, find the slope $f'(t)$ of the tangent line.

1. $f(x) = x^2$
2. $f(x) = x^3$
3. $f(x) = 1/x$
4. $f(x) = 1/x^2$
5. $f(x) = \dfrac{2x + 1}{5x + 3}$
6. $f(x) = \dfrac{5x - 1}{4x + 3}$
7. $f(x) = x^{1/2}$
8. $f(x) = x^{3/2}$
9. $f(x) = x^{1/3}$
10. $f(x) = \dfrac{x}{x^2 + 1}$

11. Find the dimensions of the box with maximum volume that can be obtained in a manner similar to that in Example 2 if the rectangular piece of metal measures 10 inches by 16 inches.

12. Find the dimensions of the box with maximum volume that can be ob-

tained in a manner similar to that in Example 2 if the rectangular piece of metal measures 12 inches by 18 inches.

13. Find the two nonnegative real numbers such that the square of the first added to the second has 18 as sum and their product is a maximum.

14. The sum of two positive numbers is 9 and the product of the first times the square of the second is to be maximum. What are the two positive numbers?

2. THE DERIVATIVE

In the last section we found several examples where the expression

$$\frac{f(x) - f(t)}{x - t}$$

had significant importance for a function *f*. The ratio is not only the slope of the line containing two points $(x, f(x))$ and $(t, f(t))$ on the graph of *f* but it is also the average velocity of an object in rectilinear motion where *f* is the distance function. The expression is called the *Newton quotient*. More importantly, we found that the slope of the tangent line to *f* at *t* and the velocity of an object at time *t* where *f* is the distance function are given by the following limit:

Newton quotient

$$\lim_{x \to t} \frac{f(x) - f(t)}{x - t}$$

Since the above limit is so important in not only the two applications discussed but also in many others, we shall study it in a general setting. If

$$\lim_{x \to t} \frac{f(x) - f(t)}{x - t}$$

derivative

exists then we call the limit the *derivative* of *f* at *t*; the derivative of *f* at *t* is often denoted by $f'(t)$. Thus, by definition,

$$f'(t) = \lim_{x \to t} \frac{f(x) - f(t)}{x - t}$$

provided the limit exists. The process of finding derivatives is called *differentiation*.

We now encounter two important tasks: (1) obtaining the derivatives of specific functions and (2) determining theorems that will enable us to find derivatives of more general functions. Afterwards, of course, our attention will be turned again to applications of the derivative.

Example 1. If $f(x) = x$, find $f'(t)$.

Solution: $f'(t) = \lim\limits_{x \to t} \dfrac{x - t}{x - t}$. Since $\dfrac{x - t}{x - t} = 1$ for *every* $x \neq t$, the limit of f as x approaches t is 1. Hence, for any real number t, $f'(t) = 1$ if $f(x) = x$. [The result should not be surprising since the graph of $f(x) = x$ is a line with 1 as slope.]

Example 2. If $f(x) = x^4$, find $f'(t)$.

Solution:
$$f'(t) = \lim_{x \to t} \frac{x^4 - t^4}{x - t}$$

$$= \lim_{x \to t} \frac{(x - t)(x + t)(x^2 + t^2)}{x - t}$$

$$= \lim_{x \to t} (x + t)(x^2 + t^2)$$

$$= 4t^3$$

Example 3. If $H(x) = x^5$, find $H'(t)$.

Solution:
$$H'(t) = \lim_{x \to t} \frac{x^5 - t^5}{x - t}$$

$$= \lim_{x \to t} \frac{(x - t)(x^4 + x^3 t + x^2 t^2 + x t^3 + t^4)}{x - t}$$

Hence, $H'(t) = 5t^4$

Essentially, we now have two avenues to explore. First, suppose $f(x) = x^2 + 7$ and $g(x) = \sqrt{x^4 + 3}$. What is the derivative at t for each function? Second, suppose the derivative of each function is known and suppose new functions are built up from f and g using the operations of addition, multiplication, subtraction, and division. How can the known derivatives of f and g be used to determine the derivatives of each of the constructed functions? In other words, knowing $f'(t)$ and $g'(t)$, what is $h'(t)$ in each of the following?

(1) $h(x) = f(x) + g(x) = x^2 + 7 + \sqrt{x^4 + 3}$

(2) $h(x) = f(x) \cdot g(x) = (x^2 + 7)\sqrt{x^4 + 3}$

(3) $h(x) = f(x) - g(x) = x^2 + 7 - \sqrt{x^4 + 3}$

(4) $h(x) = \dfrac{f(x)}{g(x)} = \dfrac{x^2 + 7}{\sqrt{x^4 + 3}}$

The student might guess (correctly) that the derivative of the sum of two functions f and g is the sum of the derivatives of each of the two functions. However, Examples 1, 2, and 3 clearly indicate that the derivative of the product of two functions is *not* the product of the derivatives of the two functions. Let us state the basic differentiation theorems for sum, difference, product, and quotient of two functions and examine some of the immediate consequences.

Theorem 1. Assume f and g are two differentiable functions.

    (a) If $h(x) = f(x) + g(x)$, then $h'(t) = f'(t) + g'(t)$

    (b) If $h(x) = cf(x)$ where c is a constant, then $h'(t) = cf'(t)$

    (c) If $h(x) = f(x) - g(x)$, then $h'(t) = f'(t) - g'(t)$

    (d) If $h(x) = f(x)g(x)$, then $h'(t) = f(t)g'(t) + f'(t)g(t)$

    (e) If $h(x) = \dfrac{f(x)}{g(x)}$, then $h'(t) = \dfrac{g(t)f'(t) - f(t)g'(t)}{[g(t)]^2}$ provided $g(t) \neq 0$.

Proof: Left for the exercises.

Part (d) of the preceding theorem generalizes quite readily and leads to several important results. Let

$$h(x) = [f(x)]^3 = f(x)f(x)f(x)$$

Thus, $h(x) = [f(x)f(x)]f(x)$

and using part (d) of Theorem 1 we obtain

$$h'(t) = [f(t)f(t)]f'(t) + [f(t)f(t)]'f(t)$$
$$h'(t) = [f(t)]^2f'(t) + [f(t)f'(t) + f(t)f'(t)]f(t)$$
$$h'(t) = [f(t)]^2f'(t) + [f(t)]^2f'(t) + [f(t)]^2f'(t)$$
$$h'(t) = 3[f(t)]^2f'(t)$$

In particular, if $f(x) = x$ and $h(x) = [f(x)]^3$, then

$$h(x) = x^3$$

and $h'(t) = 3t^2$

[We use the fact from Example 1 that $f'(t) = 1$.]

In general, part (d) of Theorem 1 can be used to prove for any positive integer n that if

$$h(x) = [f(x)]^n$$

then $h'(t) = n[f(t)]^{n-1}f'(t)$

Consequently, if $h(x) = x^n$

then $h'(t) = nt^{n-1}$

Example 4. If $h(x) = x^6 + 3x^4$, then $h'(t) = 6t^5 + 12t^3$.

Example 5. If $h(x) = (x^6 + 3x^4)^{10}$, then $h'(t) = 10(t^6 + 3t^4)^9(6t^5 + 12t^3)$.

Example 6. If $f(x) = \dfrac{3x - 7}{x^2 + 1}$, find $f'(2)$ by each of the following methods.

(a) Find $f'(2)$ by direct use of the definition of the derivative. (b) Find $f'(t)$ by using Theorem 1 and then determine $f'(2)$.

Solution:

(a)
$$f'(2) = \lim_{x \to 2} \frac{(3x + 7)/(x^2 + 1) - {}^{13}/_5}{x - 2}$$

$$= \lim_{x \to 2} \frac{5(3x + 7) - 13(x^2 + 1)}{5(x - 2)(x^2 + 1)}$$

$$= \lim_{x \to 2} \frac{-13x^2 + 15x + 22}{5(x - 2)(x^2 + 1)}$$

$$= \lim_{x \to 2} \frac{-(13x + 11)(x - 2)}{5(x - 2)(x^2 + 1)}$$

$$= \lim_{x \to 2} \frac{-(13x + 11)}{5(x^2 + 1)}$$

$$= -\frac{37}{25}$$

(b) If $f(x) = \dfrac{3x + 7}{x^2 + 1}$, then from Theorem 1 it follows that

$$f'(t) = \frac{(t^2 + 1)(3) - (3t + 7)(2t)}{(t^2 + 1)^2}$$

Thus,
$$f'(t) = \frac{-3t^2 - 14t + 3}{(t^2 + 1)^2}$$

and
$$f'(2) = -\frac{37}{25}$$

To differentiate any algebraic function we need one additional technique; it is a method to find the derivative of $[f(x)]^{p/q}$ where p and q are positive integers. First, let $h(x) = [f(x)]^{1/q}$ where f is a differentiable function and q is a positive integer. Thus,

$$[h(x)]^q = f(x)$$

Furthermore, by finding the derivative of both sides we obtain

$$q[h(x)]^{q-1}h'(x) = f'(x)$$

319

Hence,
$$h'(x) = \frac{1}{q} \frac{f'(x)}{[h(x)]^{q-1}}$$

$$= \frac{1}{q} \frac{f'(x)}{[(f(x))^{1/q}]^{q-1}}$$

$$= \frac{1}{q} \frac{f'(x)}{[f(x)]^{1-(1/q)}}$$

$$= \frac{1}{q} [f(x)]^{(1/q)-1} \cdot f'(x)$$

Consequently, for a positive rational number r where $r = 1/q$ we have shown if

$$h(x) = [f(x)]^r$$

then
$$h'(x) = r[f(x)]^{r-1} \cdot f'(x)$$

Finally, if $r = p/q$ and $h(x) = [f(x)]^{p/q}$ then

$$h(x) = \{[f(x)]^p\}^{1/q}$$

Hence,
$$h'(x) = \frac{1}{q} \{[f(x)]^p\}^{(1/q)-1} \cdot p[f(x)]^{p-1} \cdot f'(x)$$

$$= \frac{1}{q} [f(x)]^{(p/q)-p} \cdot p[f(x)]^{p-1} \cdot f'(x)$$

$$= \frac{p}{q} [f(x)]^{(p/q)-1} \cdot f'(x)$$

Thus,
$$h'(x) = r[f(x)]^{r-1} \cdot f'(x)$$

Example 7. If $h(x) = (x^3 + 2x + 1)^{2/3}$, then $h'(x) = \frac{2}{3}(x^3 + 2x + 1)^{-1/3}(3x^2 + 2)$.

Example 8. If $f(x) = \sqrt{x^4 + 7}$, then $f(x) = (x^4 + 7)^{1/2}$ and

$$f'(x) = \frac{1}{2}(x^4 + 7)^{-1/2}(4x^3)$$

Example 9. If $g(x) = \dfrac{(x^3 + 2)^{5/3}}{3x + 1}$, then

$$g'(x) = \frac{(3x + 1)(\frac{5}{3})(x^3 + 2)^{2/3}(3x^2) - (x^3 + 2)^{5/3}(3)}{(3x + 1)^2}$$

$$= \frac{(3x + 1)(x^3 + 2)^{2/3}(5x^2) - (x^3 + 2)^{5/3}(3)}{(3x + 1)^2}$$

$$= \frac{(x^3 + 2)^{2/3}(15x^3 + 5x^2 - 3x^3 - 6)}{(3x + 1)^2}$$

$$= \frac{(x^3 + 2)^{2/3}(12x^3 + 5x^2 - 6)}{(3x + 1)^2}$$

EXERCISES

For each function f in Exercises 1 through 20, find the derivative $f'(x)$ by using the stated theorems.

1. $f(x) = 5x^3 + 7x$

2. $f(x) = 4x^3 - 3x^2 + 15$

3. $f(x) = x^{15} - 6x^3 + 11$

4. $f(x) = 5x^2 - 9x + 3$

5. $f(x) = x^{4/3}$

6. $f(x) = x^{2/3}$

7. $f(x) = x^{-2/3}$

8. $f(x) = 4x^{1/2} + 6x^{2/3}$

9. $f(x) = \dfrac{3x + 5}{2x - 6}$

10. $f(x) = \dfrac{4x + 3}{5x + 2}$

11. $f(x) = \dfrac{3x + 1}{x^2 + 4}$

12. $f(x) = \dfrac{3x^2 - 5}{x^3 + 1}$

13. $f(x) = (3x^5 - 4x)^{2/3}$

14. $f(x) = (7x^2 - 2x + 5)^{5/7}$

15. $f(x) = x(3x + 2)^{4/3}$

16. $f(x) = x(x^2 + 9)^{2/9}$

17. $f(x) = x^2(x + 3)^{1/2}$

18. $f(x) = x^3(3x^2 + 2)^{2/5}$

19. $f(x) = \dfrac{x + 3}{(2x + 5)^{1/2}}$

20. $f(x) = \dfrac{3x - 11}{(x^2 + 5)^{3/2}}$

*21. Prove part (a) of Theorem 1. *Hint:*

$$\frac{h(x) - h(t)}{x - t} = \frac{[f(x) + g(x)] - [f(t) + g(t)]}{x - t}$$

$$= \frac{f(x) - f(t)}{x - t} + \frac{g(x) - g(t)}{x - t}$$

*22. Prove part (b) of Theorem 1.

*23. Prove part (c) of Theorem 1. *Hint:* $f(x) - g(x) = f(x) + (-1)g(x)$

*24. Prove part (d) of Theorem 1. *Hint:*

$$\frac{f(x)g(x) - f(t)g(t)}{x - t} = \frac{f(x)g(x) - f(x)g(t) + f(x)g(t) - f(t)g(t)}{x - t}$$

$$= f(x)\frac{g(x) - g(t)}{x - t} + g(t)\frac{f(x) - f(t)}{x - t}$$

*25. Prove part (e) of Theorem 1. *Hint:*

$$\frac{[f(x)/g(x)] - [f(t)/g(t)]}{x - t} = \frac{f(x)g(t) - g(x)f(t)}{g(x)g(t)(x - t)}$$

$$= \frac{f(x)g(t) - f(t)g(t) + f(t)g(t) - f(t)g(x)}{g(x)g(t)(x - t)}$$

3. MAXIMA AND MINIMA

As we have seen, one very important application of the derivative is solving maxima and minima problems.   Let us look more carefully at the basic concepts involved and the associated theory.

absolute maximum

A function f is said to have an *absolute maximum* at t if t is in the domain of f and $f(t) \geq f(x)$ for *every* x in the domain of f.   Similarly, a function f is said to have an *absolute minimum* at t if t is in the domain of f and $f(t) \leq f(x)$ for *every* x in the domain of f.   Let f be the function defined by $f(x) = (x - 1)^2$.   It is obvious from the graph of f in Figure 12.5 that f has an absolute minimum *at* 1; the absolute minimum of f is $f(1) = 0$.   The function does not have an absolute maximum.

absolute minimum

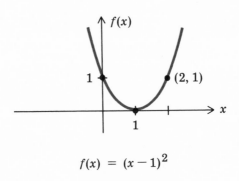

$$f(x) \;=\; (x-1)^2$$

FIGURE 12.5

local maximum

Consider an open interval $a < x < b$ in the domain of a function f.   If there exists a number t in the open interval such that $f(t) \geq f(x)$ for each x in the open interval then $f(t)$ is called a *local maximum* of f.   Similarly, if there exists a number t in the open interval such that $f(t) \leq f(x)$ for each x in the open interval then $f(t)$ is called a *local minimum* of f.   For f defined by $f(x) = (x - 1)^2$, $f(1) = 0$ is a local minimum as well as an absolute minimum.

local minimum

Consider the function g defined by $g(x) = x^3 - 5x^2 - 6x$; its graph is given in Figure 12.6.   Geometrically, it is obvious that the function has neither an absolute maximum nor an absolute minimum.   However, it is geometrically obvious that the function does have a local maximum between -1 and 0 and a local minimum between 0 and 6. In Example 1, we shall actually determine the local maximum and local minimum of g.

What is needed are necessary conditions for local maxima (or minima).   If f is a differentiable function in some open interval and if $f(t)$ is a local maximum (or local minimum) then we can conclude that

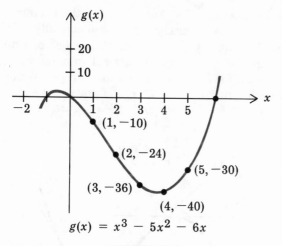

$$g(x) = x^3 - 5x^2 - 6x$$

FIGURE 12.6

$f'(t) = 0$; that is, the slope of the tangent line at the point is zero. It is extremely important to understand that we have not asserted that if $f'(t) = 0$ then $f(t)$ must be a local maximum (or local minimum). In fact, it need not be the case. For example, for the function f defined by $f(x) = x^3$ we see that $f'(0) = 0$ but $f(0) = 0$ is neither a local maximum nor local minimum; $f(x) < 0$ for $x < 0$ and $f(x) > 0$ for $x > 0$. (See Figure 12.7.)

For a differentiable function we have stated that the values for x such that $f'(x) = 0$ are "candidates" for maxima and minima points. Next, what is needed are sufficient conditions for local maxima (or local minima). If f is a differentiable function in some open interval containing t such that $f'(t) = 0$, $f'(x) > 0$ for each x in the open in-

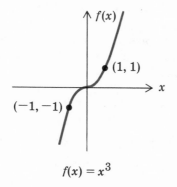

$$f(x) = x^3$$

FIGURE 12.7

terval where $x < t$, and $f'(x) < 0$ for each x in the open interval where $x > t$, then $f(t)$ is a local maximum. Geometrically, if the tangent line has zero slope at t, positive slope to the left of t and negative slope to the right of t, then $f(t)$ is a local maximum. (See Figure 12.8.) Similarly, if f is a differentiable function in some open interval containing u such that $f'(u) = 0$, $f'(x) < 0$ for $x < u$ and $f'(x) > 0$ for $x > u$, then $f(u)$ is a local minimum. (See Figure 12.8.)

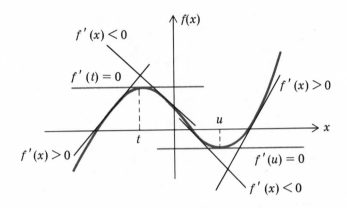

f(t) is a local maximum
f(u) is a local minimum

FIGURE 12.8

For a differentiable function f we need to determine at each t where $f'(t) = 0$ if $f(t)$ is a local maximum or local minimum. Fortunately, however, in many practical applications it is obvious that the function has one and only one local maximum (or local minimum) and evaluating the derivative on each side of t is not necessary (though perhaps comforting).

The following examples are not only of considerable interest but should adequately exhibit the techniques involved in finding maxima and minima of functions.

Example 1. Find any local maxima or minima for the function g defined by $g(x) = x^3 - 5x^2 - 6x$. (See Figure 12.6.)

Solution: $g'(x) = 3x^2 - 10x - 6$. Now, $3x^2 - 10x - 6 = 0$ if and only if

$$x = \frac{10 \pm \sqrt{100 + 72}}{6}$$

Thus, $\quad x_1 = \dfrac{10 + 2\sqrt{43}}{6} = \dfrac{5 + \sqrt{43}}{3} \quad$ and $\quad x_2 = \dfrac{5 - \sqrt{43}}{3}$

Since
$$3 < \frac{5 + \sqrt{43}}{3} < 4,$$

since $\qquad\qquad g'(3) = 27 - 30 - 6 = -9 < 0$

and since $\qquad\qquad g'(4) = 48 - 40 - 6 = 2 > 0$

it follows that $g\left(\dfrac{5 + \sqrt{43}}{3}\right)$ is a local minimum. Similarly, we can prove

that $g\left(\dfrac{5 - \sqrt{43}}{3}\right)$ is a local maximum.

Example 2. Find the positive real number such that the sum of the number and its reciprocal is a minimum.

Solution: If x is the number then $x > 0$ and the sum we wish to minimize is given by

$$s(x) = x + \frac{1}{x}$$

Now, $s'(x) = 1 - 1/x^2$. Setting $s'(x) = 0$ we obtain that the only positive number for which $1 - 1/x^2 = 0$ is $x = 1$. Provided the problem has a solution it must be 1; however, let us make certain. We see that $s'(x) < 0$ where $\frac{1}{2} < x < 1$ and $s'(x) > 0$ where $1 < x < 2$; thus, $s(1) = 2$ is a local minimum. Furthermore, since $s'(x)$ is not zero for any other positive x and since $s(x) > 0$ for $x > 0$, the absolute minimum is 2 and it is at $x = 1$.

Example 3. Find two numbers whose sum is 30 such that the sum of their squares is a minimum.

Solution: Let x be one number. Then $30 - x$ is the second and

$$f(x) = x^2 + (30 - x)^2 = 2x^2 - 60x + 900$$

is the function we wish to minimize. Now, $f'(x) = 4x - 60$, and $f'(x) = 0$ for $x = 15$. Furthermore, $f'(x) < 0$ for $x < 15$ and $f'(x) > 0$ for $x > 15$. Thus, $x = 15$ and $30 - x = 15$ are the numbers.

Example 4. A rectangular box with a square bottom is to contain 100 cubic inches. If the cost of the material for the top and bottom is 4 cents per square inch and the cost of the material for the sides is 5 cents per square inch, what dimensions should be used in order to minimize the cost of the box?

Solution: Let x be the length of one side of the square bottom. Thus, x is the width. If y is the height then $x^2 y = 100$ and $y = 100/x^2$. The total area of the bottom and top is $2x^2$ so the total cost of the top and bottom is $8x^2$. The area of all four sides is $4xy = 4x(100/x^2) = 400/x$ and the total cost of all four sides is $2{,}000/x$. Therefore, the cost function is given by

$$c(x) = 8x^2 + \frac{2{,}000}{x}$$

Thus, $c'(x) = 16x - \dfrac{2{,}000}{x^2} = \dfrac{16x^3 - 2{,}000}{x^2}$. We find that $c'(x) = 0$ if and only if $16x^3 - 2{,}000 = 0$, $16x^3 = 2{,}000$, $x^3 = 125$. Thus, $x = 5$, and it is easy to verify that the function has a minimum at 5. Consequently, the dimensions should be $5 \times 5 \times 4$ to minimize the cost.

Example 5. If the surface area of a rectangular box is 60 square inches, determine the dimensions that will maximize the volume if the length of the base is twice the width.

Solution: Let x be the width of the bottom; thus, the length of the bottom and top is $2x$ and the total surface area of the top and bottom is $4x^2$. If h is the height then $2xh$ is the total surface area of two sides and $4xh$ is the total surface area of the other two sides. Therefore,

$$2xh + 4xh + 4x^2 = 60$$
$$6xh = 60 - 4x^2$$

and
$$h = \frac{30 - 2x^2}{3x}$$

The volume of the box is given by

$$V(x) = 2x^2 \left(\frac{30 - 2x^2}{3x} \right)$$

or
$$V(x) = 20x - \frac{4x^3}{3}$$

Now,
$$V'(x) = 20 - 4x^2$$

and $V'(x) = 0$ if $4x^2 = 20$, $x^2 = 5$. Therefore, the dimensions that maximize the volume are width $= \sqrt{5}$, length $= 2\sqrt{5}$, and height $= \tfrac{4}{3}\sqrt{5}$.

Example 6. A man on an island is 3 miles from a straight shore line and wishes to reach, as soon as possible, a point on shore 4 miles from the closest point on shore. If he can average 2 miles per hour rowing in a boat and 4 miles per hour walking, what route should he take?

Solution: Let P be the nearest point on shore; let D be the destination point, and let x be the distance in miles from P to the point on shore to which he should row to minimize the time. (See Figure 12.9.)

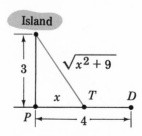

FIGURE 12.9

The distance from the island to point T is $\sqrt{x^2+9}$. Thus, the time spent rowing is $\dfrac{\text{distance}}{\text{rate}} = \dfrac{\sqrt{x^2+9}}{2}$. From T to D is $4-x$ so the time spent walking is $\dfrac{4-x}{4}$. Therefore, the total time for the trip is given by the term $f(x) = \dfrac{\sqrt{x^2+9}}{2} + \dfrac{4-x}{4} = \dfrac{(x^2+9)^{1/2}}{2} + 1 - \dfrac{x}{4}$. Thus, $f'(x) = \tfrac{1}{4}(x^2+9)^{-1/2}(2x)\tfrac{1}{4}$ and $f'(x) = 0$ if and only if $\tfrac{1}{4}(x^2+9)^{-1/2}(2x) = \tfrac{1}{4}$.

Therefore,
$$2x = (x^2+9)^{1/2}$$
$$4x^2 = x^2 + 9$$
$$3x^2 = 9$$
$$x^2 = 3$$

Since $x > 0$ in our application, $x = \sqrt{3}$ miles is the distance from P toward which he should row to minimize the time.

Example 7. A vertical wall 6 feet high stands on level ground 3 feet from a building. What is the shortest ladder resting on the ground that can reach over the wall and lean against the building?

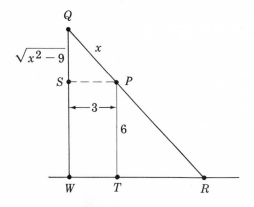

FIGURE 12.10

Solution: (See Figure 12.10.) $x = |QP|$. Thus, $|QS| = \sqrt{x^2-9}$. By similar right triangles,
$$\frac{|PR|}{x} = \frac{6}{\sqrt{x^2-9}} \quad \text{and} \quad |PR| = 6x(x^2-9)^{-1/2}$$

Therefore, the length L of the ladder is given by
$$L(x) = x + 6x(x^2-9)^{-1/2}$$

Hence, $L'(x) = 1 + 6x(-\tfrac{1}{2})(x^2-9)^{-3/2}(2x) + (x^2-9)^{-1/2}(6)$

and $L'(x) = 0$ if and only if
$$1 - 6x^2(x^2-9)^{-3/2} + 6(x^2-9)^{-1/2} = 0$$

327

Thus,
$$(x^2 - 9)^{3/2} - 6x^2 + 6x^2 - 54 = 0$$
$$(x^2 - 9)^{3/2} = 54$$
$$(x^2 - 9)^3 = (54)^2$$
$$x^2 - 9 = \sqrt[3]{54^2}$$
$$x^2 = 9 + 9\sqrt[3]{4}$$
$$x = \sqrt{9 + 9\sqrt[3]{4}}$$
$$x = 3(1 + 2^{2/3})^{1/2}$$

Substituting in $L(x) = x + 6x(x^2 - 9)^{-1/2}$, we obtain
$$L(x) = 3(2^{2/3} + 1)^{3/2}$$
$$\approx 12.5 \text{ ft}$$

Example 8. Suppose a large soup company wants to minimize the cost of a can (right circular cylinder) that is to contain K cubic inches. What should be the ratio of the height to the radius of the can?

Solution: The volume of the can is the area of the circular base times the altitude h. If r is the radius of the base, then
$$K = \pi r^2 h$$

Consequently,
$$h = \frac{K}{\pi r^2}$$

The surface area of the can (amount of metal needed) is the sum of the areas of the top, bottom, and side. The top and bottom areas are each πr^2. The area of the side is $2\pi rh$. (The area of the side could be derived by cutting the can vertically down the side and flattening it into a rectangular surface whose width is h and length is the circumference of the can. See Figure 12.11.)

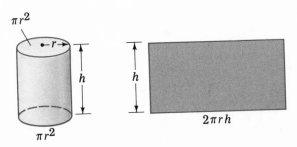

FIGURE 12.11

Thus, the total surface area is
$$2\pi rh + 2\pi r^2$$

Since $h = K/\pi r^2$, we can determine the surface area S in terms of the variable r.

$$S(r) = 2\pi r \, \frac{K}{\pi r^2} + 2\pi r^2$$

$$S(r) = \frac{2K}{r} + 2\pi r^2$$

We could sketch a graph of the function but the physical aspects tell us that there must exist a given radius that minimizes S. Furthermore, it will be the r such that $S'(r) = 0$.

$$S'(r) = \frac{-2K}{r^2} + 4\pi r$$

$S'(r) = 0$ if and only if

$$4\pi r = \frac{2K}{r^2}$$

$$r^3 = \frac{K}{2\pi}$$

Since $K = \pi r^2 h$, it follows that S will be minimized when

$$r^3 = \frac{\pi r^2 h}{2\pi}$$

or

$$r = \frac{h}{2}$$

Hence, the most economical ratio for the height to the radius is 2; in other words, the most economical can should have the diameter equal to the height.

Example 9. (Rate of Change.) Let a cistern be the shape of an inverted right circular cone with altitude 15 feet and radius 5 feet. If water is being pumped in at 12 cubic feet per minute, at what rate is the depth h of the water increasing when the depth is 4 feet? (See Figure 12.12.)

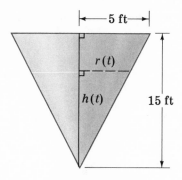

FIGURE 12.12

Solution: [As we observed with velocity, the derivative represents a rate of change. We are given that the rate of change of volume V with respect to time t is 12 cubic feet per minute; hence, $V'(t) = 12$. We wish to find $h'(t)$ when $h(t) = 4$ feet.] By similar right triangles we see from the figure that

$$\frac{5}{15} = \frac{r(t)}{h(t)}$$

Thus, $r(t) = \frac{1}{3}h(t)$. Since the volume of water $V(t)$ is given by

$$V(t) = \frac{1}{3} \pi [r(t)]^2 h(t)$$

$$= \frac{\pi}{3} \left[\frac{1}{3} h(t)\right]^2 h(t)$$

$$= \frac{\pi}{27} [h(t)]^3$$

we obtain

$$V'(t) = \frac{\pi}{9} [h(t)]^2 h'(t)$$

Since $V'(t) = 12$

$$12 = \frac{\pi}{9} [h(t)]^2 h'(t)$$

and

$$h'(t) = \frac{108}{\pi [h(t)]^2}$$

Therefore, when $h(t) = 4$,

$$h'(t) = \frac{108}{\pi(4)^2} = \frac{27}{4\pi}$$

and the depth is increasing at $27/4\pi$ feet per minute.

EXERCISES

Find any relative maxima or minima of the functions defined in Exercises 1 through 6. Sketch the graph.

1. $f(x) = x^3 + x^2$

2. $f(t) = x^2 - x^3$

3. $g(x) = 3x^3 + 9x + 3$

4. $F(x) = 2x^3 - 12x + 3$

5. $G(x) = x^3 - 6x^2 - 15x$

6. $h(x) = x^3 - x^2 + x - 1$

7. Find the positive real number such that the sum of the number and twice its reciprocal is a minimum.

8. A rectangular box with a square bottom is to be made from two different materials and contain 200 cubic inches. If the cost of the top and bottom is six cents per square inch and the cost of the sides is two cents per square inch, find the most economical dimensions for the box.

9. Suppose a rectangular piece of metal with dimensions 13 inches by 20 inches is to be made into a box with an open top by cutting out squares from the corners and turning up the sides. What is the length of the sides of the squares to be cut out that would maximize the volume?

10. Find the most economical dimensions for a box open at the top with fixed volume whose base is a rectangle with a length three times as long as its width.

11. Find the most economical dimensions for a covered box with a fixed volume whose base is a rectangle with length three times as long as its width.

12. A ship starts from a point A 50 miles directly north of a point B and sails east at 15 miles per hour. At the same time the first ship sails, a second ship sails north from point B at 20 miles per hour. How long after they set sail are the ships closest to each other?

13. A printed page is to contain 50 square inches of print. If the top and bottom margins are to be 1 inch in width and the margins at the sides are to be $1/2$ inch, what are the most economical dimensions for the page?

14. Ship A leaves point P at noon and sails due north at 10 miles per hour. Ship B starts at noon at a point 80 miles east of P and sails due west at 6 miles per hour. At what time is the distance between the ships a minimum?

15. The volume of a cube is increasing at 200 cubic inches per minute. How fast is the edge increasing when it is 10 inches?

16. A cistern in the shape of an inverted right circular cone has altitude 16 feet and radius 4 feet. If water is being pumped in at 13 cubic feet per minute, at what rate is the depth of the water increasing when the depth is 6 feet?

*17. Find the dimensions of the right circular cylinder of maximum volume that can be inscribed in a sphere of radius R.

*18. Suppose a cylindrical tank with fixed volume K is to be open at the top. What should the ratio of the height h to the radius r be in order to minimize the cost?

*19. Water is being pumped into a hemispherical tank of radius 12 feet at the rate of 10 cubic feet per minute. How fast is the water level rising when the water is 4 feet deep at the center?

*20. Water is being pumped at 15 cubic feet per second into a right circular cone that rests on its base. Its altitude is 10 feet and the radius of the base is 15 feet. If, when the depth of water is 4 feet, the depth is increasing at 0.05 feet per second, how fast is the water draining through a hole in the bottom of the tank?

4. ANTIDERIVATIVES

antiderivative

Suppose $f(x) = 2x$. A function F such that $F'(x) = f(x)$ for each real number x is called an *antiderivative* of f. From our experience in the last section, we know that $F(x) = x^2$ is an antiderivative of f since $F'(x) = 2x = f(x)$. Of course, $G(x) = x^2 + 5$ is another antiderivative of f since $G'(x) = 2x = f(x)$.

In general, let F and f be functions such that $F'(x) = f(x)$ for each x in the domain of f, then F is called an *antiderivative* of f. If F is an antiderivative of f, we write

$$\int f = F \qquad \text{or} \qquad \int f(x) \; dx = F(x)$$

Thus, we conclude from the preceding paragraph that

$$\int 2x \; dx = x^2 \qquad \text{and} \qquad \int 2x \; dx = x^2 + 5$$

Suppose F and G are two antiderivatives of a function f. $F'(x) = f(x)$ and $G'(x) = f(x)$. If we let D be the difference of the functions F and G then

$$D(x) = F(x) - G(x)$$

Thus,
$$D'(x) = F'(x) - G'(x)$$
and
$$D'(x) = f(x) - f(x) = 0$$

In the last section we proved that the derivative of a constant function was zero but we did not prove the converse theorem. However, it is true that if the derivative of a function is zero for each x in the domain then the function is a constant function. Hence, $D'(x) = 0$ implies $D(x) = C$ where C is a constant; consequently,

$$F(x) - G(x) = C$$
and
$$F(x) = G(x) + C$$

Therefore, antiderivatives of a function differ at most by a constant.

Finding the antiderivative, if it exists, of a given function is often more difficult than finding its derivative. We do have a few theorems that will help us to obtain antiderivatives. First, however, we should realize that each time we find the derivative of a given function we automatically have an antiderivative "formula." Consider the following examples.

Example 1. Let F be defined by $F(x) = x^3 + 6x^2 - 5x + 10$. Since $F'(x) = 3x^2 + 12x - 5$, it follows that

$$\int (3x^2 + 12x - 5) \ dx = x^3 + 6x^2 - 5x + C$$

Example 2. Let F be defined by $F(x) = (x^2 + 5)^{5/3}$. Since $F'(x) = \tfrac{5}{3}(x^2 + 5)^{2/3}(2x)$, it follows that

$$\int \tfrac{5}{3}(x^2 + 5)^{2/3}(2x) \ dx = (x^2 + 5)^{5/3} + C$$

Let us discuss a few important antidifferentiation theorems that are of considerable value in finding antiderivatives. Each theorem is an immediate consequence of one of the differentiation theorems stated in the last section and are usually remembered as follows: (1) The antiderivative of a constant times a function is the constant times the antiderivative of the function. (2) The antiderivative of the sum of two functions is the sum of the antiderivatives of the given functions. (3) The antiderivative of the difference of two functions is the difference of the antiderivatives of the given functions.

Theorem 1.

$$\int kf(x) \ dx = k \int f(x) \ dx + C$$

Theorem 2.

$$\int [f(x) + g(x)] \ dx = \int f(x) \ dx + \int g(x) \ dx + C$$

Theorem 3.

$$\int [f(x) - g(x)] \ dx = \int f(x) \ dx - \int g(x) \ dx + C$$

Let $F(x) = \dfrac{[f(x)]^{r+1}}{r+1}$ where r is a rational number *different* from

333

−1. Since

$$F'(x) = \frac{(r+1)[f(x)]^r \cdot f'(x)}{r+1} = [f(x)]^r \cdot f'(x)$$

we have the following very useful theorem:

Theorem 4.

$$\int [f(x)]^r \cdot f'(x) \ dx = \frac{[f(x)]^{r+1}}{r+1} + C \qquad \text{provided } r \neq -1$$

Example 3.

$$\int (x^2 + 1)^{5/3} 2x \ dx = \tfrac{3}{8}(x^2 + 1)^{8/3} + C$$

Example 4.

$$\int (x^3 + 1)^{10} x^2 \ dx = \frac{1}{3} \int (x^3 + 1)^{10} 3x^2 \ dx$$

$$= \frac{1}{3} \frac{(x^3 + 1)^{11}}{11} + C$$

Example 5.

$$\int (x^2 + 3x + 1)^{1/2} (2x + 3) \ dx = \tfrac{2}{3}(x^2 + 3x + 1)^{3/2} + C$$

Example 6.

$$\int \frac{x}{(x^2 + 4)^{4/3}} \ dx = \frac{1}{2} \int (x^2 + 4)^{-4/3} 2x \ dx$$

$$= -\tfrac{3}{2}(x^2 + 4)^{-1/3} + C$$

EXERCISES

In Exercises 1 through 14, find the indicated antiderivatives.

1. $\int (x^2 - 5x + 3) \ dx$

2. $\int (x^3 + 10x^2 - 6) \ dx$

3. $\int (x^3 - x) \ dx$

4. $\int (x^6 - 5x^2 + 7x - 3) \ dx$

5. $\int (x^{3/2} - 7x) \ dx$

6. $\int (2x^{1/2} - 4x^{1/3}) \ dx$

7. $\int \frac{x^4 - 6x^3 + 5}{x^2} \ dx$

8. $\int \frac{x^{17} - 6x^3 - 3}{x^2} \ dx$

9. $\displaystyle\int (x^2+1)^5\, 2x\, dx$

10. $\displaystyle\int \sqrt{7x^3+6}\;(21x^2)\, dx$

11. $\displaystyle\int (3x^2-5)^{4/3}x\, dx$

12. $\displaystyle\int x\sqrt{x^2+1}\, dx$

13. $\displaystyle\int \frac{2x-5}{\sqrt{x^2-5x+6}}\, dx$

14. $\displaystyle\int \frac{x^3}{(x^4+1)^{5/3}}\, dx$

Gottfried Wilhelm Leibniz (1646–1716)

Gottfried Wilhelm Leibniz was born in Leipzig, Germany, on July 1, 1646. He entered the University of Leipzig as a student of law at the age of fifteen, and in 1666 he obtained his doctorate in law. It was not until 1672, at the age of twenty-six, that he developed his interest in mathematics; this interest was initiated and encouraged by the famous physicist and mathematician, Christiaan Huygens (1629–1695).

Leibniz developed calculus between 1673 and 1676, some time after Newton developed the calculus but considerably before Newton published any of his results. Unfortunately, a battle raged for years over whether Newton or Leibniz should have had the credit for creating the calculus; during the fray, both Newton and Leibniz were accused of plagiarism. But in fact, as has been the occasion before and since in mathematics, the time was right for two fertile minds to make similar mathematical discoveries independently. Although Euler originated the sigma notation Σ, Leibniz introduced into calculus the integral sign $\int$ and many other notations. Eventually, he was made a member of the Royal Society in England, and both he and Newton were among the first foreigners to be made members of the French Academy of Sciences. Leibniz founded the Berlin Academy of Sciences and became its first President. Truly a universal genius, he was a "Jack of all trades," and, as stated by E. T. Bell, "as a diplomat and statesman Leibniz was as good as the cream of the best of them in any time or any place, and far brainier than all of them together."

13 Integral Calculus

1. Introduction
2. The Riemann Integral
3. Volume (Optional)

There is no branch of mathematics however abstract which may not some day be applied to phenomena of the real world.

NICHOLAUS IVANOVICH LOBACHEVSKI

1. INTRODUCTION

Consider a function f defined by $f(x) = x^2 + 1$. (See Figure 13.1.) What is the area of the shaded region bounded by the graph of f, the x axis, the y axis and the line $x = 4$?

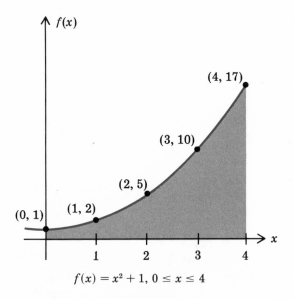

$$f(x) = x^2 + 1, \ 0 \le x \le 4$$

FIGURE 13.1

We learned techniques in geometry to assign area to regions such as squares, rectangles, triangles, trapezoids, parallelograms, etc. But no technique was discussed to assign area to such regions as in Figure 13.1. Let us analyze the problem carefully.

338

We see by the graph that the area A of the shaded region in Figure 13.1 must be less than the area of the trapezoid shown in Figure 13.2. Since the area of the trapezoid is

$$\tfrac{1}{2}(b_1 + b_2)h = \tfrac{1}{2}(1 + 17)(4) = 36 \text{ square units}$$

it is obvious that $A < 36$ square units.

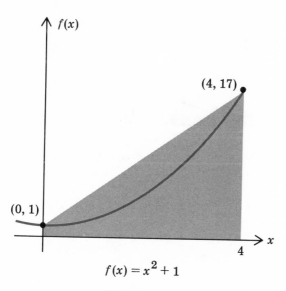

$$f(x) = x^2 + 1$$

FIGURE 13.2

If we inscribe two rectangles of equal widths as in Figure 13.3a and denote their total area by L_2, we see that

$$L_2 = (2 \times 1) + (2 \times 5) = 12 \text{ square units}$$

Similarly, if U_2 denotes the total area of the two circumscribed rectangles with equal widths as indicated in Figure 13.3b, then

$$U_2 = (2 \times 5) + (2 \times 17) = 44 \text{ square units}$$

One might deduce that the area would be close to the (arithmetic) mean of L_2 and U_2; thus, $\dfrac{L_2 + U_2}{2} = \dfrac{12 + 44}{2} = 28$ square units would be an approximation of the area. Although we might guess whether or not this approximation is too small, what is needed is a more systematic approach to the problem.

Let us refine our technique of using inscribed and circumscribed rectangles with equal widths to approximate the area. In order to

339

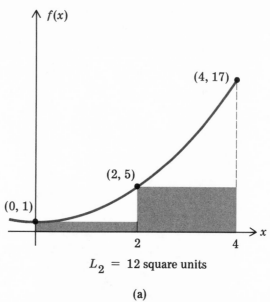

$L_2 = 12$ square units

(a)

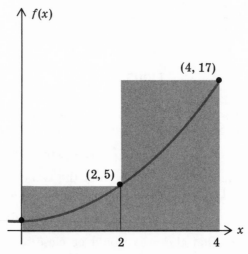

$U_2 = 44$ square units

(b)

$$L_2 < A < U_2$$

FIGURE 13.3

increase our accuracy in approximation, we increase the number of rectangles used. If eight inscribed rectangles with equal widths are used to obtain a lower approximation of the area, then the total area L_8 is given by

$$L_8 = \frac{1}{2}(1 + \frac{5}{4} + 2 + \frac{13}{4} + 5 + \frac{29}{4} + 10 + \frac{53}{4})$$
$$= \frac{43}{2} = 21\frac{1}{2} \text{ square units}$$

(See Figure 13.4.)

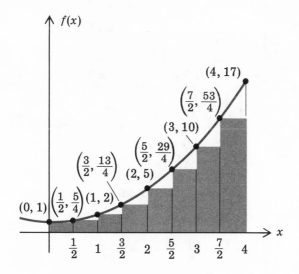

$$L_8 = 21\frac{1}{2} \text{ square units}$$

FIGURE 13.4

If U_8 is the total area of the eight circumscribed rectangles with equal widths, then an (upper) approximation is

$$U_8 = \frac{1}{2}(\frac{5}{4} + 2 + \frac{13}{4} + 5 + \frac{29}{4} + 10 + \frac{53}{4} + 17)$$
$$= \frac{59}{2} = 29\frac{1}{2} \text{ square units}$$

Notice that the arithmetic mean of L_8 and U_8 is $25\frac{1}{2}$; thus, $25\frac{1}{2}$ should be a good approximation of the area. But how good?

Let us consider a more general approach to finding the area of the indicated region. Our experience tells us that such a step may reap handsome dividends. First, divide the closed interval [0, 4] into *n equal* subintervals. (See Figure 13.5.) Since the width of the interval is 4, the width of each subinterval will be $4/n$. If we label each point of the subdivision by $x_0, x_1, x_2, x_3, \ldots, x_n$ where $x_0 = 0$ and x_n

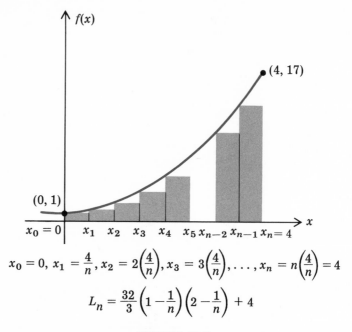

$$x_0 = 0, \ x_1 = \frac{4}{n}, x_2 = 2\left(\frac{4}{n}\right), x_3 = 3\left(\frac{4}{n}\right), \ldots , \ x_n = n\left(\frac{4}{n}\right) = 4$$

$$L_n = \frac{32}{3}\left(1 - \frac{1}{n}\right)\left(2 - \frac{1}{n}\right) + 4$$

FIGURE 13.5

is the endpoint of the nth subinterval, we see that

$$x_0 = 0, \quad x_1 = \frac{4}{n}, \quad x_2 = 2\left(\frac{4}{n}\right), \quad x_3 = 3\left(\frac{4}{n}\right), \ldots , \quad x_n = n\left(\frac{4}{n}\right) = 4$$

Since the function f is increasing on $[0, 4]$, the minimum value of f occurs at the left-hand endpoint of each subinterval. (See Figure 13.5.) Thus, if L_n denotes the total area of the inscribed rectangles, then L_n is given by

$$L_n = \frac{4}{n}\,f(x_0) + \frac{4}{n}\,f(x_1) + \frac{4}{n}\,f(x_2) + \frac{4}{n}\,f(x_3) + \cdots + \frac{4}{n}\,f(x_{n-1})$$

or

$$L_n = \frac{4}{n}\,[f(x_0) + f(x_1) + f(x_2) + f(x_3) + \cdots + f(x_{n-1})]$$

Thus,

$$L_n = \frac{4}{n}\,[x_0^2 + 1 + x_1^2 + 1 + x_2^2 + 1 + x_3^2 + 1 + \cdots + x_{n-1}^2 + 1]$$

$$L_n = \frac{4}{n}\,[x_0^2 + x_1^2 + x_2^2 + x_3^2 + \cdots + x_{n-1}^2 + n]$$

$$L_n = \frac{4}{n}\left[0 + \left(\frac{4}{n}\right)^2 + 2^2\left(\frac{4}{n}\right)^2 + 3^2\left(\frac{4}{n}\right)^2 + \cdots + (n-1)^2\left(\frac{4}{n}\right)^2\right] + 4$$

$$L_n = \left(\frac{4}{n}\right)^3 [1^2 + 2^2 + 3^2 + \cdots + (n-1)^2] + 4$$

We found on page 124 that the sum of the squares of the first k integers was $\dfrac{k(k+1)(2k+1)}{6}$. Thus, the sum of the squares of the first $n-1$ integers is $\dfrac{(n-1)n(2n-1)}{6}$. Consequently,

$$L_n = \left(\frac{4}{n}\right)^3 \left[\frac{(n-1)n(2n-1)}{6}\right] + 4$$

$$L_n = \frac{64}{6} \left[\frac{(n-1)n(2n-1)}{n^3}\right] + 4$$

and
$$L_n = \frac{32}{3} \left(1 - \frac{1}{n}\right)\left(2 - \frac{1}{n}\right) + 4$$

(As a check on our formula for L_n we should let $n = 2$ and let $n = 8$ to see if the results correspond with those previously derived. This is left as an exercise.) Obviously, $1/n \approx 0$ for large values of n. Thus,

$$L_n \approx {}^{32}\!/_3 (2) + 4 = {}^{76}\!/_3 = 25\frac{1}{3} \text{ square units}$$

We can derive in a similar fashion the formula for the area U_n of n circumscribed rectangles with equal widths where $f(x) = x^2 + 1$ with $[0, 4]$ as domain. It is given by

$$U_n = \frac{32}{3} \left(1 + \frac{1}{n}\right)\left(2 + \frac{1}{n}\right) + 4$$

We see for large n that

$$U_n \approx {}^{32}\!/_3 (2) + 4 = 25\frac{1}{3} \text{ square units}$$

Of course, $\qquad U_n > 25\frac{1}{3} \qquad$ for each n

It is an easy algebraic problem to prove that

$$U_n - L_n = \frac{64}{n}$$

Hence, the difference between U_n and L_n can be made as small as we please (as expected). We conclude that

Area $= 25\frac{1}{3}$ square units

We shall soon discover a remarkable technique that makes it quite easy to obtain such areas. However, if we are to understand fully the technique and have any real appreciation of its merit, it is important that we first consider several numerical examples.

EXERCISES

In Exercises 1 through 8, use the function f defined by $f(x) = x^2 + 1$ where $0 \leq x \leq 4$ and the facts derived in this section.

1. Use the formula for L_n on page 343 to verify that $L_2 = 12$ square units.
2. Use the formula for U_n on page 343 to verify that $U_2 = 44$ square units.
3. Use the formula for L_n on page 343 to verify that $L_8 = 21\frac{1}{2}$ square units.
4. Use the formula for U_n on page 343 to verify that $U_8 = 29\frac{1}{2}$ square units.
5. Use the formula for L_n on page 343 to obtain a three-place decimal approximation for L_{50}?
6. Use the formula for U_n on page 343 to obtain a three-place decimal approximation for U_{50}?
7. Derive the formula for U_n on page 343.
8. Show that $U_n - L_n = \dfrac{64}{n}$.

In Exercises 9 through 13, let f be the function defined by $f(x) = x^2$ where $1 \leq x \leq 7$ and let A be the area of the region bounded by the graph of f, the x axis and the lines $x = 1$ and $x = 7$.

9. (a) If L_6 is the total area of the six inscribed rectangles with equal widths, find L_6.
   (b) If U_6 is the total area of the six circumscribed rectangles with equal widths, find U_6.
   (c) Find the arithmetic mean of L_6 and U_6.
10. (a) If L_{12} is the total area of the twelve inscribed rectangles with equal widths, find L_{12}.
    (b) If U_{12} is the total area of the twelve circumscribed rectangles with equal widths, find U_{12}.
    (c) Find the arithmetic mean of L_{12} and U_{12}.
11. (a) If L_n is the total area of the n inscribed rectangles with equal widths, show that $L_n = 6 + 36\left(1 - \dfrac{1}{n}\right) + 36\left(1 - \dfrac{1}{n}\right)\left(2 - \dfrac{1}{n}\right)$.
    (b) Use the formula in part (a) to check your answers in 9a and 10a.
12. (a) If U_n is the total area of the n circumscribed rectangles with equal widths, show that $U_n = 6 + 36\left(1 + \dfrac{1}{n}\right) + 36\left(1 + \dfrac{1}{n}\right)\left(2 + \dfrac{1}{n}\right)$.
    (b) Use the formula in part (a) to check your answers in 9b and 10b.
13. Using the fact that $L_n \leq A \leq U_n$, determine the area A of the given region.
14. (a) Find the area of the trapezoid bounded by f defined by $f(x) = 2x + 7$, the x axis, and the lines $x = 5$ and $x = 16$.
    (b) Find an antiderivative F of $f(x) = 2x + 7$.

(c) Evaluate $F(16) - F(5)$.

(d) Compare the answer in part (c) with the area of the region.

15. (a) Find an antiderivative F of $f(x) = x^2 + 1$.

(b) Evaluate $F(4) - F(0)$.

(c) Compare the answer in part (b) with the area of the region bounded by $f(x) = x^2 + 1$, the x axis, and the lines $x = 0$ and $x = 4$.

16. (a) Find an antiderivative F of $f(x) = x^2$.

(b) Evaluate $F(7) - F(1)$.

(c) Compare the answer in part (b) with the area obtained in Exercise 13 of the region bounded by the graph of f, the x axis, and the lines $x = 1$ and $x = 7$.

In Exercises 17 and 18, let f be the function defined by $f(x) = x^3$ where $1 \le x \le 7$, and let A be the area of the region bounded by the graph of f, the x axis, and the lines $x = 1$ and $x = 7$.

17. (a) If L_6 is the total area of the six inscribed rectangles with equal widths, find L_6.

(b) If U_6 is the total area of the six circumscribed rectangles with equal widths, find U_6.

(c) Find the arithmetic mean of L_6 and U_6.

18. (a) If L_{12} is the total area of the twelve inscribed rectangles with equal widths, find L_{12}.

(b) If U_{12} is the total area of the twelve circumscribed rectangles with equal widths, find U_{12}.

(c) Find the arithmetic mean of L_{12} and U_{12}.

2. THE RIEMANN INTEGRAL

In this section, we shall define the Riemann integral by relying heavily on the examples and exercises in the last section and by using our geometric intuition to motivate the associated theory.

Let f be a function continuous on a closed interval $[a, b]$ and let $a = x_0, x_1, x_2, x_3, \ldots, x_n = b$ be the endpoints of the n-subintervals of $[a, b]$ having equal widths. If Δx (read, "delta x") represents the width of each subinterval, then $\Delta x = (b - a)/n$.

Since f is continuous on each subinterval of $[a, b]$, the function attains its minimum value at least once in each subinterval. Let $f(u_k)$ be the minimum value of f in the kth subinterval and define the *lower sum L_n of f by*   *lower sum*

$$L_n = f(u_1)\,\Delta x + f(u_2)\,\Delta x + f(u_3)\,\Delta x + \cdots + f(u_n)\,\Delta x$$

Thus, $L_n = [f(u_1) + f(u_2) + f(u_3) + \cdots + f(u_n)]\,\Delta x$

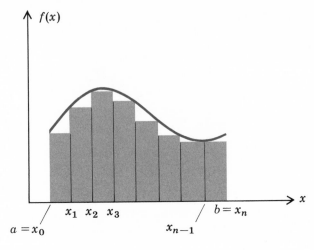

$$L_n = [f(u_1) + f(u_2) + f(u_3) + \cdots + f(u_n)] \, \Delta x$$

FIGURE 13.6

If $f(x) \geq 0$ for each x in $[a, b]$, then L_n is the area of the n-inscribed rectangles under the graph of f and above the x axis. (See Figure 13.6.)

Similarly, since f is continuous on $[a, b]$, it attains its maximum value at least once in each interval. Let $f(v_k)$ be the maximum value *upper sum* of f in the kth subinterval and defined the *upper sum* U_n of f by

$$U_n = f(v_1) \, \Delta x + f(v_2) \, \Delta x + f(v_3) \, \Delta x + \cdots + f(v_n) \, \Delta x$$

Thus, $U_n = [f(v_1) + f(v_2) + f(v_3) + \cdots + f(v_n)] \, \Delta x$

If $f(x) \geq 0$ for each x in $[a, b]$, then U_n is the area of the n-circumscribed rectangles.

For a continuous function f on $[a, b]$ we can prove that both L_n and U_n can be made arbitrarily close to a unique real number L by taking n large enough. We say that the limit of a sequence $\{L_n\}$ is L; it is denoted by

$$\lim_{n \to \infty} L_n = L$$

Of course, it also follows that

$$\lim_{n \to \infty} U_n = L$$

The real number L is called the *Riemann integral* of f (or *definite inte-*

gral of *f*) from *a* to *b*, and it is generally denoted by $\int_a^b f(x)\ dx$, or $\int_a^b f$.
Thus,

$$\lim_{n \to \infty} L_n = \lim_{n \to \infty} U_n = \int_a^b f(x)\ dx$$

If $f(x) \geq 0$ for each *x* in [*a*, *b*], then we are already aware of one *Riemann* application of the Riemann integral of *f* from *a* to *b*; it is the area *integral* bounded by the graph of *f*, the *x* axis, and the lines $x = a$ and $x = b$.

An immediate goal is to obtain an easier technique to find the Riemann integral of a given function than the one indicated in the definition. However, before stating and proving the important *Fundamental Theorem of Calculus,* which exhibits the standard technique for finding the Riemann integral of a function, let us state some theorems that can be made geometrically obvious by interpreting the Riemann integral as area of a region.

Theorem 1. *Let f be a continuous function on* [*a*, *b*]. *If a < c < b, then*

$$\int_a^c f(x)\ dx + \int_c^b f(x)\ dx = \int_a^b f(x)\ dx$$

Theorem 2. *Let f be a continuous function on* [*a*, *b*]. *If c is a constant, then*

$$\int_a^b cf(x)\ dx = c \int_a^b f(x)\ dx$$

Theorem 3. *Let f and g be continuous functions on* [*a*, *b*]. *Then*

$$\int_a^b [f(x) + g(x)]\ dx = \int_a^b f(x)\ dx + \int_a^b g(x)\ dx$$

If $f(x) \geq 0$, then Theorem 1 states that the area under the graph of *f* from *a* to *c* plus the area under the graph from *c* to *b* is the same as the area under the graph from *a* to *b*. In Theorem 2, if $c = 2$, for example, then it states that the area under the graph of the function obtained by doubling the function values of *f* is the same as twice the area under the graph of *f* between *a* and *b*. If one considers how the graph of $f + g$ can be obtained from the graphs of *f* and *g*, then Theorem 3 is also geometrically obvious.

Another important theorem that is practically as intuitively obvious as the preceding three theorems is called the *First Mean Value Theorem for Integrals.* Geometrically, it states that a rectangle exists with $b - a$ as width and a function value in the interval

347

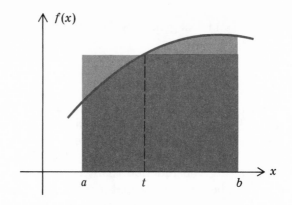

$$f(t)\,(b-a) = \int_a^b f(x)\ dx$$

FIGURE 13.7

as height such that the area of the rectangle is equal to the area under the graph of f, above the x axis, and between the lines $x = a$ and $x = b$. (See Figure 13.7.)

Theorem 4. (First Mean Value Theorem for Integrals.) *Let f be a continuous function on $[a, b]$. Then there exists a real number t in the interval such that*

$$f(t)\,(b-a) = \int_a^b f(x)\ dx$$

In order that the Riemann integral be defined from a to b where a and b are any real numbers we make the following definitions. Let f be a continuous function on a closed interval $[a, b]$. Then

$$\int_a^a f(x)\ dx = 0$$

and

$$\int_b^a f(x)\ dx = -\int_a^b f(x)\ dx$$

On the basis of the definitions, it is not difficult (though tedious) to prove that Theorems 1, 2, 3, and 4 are all valid for any two real numbers a and b.

In the last exercise set, we gave some hint of the technique used to evaluate Riemann integrals. Let us now state and prove the remarkable theorem which exhibits and verifies the correctness of the technique.

Theorem 5. (Fundamental Theorem of Calculus.) *Let f be a continuous function on* [a, b]. *Then there exists a function H such that* $H'(t) = f(t)$ *for each t in* [a, b]. *(In other words, f has an antiderivative.) Furthermore, if F is any antiderivative of f, then*

$$\int_a^b f(x)\ dx = F(b) - F(a)$$

Proof: PART 1. Since *f* is continuous on [a, b], the Riemann integral $\int_a^u f(x)\ dx$ exists for each *u* in [a, b]. Let *H* be the function defined by

$$H(u) = \int_a^u f(x)\ dx$$

From the definition of the derivative,

$$H'(t) = \lim_{u \to t} \frac{H(u) - H(t)}{u - t}$$

Thus, from the definition of *H*,

$$H'(t) = \lim_{u \to t} \frac{\displaystyle\int_a^u f(x)\ dx - \int_a^t f(x)\ dx}{u - t}$$

From Theorem 1, it follows that

$$H'(t) = \lim_{u \to t} \frac{\displaystyle\int_t^u f(x)\ dx}{u - t}$$

Using Theorem 4, the First Mean Value Theorem for Integrals, we know that there exists a *v* between *u* and *t* such that

$$H'(t) = \lim_{u \to t} \frac{f(v)(u - t)}{u - t}$$

Since *v* is between *u* and *t*, as *u* approaches *t* we know that *v* approaches *t*. The continuity of *f* implies that

$$\lim_{v \to t} f(v) = f(t)$$

hence,
$$H'(t) = f(t)$$

PART 2. Let *F* be any antiderivative of *f*. Since the function *H* defined in Part 1 is also an antiderivative of *f*, we know for each *x* in [a, b] that

$$F(x) - H(x) = C$$

349

where C is a constant. Since $H(a) = 0$, it follows that $F(a) = C$. Therefore,

$$F(b) - H(b) = F(a)$$

or
$$H(b) = F(b) - F(a)$$

From the definition of H we conclude that

$$\int_a^b f(x) \ dx = F(b) - F(a)$$

Although we used the First Mean Value Theorem for Integrals to prove Part 1 of the Fundamental Theorem of Calculus, it can also be made obvious by geometric consideration. Note that the numerator of

$$\frac{\int_t^u f(x) \ dx}{u - t}$$

is the area under the graph of f that is above the x axis and between t and u. (See Figure 13.8.) If u is close to t, then the region is almost a rectangle. Since the area of the rectangle divided by the width of the base is the height of the rectangle, we see that

$$H'(t) = f(t)$$

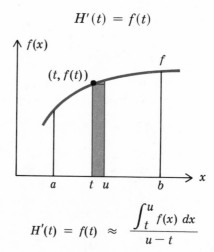

$$H'(t) = f(t) \approx \frac{\int_t^u f(x) \ dx}{u - t}$$

FIGURE 13.8

Example 1. Evaluate $\int_1^7 (3x^2 + 2) \ dx$.

Solution: Since $\int (3x^2 + 2) \ dx = x^3 + 2x$, $F(x) = x^3 + 2x$ is an antiderivative of $f(x) = 3x^2 + 2$. Thus,

$$\int_1^7 (3x^2 + 2)\ dx = F(7) - F(1)$$
$$= (343 + 14) - (1 + 2)$$
$$= 354$$

The notation $F(x)\ \Big|_a^b$ is often used to denote $F(b) - F(a)$. Therefore, the Fundamental Theorem of Calculus may also be expressed as follows:

$$\int_a^b f(x)\ dx = F(x)\ \Big|_a^b$$

Example 2. $\displaystyle\int_0^3 (x^2 - 3x + 1)\ dx = \left[\frac{x^3}{3} - \frac{3}{2}x^2 + x\right]\ \Big|_0^3$

$$= \left(9 - \frac{27}{2} + 3\right) - 0$$

$$= -\frac{3}{2}$$

Example 3. $\displaystyle\int_3^{-1} (x + 1)^{1/2}\ dx = \frac{2}{3}\ (x + 1)^{3/2}\ \Big|_3^{-1}$

$$= 0 - \frac{2}{3}\ (4)^{3/2}$$

$$= -\frac{16}{3}$$

Example 4. Find the area of the region bounded by $f(x) = x^{1/2}$ and $g(x) = x^2$.

Solution: (See Figure 13.9.) To find the intersection points of the graphs of f and g, we want to find the values for x such that $f(x) = g(x)$.

$$x^{1/2} = x^2$$
$$x^{1/2} - x^2 = 0$$
$$x^{1/2}(1 - x^{3/2}) = 0$$

Consequently, $\qquad x = 0 \qquad$ or $\qquad x = 1$

The area of the region is the difference of the area between $x = 0$ and $x = 1$, above the x axis, and under the graph of f and the area between $x = 0$ and $x = 1$, above the x axis, and under the graph of g. Thus,

$$\text{Area} = \int_0^1 x^{1/2}\ dx - \int_0^1 x^2\ dx$$

$$= \frac{2}{3}\ x^{3/2}\ \Big|_0^1 - \frac{x^3}{3}\ \Big|_0^1$$

$$= \frac{2}{3} - \frac{1}{3} = \frac{1}{3}\ \text{square units}$$

351

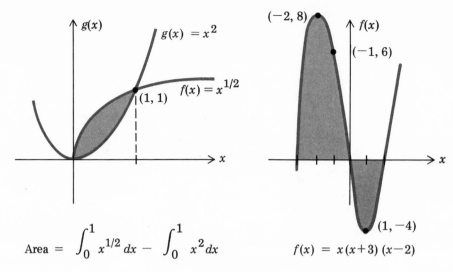

$$\text{Area} = \int_0^1 x^{1/2} \, dx - \int_0^1 x^2 \, dx \qquad f(x) = x(x+3)(x-2)$$

FIGURE 13.9

Example 5. Find the area of the regions bounded by the graph of $f(x) = x(x+3)(x-2)$ and the x axis.

Solution: (See Figure 13.9.) The area of the region between -3 and 0 is

$$\int_{-3}^0 x(x+3)(x-2) \, dx = \int_{-3}^0 (x^3 + x^2 - 6x) \, dx$$

$$= \left(\frac{x^4}{4} + \frac{x^3}{3} - \frac{6x^2}{2}\right) \Big|_{-3}^0$$

$$= 0 - \left(\frac{81}{4} - 9 - 27\right)$$

$$= \frac{63}{4} \text{ square units}$$

The area of the region between 0 and 2 will be the negative of the Riemann integral between 0 and 2; thus, the area is

$$-\int_0^2 x(x+3)(x-2) \, dx = -\int_0^2 (x^3 + x^2 - 6x) \, dx$$

$$= -\left(\frac{x^4}{4} + \frac{x^3}{3} - \frac{6x^2}{2}\right) \Big|_0^2$$

$$= -\left(4 + \frac{8}{3} - 12\right)$$

$$= \frac{16}{3} \text{ square units}$$

Therefore, the total area of the indicated regions is $^{63}/_4 + {}^{16}/_3 = {}^{253}/_{12}$ square units.

EXERCISES

In Exercises 1 through 10, evaluate each Riemann integral.

1. $\displaystyle\int_{-1}^{5} (x^2 - 2x + 5)\ dx$ 2. $\displaystyle\int_{0}^{-4} (x^3 - 5x + 7)\ dx$

3. $\displaystyle\int_{2}^{6} \left(x^3 - \frac{1}{x^3}\right) dx$ 4. $\displaystyle\int_{-1}^{1} \left(x^5 + \frac{1}{x^5}\right) dx$

5. $\displaystyle\int_{-3}^{4} (3x + 13)^{5/2}\ dx$ 6. $\displaystyle\int_{1}^{8} (3x + 1)^{3/2}\ dx$

7. $\displaystyle\int_{-2}^{2} x(x^2 + 2)^{3/2}\ dx$ 8. $\displaystyle\int_{0}^{3} x(2x^2 + 3)^{1/2}\ dx$

9. $\displaystyle\int_{0}^{1} x(x^2 + 2)^{9}\ dx$ 10. $\displaystyle\int_{0}^{-1} x(2x^2 + 1)^{5}\ dx$

In Exercises 11 through 19, find the area of each indicated region.

11. Region bounded by $f(x) = x + x^2$, $x = 1$, $x = 5$, and the x axis.
12. Region bounded by $f(x) = 3x + x^3$, $x = 1$, $x = 3$, and the x axis.
13. Region bounded by $f(x) = x^2 + 2x + 3$, $x = 0$, $x = 2$, and the x axis.
14. Region bounded by $f(x) = x^3 + 4$, $x = 0$, $x = 4$, and the x axis.
15. Region bounded by $f(x) = x^{1/2}$, $x = 4$, $x = 16$, and the x axis.
16. Region bounded by $f(x) = x^{1/3}$, $x = 8$, $x = 27$, and the x axis.
17. Region bounded by $f(x) = x^2$ and $g(x) = 18 - x^2$.
18. Region bounded by $f(x) = x$ and $g(x) = x^3$.
19. Region bounded by $f(x) = x(x - 4)(x + 5)$ and the x axis.

3. VOLUME (OPTIONAL)

The Riemann integral has many applications other than to find areas of regions in the plane. It is used in problems concerning work done by a variable force, arc length, liquid pressure, volume, etc. Let us now consider how volumes of various types of solids can be found by using the Riemann integral. We shall first find the volume of a familiar solid for which we already have a formula from geometry to obtain the volume. Next, we shall find volumes of solids for which we do not have such formulas available.

Let $f(x) = \sqrt{25 - x^2}$ where $0 \le x \le 5$. If the region bounded by the graph of f, the x axis, and the y axis is revolved about the x axis, we obtain a hemisphere with radius 5. (See Figure 13.10.)

Suppose the interval $[0, 5]$ is divided into n equal subintervals. Since f is a decreasing function on the interval, the minimum value of

353

f on the ith subinterval is $f(x_i)$. If Δx is the width of each subinterval, the volume of the ith disk obtained by revolving about the x axis the region bounded by $x = x_{i-1}$, $x = x_i$, $y = f(x_i)$ and the x axis is

$$\pi[f(x_i)]^2 \Delta x$$

since $f(x_i)$ is the radius of the disk and Δx is the width. The volume L_n of n such disks is given by

$$L_n = \pi[f(x_1)]^2 \, \Delta x + \pi[f(x_2)]^2 \, \Delta x + \pi[f(x_3)]^2 \, \Delta x + \cdots + \pi[f(x_n)]^2 \, \Delta x$$

[Actually, in our example there are only $n - 1$ inscribed disks where $f(x_i)$ is the minimum value on the ith subinterval since $f(x_n) = f(5) = 0$.]

If $F(\mathrm{x}) = \pi[f(x)]^2$, then L_n is a lower (Riemann) sum of F on $[0, 5]$. Hence, we know that $\lim\limits_{n \to \infty} L_n = \int_0^5 F(x) \, dx = \int_0^5 \pi[f(x)]^2 \, dx$. The volume V of the hemisphere is given by

$$V = \pi \int_0^5 [f(x)]^2 \, dx$$

Thus
$$V = \pi \int_0^5 (25 - x^2) \, dx$$

$$= \pi \left(25x - \frac{x^3}{3} \right) \Big|_0^5$$

$$= \pi \left(125 - \frac{125}{3} \right)$$

$$= \frac{250\pi}{3} \text{ cubic units}$$

As a check on the answer just obtained, recall that the formula for the volume of a sphere is $\frac{4}{3}\pi r^3$ where r is the radius. Hence, the volume of the given hemisphere is $\frac{1}{2}(\frac{4}{3}\pi 5^3) = 250\pi/3$.

In general, if f is a continuous function such that $f(x) \geq 0$ where x is in $[a, b]$, then the volume V of the solid obtained by revolving *about the x axis* the region bounded by the graph of f, $x = a$, $x = b$, and the x axis is given by

$$V = \pi \int_a^b [f(x)]^2 \, dx$$

disk method   This is called the *disk method* for obtaining volume.

Suppose $f(x) = \sqrt{25 - x^2}$ where $0 \leq x \leq 5$. If the region bounded by the graph of f, the x axis, and the y axis is revolved about the y axis, then we again obtain a hemisphere with radius 5. (See Figure 13.11.)

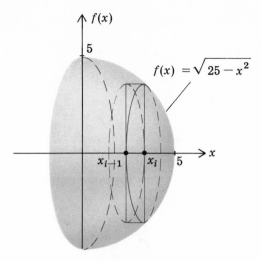

Volume of disk: $\pi[f(x_i)]^2 (x_i - x_{i-1}) = \pi[f(x_i)]^2 \Delta x$

FIGURE 13.10

Suppose the interval $[0, 5]$ is divided into n equal subintervals. Since f is decreasing in the interval, the minimum value of f on the ith subinterval is $f(x_i)$. If Δx is the width of each subinterval, the volume of the ith cylindrical shell obtained by revolving about the y axis the region bounded by $x = x_{i-1}$, $x = x_i$, $y = f(x_i)$ and the x axis is

$$2\pi\bar{x}_i f(x_i) \Delta x$$

where $\bar{x}_i$ is the midpoint between x_{i-1} and x_i. The formula for the volume of the shell can be easily verified as follows:

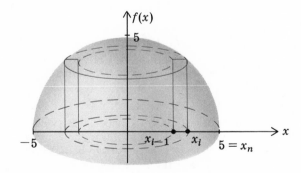

Volume of shell: $2\pi\bar{x}_i f(x_i) \Delta x$

FIGURE 13.11

355

$$2\pi \bar{x}_i\, f(x_i)\ \Delta x = 2\pi \left(\frac{x_i + x_{i-1}}{2}\right) \cdot f(x_i)(x_i - x_{i-1})$$

$$= \pi f(x_i)(x_i^2 - x_{i-1}^2)$$

$$= \pi f(x_i)x_i^2 - \pi f(x_i)\, x_{i-1}^2$$

The final difference is the volume of the outer cylinder less the volume of the inner cylinder; thus, it is the volume of the cylindrical shell.

If R_n is the volume of the n inscribed cylindrical shells, then it can be proved that $\lim\limits_{n \to \infty} R_n = \lim\limits_{n \to \infty} L_n$ where L_n is the lower sum of F defined by $F(x) = 2\pi x f(x)$. Thus, the volume V of the hemisphere is given by $V = 2\pi \displaystyle\int_0^5 x f(x)\ dx$; that is,

$$V = 2\pi \int_0^5 \sqrt{25 - x^2}\, x\ dx$$

$$= \frac{2\pi}{-2} \int_0^5 (25 - x^2)^{1/2}(-2x)\ dx$$

$$= -\pi\, \frac{2}{3}\, (25 - x^2)^{3/2}\ \Big|_0^5$$

$$= \pi\, \frac{2}{3}\, (25)^{3/2}$$

$$= \frac{250\pi}{3}\ \text{cubic units}$$

In general, if f is a continuous function such that $f(x) \geq 0$ where x is in $[a, b]$, then the volume V of the solid obtained by revolving *about the y axis* the region bounded by the graph of f, $x = a$, $x = b$, and the x axis is given by

$$V = 2\pi \int_a^b x f(x)\ dx$$

shell method   This is called the *shell method* for obtaining volumes.

Example 1. Find the volume of the solid obtained by revolving about the y axis the region bounded by $f(x) = x^2$, the y axis, and $y = 9$. (See Figure 13.12.)

Solution: The volume V of the indicated solid is the volume of the right circular cylinder with radius 3 and height 9 less the volume v of the solid obtained by revolving about the y axis the region bounded by $f(x) = x^2$, the x axis, and $x = 3$. The volume of the right circular cylinder is

$$\pi r^2 h = \pi (3)^2 9 = 81\pi$$

The volume v of the other solid is determined by the shell method.

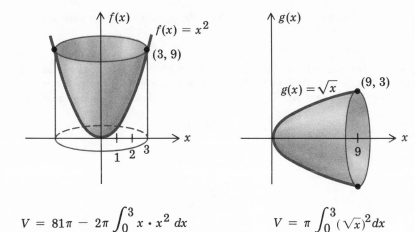

$$V = 81\pi - 2\pi \int_0^3 x \cdot x^2 \, dx \qquad\qquad V = \pi \int_0^3 (\sqrt{x})^2 dx$$

FIGURE 13.12

$$v = 2\pi \int_0^3 xf(x) \, dx$$

$$= 2\pi \int_0^3 x^3 \, dx$$

$$= 2\pi \left(\frac{x^4}{4}\right) \Big|_0^3$$

$$= \frac{81\pi}{2} \text{ cubic units}$$

Thus, the volume V of the given solid is

$$V = 81\pi - \frac{81\pi}{2} = \frac{81\pi}{2} \text{ cubic units}$$

Example 2. Check the answer to Example 1 in the following manner. Note that $g(x) = \sqrt{x}$ where $0 \le x \le 9$ is the inverse function of f. Thus, the solid obtained by revolving about the x axis the region bounded by $g(x) = \sqrt{x}$, the x axis, and $x = 9$ has the same volume. (See Figure 13.12.) Using the disk method, we find that

$$V = \pi \int_0^9 [\sqrt{x}]^2 \, dx$$

$$= \pi \int_0^9 x \, dx$$

$$= \pi \left(\frac{x^2}{2}\right) \Big|_0^9$$

$$= \frac{81\pi}{2} \text{ cubic units}$$

Example 3. Derive the formula for the volume of a right circular cone with radius r and height h.

Solution: (See Figure 13.13.) The equation of the line containing the origin and the point $(h,\, r)$ is $f(x) = (r/h)x$. Revolving about the x axis the region bounded by $f(x) = (r/h)x$, the x axis and $x = r$ generates a cone with radius r and height h. Using the disk method to obtain the volume V,

$$V = \pi \int_0^h \left[\frac{r}{h} x \right]^2 dx$$

$$= \frac{\pi r^2}{h^2} \int_0^h x^2 \, dx$$

$$= \frac{\pi r^2}{h^2} \left(\frac{x^3}{3} \right) \Big|_0^h$$

$$= \frac{\pi r^2 h}{3}$$

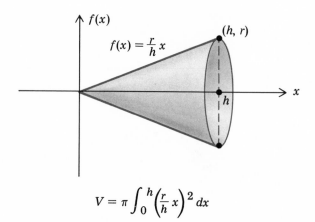

$$V = \pi \int_0^h \left(\frac{r}{h} x \right)^2 dx$$

FIGURE 13.13

EXERCISES

In Exercises 1 through 7, find the volume of the given solid.

1. The solid obtained by revolving about the x axis the region bounded by $f(x) = x^2$, the x axis, $x = 2$ and $x = 6$.

2. The solid obtained by revolving about the y axis the region bounded by $f(x) = x^2$, the x axis, $x = 2$ and $x = 6$.

3. The solid obtained by revolving about the x axis the region bounded by $f(x) = x^3$, the x axis, $x = 1$ and $x = 8$.

4. The solid obtained by revolving about the y axis the region bounded by $f(x) = x^3$, the x axis, $x = 1$ and $x = 8$.

5. The solid obtained by revolving about the x axis the region bounded by $f(x) = x - x^2$ and the x axis.

6. The solid obtained by revolving about the y axis the region bounded by $f(x) = x - x^2$ and the x axis.

7. The solid obtained by revolving about the y axis the region bounded by $f(x) = x^2$ and $g(x) = 18 - x^2$.

Richard Dedekind (1831–1916)

Richard Dedekind was born at Brunswick, Germany, on October 6, 1831. He studied under Carl Friedrich Gauss at Göttingen where he obtained his Ph.D. degree in 1852; in fact, he was the last student to receive a degree under the distinguished Gauss. Dedekind taught a short time at Göttingen and at Zurich but spent the last fifty years of his life teaching at a technical high school in Brunswick, his native city.

One of Dedekind's greatest contributions to mathematics was putting the real number system on a sound foundation. Although the existence of irrationals as nonrational lengths had been known to mathematicians for over two thousand years, it remained for Dedekind to give the first rigorous definition of irrational numbers. His development of the irrational numbers was published in 1872 in a book entitled *Continuity and Irrational Numbers.* Cantor, another great German mathematician, also developed the irrational numbers along the same lines, about the same time, but independently.

Unlike his friend, Cantor, who felt that a distinguished professorship had always been denied him because of his detractor, Leopold Kronecker, Dedekind was quite happy with his lackluster position and remained at the school by choice. Also, unlike Cantor, he maintained a great sense of humor, enjoyed life, and kept a clear and active mind until he died at the age of eighty-five.

14 Number Fields

1. Field Properties
2. Order Properties
3. Completeness Property (Optional)

1. FIELD PROPERTIES

The real number system has the properties of a *complete ordered field*. In this section, we first list the properties of a field and then show how the other familiar properties of the real number system are consequences of theorems proved using the field properties.

field

Let F be a set on which two operations are defined. The system consisting of the set and the two operations is called a *field* provided it has the following properties.

1. *Closure Property of Addition.* For each pair of elements x and y in F, a unique element in F called the *sum* is determined; it is denoted by $x + y$.
2. *Associative Property of Addition.* For each x, y, and z in F, $x + (y + z) = (x + y) + z$.
3. *Additive Identity.* There exists an element in F called the additive identity and denoted by 0 such that for each x in F, $x + 0 = x$.
4. *Additive Inverses.* For each x in F, there exists an element in F called the additive inverse of x and denoted by $-x$ such that $x + (-x) = 0$.
5. *Commutative Property of Addition.* For each pair x and y in F, $x + y = y + x$.
6. *Closure Property of Multiplication.* For each pair of elements x and y in F, a unique element in F called the *product* is determined; it is denoted by xy, or $x \cdot y$.
7. *Associative Property of Multiplication.* For each x, y, and z in F, $x(yz) = (xy)z$.
8. *Multiplicative Identity.* There exists an element in F different from the additive identity called the multiplicative identity and denoted by 1 such that for each x in F, $x \cdot 1 = x$.
9. *Multiplicative Inverses.* For each x in F, if $x \neq 0$ then there exists an element in F called the multiplicative inverse of x and denoted by x^{-1}, or $1/x$, such that $x \cdot x^{-1} = 1$.
10. *Commutative Property of Multiplication.* For each pair x and y in F, $xy = yx$.
11. *Distributive Property.* For each x, y, and z in F, $x(y + z) = xy + xz$.

From our point of view, the field properties are assumed properties (postulates) for the set of real numbers. A development of the real number system could be given where each could be derived as a theorem.

Let us use the field properties (and implicitly the properties of equality)* to prove a familiar property of the real number system.

Theorem 1. (Cancellation Property of Addition.) *Let x, y, and z be real numbers. If $x + z = y + z$, then $x = y$.*

Proof: Since z is a real number, it has an additive inverse (by Property 4 for a field). Therefore, since $x + z$ and $y + z$ are the same real number by hypothesis and since the sum of two numbers is unique by the closure property of addition, it follows that

$$(x + z) + (-z) = (y + z) + (-z)$$

From the associative property of addition, we obtain

$$x + [z + (-z)] = y + [z + (-z)]$$

Thus, $x + 0 = y + 0$ by the additive inverse property

and $x = y$ by the additive identity property

In the following exercises, we shall prove many other familiar statements about the real number system.

EXERCISES

1. Let x, y, and z be real numbers. Prove if $z + y = z + x$, then $x = y$.
2. Prove that the additive identity for the set of real numbers is unique; that is, prove if $x + 0 = x$ and $x + 0^* = x$ for each real number x, then $0 = 0^*$. (*Hint:* Why are each of the following statements true? $0 + 0^* = 0$ and $0^* + 0 = 0^*$.)
3. Prove that the multiplicative identity for the set of real numbers is unique.
4. Prove that the additive inverse of a given real number is unique.
5. Prove that the multiplicative inverse of a given real number is unique.
6. Prove that the additive inverse of the additive inverse of a real number x is x; that is, prove $[-(-x)] = x$. (*Hint:* Give reasons for the following statements.)
    (a) $x \in F$ implies $(-x) \in F$ (b) $(-x) \in F$ implies $[-(-x)] \in F$

---

* (*Equality Properties*) (a) *Reflexive.* For each x, $x = x$. (b) *Symmetric.* If $x = y$ then $y = x$. (c) *Transitive.* If $x = y$ and $y = z$ then $x = z$.

(c) $x + (-x) = 0$ (d) $(-x) + [-(-x)] = 0$
(e) $x + (-x) = [-(-x)] + (-x)$ (f) $x = -(-x)$

7. Prove for each real number x that $x \cdot 0 = 0$. (*Hint:* Give reasons for the following statements.)
(a) $0 + 1 = 1$ (b) For each $x \in F$, $x(0 + 1) = x \cdot 1$
(c) $x \cdot 0 + x \cdot 1 = x \cdot 1$ (d) $x \cdot 0 + x = x$ (e) $x \cdot 0 = 0$

8. Let x, y, and z be real numbers. Prove that if $xz = yz$ and $z \neq 0$ then $x = y$.

9. Show by example that it is necessary to assume $z \neq 0$ to prove that $xz = yz$ implies $x = y$.

10. Let x and y be real numbers. Prove that the product of x and the additive inverse of y is the additive inverse of the product xy; in other words, prove $x(-y) = -(xy)$. (*Hint:* Give reasons for the following statements.)
(a) For each x and y in F, $xy \in F$ (b) $-(xy) \in F$
(c) $-y \in F$ (d) $x(-y) \in F$
(e) $y + (-y) = 0$ (f) $x[y + (-y)] = x \cdot 0$
(g) $xy + x(-y) = 0$ (h) $xy + [-(xy)] = 0$
(i) $xy + x(-y) = xy + [-(xy)]$ (j) $x(-y) = -(xy)$

11. Let x and y be real numbers. Prove that the product of the additive inverse of x and the additive inverse of y is the product xy; that is, prove $(-x)(-y) = xy$.

12. Prove if $xy = 0$, then $x = 0$ or $y = 0$.

13. Let x and y be real numbers neither of which is zero. Prove that $(xy)^{-1} = x^{-1} \cdot y^{-1}$.

14. Prove if $x \neq 0$ then $(x^{-1})^{-1} = x$.

15. Given two real numbers a and b. If there exists a unique real number x such that $a + x = b$, then x is called the *difference of b subtract a;* symbolically, $x = b - a$. Prove that $b - a = b + (-a)$.

16. Given two real numbers a and b. If there exists a unique real number x such that $ax = b$, then x is called the *quotient of b divided by a;* symbolically, $x = b \div a$. Prove that $b \div a = b \cdot a^{-1}$ provided $a \neq 0$.

17. Let $F = \{r + s\sqrt{3} \mid r$ and s are rational numbers$\}$. Use your previous knowledge of the rational and real number systems to show that F has the field properties with respect to addition and multiplication.

18. Determine if the following mathematical system is a field where the two operations of addition and multiplication are defined on the set $\{O, I, a, b\}$ by the following tables:

+	O	I	a	b
O	O	I	a	b
I	I	O	b	a
a	a	b	O	I
b	b	a	I	O

×	O	I	a	b
O	O	O	O	O
I	O	I	a	b
a	O	a	b	I
b	O	b	I	a

2. ORDER PROPERTIES

In our effort to characterize the real number system, we have stated the field properties and studied some of their immediate consequences. Now let us state the properties of an *ordered field*.   *ordered field*

Definition. A set F with the field properties is said to be an ordered field (with respect to P) if and only if there exists a nonempty subset P of F such that each of the following is true.
1. *If $x \in P$ and $y \in P$, then $(x + y) \in P$ and $xy \in P$.*
2. *$0 \notin P$.*
3. *If $x \in F$ and $x \neq 0$, then $x \in P$ or $-x \in P$, but not both.*

We assume that the real number system has the ordered field properties. It can be proved (with some difficulty) that the real number field can be ordered with respect to only one subset P; we call this (familiar) subset P the set of *positive real numbers*. The concept   *positive real* of *positiveness* is used to define the important less-than relation on   *numbers* the set of real numbers. (We now repeat the definition given earlier.)

Definition. Let a and b be real numbers. The number a is said to be less than *the number b if and only if there exists a positive number x*   *less than* *such that $a + x = b$; symbolically, $a < b$. Furthermore, b is* greater than *a, denoted by $b > a$ if and only if $a < b$; $a \leq b$ if and only if $a < b$ or $a = b$; and $a \geq b$ if and only if $a > b$ or $a = b$.*   *greater than*

It follows from the ordered field properties and the above definitions that a real number a is positive if and only if $a > 0$. Let us prove this fact. If $a > 0$, then there exists a *positive* real number x such that $0 + x = a$. Thus, $x = a$ and a is positive. Now, suppose a is positive. Since $0 + a = a$, it follows from the definition of less-than that $0 < a$. Consequently, we have proved that $a > 0$ if and only if a is positive. We *define* a real number a to be *negative* if and only if   *negative* $a < 0$. By Assumption 2 of the order properties and by definition, zero is neither positive nor negative.

If a and b are real numbers, then one and only one of the following is true: $a < b$, $a = b$, $a > b$. This is called the *trichotomy prop-*   *trichotomy* *erty*. Let us prove the trichotomy property as a consequence of the   *property* ordered field properties and the definition of less-than.

Theorem 2. (Trichotomy Property.) *Let a and b be real numbers. Then, one and only one of the following is true: $a < b$, $a = b$, or $a > b$.*

Proof:

Statements	*Reasons*
1. Let $x = (-a) + b$	By field property 4, the additive inverse of a exists, and by field property 1 the sum of $(-a)$ and b is unique
2. $a + x = a + [(-a) + b]$	Property 1 and the reflexive property of equality
3. $a + x = [a + (-a)] + b$	Property 2 and equality properties
4. $a + x = 0 + b$	Property 4 and equality properties
5. $a + x = b$	Property 3 and equality properties
6. $(a + x) + (-x) = b + (-x)$	Step 5 and Property 1*
7. $a + [x + (-x)] = b + (-x)$	Property 2
8. $a + 0 = b + (-x)$	Property 4
9. $a = b + (-x)$	Property 3

From step 9, it follows that if $x = 0$ then $a = b$. Furthermore, if $x = 0$ then x is not positive and $-x$ is not positive; hence, $a < b$ and $a > b$ are both false. If $x \neq 0$, then x is positive or $-x$ is positive, but not both. If x is positive, $a + x = b$ in step 5 implies $a < b$ by definition of less-than. If $-x$ is positive, then from $a = b + (-x)$ in step 9 we conclude that $a > b$.

transitive property

Another important property for the ordered field of real numbers is the *transitive property* of less-than. The validity of the transitive property is intuitively obvious if we think of the usual association of real numbers with points on a number line. However, let us state it as a theorem. The proof, which is left as an exercise, is obtained by using the ordered field properties and the definition of less-than.

Theorem 3. (Transitive Property.) *Let a, b, and c be real numbers. If $a < b$ and $b < c$, then $a < c$.*

Proof: Left as an exercise.

Let us next state several theorems concerned with the less-than relation. Proofs for a few of the theorems are given; outlines for proofs of some are given; and many proofs are left as exercises for the student.

---

* Henceforth, we shall not note the obvious use of the equality properties.

Theorem 4. If $a < b$, then $a + c < b + c$.

Proof:

Statements	Reasons
1. $a < b$	1. Why?
2. There is a positive number x such that $a + x = b$	2. Why?
3. $(a + x) + c = b + c$	3. Why?
4. $a + (x + c) = b + c$	4. Why?
5. $a + (c + x) = b + c$	5. Why?
6. $(a + c) + x = b + c$	6. Why?
7. $a + c < b + c$	7. Why?

Theorem 5. Let a be a real number. If $a < 0$, then $-a > 0$.

Proof:

Statements	Reasons
1. $a < 0$	Given.
2. $a + (-a) < 0 + (-a)$	Theorem 4.
3. $0 < -a$	Field properties 3 and 4.
4. $-a > 0$	Definition of greater-than.

Theorem 6. If $a < b$, then $a - c < b - c$.

Proof: Left as an exercise.

Theorem 7. If $a < b$ and $c > 0$, then $ac < bc$.

Proof:

Statements	Reasons
1. $a < b$	1. Why?
2. $a + x = b$ where $x > 0$	2. Why?
3. $c(a + x) = cb$	3. Why?
4. $ca + cx = cb$	4. Why?
5. $ac + cx = bc$	5. Why?
6. $ac < bc$	6. Why?

Theorem 8. If $a < b$ and $c < 0$, then $ac > bc$.

Proof: Left as an exercise.

Theorem 9. Let a be any real number different from zero. Then, $a^2 > 0$.

Proof: Left as an exercise.

Theorem 10. *The multiplicative identity is greater than the additive identity; that is, $1 > 0$.*

Proof:

Statements	Reasons
1. $1 < 0$, $1 = 0$, or $1 > 0$	1. Why?
2. $1 \neq 0$	2. Why?
3. If $1 < 0$, then $1 \cdot 1 > 1 \cdot 0$.	3. Why?
4. Thus, $1 > 0$.	4. Why?
5. Statement 4 contradicts Statement 3.	5. Why?
6. Since $1 = 0$ and $1 < 0$ are both false statements, $1 > 0$.	6. Why?

Theorem 11. *Let a be any real number. If $a > 0$ then $a^{-1} > 0$.*

Proof: Left as an exercise.

Theorem 12. *Let a be any real number. If $a < 0$ then $a^{-1} < 0$.*

Proof: Left as an exercise.

Theorem 13. *Let a, b, c, and d be any real numbers.*
(a) *If $a < b$ and $c < d$, then $a + c < b + d$.*
(b) *If $a \leq b$ and $c \leq d$, then $a + c \leq b + d$.*
(c) *If $a < b$ and $c \leq d$, then $a + c < b + d$.*

Proof: Part (a)

Statements	Reasons
1. $a < b$ and $c < d$	1. Why?
2. $a + c < b + c$	2. Why?
3. $b + c < b + d$	3. Why?
4. $a + c < b + d$	4. Why?

Parts (b) and (c) are left as exercises.

Theorem 14. *If $a < b$ and $ab > 0$, then $\dfrac{1}{a} > \dfrac{1}{b}$.*

Proof: Left as an exercise.

Theorem 15. *If $ab < 0$ then either $a > 0$ and $b < 0$ or $a < 0$ and $b > 0$.*

Proof:

Statements	*Reasons*
1. $ab < 0$	Given.
2. $a \neq 0$	If a = 0, ab = 0, a contradiction.
3. $a < 0$ or $a > 0$	Trichotomy property.
4. If $a < 0$, then $a^{-1} < 0$	Theorem 12.
5. Then, $a^{-1}(ab) > a^{-1} \cdot 0$	Theorem 8.
6. $(a^{-1}a)b > 0$	Property 7 and Exercise 7, Section 1.
7. $b > 0$	Properties 9 and 8.

Thus, if $a < 0$, then $b > 0$. (It can be proved in a similar manner that if $a > 0$, then $b < 0$. This is left as an exercise.)

Theorem 16. *If $ab > 0$, then either $a > 0$ and $b > 0$ or $a < 0$ and $b < 0$.*

Proof: Left as an exercise.

EXERCISES

1. (a) Give a geometric interpretation of the trichotomy and transitive properties. (b) Prove Theorem 3.
2. Answer the questions in the proof of Theorem 4.
3. Prove Theorem 6.
4. Answer the questions in the proof of Theorem 7.
5. Prove Theorem 8.
6. Prove Theorem 9.
7. Answer the questions in the proof of Theorem 10.
8. Prove Theorem 11.
9. Prove Theorem 12.
10. Answer the questions in the proof of part (a) of the proof of Theorem 13.
11. Prove parts (b) and (c) of Theorem 13.
12. Prove Theorem 14.
13. Complete the proof of Theorem 15.
14. Prove Theorem 16.

Determine the solution set for each of the inequalities in Exercises 15 through 20.

15. $(2x + 1)(3x - 5) > 0$ 16. $(7x - 5)(5x + 3) \leq 0$

369

17. $\dfrac{3x + 13}{5x - 2} > 0$ **18.** $\dfrac{4x - 7}{5x + 8} \leq 0$

19. $\dfrac{3x - 14}{2x + 11} \leq 0$ **20.** $\dfrac{3x + 5}{2x - 4} < 8$

21. Observe that Theorem 9 is a consequence of the ordered field properties and use your previous knowledge of number systems to give an example of a field with infinitely many elements that cannot have the ordered field properties.

22. Use your previous knowledge of number systems to determine if the rational number system has the ordered field properties. (No proofs are required.)

*23. Let $<$ be defined as usual on the set of real numbers. Let $F = \{r + s\sqrt{3} \mid r$ and s are rational numbers$\}$ and let $P_1 = \{r + s\sqrt{3} \mid r + s\sqrt{3} > 0\}$. Is F an ordered field with respect to P_1? (See Section 1, Exercise 17.)

*24. Let $<$ be defined as usual on the set of real numbers. Let $F = \{r + s\sqrt{3} \mid r$ and s are rational numbers$\}$ and let $P_2 = \{r + s\sqrt{3} \mid r - s\sqrt{3} > 0\}$. Is F an ordered field with respect to P_2?

*25. Give an example of a field that can be ordered with respect to two different subsets P and P^*.

3. COMPLETENESS PROPERTY (OPTIONAL)

We should be aware of the fact that not only is the real number system a field but also the rational and complex number systems have the field properties. Thus, we speak of the real number field, the rational number field and the complex number field. As a result of Theorem 9, Section 2, we know that the complex number field cannot be an ordered field since there exists at least one element in the complex field whose square is negative. However, the rational number system does have the ordered field properties. In this section we exhibit the main distinguishing feature between the ordered field of real numbers and the ordered field of rational numbers. First, we need the concepts of least element in a set and upper bound of a set.

least element

Definition. Let S be a nonempty set of real numbers. A real number t is called the least element in S if and only if $t \in S$ and $t \leq x$ for each $x \in S$.

The least element in the set of positive integers is 1 and the least element in the set of even positive integers is 2. Some subsets of the set of real numbers have no least element. For example, the set of positive rational numbers has no least element. However, it is not difficult to prove that if a subset of the set of real numbers has a least element then it is unique.

Definition. *Let S be a nonempty set of real numbers. A real number u is called an* upper bound *of S if and only if $x \leq u$ for each $x \in S$.*   *upper bound*

Since every number in $\{3, 11, 17\}$ is less than, say, 65, it follows that 65 is an upper bound of the set. Of course, 90, 75, and $\sqrt{401}$ are also upper bounds of the set. If $T = \{x \mid x < 7\}$, then any real number greater than or equal to 7 is an upper bound of T. If $W = \{x \mid x \leq 7\}$, then any real number greater than or equal to 7 is an upper bound of W. It should be noted that although $T \neq W$, the set of upper bounds for each set is the same.

If the set of upper bounds of some given set S has a least number z in it, then z is said to be the *least upper bound* of S. Symbolically, $z = \mathrm{lub}\ S$. If $S = \{3, 11, 17\}$, $T = \{x \mid x < 7\}$, and $W = \{x \mid x \leq 7\}$, then lub $S = 17$, lub $T = 7$, and lub $W = 7$. Since $7 \notin T$ and $7 \in W$, it is obvious that if a set has a least upper bound then the least upper bound may or may not be an element in the set.

We can now state another property of the real number system.

Completeness Property. *Any nonempty set of real numbers with an*   *least upper*
upper bound has a least upper bound.   *bound*

We take completeness as an assumed property of the real number system; that is, we assume that every bounded set of real numbers has a least upper bound. It is important to observe that we do *not* assume that a set with an upper bound *contains* its least upper bound; it may or may not be a member of the set. Since the real number system   *complete*
has the ordered field and completeness properties, it is often referred to   *ordered field*
as a *complete ordered field.**

It can be proved that although $\{x \mid x$ is a positive rational number and $x^2 < 2\}$ has an upper bound, the set does not have a *rational* least upper bound. However, it does have the irrational number $\sqrt{2}$ as its least upper bound. Since both the rational number and real number systems have the ordered field properties, the completeness property is the distinguishing feature for the real number system.

Definition. *Let S be a nonempty set of real numbers. A real number t*   *greatest*
is called the greatest element *in S if and only if $t \in S$ and $x \leq t$ for*   *element*
each $x \in S$.

---

* The ordered field properties and completeness property characterize uniquely the real number system. In other words, one can prove that any system with these properties is isomorphic to the real number system.

<table>
<tr><td>lower bound</td><td>Definition. Let S be a nonempty set of real numbers. A real number v is called a lower bound of S if and only if $x \geq v$ for each $x \in S$.</td></tr>
</table>

<table>
<tr><td>greatest
lower bound</td><td>If the set of lower bounds of some given set S has a greatest number z in it, then z is said to be the greatest lower bound of S. Symbolically, $z = \text{glb } S$. If a set has an upper bound, we occasionally say that it is bounded above. Similarly, if a set has a lower bound, we say that it is bounded below. A set is said to be bounded if and only if it is bounded above and below.</td></tr>
<tr><td>bounded</td><td></td></tr>
</table>

<table>
<tr><td>Archimedean</td><td>Definition. An ordered field is called Archimedean if and only if for each $a > 0$ and $b > 0$ there exists a positive integer m such that $ma > b$.</td></tr>
</table>

It is not too difficult to prove that every ordered field which has the completeness property also has the Archimedean property. Let us complete the section by proving the real number system has the Archimedean property.

Theorem. *The complete ordered field of real numbers has the Archimedean property.*

Proof:

Statements	Reasons
1. If $a > 0$, $b > 0$ and $a \geq b$, then there exists a positive integer m such that $ma > b$.	1. Why?
2. Let $a < b$. Assume for each positive integer m that $ma \leq b$. Then, $S = \{ma \mid m \in N\}$ is a set of real numbers with an upper bound.	2. Why?
3. The set S has a least upper bound t.	3. Why?
4. Now, for each positive integer m, $(m + 1)a \leq t$.	4. Why?
5. Hence, for each positive integer m, $ma \leq t - a$.	5. Why?
6. Since $t - a < t$, Statement 5 contradicts the fact that t is the least upper bound of S.	6. Why?
7. Consequently, for $a < b$, there exists a positive integer m such that $ma > b$.	7. Why?

EXERCISES

1. What is the least element in each of the following sets?
   (a) $\{p \mid p \text{ is a positive prime}\}$
   (b) $\{n \mid n \text{ is a positive multiple of 4, 12, and 15}\}$
   (c) $\{n \mid n \text{ is a positive multiple of 13 and 21}\}$

(d) $\{n \mid n$ is a positive integer and $4n^2 < 2^n\}$

2. Prove that a set of real numbers cannot have two different least elements.

3. What is the least upper bound of each of the following sets?
   (a) $\{-2, -3, -\frac{3}{2}\}$
   (b) $\{x \mid x$ is a prime and $x < 138\}$
   (c) $\{x \mid x$ is a real number and $x^2 < 16\}$
   (d) $\{x \mid -x$ is a positive real number$\}$

4. Prove if z is the least upper bound of a set S of real numbers, then for each positive real number d there exists an $x \in S$ such that $x > z - d$. (Geometrically, if z is the least upper bound of S, then for any point on the number line to the left of z there must be a point in S to the right of the point.)

5. Let $S = \{3, 11, 17\}$. For any $d > 0$, what is an element in S greater than $z - d$ where z is the least upper bound of S?

6. Let $T = \{x \mid x < 7\}$. For any given $d > 0$, what is an element in T greater than $z - d$ where z is the least upper bound of T?

7. Let z be the least upper bound of a set S. (a) If $z \in S$, can there be a finite number of elements in S greater than $z - d$ for a given $d > 0$? (b) If $z \notin S$, can there be a finite number of elements in S greater than $z - d$ for a given $d > 0$? (Verify your answers.)

8. Determine the greatest lower bound, if it exists, of each of the following sets.
   (a) $\{1, -2, 11, 19\}$
   (b) $\{x \mid x$ is a real number and $x < 5\}$
   (c) $\{t \mid t$ is a real number and $-1 < t \le 3\}$
   (d) $\{t \mid t$ is an integer and $t > 5\}$
   (e) $\{x \mid x$ is a positive prime and $x > 41\}$
   (f) $\{x \mid x$ is a real number and $x^2 < 3\}$

9. Let w be the greatest lower bound of a set S of real numbers. Prove for each positive real number d that there exists an $x \in S$ such that $x < w + d$.

10. *Theorem:* If S is a set of real numbers with a lower bound, then S has a greatest lower bound. Prove the theorem in the following manner. Explain why the set T of lower bounds of S has a least upper bound and prove that lub T is the greatest lower bound of S.

11. Prove the theorem in Exercise 10 in the following way. Explain why $\{-x \mid x \in S\}$ has an upper bound and prove that the additive inverse of the least upper bound of this set is the greatest lower bound of S.

12. Answer the questions in the proof of the theorem that states the complete ordered field of real numbers is Archimedean.

13. Give an example of an ordered field which does not have the completeness property but does have the Archimedean property. (No proofs required.)

*14. Let S be a set of real numbers with an upper bound. Let $s = $ lub S. Prove that $s \in S$ if and only if S has a greatest element.

Evariste Galois (1811–1832)

Evariste Galois was born at Bourg-la-Reine, near Paris, on October 25, 1811. Although Galois had a brilliant mind, he did not distinguish himself in school. He was capable of mathematical insights that he found difficult to explain to others; many of his insights took able mathematicians considerable time to clearly understand. Unfortunately, Galois never seemed to have a teacher who understood his abilities or a mentor to help him. He submitted some of his first important work to the Academy of Science as a competitive paper for the Grand Prize in Mathematics given by the Academy, but the Academy lost the important manuscript.

Because Galois disliked the Crown, he joined the radical Republicans. His revolutionary activities led to two short prison terms. The account of the last few days of his life is sketchy. He apparently entered into a duel to defend the honor of a girl of doubtful reputation named Eve, a girl with whom he evidently had his first (and last) love affair. There is some speculation that the duel, which everyone expected Galois to lose, had been promoted by the authorities to rid themselves of the radical revolutionist. He worked laboriously and finished writing a summary of his mathematical discoveries on the night before the duel; among them were ideas that would lead to important new areas in modern algebra. The summary of his work was sent to a friend and ended with the following statements. "You will publicly ask Jacobi or Gauss to give their opinion not on the truth, but on the importance of the theorems. After this there will be, I hope, some people who will find it to their advantage to decipher all this mess." On the next day, May 30, 1832, the duel took place; Galois lost and died on the following day at the age of twenty.

15

A Look at Modern Algebra

1. Examples of Groups
2. Elementary Theory of Groups

1. EXAMPLES OF GROUPS

Let G be a nonempty (finite or infinite) set. Suppose a binary operation, such as addition or multiplication, is defined on pairs of elements of G. Let $*$ denote the operation and assume the system consisting of G and this operation has the following properties:

1. If $a \in G$ and $b \in G$, then $a * b$ is a unique element of G. (Closure Property)
2. If $a \in G$, $b \in G$, and $c \in G$, then $(a * b) * c = a * (b * c)$. (Associative Property)

identity

3. There exists an element of G called an *identity* and denoted by e such that $a * e = e * a = a$ for every $a \in G$. (Existence of an Identity)

inverse

4. For each $a \in G$, there exists an element in G called the *inverse* of a and denoted by a^{-1} such that $a * a^{-1} = a^{-1} * a = e$. (Existence of Inverses)

group

Such a system consisting of a set G and a binary operation having the given properties is called a *group*. Although this is an abstract mathematical system, let us give several examples of groups. In the next section, we shall develop some elementary theory of groups; that is, we shall prove theorems which will reveal certain properties common to all groups. Having several examples of groups to look at should help us not only to prove the theorems but also to "discover" some theorems.

Example 1. Let $G = \{1, -1\}$ and let $*$ be (ordinary) multiplication.
(a) Since $1 \times 1 = 1$, $(-1) \times 1 = -1$, $1 \times (-1) = -1$, and $(-1) \times (-1) = 1$, the system has the closure property.
(b) Multiplication is an associative operation.
(c) 1 is the identity.
(d) Since $1 \times 1 = 1$, the multiplicative inverse of 1 is 1; that is, $1^{-1} = 1$. Since $(-1) \times (-1) = 1$, the inverse of -1 is -1; that is $(-1)^{-1} = -1$.

Example 2. Let G be the set of all integers and let $*$ be addition.
(a) Since the sum of two integers is an integer, the system has the closure property.
(b) Addition is an associative operation.
(c) Since $a + 0 = 0 + a = a$ for every integer a, we conclude that 0 is the (additive) identity.
(d) Since $6 + (-6) = (-6) + 6 = 0$, for example, -6 is the (additive) inverse of 6. In general, $-a$ is the inverse of a.

Example 3. Let $G = \{1, -1, i, -i\}$ where $*$ is multiplication and $i \times i = -1$. (Verify that this is a group.)

Example 4. Let G be the set of real numbers and let $*$ be addition.

Example 5. Let G be the set of all real numbers different from 0 and let $*$ be multiplication.

Example 6. Let $G = \{a + b\sqrt{2} \mid a$ and b are rational numbers, a and b are not both zero$\}$ and let $*$ be multiplication. [What is the multiplicative inverse (in the form $a + b\sqrt{2}$) of $3 + 5\sqrt{2}$?]

The reader should be convinced before reading further that the preceding six examples are groups. Let us now consider some less familiar systems.

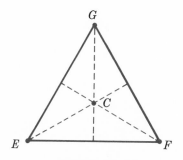

FIGURE 15.1

Example 7. Consider the equilateral triangle EFG as indicated in the figure above. Let C be the centroid of the plane figure (the geometric center where the medians of the triangle meet). Let p represent a counterclockwise rotation of $120°$ about C, let q represent a counterclockwise rotation of $240°$ about C, and let e represent no rotation. The operation $p * q$, for example, is defined to be rotation p followed by q. Since a rotation of $120°$ followed by one of $240°$ is a complete revolution, it is equivalent to no rotation at all with respect to the final position of the figure; thus, $p * q = e$.

377

Notice that $p * p = q$ and $q * q = p$. Often, we say that e is the "product" of p "times" q even though the operation is not multiplication.

group table

For a finite set we can represent all products in what is called a "multiplication table"; it is also called a *group table* provided the system has the group properties. This table is constructed similar to the multiplication tables we used in elementary school. The elements are entered along the headline and sideline usually in the same

*	e	p	q
e	e	p	q
p	p	q	e
q	q	e	p

order with the identity if there is one in the first position. The product of the mth element in the sideline times the nth element in the headline is entered in the mth row and nth column of the table.

The group table for $\{1, -1, i, -i\}$ with multiplication as the operation is as follows:

×	1	−1	i	−i
1	1	−1	i	−i
−1	−1	1	−i	i
i	i	−i	−1	1
−i	−i	i	1	−1

Example 8. Often a mathematical system with a finite number of elements is defined by a multiplication table. For example, for the set

$$G = \{e, p, q, r, s, t\}$$

let the operation $*$ be defined by the "multiplication" table on the facing page.

An obvious question would be "Is this system a group?" To answer, we must find if the system has the four properties of a group.

(a) Since there are no blank spaces in the table, the product of every pair is defined. Also, since each of the entries in the table is one and only one of the elements e, p, q, r, s, t, the system has the closure property.

(b) To show that the system has the associative property is not an easy task if all $6 \times 6 \times 6 \times 2 = 432$ possibilities for the (two associated) products

*	e	p	q	r	s	t
e	e	p	q	r	s	t
p	p	q	e	s	t	r
q	q	e	p	t	r	s
r	r	t	s	e	q	p
s	s	r	t	p	e	q
t	t	s	r	q	p	e

of any three elements are individually checked. Of course, this number can be reduced in various ways, but the check is still tedious. For now, let us state that the system has the associative property.

(c) Since the first row is the same as the headline and the first column is the same as the sideline, it is easily seen that e is an identity for the system.

(d) For an element such as p to have an inverse, an e must appear in the row with p at the sideline. Since e appears under q, we have that $p * q = e$. However, this is not enough to ensure that q is an inverse of p since we must also have that $q * p = e$. Assuming the standard arrangement for the table, not only must an e appear in every row but all of them must either appear on the (main) diagonal from the upper left corner to the lower right corner or they must be symmetrically placed with respect to this main diagonal. Since this is the case for the given table, every element has an inverse. Consequently, (a), (b), (c), and (d) show that the system is a group.

Example 9. Consider the square *EFGH* as indicated in Figure 15.2. Let C be the centroid of the plane figure. Let p represent a counterclockwise rotation of 90° about C, let q represent a counterclockwise rotation of 180° about C let r represent a 270° counterclockwise rotation about C and let e

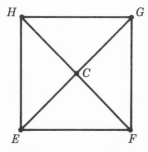

FIGURE 15.2

379

represent no rotation. The product $p * q$ is the element in the set $\{e, p, q, r\}$ which results in the same position of the square as when p is followed by q. This system is a group and the group table is as follows:

*	e	p	q	r
e	e	p	q	r
p	p	q	r	e
q	q	r	e	p
r	r	e	p	q

We notice that the group table having six elements (Example 8) is different in one major respect from the tables with three and four elements. Namely, *all* elements in the three and four element groups are symmetrically placed with respect to the main diagonal of the group table; this is not the case for the six element group table. In other words, $a * b = b * a$, if a and b are any elements of the groups with three or four elements, but this is not the case for the latter group with six elements. Any group for which $a * b = b * a$ for *every* *commutative,* *pair* of elements of the group is called *commutative,* or *abelian.* [The *or abelian* first name is a rather obvious choice; the second is in honor of the famous Norwegian mathematician Niels Henrik Abel (1802–1829).]

Let $G = \{e, p, q, r, s, t\}$ and let $*$ be defined by the following multiplication table:

*	e	p	q	r	s	t
e	e	p	q	r	s	t
p	p	q	e	t	r	s
q	q	e	p	s	t	r
r	r	t	s	e	p	q
s	s	r	t	q	e	p
t	t	s	r	p	q	e

Before reading further, try to determine if this system is a group.

Let us look more closely at the two groups with four elements which we discussed earlier (Examples 3 and 9). One group was $S = \{1, -1, i, -i\}$ with multiplication as the operation and the other was a set of rotations of a square about its centroid where the operation was successive rotations. Are these two groups different? Of course, the answer depends on what we mean by "different." From an abstract point of view, they are not different. What we mean by this is that there is a way of pairing the elements in both sets so that the product of any two corresponding pairs in the two sets preserves the correspondence. For example, let the correspondence between the two sets be given by

$$
\begin{array}{cc}
S & T \\
1 \leftrightarrow e \\
-1 \leftrightarrow q \\
i \leftrightarrow r \\
-i \leftrightarrow p
\end{array}
$$

Then, for example,

$$
\begin{aligned}
-1 = (1)(-1) &\leftrightarrow e * q = q \\
-1 = (i)(i) &\leftrightarrow r * r = q \\
1 = (-i)(i) &\leftrightarrow p * r = e \\
-i = (-1)(i) &\leftrightarrow q * r = p
\end{aligned}
$$

We have exhibited a one-to-one correspondence between the two sets such that the products of any two corresponding pairs will also correspond. (The student should check the other pairs.) In modern algebra, two such groups are said to be *isomorphic* (same structure) and in most situations such groups are not considered to be different. Roughly speaking, two groups are isomorphic if we can rename the elements in one group such that its group table will be exactly like that of the other group. If we replace 1 by e, -1 by q, i by r, and $-i$ by p in the group table for Example 3 we will get the group table for Example 9. (Do it.)

isomorphic

As stated earlier, having several examples of groups to look at helps us anticipate theorems that might be true and, perhaps, gives us some indication of the methods of proofs for such theorems. For example, we notice that in the examples of group tables that every element appears once and only once in each row and in each column. Might this be a general property for finite group tables? Can a group have more than one identity? (None of our examples do.) A number of other interesting questions present themselves at this time.

---

1. Is there a group with n elements where n is any given positive integer?

2. How many different groups are there with one element?

Questions

Questions

> 3. How many different groups are there with two elements?
>
> 4. How many different groups are there with three elements?
>
> 5. How many different groups are there with four elements?
>
> 6. How many different groups are there with five elements?
>
> 7. How many different groups are there with six elements?
>
> 8. How many different groups are there with seven elements?
>
> 9. Are there any noncommutative groups with two elements? Three elements? Four elements? Five elements? Six elements? Seven elements?
>
> 10. What are some of the properties which are common to all groups?

The answer to Question 1 is "yes." The system consisting of the set with only the integer 1 and the operation of multiplication is a group with one element. We have seen examples of groups with two, three, four, and six elements. An example of a group with n elements can be obtained from an n-sided regular polygon. Let C be the centroid of the polygon, let p_1 be the counterclockwise rotation about C of $360°/n$, let p_2 be the counterclockwise rotation about C of $2(360°/n)$, let p_3 be the counterclockwise rotation about C of $3(360°/n)$, etc. If the operation is as explained in our examples with the equilateral triangle and the square, then $p_1 * p_1 = p_2$. In fact, if we let p_1^n be the "product" of n of the p_1 rotations, we see that $p_1^3 = p_3$, $p_1^4 = p_4$, $p_1^5 = p_5$, and $p_1^n = e$ where e represents no rotation. This rotation group is generally called a cyclic group.

cyclic

Definition. *Let G be a set with an operation $*$ defined having the group properties. The group is called* cyclic *if and only if there exists an $a \in G$ such that $G = \{a^n \mid n \text{ is an integer}\}$. The element a is said to* gener-

generate

ate *the group.*

In the group table on page 380, notice how the elements in the rows "cycle" — *epqr, pqre, qrep, repq*. This property can be used to construct a cyclic group with n elements where n is any positive integer.

To show that the system consisting of $G = \{1, -1, i, -i\}$ with multiplication as the operation is a cyclic group we need only find one $a \in G$ such that $\{a, a^2, a^3, a^4\} = \{1, -1, i, -i\}$. Let $a = i$. Then $a^2 = i^2 = -1$, $a^3 = -i$, and $a^4 = 1$. Thus, the group is cyclic and i is a generator of the group. It should be noted that 1 and -1 are not generators of this group, while both i and $-i$ are.

Not all groups are cyclic; this can be seen by looking at our example of the noncommutative group with six elements in Example 8.

One might guess (incorrectly) that if a finite group is commutative then the group would be cyclic. (This is true for all of the examples we have seen.) However, this is not the case as is exhibited by the following commutative group with four elements.

Example 10. Let $G = \{e, a, b, c\}$ and let $*$ be defined by

$*$	e	a	b	c
e	e	a	b	c
a	a	e	c	b
b	b	c	e	a
c	c	b	a	e

A finite group with n elements is called a group of *order n*. Now, let us consider how many different groups there are of order n where $n = 1, 2, 3, 4, 5, 6,$ and 7. Since a group must contain an identity, there is only one group of order 1 and its group table is as shown in the marginal area.

$*$	e
e	e

There is only one group of order two and only one group with three elements; they are the cyclic groups with the following group tables:

$*$	e	a
e	e	a
a	a	e

$*$	e	a	b
e	e	a	b
a	a	b	e
b	b	e	a

As the student should be able to verify, it is a fact for a finite group table that the first row must be the same as the headline with the standard arrangement of the elements, the first column must be the same as the sideline, and every element must appear in each row and column once and only once. With this information, it is not very difficult to prove that these are the only possible multiplication tables with these properties. (Do it.) Hence, all groups of order two and three are isomorphic to one of these two groups.

Using the yet unproved statements stated above, it can be shown that every group with four elements must be isomorphic to one of the following groups of order four.

*	e	a	b	c
e	e	a	b	c
a	a	b	c	e
b	b	c	e	a
c	c	e	a	b

*	e	a	b	c
e	e	a	b	c
a	a	e	c	b
b	b	c	e	a
c	c	b	a	e

Things begin to become rather tedious if the approach is essentially trial and error in trying to construct group tables of groups which are not cyclic and where the order is higher than four. Fortunately, it is possible to prove an important theorem which states that there is only one group with n elements if n is a prime number. From this fact, we can conclude that there is only one group of order five and only one group of order seven; they are the cyclic groups. It is not particularly easy to determine the number of groups of order six. (We leave this question unanswered in hope that some students will accept the challenge to attempt to answer it on their own.)

It is rather easy to see by studying the tables of cyclic groups that the entries must be symmetrically placed with respect to the main diagonal. Thus, the cyclic groups of orders two, three, five, and seven are all commutative. We can observe that the two groups of order four are commutative. A noncommutative group with less than eight elements is the one given in Example 8.

An answer to Question 10 and some of the others stated in this section will be given in the next section.

EXERCISES

1. Verify that the system consisting of $G = \{a + b\sqrt{2} \mid a$ and b are rational numbers and not both zero$\}$ and ordinary multiplication as the operation is a group.

2. Let $S = \{2^t \mid t$ is any integer$\}$. Is the system consisting of this set and the operation of multiplication a group?

3. Verify that the system consisting of $G = \{a + b\sqrt{3} \mid a$ and b are rational numbers and not both zero$\}$ and the operation of multiplication is a group.

4. Let $a = (-1 + i\sqrt{3})/2$. Show that powers of a generate a cyclic group with respect to multiplication. What is the order of this group?

5. Let a set G with an operation $*$ define on it be a group. A system consisting of a nonempty subset of G and the group operation is called a *subgroup* of the given group if and only if it has the group properties.

(a) Explain why the cyclic group of order three has two subgroups.

(b) List the subgroups of the noncyclic group of order four.

(c) List the subgroups of the group of order six given in Example 8.

6. Give some examples of groups not already discussed in this chapter.

7. Let G be the following set of wheel "exchanges" that could be made on a three-wheeled vehicle.

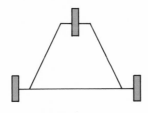

FIGURE 15.3

e: no change

p: 120° rotation of all three wheels counterclockwise

q: 240° rotation of all three wheels counterclockwise

r: exchange the rear wheels

s: exchange right rear wheel and front wheel

t: exchange left rear wheel and front wheel

Let the product $p * q$, for example, be p followed by q. Since $p * q$ is equivalent to no rotation, we have that $p * q = e$.

(a) Show that the group table for Example 8 represents this system.

(b) Is it true for this group that $(p * r)^{-1} = p^{-1} * r^{-1}$?

(c) Is it true that $(p * r)^{-1} = r^{-1} * p^{-1}$?

8. (a) List all of the subgroups of the group in Exercise 7. (b) Is each a cyclic subgroup? (c) Is the order of each a factor of the order of the group?

9. (a) Complete the table at right below so that there will be one and only one of e, a, b, c, d, in each row and column.

(b) Prove that the associated system is isomorphic to the cyclic group whose table is given at the left.

	e	p	q	r	s
e	e	p	q	r	s
p	p	q	r	s	e
q	q	r	s	e	p
r	r	s	e	p	q
s	s	e	p	q	r

	e	a	b	c	d
e	e	a	b	c	d
a	a	b	c	d	
b	b	c			
c	c				
d	d				

385

10. (a) List all the subgroups of the group in Exercise 9.
    (b) Is each a cyclic subgroup?
    (c) Is the order of each a factor of the order of the group?

11. (a) Consider the equilateral triangle below with each indicated point tagged with the given letters. Let $\{e, p, q, r, s, t\}$ be the following rotations:

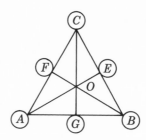

FIGURE 15.4

e: no rotation
p: 120° counterclockwise rotation about 0
q: 240° counterclockwise rotation about 0
r: 180° rotation about the line segment AE (assume the letters are attached to the triangle and flip the figure about AE)
s: 180° rotation about the line segment CG
t: 180° rotation about the line segment BF

Let $p * r$ represent p followed by r; thus, $p * r = q$. Show that the table for this system is given on page 380.

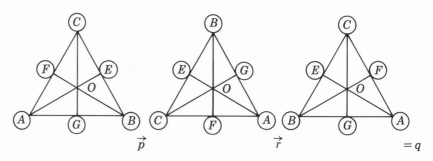

FIGURE 15.5

(b) Show that this system does not have the associative property.
(c) Is $(p * r)^{-1} = p^{-1} * r^{-1}$?
(d) Is $(p * r)^{-1} = r^{-1} * p^{-1}$?

12. Use the group table for Example 8 to show that it need not be true that if a, b, and c are elements of a group and $a * c = c * b$ then $a = b$.

13. (a) Make a table similar to that in Exercise 7 for the following "exchange" of the wheels on an automobile:

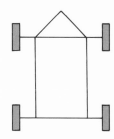

FIGURE 15.6

    e: no rotation
    p: 90° counterclockwise rotation of all four wheels
    q: 180° counterclockwise rotation of all four wheels
    r: 270° counterclockwise rotation of all four wheels
    s: exchange right front and left rear wheels
    t: exchange two front wheels for two rear wheels
    u: exchange left front and right rear wheels
    v: exchange two right wheels for two left wheels

  (b) Is it a group table?

14. (a) List all the subgroups of the group in Exercise 13.
  (b) Is each a cyclic subgroup?
  (c) Is the order of each a factor of the order of the group?

15. By looking at several examples, make a conjecture concerning the order of a subgroup of a given finite group as it relates to the order of the group.

2. ELEMENTARY THEORY OF GROUPS

Let us now take the axioms for a group listed on page 376 and proceed to prove theorems that will exhibit further properties common to all groups.

Theorem 1. *A group cannot have two different identities.* (*The identity for a group is unique.*)

Proof: Let e and e' be two identities for a group. If e' is an identity for the group, then

$$e * e' = e$$

(Anything times the identity e' is again the given element.) Similarly, if e is an identity for the group, then

$$e * e' = e'$$

Since $e * e'$ is a unique element of G, we conclude that

$$e' = e$$

Theorem 2. *Let a, b, and c be elements of a group. If $a * c = b * c$, then $a = b$.*

Proof:

$a * c = b * c$	Why? (1)
The element c has an inverse c^{-1}	Why? (2)
$(a * c) * c^{-1} = (b * c) * c^{-1}$	Why? (3)
$a * (c * c^{-1}) = b * (c * c^{-1})$	Why? (4)
$a * e = b * e$	Why? (5)
$a = b$	Why? (6)

Theorem 3. *Let a, b, and c be elements of a group. If $c * a = c * b$, then $a = b$.*

Proof: Left as an exercise.

The properties expressed in Theorems 2 and 3 are generally called the right and left cancellation laws, respectively. We should emphasize that cancellation "on the same side" is important. As we saw in Exercise 12 in the last section, it need not be true in a group that if $a * c = c * b$, then $a = b$.

Not only is it true that the identity for a group is unique, but it is also true that the inverse of a given element in a group is unique. Let us prove this theorem.

Theorem 4. *Let a be an element of a group. The inverse of a is unique.*

Proof: Let x and y be two inverses of a. Then,

	$a * x = e$	Why? (1)
Also,	$a * y = e$	Why? (2)
Thus,	$a * x = a * y$	Why? (3)
Consequently,	$x = y$	Why? (4)

If a group were commutative, it would be true that $(a \quad b)^{-1} = a^{-1} * b^{-1}$; but as we saw in Exercise 7 of the last section this need not be true for noncommutative groups. However, we do have an interesting theorem concerning the inverse of the product of any pair of elements in a group. It is as follows.

Theorem 5. *If a, b are elements of a group, then $(a * b)^{-1} = b^{-1} * a^{-1}$. (The inverse of a product is the product of the inverse in reverse order.)*

Proof:

$$a^{-1} * a = e \qquad \text{Why? (1)}$$
$$(a^{-1} * a) * b = e * b \qquad \text{Why? (2)}$$
$$a^{-1} * (a * b) = b \qquad \text{Why? (3)}$$
$$b^{-1} * [a^{-1} * (a * b)] = b^{-1} * b \qquad \text{Why? (4)}$$
$$(b^{-1} * a^{-1}) * (a * b) = e \qquad \text{Why? (5)}$$

Thus,
$$(a * b)^{-1} = b^{-1} * a^{-1} \qquad \text{Why? (6)}$$

Theorem 6. *If a is an element of a group, then $(a^{-1})^{-1} = a$.*

Proof:
$$(a^{-1}) * (a^{-1})^{-1} = e \qquad \text{Why? (1)}$$
Also
$$(a^{-1}) * a = e \qquad \text{Why? (2)}$$
Thus,
$$(a^{-1}) * (a^{-1})^{-1} = (a^{-1}) * a \qquad \text{Why? (3)}$$
and
$$(a^{-1})^{-1} = a \qquad \text{Why? (4)}$$

Theorem 7. *Let G be a group and let a and b be any elements of G. $(a * b)^2 = a^2 * b^2$ if and only if $a * b = b * a$.*

Proof: (We have essentially two theorems to prove, an implication and its converse.)
PART 1. Assume $a * b = b * a$ for all pairs of G. Then

$$(a * b) * (a * b) = (b * a) * (b * a) \qquad \text{Why? (1)}$$
Thus,
$$(a * b)^2 = (b * a) * (a * b) \qquad \text{Why? (2)}$$
$$= b * [a * (a * b)] \qquad \text{Why? (3)}$$
$$= b * (a^2 * b) \qquad \text{Why? (4)}$$
$$= b * (b * a^2) \qquad \text{Why? (5)}$$
$$= b^2 * a^2 \qquad \text{Why? (6)}$$
$$= a^2 * b^2 \qquad \text{Why? (7)}$$

PART 2. Assume $(a * b)^2 = a^2 * b^2$ for every pair a and b of G. Then
$$(a * b) * (a * b) = (a * a) * (b * b) \qquad \text{Why? (1)}$$

$$a^{-1}[(a * b) * (a * b)] = a^{-1}[(a * a) * (b * b)] \qquad \text{Why?} \quad (2)$$
$$[a^{-1} * (a * b)] * (a * b) = [a^{-1} * (a * a)] * (b * b) \qquad \text{Why?} \quad (3)$$
$$[(a^{-1} * a) * b] * (a * b) = [(a^{-1} * a) * a] * (b * b) \qquad \text{Why?} \quad (4)$$
$$(e * b) * (a * b) = (e * a) * (b * b) \qquad \text{Why?} \quad (5)$$
$$b * (a * b) = a * (b * b) \qquad \text{Why?} \quad (6)$$
$$(b * a) * b = (a * b) * b \qquad \text{Why?} \quad (7)$$
$$[(b * a) * b] * b^{-1} = [(a * b) * b] * b^{-1} \qquad \text{Why?} \quad (8)$$
$$(b * a) * (b * b^{-1}) = (a * b) * (b * b^{-1}) \qquad \text{Why?} \quad (9)$$
$$(b * a) * e = (a * b) * e \qquad \text{Why?} \quad (10)$$
$$b * a = a * b \qquad \text{Why?} \quad (11)$$

Let G be a set with an operation $*$ defined having the group properties and let H be a subset of G also having the group properties with respect to the operation $*$. (As defined in Exercise 5 of the last section, this subsystem is called a subgroup.) For any given element a in G, the set of all elements of the form $h * a$ where $h \in H$ is called a *right coset of H* and is denoted by Ha. (Notice that Ha does not represent a product; it represents a set.) Similarly, the set of all elements of the form $a * h$ where $h \in H$ is called a *left coset of H*. To better understand the concept of cosets, let us look at all of the right and left cosets of two different subgroups of the group given in Example 8 of the last section. (It would be advisable to have that table available.)

Example 1. Recall that $G = \{e, p, q, r, s, t\}$ and let $H = \{e, p, q\}$. The right coset Hr is the set $\{e * r, p * r, q * r\} = \{r, s, t\}$.

Right Cosets	Left Cosets
$He = \{ e * e, p * e, q * e\} = \{e, p, q\}$	$eH = \{e, p, q\}$
$Hp = \{e * p, p * p, q * p\} = \{p, q, e\}$	$pH = \{e, p, q\}$
$Hq = \{e * q, p * q, q * q\} = \{ q, e, p\}$	$qH = \{e, p, q\}$
$Hr = \{e * r, p * r, q * r\} = \{r, s, t\}$	$rH = \{r, s, t\}$
$Hs = \{e * s, p * s, q * s\} = \{s, t, r\}$	$sH = \{r, s, t\}$
$Ht = \{e * t, p * t, q * t\} = \{t, r, s\}$	$tH = \{r, s, t\}$

We should notice a number of things. (1) There are only two right cosets of H and only two left cosets of H. (2) The right and left cosets are $\{e, p, q\}$ and $\{r, s, t\}$. (3) The two cosets of H have no elements in common. (4) The union of the cosets of H is the set G.

We should also notice that $pH = Hp$, for example. However, as the next example will show, this is not a general property. (Of course, if the group is commutative, then the left and right cosets with respect to a given subgroup would be the same.)

Example 2. Again, using Example 8 of the last section where $G = \{e, p, q, r, s, t\}$ let $H = \{e, r\}$.

Right Cosets	*Left Cosets*
$He = \{e, r\}$	$eH = \{e, r\}$
$Hp = \{p, t\}$	$pH = \{p, s\}$
$Hq = \{q, s\}$	$qH = \{q, t\}$
$Hr = \{e, r\}$	$rH = \{e, r\}$
$Hs = \{q, s\}$	$sH = \{s, p\}$
$Ht = \{t, p\}$	$tH = \{t, q\}$

Here there are three different right cosets with respect to H which are disjoint sets and whose union is G. We call particular attention to the fact that $pH \neq Hp$.

EXERCISES

1. Let $G = \{1, 2, 3, 4, 5, 6\}$. If $a \in G$ and $b \in G$, let $a \circ b$ represent an element $c \in G$ (if there is one) such that $a \times b = c$, mod 7. For example, since $3 \times 4 \equiv 5$, mod 7, $3 \circ 4 = 5$. (See page 251.) (a) Construct a table for this system. (b) Is it a group? (c) Is it cyclic?

2. Let $G = \{1, 2, 3, 4, 5, 6, 7\}$. Define $a \circ b = c$ if and only if $c \in G$ and $a \times b \equiv c$, mod 8. (See Exercise 1.) Is this system a group?

3. Let $G = \{0, 1, 2, 3, 4, 5, 6\}$. Define $a \circ b = c$ if and only if $c \in G$ and $a + b \equiv c$, mod 7. (a) Construct a table for this system. (b) Is it a group? (c) Is it cyclic?

4. Use the left and right cancellation properties to explain why the group table for a finite group cannot have two elements alike in the same row (or column).

5. Let G be a group with n elements. Suppose that there is an element a in G such that $a^n = e$ and suppose that n is the smallest positive integer such that a^n is the identity. Prove that $e, a, a^2, a^3, \ldots, a^{n-1}$ are n *different* elements of G. (Thus, a generates the group and it is cyclic.) *Hint:* Suppose $a^i = a^j$ where $1 \leq i \leq n$, $1 \leq j \leq n$, and $i \neq j$. If $i < j$ then there is a positive integer k less than n such that $i + k = j$. $a^{i+k} = a^i * a^k = a^i$.

6. Answer the questions in the proof of Theorem 2.

7. Prove Theorem 3.

8. Answer the questions in the proof of Theorem 4.

9. Answer the questions in the proof of Theorem 5.

10. Answer the questions in the proof of Theorem 6.

11. Answer the questions in the proof of Theorem 7.

12. If for every element a of a group we have that $a^2 = e$, prove the group is commutative.

13. (a) Let G be a finite set with a binary operation $*$ defined having the closure and associative properties. Assume $a * b = a * c$ implies $b = c$ and $a * c = b * c$ implies $a = b$ for all elements a, b, c in G. Show that G is a group with respect to this operation.
    (b) What if G is not finite?

*14. Prove that if a and b are any elements of a subgroup of a given group that $a * b^{-1}$ is also an element of the subgroup.

*15. Let G be a cyclic group generated by a. If G is of order m, then a^n generates G if m and n have no factors in common other than 1 and -1.

*16. Let G be a group and H be a subgroup of order m. What is the number of elements in a right coset of H?

*17. Let Ha and Hb be the two right cosets of a subgroup H of a group G. Prove if $Ha \neq Hb$ then $Ha \cap Hb = \emptyset$.

*18. Let G be a group of order n and let H be a subgroup of order m. Prove that m is a factor of n. (*Hint:* See Exercise 16 and consider all of the right cosets of H.)

APPENDIX A

Suggested Reading

Ball, W. W. R.: *Mathematical Recreations and Essays,* 11th ed. (New York: The Macmillan Company, 1962.)

———: *A Short Account of the History of Mathematics,* 3rd ed. (New York: The Macmillan Company, 1901.)

Beiler, A. H.: *Recreations in the Theory of Numbers.* (New York: Cover Publications, Inc., 1966.)

Bell, E. T.: *The Development of Mathematics,* 2nd ed. (New York: McGraw-Hill Book Company, 1944.)

———: *The Handmaiden of the Sciences.* (Baltimore: The Williams & Wilkins Company, 1937.)

———: *Men of Mathematics.* (New York: Simon & Schuster, Inc., 1937.)

Blumenthal, L. M.: *A Modern View of Geometry.* (San Francisco: W. H. Freeman and Company, 1961.)

Boyer, Carl B.: *A History of Mathematics.* (New York: John Wiley & Sons, Inc., 1968.)

Bowden, L.: "The Language of Computers," *American Scientist,* vol. 58, no. 1, Jan.–Feb., 1970, pp. 43–53.

Computers and Computation, introduction by R. Fenichel and J. Weizenbaum. (San Francisco: W. H. Freeman and Company, 1971.) Paperback. A collection of twenty-two articles reprinted from *Scientific American.*

Courant, R., and H. Robbins: *What is Mathematics?* (New York: Oxford University Press, 1941.)

Dantzig, T.: *Number: The Language of Science,* 4th ed. rev. (New York: The Macmillan Company, 1959.)

Eves, H.: *An Introduction to the History of Mathematics,* rev. ed. (New York: Holt, Rinehart, and Winston, Inc., 1964.)

Eves, H., and C. V. Newsom: *An Introduction to the Foundations and Fundamental Concepts of Mathematics,* rev. ed. (New York: Holt, Rinehart and Winston, Inc., 1965.)

Gateley, W. Y. and G. G. Bitter: *BASIC for Beginners.* (New York: McGraw-Hill Book Company, 1970.)

Goldstein, M.: "Computer Languages," *American Mathematical Monthly,* vol. 72, no. 2, part II, Feb. 1965, pp. 141–146.

Karpinski, L. C., and D. E. Smith: *The Hindu-Arabic Numerals.* (Boston: Ginn and Company, 1961.)

Karpinski, L. C.: *The History of Arithmetic.* (Chicago: Rand McNally and Company, 1925.)

Kasner, E., and J. Newman: *Mathematics and the Imagination.* (New York: Simon & Schuster, Inc., 1963.)

Kemeny, J. G., and T. E. Kurtz: *BASIC Programming,* (New York: John Wiley & Sons, Inc., 1967.)

Kemeny, J. G.: "Man Viewed as a Machine," *Scientific American,* vol. 192, no. 4, April 1955, pp. 58–67.

Kline, M.: *Mathematical Thought from Ancient to Modern Times.* (New York: Oxford University Press, 1972.)

_____: *Mathematics in Western Culture.* (New York: Oxford University Press, 1953.)

Kramer, E.: *The Mainstream of Mathematics.* (New York: Oxford University Press, 1951.)

Minsky, M. L.: "Artificial Intelligence," *Scientific American,* vol. 215, no. 3, Sept. 1966, pp. 246–260.

Newman, J. R., ed.: *The World of Mathematics,* 4 vols. (New York: Simon & Schuster, Inc., 1956.)

Pavlovich, J. P., and T. E. Tahan: *Computer Programming in BASIC.* (San Francisco: Holden-Day, Inc., 1971.) Paperback.

Sawyer, W.: *Prelude to Mathematics.* (Baltimore: Penguin Books, Inc., 1955.)

Stein, S.: *Mathematics, The Man-Made Universe,* 2nd ed. (San Francisco: W. H. Freeman and Company, 1968.)

Tietze, H.: *Famous Problems of Mathematics,* 2nd ed. (New York: Graylock Press, 1965.)

von Neumann, John: *The Computer and the Brain.* (New Haven: Yale University Press, 1956.)

Wilder, Raymond L.: *Evolution of Mathematical Concepts: An Elementary Study.* (New York: John Wiley & Sons, Inc., 1968.)

Youse, B.: *Arithmetic: An Introduction to Mathematics.* (San Francisco: Canfield Press, 1971.)

_____: *Introduction to Real Analysis.* (Boston: Allyn and Bacon, Inc., 1972.)

APPENDIX
B

Lame's Theorem

Consider the special sequence of numbers a_1, a_2, a_3, . . . where $a_1 = 1$, $a_2 = 1$, and $a_{n+2} = a_{n+1} + a_n$ for $n \geq 1$; that is, consider the sequence of numbers whose first two terms are 1 and where each succeeding term is obtained by adding the two preceding terms. The numbers in this sequence are called *Fibonacci numbers;* the first few are 1, 1, 2, 3, 5, 8, 13, 21, 34, 55, 89, 144, 233, 377, ... (At one time botanists felt there was a strong relationship between phyllotaxis and the Fibonacci sequence.)

Let us compare the terms of the geometric sequence

$$1, t, t^2, t^3, t^4, \ldots \qquad \text{where } t = \frac{1 + \sqrt{5}}{2}$$

with the Fibonacci numbers

$$1, 1, 2, 3, 5, 8, 13, 21, 34, 55, 89, \ldots$$

It is easily checked by direct substitution or by the quadratic formula that t is a root of the equation $t^2 - t - 1 = 0$. Since $t < 2$

$$t^2 = t + 1 < 2 + 1 = a_3 + a_2 = a_4$$

Multiplying $t^2 = t + 1$ by t we get

$$t^3 = t^2 + t$$

Since $t < 2 = a_3$ and $t^2 < a_4$, it follows that $t^2 + t < a_4 + a_3 = a_5$;

thus, $$t^3 < a_5$$

Similarly, $$t^4 = t^3 + t^2 < a_5 + a_4 = a_6$$

Continuing, $$t^k < a_{k+2}$$

Having obtained this important result comparing the terms of the geometric sequence with 1 as first term and t as common ratio with the terms of the Fibonacci sequence, let us return to our consideration of the euclidean algorithm.

Let a and b be positive integers where $a > b$. In the euclidean algorithm if $r_n = 0$ and $r_i \neq 0$ for $1 \leq i < n$, then

$$a = bq_1 + r_1$$
$$b = r_1 q_2 + r_2$$
$$r_1 = r_2 q_3 + r_3$$
$$r_2 = r_3 q_4 + r_4$$
$$\cdot \cdot \cdot \cdot \cdot \cdot \cdot \cdot$$
$$r_{n-3} = r_{n-2} q_{n-1} + r_{n-1}$$
$$r_{n-2} = r_{n-1} q_n$$

Since $r_{n-2} > r_{n-1}$, $q_n \geq 2$. Thus, $r_{n-2} = r_{n-1} q_n \geq 2 r_{n-1}$. Since q_1, $q_2, \ldots q_{n-1} \geq 1$, it follows that

$$r_{n-3} \geq r_{n-2} + r_{n-1}$$
$$r_{n-4} \geq r_{n-3} + r_{n-2}$$
$$r_{n-5} \geq r_{n-4} + r_{n-3}$$
$$\cdot \cdot \cdot \cdot \cdot \cdot \cdot \cdot \cdot \cdot$$
$$b \geq r_1 + r_2$$

For the Fibonacci sequence we also have

$$r_{n-1} \geq a_2$$
$$r_{n-2} \geq a_3$$
$$r_{n-3} \geq r_{n-2} + r_{n-1} \geq a_2 + a_3 = a_4$$
$$r_{n-4} \geq r_{n-3} + r_{n-2} \geq a_3 + a_4 = a_5$$
$$\cdot \cdot \cdot \cdot \cdot \cdot \cdot \cdot \cdot \cdot \cdot \cdot \cdot \cdot \cdot \cdot$$
$$r_{n-k} \geq r_{n-k+1} + r_{n-k+2} \geq a_{k-1} + a_k = a_{k+1}$$

Consequently, $a_{n+1} = a_n + a_{n-1} \leq r_1 + r_2 \leq b$.

Since $t^k < a_{k+2}$ where $t = (1 + \sqrt{5})/2$, it follows that

$$t^{n-1} < a_{n+1}$$

and
$$t^{n-1} < b$$

Using logarithms, $\log_{10} t^{n-1} < \log_{10} b$ and

$$(n - 1) \log_{10} t < \log_{10} b$$

Since $\log_{10} t$ is a positive number,

$$n - 1 < \frac{\log_{10} b}{\log_{10} t}$$

If b has m digits, then $b < 10^m$ and $\log_{10} b < m$. Therefore,

$$n - 1 < \frac{m}{\log_{10} t}$$

As can be readily checked in logarithm tables, $\log_{10} t > \frac{1}{5}$; thus,

$$n - 1 < 5m$$

and
$$n \leq 5m$$

Thus, we have proved that the number of divisions n required in the euclidean algorithm is less than or equal to five times the number of digits in the smaller of the two given numbers.

APPENDIX C

Tables

1. Exponential Functions
2. Four-place Mantissas for Common Logarithms
3. Amount at Compound Interest $(1 + i)^n$

The tables in this section are taken from Samuel Selby, Ed., *CRC Standard Mathematics Tables,* 20th ed., © The Chemical Rubber Co., 1972. Used by permission of The Chemical Rubber Co.

x	e^x	x	e^x	x	e^x	x	e^x
0.00	1.0000	**0.50**	1.6487	**1.00**	2.7183	**1.50**	4.4817
0.01	1.0101	0.51	1.6653	1.01	2.7456	1.51	4.5267
0.02	1.0202	0.52	1.6820	1.02	2.7732	1.52	4.5722
0.03	1.0305	0.53	1.6989	1.03	2.8011	1.53	4.6182
0.04	1.0408	0.54	1.7160	1.04	2.8292	1.54	4.6646
0.05	1.0513	**0.55**	1.7333	**1.05**	2.8577	**1.55**	4.7115
0.06	1.0618	0.56	1.7507	1.06	2.8864	1.56	4.7588
0.07	1.0725	0.57	1.7683	1.07	2.9154	1.57	4.8066
0.08	1.0833	0.58	1.7860	1.08	2.9447	1.58	4.8550
0.09	1.0942	0.59	1.8040	1.09	2.9743	1.59	4.9037
0.10	1.1052	**0.60**	1.8221	**1.10**	3.0042	**1.60**	4.9530
0.11	1.1163	0.61	1.8404	1.11	3.0344	1.61	5.0028
0.12	1.1275	0.62	1.8589	1.12	3.0649	1.62	5.0531
0.13	1.1388	0.63	1.8776	1.13	3.0957	1.63	5.1039
0.14	1.1503	0.64	1.8965	1.14	3.1268	1.64	5.1552
0.15	1.1618	**0.65**	1.9155	**1.15**	3.1582	**1.65**	5.2070
0.16	1.1735	0.66	1.9348	1.16	3.1899	1.66	5.2593
0.17	1.1853	0.67	1.9542	1.17	3.2220	1.67	5.3122
0.18	1.1972	0.68	1.9739	1.18	3.2544	1.68	5.3656
0.19	1.2092	0.69	1.9937	1.19	3.2871	1.69	5.4195
0.20	1.2214	**0.70**	2.0138	**1.20**	3.3201	**1.70**	5.4739
0.21	1.2337	0.71	2.0340	1.21	3.3535	1.71	5.5290
0.22	1.2461	0.72	2.0544	1.22	3.3872	1.72	5.5845
0.23	1.2586	0.73	2.0751	1.23	3.4212	1.73	5.6407
0.24	1.2712	0.74	2.0959	1.24	3.4556	1.74	5.6973
0.25	1.2840	**0.75**	2.1170	**1.25**	3.4903	**1.75**	5.7546
0.26	1.2969	0.76	2.1383	1.26	3.5254	1.76	5.8124
0.27	1.3100	0.77	2.1598	1.27	3.5609	1.77	5.8709
0.28	1.3231	0.78	2.1815	1.28	3.5966	1.78	5.9299
0.29	1.3364	0.79	2.2034	1.29	3.6328	1.79	5.9895
0.30	1.3499	**0.80**	2.2255	**1.30**	3.6693	**1.80**	6.0496
0.31	1.3634	0.81	2.2479	1.31	3.7062	1.81	6.1104
0.32	1.3771	0.82	2.2705	1.32	3.7434	1.82	6.1719
0.33	1.3910	0.83	2.2933	1.33	3.7810	1.83	6.2339
0.34	1.4049	0.84	2.3164	1.34	3.8190	1.84	6.2965
0.35	1.4191	**0.85**	2.3396	**1.35**	3.8574	**1.85**	6.3598
0.36	1.4333	0.86	2.3632	1.36	3.8962	1.86	6.4237
0.37	1.4477	0.87	2.3869	1.37	3.9354	1.87	6.4883
0.38	1.4623	0.88	2.4109	1.38	3.9749	1.88	6.5535
0.39	1.4770	0.89	2.4351	1.39	4.0149	1.89	6.6194
0.40	1.4918	**0.90**	2.4596	**1.40**	4.0552	**1.90**	6.6859
0.41	1.5068	0.91	2.4843	1.41	4.0960	1.91	6.7531
0.42	1.5220	0.92	2.5093	1.42	4.1371	1.92	6.8210
0.43	1.5373	0.93	2.5345	1.43	4.1787	1.93	6.8895
0.44	1.5527	0.94	2.5600	1.44	4.2207	1.94	6.9588
0.45	1.5683	**0.95**	2.5857	**1.45**	4.2631	**1.95**	7.0287
0.46	1.5841	0.96	2.6117	1.46	4.3060	1.96	7.0993
0.47	1.6000	0.97	2.6379	1.47	4.3492	1.97	7.1707
0.48	1.6161	0.98	2.6645	1.48	4.3929	1.98	7.2427
0.49	1.6323	0.99	2.6912	1.49	4.4371	1.99	7.3155
0.50	1.6487	**1.00**	2.7183	**1.50**	4.4817	**2.00**	7.3891

EXPONENTIAL FUNCTIONS

x	e^x	x	e^x	x	e^x	x	e^x
2.00	7.3891	**2.50**	12.182	**3.00**	20.086	**3.50**	33.115
2.01	7.4633	2.51	12.305	3.01	20.287	3.51	33.448
2.02	7.5383	2.52	12.429	3.02	20.491	3.52	33.784
2.03	7.6141	2.53	12.554	3.03	20.697	3.53	34.124
2.04	7.6906	2.54	12.680	3.04	20.905	3.54	34.467
2.05	7.7679	**2.55**	12.807	3.05	21.115	**3.55**	34.813
2.06	7.8460	2.56	12.936	3.06	21.328	3.56	35.163
2.07	7.9248	2.57	13.066	3.07	21.542	3.57	35.517
2.08	8.0045	2.58	13.197	3.08	21.758	3.58	35.874
2.09	8.0849	2.59	13.330	3.09	21.977	3.59	36.234
2.10	8.1662	**2.60**	13.464	**3.10**	22.198	**3.60**	36.598
2.11	8.2482	2.61	13.599	3.11	22.421	3.61	36.966
2.12	8.3311	2.62	13.736	3.12	22.646	3.62	37.338
2.13	8.4149	2.63	13.874	3.13	22.874	3.63	37.713
2.14	8.4994	2.64	14.013	3.14	23.104	3.64	38.092
2.15	8.5849	**2.65**	14.154	**3.15**	23.336	**3.65**	38.475
2.16	8.6711	2.66	14.296	3.16	23.571	3.66	38.861
2.17	8.7583	2.67	14.440	3.17	23.807	3.67	39.252
2.18	8.8463	2.68	14.585	3.18	24.047	3.68	39.646
2.19	8.9352	2.69	14.732	3.19	24.288	3.69	40.045
2.20	9.0250	**2.70**	14.880	**3.20**	24.533	**3.70**	40.447
2.21	9.1157	2.71	15.029	3.21	24.779	3.71	40.854
2.22	9.2073	2.72	15.180	3.22	25.028	3.72	41.264
2.23	9.2999	2.73	15.333	3.23	25.280	3.73	41.679
2.24	9.3933	2.74	15.487	3.24	25.534	3.74	42.098
2.25	9.4877	**2.75**	15.643	**3.25**	25.790	**3.75**	42.521
2.26	9.5831	2.76	15.800	3.26	26.050	3.76	42.948
2.27	9.6794	2.77	15.959	3.27	26.311	3.77	43.380
2.28	9.7767	2.78	16.119	3.28	26.576	3.78	43.816
2.29	9.8749	2.79	16.281	3.29	26.843	3.79	44.256
2.30	9.9742	**2.80**	16.445	**3.30**	27.113	**3.80**	44.701
2.31	10.074	2.81	16.610	3.31	27.385	3.81	45.150
2.32	10.176	2.82	16.777	3.32	27.660	3.82	45.604
2.33	10.278	2.83	16.945	3.33	27.938	3.83	46.063
2.34	10.381	2.84	17.116	3.34	28.219	3.84	46.525
2.35	10.486	**2.85**	17.288	**3.35**	28.503	**3.85**	46.993
2.36	10.591	2.86	17.462	3.36	28.789	3.86	47.465
2.37	10.697	2.87	17.637	3.37	29.079	3.87	47.942
2.38	10.805	2.88	17.814	3.38	29.371	3.88	48.424
2.39	10.913	2.89	17.993	3.39	29.666	3.89	48.911
2.40	11.023	**2.90**	18.174	**3.40**	29.964	**3.90**	49.402
2.41	11.134	2.91	18.357	3.41	30.265	3.91	49.899
2.42	11.246	2.92	18.541	3.42	30.569	3.92	50.400
2.43	11.359	2.93	18.728	3.43	30.877	3.93	50.907
2.44	11.473	2.94	18.916	3.44	31.187	3.94	51.419
2.45	11.588	**2.95**	19.106	**3.45**	31.500	**3.95**	51.935
2.46	11.705	2.96	19.298	3.46	31.817	3.96	52.457
2.47	11.822	2.97	19.492	3.47	32.137	3.97	52.985
2.48	11.941	2.98	19.688	3.48	32.460	3.98	53.517
2.49	12.061	2.99	19.886	3.49	32.786	3.99	54.055
2.50	12.182	**3.00**	20.086	**3.50**	33.115	**4.00**	54.598

x	e^x	x	e^x	x	e^x	x	e^x
4.00	54.598	**4.50**	90.017	**5.00**	148.41	**5.50**	244.69
4.01	55.147	4.51	90.922	5.01	149.90	5.55	257.24
4.02	55.701	4.52	91.836	5.02	151.41	5.60	270.43
4.03	56.261	4.53	92.759	5.03	152.93	5.65	284.29
4.04	56.826	4.54	93.691	5.04	154.47	5.70	298.87
4.05	57.397	**4.55**	94.632	**5.05**	156.02	**5.75**	314.19
4.06	57.974	4.56	95.583	5.06	157.59	5.80	330.30
4.07	58.557	4.57	96.544	5.07	159.17	5.85	347.23
4.08	59.145	4.58	97.514	5.08	160.77	5.90	365.04
4.09	59.740	4.59	98.494	5.09	162.39	5.95	383.75
4.10	60.340	**4.60**	99.484	**5.10**	164.02	**6.00**	403.43
4.11	60.947	4.61	100.48	5.11	165.67	6.05	424.11
4.12	61.559	4.62	101.49	5.12	167.34	6.10	445.86
4.13	62.178	4.63	102.51	5.13	169.02	6.15	468.72
4.14	62.803	4.64	103.54	5.14	170.72	6.20	492.75
4.15	63.434	**4.65**	104.58	**5.15**	172.43	**6.25**	518.01
4.16	64.072	4.66	105.64	5.16	174.16	6.30	544.57
4.17	64.715	4.67	106.70	5.17	175.91	6.35	572.49
4.18	65.366	4.68	107.77	5.18	177.68	6.40	601.85
4.19	66.023	4.69	108.85	5.19	179.47	6.45	632.70
4.20	66.686	**4.70**	109.95	**5.20**	181.27	**6.50**	655.14
4.21	67.357	4.71	111.05	5.21	183.09	6.55	699.24
4.22	68.033	4.72	112.17	5.22	184.93	6.60	735.10
4.23	68.717	4.73	113.30	5.23	186.79	6.65	772.78
4.24	69.408	4.74	114.43	5.24	188.67	6.70	812.41
4.25	70.105	**4.75**	115.58	**5.25**	190.57	**6.75**	854.06
4.26	70.810	4.76	116.75	5.26	192.48	6.80	897.85
4.27	71.522	4.77	117.92	5.27	194.42	6.85	943.88
4.28	72.240	4.78	119.10	5.28	196.37	6.90	992.27
4.29	72.966	4.79	120.30	5.29	198.34	6.95	1043.1
4.30	73.700	**4.80**	121.51	**5.30**	200.34	**7.00**	1096.6
4.31	74.440	4.81	122.73	5.31	202.35	7.05	1152.9
4.32	75.189	4.82	123.97	5.32	204.38	7.10	1212.0
4.33	75.944	4.83	125.21	5.33	206.44	7.15	1274.1
4.34	76.708	4.84	126.47	5.34	208.51	7.20	1339.4
4.35	77.478	**4.85**	127.74	**5.35**	210.61	**7.25**	1408.1
4.36	78.257	4.86	129.02	5.36	212.72	7.30	1480.3
4.37	79.044	4.87	130.32	5.37	214.86	7.35	1556.2
4.38	79.838	4.88	131.63	5.38	217.02	7.40	1636.0
4.39	80.640	4.89	132.95	5.39	219.20	7.45	1719.9
4.40	81.451	**4.90**	134.29	**5.40**	221.41	**7.50**	1808.0
4.41	82.269	4.91	135.64	5.41	223.63	7.55	1900.7
4.42	83.096	4.92	137.00	5.42	225.88	7.60	1998.2
4.43	83.931	4.93	138.38	5.43	228.15	7.65	2100.6
4.44	84.775	4.94	139.77	5.44	230.44	7.70	2208.3
4.45	85.627	**4.95**	141.17	**5.45**	232.76	**7.75**	2321.6
4.46	86.488	4.96	142.59	5.46	235.10	7.80	2440.6
4.47	87.357	4.97	144.03	5.47	237.46	7.85	2565.7
4.48	88.235	4.98	145.47	5.48	239.85	7.90	2697.3
4.49	89.121	4.99	146.94	5.49	242.26	7.95	2835.6
4.50	90.017	**5.00**	148.41	**5.50**	244.69	**8.00**	2981.0

EXPONENTIAL FUNCTIONS
(*continued*)

FOUR-PLACE MANTISSAS FOR COMMON LOGARITHMS

N	0	1	2	3	4	5	6	7	8	9			Proportional Parts						
											1	2	3	4	5	6	7	8	9
10	0000	0043	0086	0128	0170	0212	0253	0294	0334	0374	*4	8	12	17	21	25	29	33	37
11	0414	0453	0492	0531	0569	0607	0645	0682	0719	0755	4	8	11	15	19	23	26	30	34
12	0792	0828	0864	0899	0934	0969	1004	1038	1072	1106	3	7	10	14	17	21	24	28	31
13	1139	1173	1206	1239	1271	1303	1335	1367	1399	1430	3	6	10	13	16	19	23	26	29
14	1461	1492	1523	1553	1584	1614	1644	1673	1703	1732	3	6	9	12	15	18	21	24	27
15	1761	1790	1818	1847	1875	1903	1931	1959	1987	2014	*3	6	8	11	14	17	20	22	25
16	2041	2068	2095	2122	2148	2175	2201	2227	2253	2279	3	5	8	11	13	16	18	21	24
17	2304	2330	2355	2380	2405	2430	2455	2480	2504	2529	2	5	7	10	12	15	17	20	22
18	2553	2577	2601	2625	2648	2672	2695	2718	2742	2765	2	5	7	9	12	14	16	19	21
19	2788	2810	2833	2856	2878	2900	2923	2945	2967	2989	2	4	7	9	11	13	16	18	20
20	3010	3032	3054	3075	3096	3118	3139	3160	3181	3201	2	4	6	8	11	13	15	17	19
21	3222	3243	3263	3284	3304	3324	3345	3365	3385	3404	2	4	6	8	10	12	14	16	18
22	3424	3444	3464	3483	3502	3522	3541	3560	3579	3598	2	4	6	8	10	12	14	15	17
23	3617	3636	3655	3674	3692	3711	3729	3747	3766	3784	2	4	6	7	9	11	13	15	17
24	3802	3820	3838	3856	3874	3892	3909	3927	3945	3962	2	4	5	7	9	11	12	14	16
25	3979	3997	4014	4031	4048	4065	4082	4099	4116	4133	2	3	5	7	9	10	12	14	15
26	4150	4166	4183	4200	4216	4232	4249	4265	4281	4298	2	3	5	7	8	10	11	13	15
27	4314	4330	4346	4362	4378	4393	4409	4425	4440	4456	2	3	5	6	8	9	11	13	14
28	4472	4487	4502	4518	4533	4548	4564	4579	4594	4609	2	3	5	6	8	9	11	12	14
29	4624	4639	4654	4669	4683	4698	4713	4728	4742	4757	1	3	4	6	7	9	10	12	13
30	4771	4786	4800	4814	4829	4843	4857	4871	4886	4900	1	3	4	6	7	9	10	11	13
31	4914	4928	4942	4955	4969	4983	4997	5011	5024	5038	1	3	4	6	7	8	10	11	12
32	5051	5065	5079	5092	5105	5119	5132	5145	5159	5172	1	3	4	5	7	8	9	11	12
33	5185	5198	5211	5224	5237	5250	5263	5276	5289	5302	1	3	4	5	6	8	9	10	12
34	5315	5328	5340	5353	5366	5378	5391	5403	5416	5428	1	3	4	5	6	8	9	10	11
35	5441	5453	5465	5478	5490	5502	5514	5527	5539	5551	1	2	4	5	6	7	9	10	11
36	5563	5575	5587	5599	5611	5623	5635	5647	5658	5670	1	2	4	5	6	7	8	10	11
37	5682	5694	5705	5717	5729	5740	5752	5763	5775	5786	1	2	3	5	6	7	8	9	10
38	5798	5809	5821	5832	5843	5855	5866	5877	5888	5899	1	2	3	5	6	7	8	9	10
39	5911	5922	5933	5944	5955	5966	5977	5988	5999	6010	1	2	3	4	5	7	8	9	10
40	6021	6031	6042	6053	6064	6075	6085	6096	6107	6117	1	2	3	4	5	6	8	9	10
41	6128	6138	6149	6160	6170	6180	6191	6201	6212	6222	1	2	3	4	5	6	7	8	9
42	6232	6243	6253	6263	6274	6284	6294	6304	6314	6325	1	2	3	4	5	6	7	8	9
43	6335	6345	6355	6365	6375	6385	6395	6405	6415	6425	1	2	3	4	5	6	7	8	9
44	6435	6444	6454	6464	6474	6484	6493	6503	6513	6522	1	2	3	4	5	6	7	8	9
45	6532	6542	6551	6561	6571	6580	6590	6599	6609	6618	1	2	3	4	5	6	7	8	9
46	6628	6637	6646	6656	6665	6675	6684	6693	6702	6712	1	2	3	4	5	6	7	7	8
47	6721	6730	6739	6749	6758	6767	6776	6785	6794	6803	1	2	3	4	5	5	6	7	8
48	6812	6821	6830	6839	6848	6857	6866	6875	6884	6893	1	2	3	4	4	5	6	7	8
49	6902	6911	6920	6928	6937	6946	6955	6964	6972	6981	1	2	3	4	4	5	6	7	8
50	6990	6998	7007	7016	7024	7033	7042	7050	7059	7067	1	2	3	3	4	5	6	7	8
51	7076	7084	7093	7101	7110	7118	7126	7135	7143	7152	1	2	3	3	4	5	6	7	8
52	7160	7168	7177	7185	7193	7202	7210	7218	7226	7235	1	2	2	3	4	5	6	7	7
53	7243	7251	7259	7267	7275	7284	7292	7300	7308	7316	1	2	2	3	4	5	6	6	7
54	7324	7332	7340	7348	7356	7364	7372	7380	7388	7396	1	2	2	3	4	5	6	6	7
55	7404	7412	7419	7427	7435	7443	7451	7459	7466	7474	1	2	2	3	4	5	5	6	7
56	7482	7490	7497	7505	7513	7520	7528	7536	7543	7551	1	2	2	3	4	5	5	6	7
57	7559	7566	7574	7582	7589	7597	7604	7612	7619	7627	1	2	2	3	4	5	5	6	7
58	7634	7642	7649	7657	7664	7672	7679	7686	7694	7701	1	1	2	3	4	4	5	6	7
59	7709	7716	7723	7731	7738	7745	7752	7760	7767	7774	1	1	2	3	4	4	5	6	7
N	0	1	2	3	4	5	6	7	8	9	1	2	3	4	5	6	7	8	9

* Interpolation in this section of the table is inaccurate.

N	0	1	2	3	4	5	6	7	8	9	Proportional Parts								
											1	2	3	4	5	6	7	8	9
60	7782	7789	7796	7803	7810	7818	7825	7832	7839	7846	1	1	2	3	4	4	5	6	6
61	7853	7860	7868	7875	7882	7889	7896	7903	7910	7917	1	1	2	3	4	4	5	6	6
62	7924	7931	7938	7945	7952	7959	7966	7973	7980	7987	1	1	2	3	3	4	5	6	6
63	7993	8000	8007	8014	8021	8028	8035	8041	8048	8055	1	1	2	3	3	4	5	5	6
64	8062	8069	8075	8082	8089	8096	8102	8109	8116	8122	1	1	2	3	3	4	5	5	6
65	8129	8136	8142	8149	8156	8162	8169	8176	8182	8189	1	1	2	3	3	4	5	5	6
66	8195	8202	8209	8215	8222	8228	8235	8241	8248	8254	1	1	2	3	3	4	5	5	6
67	8261	8267	8274	8280	8287	8293	8299	8306	8312	8319	1	1	2	3	3	4	5	5	6
68	8325	8331	8338	8344	8351	8357	8363	8370	8376	8382	1	1	2	3	3	4	4	5	6
69	8388	8395	84fil	8407	8414	8420	8426	8432	8439	8445	1	1	2	2	3	4	4	5	6
70	8451	8457	8463	8470	8476	8482	8488	8494	8500	8506	1	1	2	2	3	4	4	5	6
71	8513	8519	8525	8531	8537	8543	8549	8555	8561	8567	1	1	2	2	3	4	4	5	5
72	8573	8579	8585	8591	8597	8603	8609	8615	8621	8627	1	1	2	2	3	4	4	5	5
73	8633	8639	8645	8651	8657	8663	8669	8675	8681	8686	1	1	2	2	3	4	4	5	5
74	8692	8698	8704	8710	8716	8722	8727	8733	8739	8745	1	1	2	2	3	4	4	5	5
75	8751	8756	8762	8768	8774	8779	8785	8791	8797	8802	1	1	2	2	3	3	4	5	5
76	8808	8814	8820	8825	8831	8837	8842	8848	8854	8859	1	1	2	2	3	3	4	5	5
77	8865	8871	8876	8882	8887	8893	8899	8904	8910	8915	1	1	2	2	3	3	4	4	5
78	8921	8927	8932	8938	8943	8949	8954	8960	8965	8971	1	1	2	2	3	3	4	4	5
79	8976	8982	8987	8993	8998	9004	9009	9015	9020	9025	1	1	2	2	3	3	4	4	5
80	9031	9036	9042	9047	9053	9058	9063	9069	9074	9079	1	1	2	2	3	3	4	4	5
81	9085	9090	9096	9101	9106	9112	9117	9122	9128	9133	1	1	2	2	3	3	4	4	5
82	9138	9143	9149	9154	9159	9165	9170	9175	9180	9186	1	1	2	2	3	3	4	4	5
83	9191	9196	9201	9206	9212	9217	9222	9227	9232	9238	1	1	2	2	3	3	4	4	5
84	9243	9248	9253	9258	9263	9269	9274	9279	9284	9289	1	1	2	2	3	3	4	4	5
85	9294	9299	9304	9309	9315	9320	9325	9330	9335	9340	1	1	2	2	3	3	4	4	5
86	9345	9350	9355	9360	9365	9370	9375	9380	9385	9390	1	1	2	2	3	3	4	4	5
87	9395	9400	9405	9410	9415	9420	9425	9430	9435	9440	0	1	1	2	2	3	3	4	4
88	9445	9450	9455	9460	9465	9469	9474	9479	9484	9489	0	1	1	2	2	3	3	4	4
89	9494	9499	9504	9509	9513	9518	9523	9528	9533	9538	0	1	1	2	2	3	3	4	4
90	9542	9547	9552	9557	9562	9566	9571	9576	9581	9586	0	1	1	2	2	3	3	4	4
91	9590	9595	9600	9605	9609	9614	9619	9624	9628	9633	0	1	1	2	2	3	3	4	4
92	9638	9643	9647	9652	9657	9661	9666	9671	9675	9680	0	1	1	2	2	3	3	4	4
93	9685	9689	9694	9699	9703	9708	9713	9717	9722	9727	0	1	1	2	2	3	3	4	4
94	9731	9736	9741	9745	9750	9754	9759	9763	9768	9773	0	1	1	2	2	3	3	4	4
95	9777	9782	9786	9791	9795	9800	9805	9809	9814	9818	0	1	1	2	2	3	3	4	4
96	9823	9827	9832	9836	9841	9845	9850	9854	9859	9863	0	1	1	2	2	3	3	4	4
97	9868	9872	9877	9881	9886	9890	9894	9899	9903	9908	0	1	1	2	2	3	3	4	4
98	9912	9917	9921	9926	9930	9934	9939	9943	9948	9952	0	1	1	2	2	3	3	4	4
99	9956	9961	9965	9969	9974	9978	9983	9987	9991	9996	0	1	1	2	2	3	3	4	4
N	0	1	2	3	4	5	6	7	8	9	1	2	3	4	5	6	7	8	9

Periods	Rate i				
n	.0025(¼%)	.004167(⁵/₁₂%)	.005(½%)	.005833(⁷/₁₂%)	.0075(¾%)
1	1.0025 0000	1.0041 6667	1.0050 0000	1.0058 3333	1.0075 0000
2	1.0050 0625	1.0083 5069	1.0100 2500	1.0117 0069	1.0150 5625
3	1.0075 1877	1.0125 5216	1.0150 7513	1.0176 0228	1.0226 6917
4	1.0100 3756	1.0167 7112	1.0201 5050	1.0235 3830	1.0303 3919
5	1.0125 6266	1.0210 1767	1.0252 5125	1.0295 0894	1.0280 6673
6	1.0150 9406	1.0252 6187	1.0303 7751	1.0355 1440	1.0458 5224
7	1.0176 3180	1.0295 3379	1.0355 2940	1.0415 5490	1.0536 9613
8	1.0201 7588	1.0338 2352	1.0407 0704	1.0476 3064	1.0615 9885
9	1.0227 2632	1.0381 3111	1.0459 1058	1.0537 4182	1.0696 6084
10	1.0252 8313	1.0424 5666	1.0511 4013	1.0598 8865	1.0775 8255
11	1.0278 4634	1.0468 0023	1.0563 9583	1.0660 7133	1.0856 6441
12	1.0304 1596	1.0511 6190	1.0616 7781	1.0722 9008	1.0938 0690
13	1.0329 9200	1.0555 4174	1.0669 8620	1.0785 4511	1.1020 1045
14	1.0355 7448	1.0599 3983	1.0723 2113	1.0848 3662	1.1102 7553
15	1.0381 6341	1.0643 5625	1.0776 8274	1.0911 6483	1.1186 0259
16	1.0407 5882	1.0687 9106	1.0830 7115	1.0975 2996	1.1269 9211
17	1.0433 6072	1.0732 4436	1.0884 8651	1.1039 3222	1.1354 4455
18	1.0459 6912	1.0777 1621	1.0939 2894	1.1103 7182	1.1439 6039
19	1.0485 8404	1.0822 0670	1.0993 9858	1.1168 4899	1.1525 4009
20	1.0512 0550	1.0867 1589	1.1048 9558	1.1233 6395	1.1611 8414
21	1.0538 3352	1.0912 4387	1.1104 2006	1.1299 1690	1.1698 9302
22	1.0564 6810	1.0957 9072	1.1159 7216	1.1365 0808	1.1786 6722
23	1.0591 0927	1.1003 5652	1.1215 5202	1.1431 3771	1.1875 0723
24	1.0617 5704	1.1049 4134	1.1271 5978	1.1498 0602	1.1964 1353
25	1.0644 1144	1.1095 4526	1.1327 9558	1.1565 1322	1.2053 8663
26	1.0670 7247	1.1141 6836	1.1384 5955	1.1632 5955	1.2144 2703
27	1.0697 4015	1.1188 1073	1.1441 5185	1.1700 4523	1.2235 3523
28	1.0724 1450	1.1234 7244	1.1498 7261	1.1768 7049	1.2327 1175
29	1.0750 9553	1.1281 5358	1.1556 2197	1.1837 3557	1.2419 5709
30	1.0777 8327	1.1328 5422	1.1614 0008	1.1906 4069	1.2512 7176
31	1.0804 7773	1.1375 7444	1.1672 0708	1.1975 8610	1.2606 5630
32	1.0831 7892	1.1423 1434	1.1730 4312	1.2045 7202	1.2701 1122
33	1.0858 8687	1.1470 7398	1.1789 0833	1.2115 9869	1.2796 3706
34	1.0886 0159	1.1518 5346	1.1848 0288	1.2186 6634	1.2892 3434
35	1.0913 2309	1.1566 5284	1.1907 2689	1.2257 7523	1.2989 0359
36	1.0940 5140	1.1614 7223	1.1966 8052	1.2329 2559	1.3086 4537
37	1.0967 8653	1.1663 1170	1.2026 6393	1.2401 1765	1.3184 6021
38	1.0995 2850	1.1711 7133	1.2086 7725	1.2473 5167	1.3283 4866
39	1.1022 7732	1.1760 5121	1.2147 2063	1.2546 2789	1.3383 1128
40	1.1050 3301	1.1809 5142	1.2207 9424	1.2619 4655	1.3483 4861
41	1.1077 9559	1.1858 7206	1.2268 9821	1.2693 0791	1.3584 6123
42	1.1105 6508	1.1908 1319	1.2330 3270	1.2767 1220	1.3686 4969
43	1.1133 4149	1.1957 7491	1.2391 9786	1.2841 5969	1.3789 1456
44	1.1161 2485	1.2007 5731	1.2453 9385	1.2916 5062	1.3892 5642
45	1.1189 1516	1.2057 6046	1.2516 2082	1.2991 8525	1.3996 7584
46	1.1217 1245	1.2107 8446	1.2578 7892	1.3067 6383	1.4101 7341
47	1.1245 1673	1.2158 2940	1.2641 6832	1.3143 8662	1.4207 4971
48	1.1273 2802	1.2208 9536	1.2704 8916	1.3220 5388	1.4314 0533
49	1.1301 4634	1.2259 8242	1.2768 4161	1.3297 6586	1.4421 4087
50	1.1329 7171	1.2310 9068	1.2832 2581	1.3375 2283	1.4529 5693

Periods	Rate i				
n	.0025(¼%)	.004167(⁵⁄₁₂%)	.005(½%)	.005833(⁷⁄₁₂%)	.0075(¾%)
51	1.1358 0414	1.2362 2022	1.2896 4194	1.3453 2504	1.4638 5411
52	1.1386 4365	1.2413 7114	1.2960 9015	1.3531 7277	1.4748 3301
53	1.1414 9026	1.2465 4352	1.3025 7060	1.3610 6628	1.4858 9426
54	1.1443 4398	1.2517 3745	1.3090 8346	1.3690 0583	1.4970 3847
55	1.1472 0484	1.2569 5302	1.3156 2887	1.3769 9170	1.5082 6626
56	1.1500 7285	1.2621 9033	1.3222 0702	1.3850 2415	1.5195 7825
57	1.1529 4804	1.2674 4946	1.3288 1805	1.3931 0346	1.5309 7509
58	1.1558 3041	1.2727 3050	1.3354 6214	1.4012 2990	1.5424 5740
59	1.1587 1998	1.2780 3354	1.3421 3946	1.4094 0374	1.5540 2583
60	1.1616 1678	1.2833 5868	1.3488 5015	1.4176 2526	1.5656 8103
61	1.1645 2082	1.2887 0601	1.3555 9440	1.4258 9474	1.5774 2363
62	1.1674 3213	1.2940 7561	1.3623 7238	1.4342 1246	1.5892 5431
63	1.1703 5071	1.2994 6760	1.3691 8424	1.4425 7870	1.6011 7372
64	1.1732 7658	1.3048 8204	1.3760 3016	1.4509 9374	1.6131 8252
65	1.1762 0977	1.3103 1905	1.3829 1031	1.4594 5787	1.6252 8139
66	1.1791 5030	1.3157 7872	1.3898 2486	1.4679 7138	1.6374 7100
67	1.1820 9817	1.3212 6113	1.3967 7399	1.4765 3454	1.6497 5203
68	1.1850 5342	1.3267 6638	1.4037 5785	1.4851 4766	1.6621 2517
69	1.1880 1605	1.3322 9458	1.4107 7664	1.4938 1102	1.6745 9111
70	1.1909 8609	1.3378 4580	1.4178 3053	1.5025 2492	1.6871 5055
71	1.1939 6356	1.3434 2016	1.4249 1968	1.5112 8965	1.6998 0418
72	1.1969 4847	1.3490 1774	1.4320 4428	1.5201 0550	1.7125 5271
73	1.1999 4084	1.3546 3865	1.4392 0450	1.5289 7279	1.7253 9685
74	1.2029 4069	1.3602 8298	1.4464 0052	1.5378 9179	1.7383 3733
75	1.2059 4804	1.3659 5082	1.4536 3252	1.5468 6283	1.7513 7486
76	1.2089 6291	1.3716 4229	1.4609 0069	1.5558 8620	1.7645 1017
77	1.2119 8532	1.3773 5746	1.4682 0519	1.5649 6220	1.7777 4400
78	1.2150 1528	1.3830 9645	1.4755 4622	1.5740 9115	1.7910 7708
79	1.2180 5282	1.3888 5935	1.4829 2395	1.5832 7334	1.8045 1015
80	1.2210 9795	1.3946 4627	1.4903 3857	1.5925 0910	1.8180 4398
81	1.2241 5070	1.4004 5729	1.4977 9026	1.6017 9874	1.8316 7931
82	1.2272 1108	1.4062 9253	1.5052 7921	1.6111 4257	1.8454 1691
83	1.2302 7910	1.4121 5209	1.5128 0561	1.6205 4090	1.8592 5753
84	1.2333 5480	1.4180 3605	1.5203 6964	1.6299 9405	1.8732 0196
85	1.2364 3819	1.4239 4454	1.5279 7148	1.6395 0235	1.8872 5098
86	1.2395 2928	1.4298 7764	1.5356 1134	1.6490 6612	1.9014 0536
87	1.2426 2811	1.4358 3546	1.5432 8940	1.6586 8567	1.9156 6590
88	1.2457 3468	1.4418 1811	1.5510 0585	1.6683 6134	1.9300 3339
89	1.2488 4901	1.4478 2568	1.5587 6087	1.6780 9344	1.9445 0865
90	1.2519 7114	1.4538 5829	1.5665 5468	1.6878 8232	1.9590 9246
91	1.2551 0106	1.4599 1603	1.5743 8745	1.6977 2830	1.9737 8565
92	1.2582 3882	1.4659 9902	1.5822 5939	1.7076 3172	1.9885 8905
93	1.2613 8441	1.4721 0735	1.5901 7069	1.7175 9290	2.0035 0346
94	1.2645 3787	1.4782 4113	1.5981 2154	1.7276 1219	2.0185 2974
95	1.2676 9922	1.4844 0047	1.6061 1215	1.7376 8993	2.0336 6871
96	1.2708 6847	1.4905 8547	1.6141 4271	1.7478 2646	2.0489 2123
97	1.2740 4564	1.4967 9624	1.6222 1342	1.7580 2211	2.0642 8814
98	1.2772 3075	1.5030 3289	1.6303 2449	1.7682 7724	2.0797 7030
99	1.2804 2383	1.5092 9553	1.6384 7611	1.7785 9219	2.0953 6858
100	1.2836 2489	1.5155 8426	1.6466 6849	1.7889 6731	2.1110 8384

AMOUNT AT
COMPOUND
INTEREST
$(1 + i)^n$
(*continued*)

A-13

Periods	Rate i				
n	.01 (1%)	.01125 (1⅛%)	.0125 (1¼%)	.015 (1½%)	.0175 (1¾%)
1	1.0100 0000	1.0112 5000	1.0125 0000	1.0150 0000	1.0175 0000
2	1.0201 0000	1.0226 2656	1.0251 5625	1.0302 2500	1.0353 0625
3	1.0303 0100	1.0341 3111	1.0379 7070	1.0456 7838	1.0534 2411
4	1.0406 0401	1.0457 6509	1.0509 4534	1.0613 6355	1.0718 5903
5	1.0510 1005	1.0575 2994	1.0640 8215	1.0772 8400	1.0906 1656
6	1.0615 2015	1.0694 2716	1.0773 8318	1.0934 4326	1.1097 0235
7	1.0721 3535	1.0814 5821	1.0908 5047	1.1098 4491	1.1291 2215
8	1.0828 5671	1.0936 2462	1.1044 8610	1.1264 9259	1.1488 8178
9	1.0936 8527	1.1059 2789	1.1182 9218	1.1433 8998	1.1689 8721
10	1.1046 2213	1.1183 6958	1.1322 7083	1.1605 4083	1.1894 4449
11	1.1156 6835	1.1309 5124	1.1464 2422	1.1779 4894	1.2102 5977
12	1.1268 2503	1.1436 7444	1.1607 5452	1.1956 1817	1.2314 3931
13	1.1380 9328	1.1565 4078	1.1752 6395	1.2135 5244	1.2529 8950
14	1.1494 7421	1.1695 5186	1.1899 5475	1.2317 5573	1.2749 1682
15	1.1609 6896	1.1827 0932	1.2048 2918	1.2502 3207	1.2972 2786
16	1.1725 7864	1.1960 1480	1.2198 8955	1.2689 8555	1.3199 2935
17	1.1843 0443	1.2094 6997	1.2351 3817	1.2880 2033	1.3430 2811
18	1.1961 4748	1.2230 7650	1.2505 7739	1.3073 4064	1.3665 3111
19	1.2081 0895	1.2368 3611	1.2662 0961	1.3269 5075	1.3904 4540
20	1.2201 9004	1.2507 5052	1.2820 3723	1.3468 5501	1.4147 7820
21	1.2323 9194	1.2648 2146	1.2980 6270	1.3670 5783	1.4395 3681
22	1.2447 1586	1.2790 5071	1.3142 8848	1.3875 6370	1.4647 2871
23	1.2571 6302	1.2934 4003	1.3307 1709	1.4083 7715	1.4903 6146
24	1.2697 3465	1.3079 9123	1.3473 5105	1.4295 0281	1.5164 4279
25	1.2824 3200	1.3227 0613	1.3641 9294	1.4509 4535	1.5429 8054
26	1.2952 5631	1.3375 8657	1.3812 4535	1.4727 0953	1.5699 8269
27	1.3082 0888	1.3526 3442	1.3985 1092	1.4948 0018	1.5974 5739
28	1.3212 9097	1.3678 5156	1.4159 9230	1.5172 2218	1.6254 1290
29	1.3345 0388	1.3832 3989	1.4336 9221	1.5399 8051	1.6538 5762
30	1.3478 4892	1.3988 0134	1.4516 1336	1.5630 8022	1.6828 0013
31	1.3613 2740	1.4145 3785	1.4697 5853	1.5865 2642	1.7122 4913
32	1.3749 4068	1.4304 5140	1.4881 3051	1.6103 2432	1.7422 1349
33	1.3886 9009	1.4465 4398	1.5067 3214	1.6344 7918	1.7727 0223
34	1.4025 7699	1.4628 1760	1.5255 6629	1.6589 9637	1.8037 2452
35	1.4166 0276	1.4792 7430	1.5446 3587	1.6838 8132	1.8352 8970
36	1.4307 6878	1.4959 1613	1.5639 4382	1.7091 3954	1.8674 0727
37	1.4450 7647	1.5127 4519	1.5834 9312	1.7347 7663	1.9000 8689
38	1.4595 2724	1.5297 6357	1.6032 8678	1.7607 9828	1.9333 3841
39	1.4741 2251	1.5469 7341	1.6233 2787	1.7872 1025	1.9671 7184
40	1.4888 6373	1.5643 7687	1.6436 1946	1.8140 1841	2.0015 9734
41	1.5037 5237	1.5819 7611	1.6641 6471	1.8412 2868	2.0366 2530
42	1.5187 8989	1.5997 7334	1.6849 6677	1.8688 4712	2.0722 6624
43	1.5339 7779	1.6177 7079	1.7060 2885	1.8968 7982	2.1085 3090
44	1.5493 1757	1.6359 7071	1.7273 5421	1.9253 3302	2.1454 3019
45	1.5648 1075	1.6543 7538	1.7489 4614	1.9542 1301	2.1829 7522
46	1.5804 5885	1.6729 8710	1.7708 0797	1.9835 2621	2.2211 7728
47	1.5962 6344	1.6918 0821	1.7929 4306	2.0132 7910	2.2600 4789
48	1.6122 2608	1.7108 4105	1.8153 5485	2.0434 7829	2.2995 9872
49	1.6283 4834	1.7300 8801	1.8380 4679	2.0741 3046	2.3398 4170
50	1.6446 3182	1.7495 5150	1.8610 2237	2.1052 4242	2.3807 8893

Periods	Rate i				
n	.01 (1%)	.01125 (1⅛%)	.0125 (1¼%)	.015 (1½%)	.0175 (1¾%)
51	1.6610 7814	1.7692 3395	1.8842 8515	2.1368 2106	2.4224 5274
52	1.6776 8892	1.7891 3784	1.9078 3872	2.1688 7337	2.4648 4566
53	1.5944 6581	1.8092 6564	1.9316 8670	2.2014 0647	2.5079 8046
54	1.7114 1047	1.8296 1988	1.9558 3279	2.2344 2757	2.5518 7012
55	1.7285 2457	1.8502 0310	1.9802 8070	2.2679 4398	2.5965 2785
56	1.7458 0982	1.8710 1788	2.0050 3420	2.3019 6314	2.6419 6708
57	1.7632 6792	1.8920 6684	2.0300 9713	2.3364 9259	2.6882 0151
58	1.7809 0060	1.9133 5259	2.0554 7335	2.3715 3998	2.7352 4503
59	1.7987 0960	1.9348 7780	2.0811 6676	2.4071 1308	2.7831 1182
60	1.8166 9670	1.9566 4518	2.1071 8135	2.4432 1978	2.8318 1628
61	1.8348 6367	1.9786 5744	2.1335 2111	2.4798 6807	2.8813 7306
62	1.8532 1230	2.0009 1733	2.1601 9013	2.5170 6609	2.9317 9709
63	1.8717 4443	2.0234 2765	2.1871 9250	2.5548 2208	2.9831 0354
64	1.8904 6187	2.0461 9121	2.2145 3241	2.5931 4442	3.0353 0785
65	1.9093 6649	2.0692 1087	2.2422 1407	2.6320 4158	3.0884 2574
66	1.9284 6015	2.0924 8949	2.2702 4174	2.6715 2221	3.1423 7319
67	1.9477 4475	2.1160 2999	2.2986 1976	2.7115 9504	3.1974 6647
68	1.9672 2220	2.1398 3533	2.3273 5251	2.7522 6896	3.2534 2213
69	1.9868 9442	2.1639 0848	2.3564 4442	2.7935 5300	3.3103 5702
70	2.0067 6337	2.1882 5245	2.3858 9997	2.8354 5629	3.3682 8827
71	2.0268 3100	2.2128 7029	2.4157 2372	2.8779 8814	3.4272 3331
72	2.0470 9931	2.2377 6508	2.4459 2027	2.9211 5796	3.4872 0990
73	2.0675 7031	2.2629 3994	2.4764 9427	2.9649 7533	3.5482 3607
74	2.0882 4601	2.2883 9801	2.5074 5045	3.0094 4996	3.6103 3020
75	2.1091 2847	2.3141 4249	2.5387 9358	3.0545 9171	3.6735 1098
76	2.1302 1975	2.3401 7659	2.5705 2850	3.1004 1059	3.7377 9742
77	2.1515 2195	2.3665 0358	2.6026 6011	3.1469 1674	3.8032 0888
78	2.1730 3717	2.3931 2675	2.6351 9336	3.1941 2050	3.8697 6503
79	2.1947 6754	2.4200 4942	2.6681 3327	3.2420 3230	3.9374 8592
80	2.2167 1522	2.4472 7498	2.7014 8494	3.2906 6279	4.0063 9192
81	2.2388 8237	2.4748 0682	2.7352 5350	3.3400 2273	4.0765 0378
82	2.2612 7119	2.5026 4840	2.7694 4417	3.3901 2307	4.1478 4260
83	2.2838 8390	2.5308 0319	2.8040 6222	3.4409 7492	4.2204 2984
84	2.3067 2274	2.5592 7473	2.8391 1300	3.4925 8954	4.2942 8737
85	2.3297 8997	2.5880 6657	2.8746 0191	3.5449 7838	4.3694 3740
86	2.3530 8787	2.6171 8232	2.9105 3444	3.5981 5306	4.4459 0255
87	2.3766 1875	2.6466 2562	2.9469 1612	3.6521 2535	4.5237 0584
88	2.4003 8494	2.6764 0016	2.9837 5257	3.7069 0723	4.6028 7070
89	2.4243 8879	2.7065 0966	3.0210 4948	3.7625 1084	4.6834 2093
90	2.4486 3267	2.7369 5789	3.0588 1260	3.8189 4851	4.7653 8080
91	2.4731 1900	2.7677 4867	3.0970 4775	3.8762 3273	4.8487 7496
92	2.4978 5019	2.7988 8584	3.1357 6085	3.9343 7622	4.9336 2853
93	2.5228 2869	2.8303 7331	3.1749 5786	3.9933 9187	5.0199 6703
94	2.5480 5698	2.8622 1501	3.2146 4483	4.0532 9275	5.1078 1645
95	2.5735 3755	2.8944 1492	3.2548 2789	4.1140 9214	5.1972 0324
96	2.5992 7293	2.9269 7709	3.2955 1324	4.1758 0352	5.2881 5429
97	2.6252 6565	2.9599 0559	3.3367 0716	4.2384 4057	5.3806 9699
98	2.6515 1831	2.9932 0452	3.3784 1600	4.3020 1718	5.4748 5919
99	2.6780 3349	3.0268 7807	3.4206 4620	4.3665 4744	5.5706 6923
100	2.7048 1383	3.0609 3045	3.4634 0427	4.4320 4565	5.6681 5594

AMOUNT AT COMPOUND INTEREST
$(1 + i)^n$
(*continued*)

Periods	Rate i				
n	.02 (2%)	.0225 (2¼%)	.025 (2½%)	.0275 (2¾%)	.03 (3%)
1	1.0200 0000	1.0225 0000	1.0250 0000	1.0275 0000	1.0300 0000
2	1.0404 0000	1.0455 0625	1.0506 2500	1.0557 5625	1.0609 0000
3	1.0612 0800	1.0690 3014	1.0768 9063	1.0847 8955	1.0927 2700
4	1.0824 3216	1.0930 8332	1.1038 1289	1.1146 2126	1.1255 0881
5	1.1040 8080	1.1176 7769	1.1314 0821	1.1452 7334	1.1592 7407
6	1.1261 6242	1.1428 2544	1.1596 9342	1.1767 6836	1.1940 5230
7	1.1486 8567	1.1685 3901	1.1886 8575	1.2091 2949	1.2298 7387
8	1.1716 5938	1.1948 3114	1.2184 0290	1.2423 8055	1.2667 7008
9	1.1950 9257	1.2217 1484	1.2488 6297	1.2765 4602	1.3047 7318
10	1.2189 9442	1.2492 0343	1.2800 8454	1.3116 5103	1.3439 1638
11	1.2433 7431	1.2773 1050	1.3120 8666	1.3477 2144	1.3842 3387
12	1.2682 4179	1.3060 4999	1.3448 8882	1.3847 8378	1.4257 6089
13	1.2936 0663	1.3354 3611	1.3785 1104	1.4228 6533	1.4685 3371
14	1.3194 7876	1.3654 8343	1.4129 7382	1.4619 9413	1.5125 8972
15	1.3458 6834	1.3962 0680	1.4482 9817	1.5021 9896	1.5579 6742
16	1.3727 8571	1.4276 2146	1.4845 0562	1.5435 0944	1.6047 0644
17	1.4002 4142	1.4597 4294	1.5216 1826	1.5859 5595	1.6528 4763
18	1.4282 4625	1.4925 8716	1.5596 5872	1.6295 6973	1.7024 3306
19	1.4568 1117	1.5261 7037	1.5986 5019	1.6743 8290	1.7535 0605
20	1.4859 4740	1.5605 0920	1.6386 1644	1.7204 2843	1.8061 1123
21	1.5156 6634	1.5956 2066	1.6795 8185	1.7677 4021	1.8602 9457
22	1.5459 7967	1.6315 2212	1.7215 7140	1.8163 5307	1.9161 0341
23	1.5768 9926	1.6682 3137	1.7646 1068	1.8663 0278	1.9735 8651
24	1.6084 3725	1.7057 6658	1.8087 2595	1.9176 2610	2.0327 9411
25	1.6406 0599	1.7441 4632	1.8539 4410	1.9703 6082	2.0937 7793
26	1.6734 1811	1.7833 8962	1.9002 9270	2.0245 4575	2.1565 9127
27	1.7068 8648	1.8235 1588	1.9478 0002	2.0802 2075	2.2212 8901
28	1.7410 2421	1.8645 4499	1.9964 9502	2.1374 2682	2.2879 2768
29	1.7758 4469	1.9064 9725	2.0464 0739	2.1962 0606	2.3565 6551
30	1.8113 6158	1.9493 9344	2.0975 6758	2.2566 0173	2.4272 6247
31	1.8475 8882	1.9932 5479	2.1500 0677	2.3186 5828	2.5000 8035
32	1.8845 4059	2.0381 0303	2.2037 5694	2.3824 2138	2.5750 8276
33	1.9222 3140	2.0839 6034	2.2588 5086	2.4479 3797	2.6523 3524
34	1.9606 7603	2.1308 4945	2.3153 2213	2.5152 5626	2.7319 0530
35	1.9998 8955	2.1787 9356	2.3732 0519	2.5844 2581	2.8138 6245
36	2.0398 8734	2.2278 1642	2.4325 3532	2.6554 9752	2.8982 7833
37	2.0806 8509	2.2779 4229	2.4933 4870	2.7285 2370	2.9852 2668
38	2.1222 9879	2.3291 9599	2.5556 8242	2.8035 5810	3.0747 8348
39	2.1647 4477	2.3816 0290	2.6195 7448	2.8806 5595	3.1670 2698
40	2.2080 3966	2.4351 8897	2.6850 6384	2.9598 7399	3.2620 3779
41	2.2522 0046	2.4899 8072	2.7521 9043	3.0412 7052	3.3598 9893
42	2.2972 4447	2.5460 0528	2.8209 9520	3.1249 0546	3.4606 9589
43	2.3431 8936	2.6032 9040	2.8915 2008	3.2108 4036	3.5645 1677
44	2.3900 5314	2.6618 6444	2.9638 0808	3.2991 3847	3.6714 5227
45	2.4378 5421	2.7217 5639	3.0379 0328	3.3898 6478	3.7815 9584
46	2.4866 1129	2.7829 9590	3.1138 5086	3.4830 8606	3.8950 4372
47	2.5363 4352	2.8456 1331	3.1916 9713	3.5788 7093	4.0118 9503
48	2.5870 7039	2.9096 3961	3.2714 8956	3.6772 8988	4.1322 5188
49	2.6388 1179	2.9751 0650	3.3532 7680	3.7784 1535	4.2562 1944
50	2.6915 8803	3.0420 4640	3.4371 0872	3.8823 2177	4.3839 0602

Periods	Rate i				
n	.02 (2%)	.0225 (2¼%)	.025 (2½%)	.0275 (2¾%)	.03 (3%)
51	2.7454 1979	3.1104 9244	3.5230 3644	3.9890 8562	4.5154 2320
52	2.8003 2819	3.1804 7852	3.6111 1235	4.0987 8547	4.6508 8590
53	2.8563 3475	3.2520 3929	3.7013 9016	4.2115 0208	4.7904 1247
54	2.9134 6144	3.3252 1017	3.7939 2491	4.3273 1838	4.9341 2485
55	2.9717 3067	3.4000 2740	3.8887 7303	4.4463 1964	5.0821 4859
56	3.0311 6529	3.4765 2802	3.9859 9236	4.5685 9343	5.2346 1305
57	3.0917 8859	3.5547 4990	4.0856 4217	4.6942 2975	5.3916 5144
58	3.1536 2436	3.6347 3177	4.1877 8322	4.8233 2107	5.5534 0098
59	3.2166 9685	3.7165 1324	4.2924 7780	4.9559 6239	5.7200 0301
60	3.2810 3079	3.8001 3479	4.3997 8975	5.0922 5136	5.8916 0310
61	3.3466 5140	3.8856 3782	4.5097 8449	5.2322 8827	6.0683 5120
62	3.4135 8443	3.9730 6467	4.6225 2910	5.3761 7620	6.2504 0173
63	3.4818 5612	4.0624 5862	4.7380 9233	5.5240 2105	6.4379 1379
64	3.5514 9324	4.1538 6394	4.8565 4464	5.6759 3162	6.6310 5120
65	3.6225 2311	4.2473 2588	4.9779 5826	5.8320 1974	6.8299 8273
66	3.6949 7357	4.3428 9071	5.1024 0721	5.9924 0029	7.0348 8222
67	3.7688 7304	4.4406 0576	5.2299 6739	6.1571 9130	7.2459 2868
68	3.8442 5050	4.5405 1939	5.3607 1658	6.3265 1406	7.4633 0654
69	3.9211 3551	4.6426 8107	5.4947 3449	6.5004 9319	7.6872 0574
70	3.9995 5822	4.7471 4140	5.6321 0286	6.6792 5676	7.9178 2191
71	4.0795 4939	4.8539 5208	5.7729 0543	6.8629 3632	8.1553 5657
72	4.1611 4038	4.9631 6600	5.9172 2806	7.0516 6706	8.4000 1727
73	4.2443 6318	5.0748 3723	6.0651 5876	7.2455 8791	8.6520 1778
74	4.3292 5045	5.1890 2107	6.2167 8773	7.4448 4158	8.9115 7832
75	4.4158 3546	5.3057 7405	6.3722 0743	7.6495 7472	9.1789 2567
76	4.5041 5216	5.4251 5396	6.5315 1261	7.8599 3802	9.4542 9344
77	4.5942 3521	5.5472 1993	6.6948 0043	8.0760 8632	9.7379 2224
78	4.6861 1991	5.6720 3237	6.8621 7044	8.2981 7869	10.0300 5991
79	4.7798 4231	5.7996 5310	7.0337 2470	8.5263 7861	10.3309 6171
80	4.8754 3916	5.9301 4530	7.2095 6782	8.7608 5402	10.6408 9056
81	4.9729 4794	6.0635 7357	7.3898 0701	9.0017 7651	10.9601 1727
82	5.0724 0690	6.2000 0397	7.5745 5219	9.2493 2639	11.2889 2079
83	5.1738 5504	6.3395 0406	7.7639 1599	9.5036 8286	11.6275 8842
84	5.2773 3214	6.4821 4290	7.9580 1389	9.7650 3414	11.9764 1607
85	5.3828 7878	6.6279 9112	8.1569 6424	10.0335 7258	12.3357 0855
86	5.4905 3636	6.7771 2092	8.3608 8834	10.3094 9583	12.7057 7981
87	5.6003 4708	6.9296 0614	8.5699 1055	10.5930 0696	13.0869 5320
88	5.7123 5402	7.0855 2228	8.7841 5832	10.8843 1465	13.4795 6180
89	5.8266 0110	7.2449 4653	9.0037 6228	11.1836 3331	13.8839 4865
90	5.9431 3313	7.4079 5782	9.2288 5633	11.4911 8322	14.3004 6711
91	6.0619 9579	7.5746 3688	9.4595 7774	11.8071 9076	14.7294 8112
92	6.1832 3570	7.7450 6621	9.6960 6718	12.1318 8851	15.1713 6556
93	6.3069 0042	7.9193 3020	9.9384 6886	12.4655 1544	15.6265 0652
94	6.4330 3843	8.0975 1512	10.1869 3058	12.8083 1711	16.0953 0172
95	6.5616 9920	8.2798 0921	10.4416 0385	13.1605 4584	16.5781 6077
96	6.6929 3318	8.4660 0267	10.7026 4395	13.5224 6085	17.0755 0559
97	6.8267 9184	8.6564 8773	10.9702 1004	13.8943 2852	17.5877 7076
98	6.9633 2768	8.8512 5871	11.2444 6530	14.2764 2255	18.1154 0388
99	7.1025 9423	9.0504 1203	11.5255 7693	14.6690 2417	18.6588 6600
100	7.2446 4612	9.2540 4630	11.8137 1635	15.0724 2234	19.2186 3198

Periods	Rate i				
n	.035 (3½%)	.04 (4%)	.045 (4½%)	.05 (5%)	.055 (5½%)
1	1.0350 0000	1.0400 0000	1.0450 0000	1.0500 0000	1.0550 0000
2	1.0712 2500	1.0816 0000	1.0920 2500	1.1025 0000	1.1130 2500
3	1.1087 1788	1.1248 6400	1.1411 6613	1.1576 2500	1.1742 4138
4	1.1475 2300	1.1698 5856	1.1925 1860	1.2155 0625	1.2388 2465
5	1.1876 8631	1.2166 5290	1.2461 8194	1.2762 8156	1.3069 6001
6	1.2292 5533	1.2653 1902	1.3022 6012	1.3400 9564	1.3788 4281
7	1.2722 7926	1.3159 3178	1.3608 6183	1.4071 0042	1.4546 7916
8	1.3168 0904	1.3685 6905	1.4221 0061	1.4774 5544	1.5346 8651
9	1.3628 9735	1.4233 1181	1.4860 9514	1.5513 2822	1.6190 9427
10	1.4105 9876	1.4802 4428	1.5529 6942	1.6288 9463	1.7081 4446
11	1.4599 6972	1.5394 5406	1.6228 5305	1.7103 3936	1.8020 9240
12	1.5110 6866	1.6010 3222	1.6958 8143	1.7958 5633	1.9012 0749
13	1.5639 5606	1.6650 7351	1.7721 9610	1.8856 4914	2.0057 7390
14	1.6186 9452	1.7316 7645	1.8519 4492	1.9799 3160	2.1160 9146
15	1.6753 4883	1.8009 4351	1.9352 8244	2.0789 2818	2.2324 7649
16	1.7339 8604	1.8729 8125	2.0223 7015	2.1828 7459	2.3552 6270
17	1.7946 7555	1.9479 0050	2.1133 7681	2.2920 1832	2.4848 0215
18	1.8574 8920	2.0258 1652	2.2084 7877	2.4066 1923	2.6214 6627
19	1.9225 0132	2.1068 4918	2.3078 6031	2.5269 5020	2.7656 4691
20	1.9897 8886	2.1911 2314	2.4117 1402	2.6532 9771	2.9177 5749
21	2.0594 3147	2.2787 6807	2.5202 4116	2.7859 6259	3.0782 3415
22	2.1315 1158	2.3699 1879	2.6336 5201	2.9252 6072	3.2475 3703
23	2.2061 1448	2.4647 1554	2.7521 6635	3.0715 2376	3.4261 5157
24	2.2833 2849	2.5633 0416	2.8760 1383	3.2250 9994	3.6145 8990
25	2.3632 4498	2.6658 3633	3.0054 3446	3.3863 5494	3.8133 9235
26	2.4459 5856	2.7724 6978	3.1406 7901	3.5556 7269	4.0231 2893
27	2.5315 6711	2.8833 6858	3.2820 0956	3.7334 5632	4.2444 0102
28	2.6201 7196	2.9987 0332	3.4296 9999	3.9201 2914	4.4778 4307
29	2.7118 7798	3.1186 5145	3.5840 3649	4.1161 3560	4.7241 2444
30	2.8067 9370	3.2433 9751	3.7453 1813	4.3219 4238	4.9839 5129
31	2.9050 3148	3.3731 3341	3.9138 5745	4.5380 3949	5.2580 6861
32	3.0067 0759	3.5080 5875	4.0899 8104	4.7649 4147	5.5472 6238
33	3.1119 4235	3.6483 8110	4.2740 3018	5.0031 8854	5.8523 6181
34	3.2208 6033	3.7943 1634	4.4663 6154	5.2533 4797	6.1742 4171
35	3.3335 9045	3.9460 8899	4.6673 4781	5.5160 1537	6.5138 2501
36	3.4502 6611	4.1039 3255	4.8773 7846	5.7918 1614	6.8720 8538
37	3.5710 2543	4.2680 8986	5.0968 6049	6.0814 0694	7.2500 5008
38	3.6960 1132	4.4388 1345	5.3262 1921	6.3854 7729	7.6488 0283
39	3.8253 7171	4.6163 6599	5.5658 9908	6.7047 5115	8.0694 8699
40	3.9592 5972	4.8010 2063	5.8163 6454	7.0399 8871	8.5133 0877
41	4.0978 3381	4.9930 6145	6.0781 0094	7.3919 8815	8.9815 4076
42	4.2412 5799	5.1927 8391	6.3516 1548	7.7615 8756	9.4755 2550
43	4.3897 0202	5.4004 9527	6.6374 3818	8.1496 6693	9.9966 7940
44	4.5433 4160	5.6165 1508	6.9361 2290	8.5571 5028	10.5464 9677
45	4.7023 5855	5.8411 7568	7.2482 4843	8.9850 0779	11.1265 5409
46	4.8669 4110	6.0748 2271	7.5744 1961	9.4342 5818	11.7385 1456
47	5.0372 8404	6.3178 1562	7.9152 6849	9.9059 7109	12.3841 3287
48	5.2135 8898	6.5705 2824	8.2714 5557	10.4012 6965	13.0652 6017
49	5.3960 6459	6.8333 4937	8.6436 7107	10.9213 3313	13.7838 4948
50	5.5849 2686	7.1066 8335	9.0326 3627	11.4673 9979	14.5419 6120

Periods	Rate i				
n	.06(6%)	.065(6½%)	.07(7%)	.075(7½%)	.08(8%)
1	1.0600 0000	1.0650 0000	1.0700 0000	1.0750 0000	1.0800 0000
2	1.1236 0000	1.1342 2500	1.1449 0000	1.1556 2500	1.1664 0000
3	1.1910 1600	1.2079 4963	1.2250 4300	1.2422 9688	1.2597 1200
4	1.2624 7696	1.2864 6635	1.3107 9601	1.3354 6914	1.3604 8896
5	1.3382 2558	1.3700 8666	1.4025 5173	1.4356 2933	1.4693 2808
6	1.4185 1911	1.4591 4230	1.5007 3035	1.5433 0153	1.5868 7432
7	1.5036 3026	1.5539 8655	1.6057 8148	1.6590 4914	1.7138 2427
8	1.5938 4807	1.6549 9567	1.7181 8618	1.7834 7783	1.8509 3021
9	1.6894 7896	1.7625 7039	1.8384 5921	1.9172 3866	1.9990 0463
10	1.7908 4770	1.8771 3747	1.9671 5136	2.0610 3156	2.1589 2500
11	1.8982 9856	1.9991 5140	2.1048 5195	2.2156 0893	2.3316 3900
12	2.0121 9647	2.1290 9624	2.2521 9159	2.3817 7960	2.5181 7012
13	2.1329 2826	2.2674 8750	2.4098 4500	2.5604 1307	2.7196 2373
14	2.2609 0396	2.4148 7418	2.5785 3415	2.7524 4405	2.9371 9362
15	2.3965 5819	2.5718 4101	2.7590 3154	2.9588 7735	3.1721 6911
16	2.5403 5168	2.7390 1067	2.9521 6375	3.1807 9315	3.4259 4264
17	2.6927 7279	2.9170 4637	3.1588 1521	3.4193 5264	3.7000 1805
18	2.8543 3915	3.1066 5438	3.3799 3228	3.6758 0409	3.9960 1950
19	3.0255 9950	3.3085 8691	3.6165 2754	3.9514 8940	4.3157 0106
20	3.2071 3547	3.5236 4506	3.8696 8446	4.2478 5110	4.6609 5714
21	3.3995 6360	3.7526 8199	4.1405 6237	4.5664 3993	5.0338 3372
22	3.6035 3742	3.9966 0632	4.4304 0174	4.9089 2293	5.4365 4041
23	3.8197 4966	4.2563 8573	4.7405 2986	5.2770 9215	5.8714 6365
24	4.0489 3464	4.5330 5081	5.0723 6695	5.6728 7406	6.3411 8074
25	4.2918 7072	4.8276 9911	5.4274 3264	6.0983 3961	6.8484 7520
26	4.5493 8296	5.1414 9955	5.8073 5292	6.5557 1508	7.3963 5321
27	4.8223 4594	5.4756 9702	6.2138 6763	7.0473 9371	7.9880 6147
28	5.1116 8670	5.8316 1733	6.6488 3836	7.5759 4824	8.6271 0639
29	5.4183 8790	6.2106 7245	7.1142 5705	8.1441 4436	9.3172 7490
30	5.7434 9117	6.6143 6616	7.6122 5504	8.7549 5519	10.0626 5689
31	6.0881 0064	7.0442 9996	8.1451 1290	9.4115 7683	10.8678 6944
32	6.4533 8668	7.5021 7946	8.7152 7080	10.1174 4509	11.7370 8300
33	6.8405 8988	7.9898 2113	9.3253 3975	10.8762 5347	12.6760 4964
34	7.2510 2528	8.5091 5950	9.9781 1354	11.6919 7248	13.6901 3361
35	7.6860 8679	9.0622 5487	10.6765 8148	12.5688 7042	14.7853 4429
36	8.1472 5200	9.6513 0143	11.4239 4219	13.5115 3570	15.9681 7184
37	8.6360 8712	10.2786 3603	12.2236 1814	14.5249 0088	17.2456 2558
38	9.1542 5235	10.9467 4737	13.0792 7141	15.6142 6844	18.6252 7563
39	9.7035 0749	11.6582 8595	13.9948 2041	16.7853 3858	20.1152 9768
40	10.2857 1794	12.4160 7453	14.9744 5784	18.0442 3897	21.7245 2150
41	10.9028 6101	13.2231 1938	16.0226 6989	19.3975 5689	23.4624 8322
42	11.5570 3267	14.0826 2214	17.1442 5678	20.8523 7366	25.3394 8187
43	12.2504 5463	14.9979 9258	18.3443 5475	22.4163 0168	27.3666 4042
44	12.9854 8191	15.9728 6209	19.6284 5959	24.0975 2431	29.5559 7166
45	13.7646 1083	17.0110 9813	21.0024 5176	25.9048 3863	31.9204 4939
46	14.5904 8748	18.1168 1951	22.4726 2338	27.8477 0153	34.4740 8534
47	15.4659 1673	19.2944 1278	24.0457 0702	29.9362 7915	37.2320 1217
48	16.3938 7173	20.5485 4961	25.7289 0651	32.1815 0008	40.2105 7314
49	17.3775 0403	21.8842 0533	27.5299 2997	34.5951 1259	43.4274 1899
50	18.4201 5427	23.3066 7868	29.4570 2506	37.1897 4603	46.9016 1251

AMOUNT AT
COMPOUND
INTEREST
$(1 + i)^n$
(continued)

APPENDIX
D

Answers to Odd-numbered Problems

CHAPTER 1 *Chapter 1, Section 1, page 5*

1. It is a valuable tool for practical applications in the physical world. Man's quest for truth and his love of wisdom have also contributed to the development of mathematics. The mysticism that has surrounded numbers and primitive religious rituals made a contribution. The fact that mathematics is an art satisfies a creative instinct in man, and the fact it can be a "game" makes it possible for it to amuse, amaze, and serve as a worthwhile pastime.

CHAPTER 2 *Chapter 2, Section 1, page 11*

1. (a) $\{a, b, c, d, e, f\}$. (b) $\{a, b, c, d, e, f, g, h, k\}$. (c) $\{b, c, d, e, f, g, h, k\}$.
3. (a) $\varnothing$ (b) $\varnothing$ (c) A
5. (a) $\{d, e, f, g, h, i, j, k\}$. (b) $\{a, g, h, i, j, k\}$. (c) $\{a, b, c, i, j\}$.
7. (a) $\{a, b, c, d, e, f, g\}$. (b) $\{a, b, c, d, x, y, z\}$. (c) $\{c, d, e, f, g, x, y, z\}$.
9. (a) $\varnothing$ (b) $\varnothing$ (c) A
11. (a) $\{e, f, g, x, y, z\}$. (b) $\{a, b, x, y, z\}$. (c) $\{a, b, c, d, e, f, g\}$.
13. $\varnothing, \{a\}, \{b\}, \{c\}, \{d\}, \{a, b\}, \{a, c\}, \{a, d\}, \{b, c\}, \{b, d\}, \{c, d\}, \{a, b, c\}, \{a, b, d\}, \{a, c, d\}, \{b, c, d\}, \{a, b, c, d\}$.

Chapter 2, Section 2, page 17

1. $a \div 0$ would be the number x such that $0 \times x = a$. But $0 \times x = 0$. Since $a \neq 0$, no such number x can exist.
3. Let $A \subseteq B$, let $n(A) = a$ and $n(B) = b$. Then $b - a = n(A'_B)$.
5. Let A be the set of tea drinkers and B the set of coffee drinkers. Thus, $n(A \cup B) = 512$, $n(A) = 278$, and $n(B) = 334$. Hence, $n(A \cap B) = n(A) + n(B) - n(A \cup B) = 278 + 334 - 512 = 100$.
7. (a) Yes. (b) Yes.
9. (a) e. (b) p. (c) r. (d) q. (e) p. (f) q.

11. (a) *e.* (b) *p.* (c) *r.* (d) *q.* (e) *p.* (f) *q.*
13. (a) *p.* (b) *e.*
15. (a) Yes. (b) Yes.

Chapter 2, Section 3, page 26

1. Let $q = 0$. Then $a = r$ and r is less than b since a is less than b.

3. $q = 16$; $r = 4$.   **5.** $q = 17$; $r = 4$.

7. dodoty-do, dodoty-to, dodoty-fo, todoty, todoty-un, todoty-do, todoty-to, todoty-fo, fodoty, fodoty-un, fodoty-do, fodoty-to, fodoty-fo.

9. ᘔᘔ, ᘔƐ, ᘔh, Ɛ0, ƐI, Ɛᘔ, ƐƐ, Ɛh, h0, hI, hᘔ, hƐ, hh, 100, 10I

11. Analysis: (1) Since we "bring down" two numbers in the second and third division steps, both digits on either side of "8" in the quotient must be "0". (2) Since 8 times a three-digit number is a three-digit number, the divisor must be less than 125. (3) Since the last number in the quotient times the divisor is a four-digit number, the last digit in the divisor must be a "9". (4) In the first and second subtractions, the only way to get the resulting difference is for the first two digits in the dividend to be "1" and "0"; furthermore, the first digit in the

```
        1 0
      ****
         9
       ***
      -----
      0***
```

subtrahend must be a "9".

(5) Since $7 \times 125 = 875$, since the divisor is less than 125, and since the first digit in the quotient times the divisor gives a number over 900, the first digit in the divisor is greater than 7. We know the first digit cannot be "9" or a four-digit product would result; thus the first digit is "8". We now have the following information:

```
                 80,809
        1**) 10,***,***
             9**
             ------
             10**
              9**
             ------
              ****
              ****
```

(6) Since $10,000,000 \div 80,809$ is *greater than* 123, the divisor must be *greater than* 123 to get a quotient 80,809. Hence, the divisor is 124. (7) To find the dividend, find the product $124 \times 80,809$. The other numbers can be found by long division. The answer is as follows:

$$
\begin{array}{r}
80{,}809 \\
124{\overline{\smash{\big)}\,10{,}020{,}316}} \\
992 \\
\hline
1003 \\
992 \\
\hline
1116 \\
1116 \\
\hline
\end{array}
$$

13. The answer is unique. It is

$$
\begin{array}{r}
775 \\
33 \\
\hline
2325 \\
2325 \\
\hline
25{,}575 \\
\hline
\end{array}
$$

Chapter 2, Section 4, page 34

1. **Addition Table**

+	0	1	2	3	4	5	6	7
0	0	1	2	3	4	5	6	7
1	1	2	3	4	5	6	7	10
2	2	3	4	5	6	7	10	11
3	3	4	5	6	7	10	11	12
4	4	5	6	7	10	11	12	13
5	5	6	7	10	11	12	13	14
6	6	7	10	11	12	13	14	15
7	7	10	11	12	13	14	15	16

3. (a) 330   (b) 3,420   (c) 1,538

5. (a) 73   (b) 285   (c) 64

7. (a) 29   (b) 44   (c) 32

9. (a) 76   (b) 35   (c) 27

11. (a) 17265_{eight} (b) 3360_{eight} (c) 55004_{eight}

13. (a) 16053_{eight} (b) 5676_{eight} (c) 17657_{eight}

15. (a) Yes. (b) Remove 4 counters from Row 3.

17. (a) Yes. (b) Remove 17 counters from Row 1.

19. (a) Yes. (b) Remove 18 counters from Row 2.

Chapter 2, Section 5, page 37

1. (a) 475_{eight}
     $\dfrac{7_{\text{eight}}}{4253_{\text{eight}}}$

    (b) $7\overline{)2219}$ 317
    $\dfrac{21}{11}$
    $\dfrac{7}{49}$
    49

    In part (b), $317_{\text{ten}} = 475_{\text{eight}}$.

3. (a) 101_{two}
     $\dfrac{1010_{\text{two}}}{1111_{\text{two}}}$

     1011_{two}
     $\dfrac{1011_{\text{two}}}{10110_{\text{two}}}$

     10110_{two}
     $\dfrac{10111_{\text{two}}}{101101_{\text{two}}}$

    (b) 15
     $\dfrac{5}{10}$

     22
     $\dfrac{11}{11}$

     45
     $\dfrac{22}{23}$

5. 101_{two}
     $\dfrac{11_{\text{two}}}{101_{\text{two}}}$
     $\dfrac{101_{\text{two}}}{1111_{\text{two}}}$

     $3 = 11_{\text{two}}$
     $5\overline{)15}$
     $\dfrac{15}{0}$

7. (a) 10001_{two}
    Check: 13
     $\dfrac{4}{17}$

    (b) 100110_{two}
    12
    15
     $\dfrac{11}{38}$

    (c) 110111_{two}
    31
    9
     $\dfrac{15}{55}$

9. (a) 1101_{two}
     $\dfrac{11_{\text{two}}}{1101_{\text{two}}}$
     $\dfrac{1101_{\text{two}}}{100111_{\text{two}}}$

    Check: 13
     $\dfrac{3}{39}$

    (b) 11010_{two}
     $\dfrac{1010_{\text{two}}}{110100_{\text{two}}}$
     $\dfrac{11010_{\text{two}}}{100000100_{\text{two}}}$

    26
     $\dfrac{10}{260}$

    (c) 101101_{two}
     $\dfrac{111000_{\text{two}}}{101101_{\text{two}}}$
     101101_{two}
     $\dfrac{101101_{\text{two}}}{100111011000_{\text{two}}}$

    45
     $\dfrac{56}{270}$
     $\dfrac{225}{2520}$

11. (a) 1101_{two}
     $\dfrac{101_{\text{two}}}{1101_{\text{two}}}$
     $\dfrac{1101_{\text{two}}}{1000001_{\text{two}}}$

    (b) 110111_{two}
     $\dfrac{11101_{\text{two}}}{110111_{\text{two}}}$
     110111_{two}
     110111_{two}
     $\dfrac{110111_{\text{two}}}{11000111011_{\text{two}}}$

    (c) 101011_{two}
     $\dfrac{1110_{\text{two}}}{101011_{\text{two}}}$
     101011_{two}
     $\dfrac{101011_{\text{two}}}{1001011010_{\text{two}}}$

13. (a) 3222_{eight} (b) 4436_{eight} (c) 2257_{eight}

15.

+	0	1	2	3	4	5
0	0	1	2	3	4	5
1	1	2	3	4	5	10
2	2	3	4	5	10	11
3	3	4	5	10	11	12
4	4	5	10	11	12	13
5	5	10	11	12	13	14

×	0	1	2	3	4	5
0	0	0	0	0	0	0
1	0	1	2	3	4	5
2	0	2	4	10	12	14
3	0	3	10	13	20	23
4	0	4	12	20	24	32
5	0	5	14	23	32	41

17. (a) $\begin{array}{r} 321_{\text{six}} \\ 12_{\text{six}} \\ \hline 1042_{\text{six}} \\ 321_{\text{six}} \\ \hline 4252_{\text{six}} \end{array}$

(b) $\begin{array}{r} 432_{\text{six}} \\ 211_{\text{six}} \\ \hline 432_{\text{six}} \\ 432_{\text{six}} \\ 1304_{\text{six}} \\ \hline 135552_{\text{six}} \end{array}$

(c) $\begin{array}{r} 324_{\text{six}} \\ 235_{\text{six}} \\ \hline 2512_{\text{six}} \\ 1420_{\text{six}} \\ 1052_{\text{six}} \\ \hline 130312_{\text{six}} \end{array}$

19. (a) $\begin{array}{r} 121 \\ 8 \\ \hline 968 \end{array}$

(b) $\begin{array}{r} 164 \\ 79 \\ \hline 1476 \\ 1148 \\ \hline 12{,}956 \end{array}$

(c) $\begin{array}{r} 124 \\ 95 \\ \hline 620 \\ 1116 \\ \hline 11{,}780 \end{array}$

CHAPTER 3 *Chapter 3, Section 1, page 44*

1. $\begin{array}{r} 8\ 7\ 9 \\ 9 \\ \hline 7\ 9\ 1\ ① \end{array}$ $\begin{array}{r} 7+9+1=17 \\ 7+1=\ 8 \\ 9-8=\ ① \end{array}$

3. $\begin{array}{r} 4\ 6{,}4\ 6\ 7 \\ 9 \\ \hline 4\ 1\ 8{,}2\ 0\ ③ \end{array}$ $\begin{array}{r} 4+1+8+2+0=15 \\ 1+5=\ 6 \\ 9-6=\ ③ \end{array}$

5. $\begin{array}{r} 4\ 1{,}2\ 7\ 3 \\ 9 \\ \hline 3\ 7\ 1{,}4\ ⑤\ 7 \end{array}$ $\begin{array}{r} 3+7+1+4+7=22 \\ 2+2=\ 4 \\ 9-4=\ ⑤ \end{array}$

7. $\begin{array}{r} 2\ 1{,}5\ 2\ 5 \\ 9 \\ \hline 1\ 9\ 3{,}⑦2\ 5 \end{array}$ $\begin{array}{r} 1+9+3+2+5=20 \\ 2+0=\ 2 \\ 9-2=\ ⑦ \end{array}$

9. $\begin{array}{r} 3\,2,3\,3\,9 \\ 9 \\ \hline 2\,\circledcirc\,1,0\,5\,1 \end{array}$ $\begin{array}{l} 2+1+0+5+1=\ 9 \\ 9-9=\ \circledzero \\ \text{(\textit{Note} the difference in circled digits.)} \end{array}$

11. Obviously, it does not produce the discarded digit if the digit is a "9." See Exercise 9. It does work for all other digits.

Chapter 3, Section 2, page 53

1. (a) No. For example, 24 has both 3 and 6 as factors but it does not have 18 as a factor. The difficulty is that 3 and 6 have a common factor different from 1. A number needs only one factor of 3 to be divisible by 3 and 6 but it would need at least two factors of 3 to be divisible by 18. (b) A number is divisible by 40 if and only if it has 5 and 8 as factors.

3. 2, 4, 5, and 10.   5. 3, 9, and 11.

7. 2, 3, 4, 5, 6, 8, 10, 11, 15, and 40.

9. The number is divisible by 2, 3, 4, 5, 6, 8, 10, 11, 12, 15, and 40.

11. The number is divisible by 2, 3, 4, 6, 8, 9, 12, and 18.

13. PART 2. From Part 1,

$$(a+b+c+d+e+f) = abc,def - 3[33,33a + 3,333b + 333c + 33d + 3e].$$

If 3 is a factor of abc,def, then 3 is a factor of the difference on the right-hand side of the equality; thus, 3 is a factor of $(a+b+c+d+e+f)$.

15. *Hint:* $abc,def = 10^5a + 10^4b + 10^3c + 10^2d + 10e + f$
    $$= 5[2(10^4)a + 2(10^3)b + 2(10^2)c + 2(10)d + 2e] + f.$$

17. *Hint:* $abc,def = [1000(10^2)a + 1000(10)b + 1000c] + [10^2d + 10e + f]$
    $$= 8[125(10^2)a + 125(10)b + 125c] + [10^2d + 10e + f].$$

19. *Hint:* $abc,def = 10[(10^4)a + (10^3)b + (10^2)c + 10d + e] + f.$

21. (a) Yes.   (b) Yes.
    (c) $aba,bab = a10^5 + b10^4 + a10^3 + b10^2 + a10 + b$
    $$= a(10^5 + 10^3 + 10) + b(10^4 + 10^2 + 1)$$
    $$= 10a(10^4 + 10^2 + 1) + b(10^4 + 10^2 + 1)$$
    $$= 10a(10,101) + b(10,101).$$

    Since $10,101 \div 91 = 111$, the number has 91 as a factor. Of course, it also has 111 and 10,101 as factors.

23. $abcdef = a10^5_{\text{three}} + b10^4_{\text{three}} + c10^3_{\text{three}} + d10^2_{\text{three}} + e10_{\text{three}} + f$
    $$= a(22222_{\text{three}} + 1) + b(2222_{\text{three}} + 1) + c(222_{\text{three}} + 1)$$
    $$+ d(22_{\text{three}} + 1) + e(2_{\text{three}} + 1) + f$$
    $$= a(22222_{\text{three}}) + b(2222_{\text{three}}) + c(222_{\text{three}}) + d(22_{\text{three}})$$
    $$+ e(2_{\text{three}}) + (a + b + c + d + e + f)$$

    The conclusion follows as in the proof of the divisibility test for 9 in base ten.

Chapter 3, Section 3, page 56.

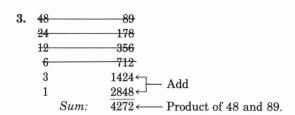

1. 21   467 ←
    ~~10~~   ~~934~~
    5   1868 ← ⎤
    ~~2~~   ~~3736~~ ⎬ Add
    1   7472 ← ⎦
        Sum: 9807 ←——— Product of 21 and 467.

3. ~~48~~   ~~89~~
    ~~24~~   ~~178~~
    ~~12~~   ~~356~~
    ~~6~~   ~~712~~
    3   1424 ← ⎤
    1   2848 ← ⎦ Add
        Sum: 4272 ←——— Product of 48 and 89.

5. 31   402 ← ⎤
    15   804 ← │
    7   1608 ← ⎬ Add
    3   3216 ← │
    1   6432 ← ⎦
        Sum: 12,462 ←——— Product of 31 and 402.

7. Yes.

9. (a) 9 *R* 1 ×   421 =   421
         3 *R* 0 ×   1263 =   0
         1 *R* 0 ×   3789 =   0
         0 *R* 1 × 11,367 = 11,367
                    Sum: 11,788 ←——— Product of 28 and 421.

    (b) 27 *R* 2 ×   279 =   558
         9 *R* 0 ×   837 =   0
         3 *R* 0 ×   2511 =   0
         1 *R* 0 ×   7533 =   0
         0 *R* 1 × 22,599 = 22,599
                    Sum: 23,157 ←——— Product of 83 and 279.

    (c) 22 *R* 0 ×   95 =   0
         7 *R* 1 ×   285 =   285
         2 *R* 1 ×   855 =   855
         0 *R* 2 ×   2,565 =   5,130
                    Sum: 6,270 ←——— Product of 66 and 95.

Chapter 3, Section 4, page 59

1. (a) $376{,}841 \to 29 \to 11 \longrightarrow ②$
   $241{,}382 \to 20 \to 2 \longleftarrow$
   $\underline{135{,}459 \to 27 \to 9 \longleftarrow}$ }—Add
   $\phantom{135{,}459 \to 27 \to }11 \longrightarrow ②$

(b) $468{,}528 \to 33 \to ⑥$
   $189{,}237 \to 30 \to 3 \longleftarrow$
   $\underline{279{,}291 \to 30 \to 3 \longleftarrow}$ }—Add
   $\phantom{279{,}291 \to 30 \to }⑥$

3. (a)
   $3784 \longrightarrow 22 \longrightarrow 4$
   $2561 \longrightarrow 14 \longrightarrow 5$
   $8124 \longrightarrow 15 \longrightarrow 6$
   $3211 \longrightarrow 7$
   $\underline{6824 \longrightarrow 20 \longrightarrow 2}$
   $24{,}504 \to 15 \to ⑥ \quad 24 \to ⑥$

(b)
   $2467 \to 19 \to 10 \to 1$
   $3145 \to 13 \longrightarrow 4$
   $4567 \to 22 \longrightarrow 4$
   $9423 \to 18 \longrightarrow 9$
   $\underline{5765 \to 23 \longrightarrow 5}$
   $25{,}367 \to 23 \to ⑤ \quad 23 \to ⑤$

5. (a)
   $3726 \longrightarrow 18 \longrightarrow 9$
   $\underline{426} \longrightarrow 12 \longrightarrow 3$
   $22356 \overline{27} \to ⑨$
   7452
   $\underline{14904}$
   $1{,}587{,}276 \to 36 \to ⑨$

(b)
   $8427 \longrightarrow 21 \longrightarrow 3$
   $\underline{683} \longrightarrow 17 \longrightarrow 8$
   $25281 \overline{24} \to ⑥$
   67416
   $\underline{50562}$
   $5{,}755{,}641 \to 33 \to ⑥$

7.
   38
   15
   53
   68
   121
   189
   $310 -$ seventh
   499
   809
   $\underline{1308}$
   Sum: $\overline{3410}$

   310
   $\underline{11}$
   310
   $\underline{310}$
   Product: 3410

9. (a) $(40)(50) + 25 = 2025$. (b) $(60)(70) + 25 = 4225$. (c) $(70)(80) + 25 = 5625$. (d) $(90)(100) + 25 = 9025$. (e) $(120)(130) + 25 = 15{,}625$.

11. No. Let $x = 17$; $x - 1 = 16$ has 8 as a factor but 17 is not a perfect square. But let $x = 25$; $x - 1 = 24$ has 8 as a factor and 25 is a perfect square.

13. It cannot be the square of an odd integer since 836 is not divisible by 8.

15. Consider the number 3784 and notice the following

$$3784 \to 3 + 7 + 8 + 4 = 22 \to 2 + 2 = ④$$
$$9\,\overline{)\,3784}$$
$$420 \quad \text{Remainder of } ④.$$

It can be proved that if the final number obtained by adding digits of a given number is not a 9, then it is the same as the remainder in the division of the number by 9. Since the remainder is the difference between the number and the largest multiple of 9 less than or equal to the number, it is the excess after all of the nines (multiples of 9) have been "cast out."

17. Let a and b be the first and second numbers. Then, the numbers obtained are as follows:

$$
\begin{array}{r}
a \\
b \\
\hline
a + b \\
a + 2b \\
2a + 3b \\
3a + 5b \\
5a + 8b - \text{seventh} \\
11a + 13b \\
13a + 21b \\
21a + 34b \\
\hline
\end{array}
$$

$$\text{Sum:} \quad 55a + 88b$$

$$
\begin{array}{r}
5a + 8b \\
11 \\
\hline
\end{array}
$$

$$\text{Product:} \quad 55a + 88b$$

CHAPTER 4

Chapter 4, Section 1, page 69

1. See technique described for natural numbers.

3. (a) Yes. $\dfrac{m}{2^n} + \dfrac{p}{2^q} = \dfrac{m2^q + p2^n}{2^{n+q}}$.

   (b) Yes.

   (c) Yes. $\dfrac{m}{2^n} \cdot \dfrac{p}{2^q} = \dfrac{mp}{2^{n+q}}$.

   (d) No. For example, $\dfrac{3}{4} \div \dfrac{7}{8} \neq \dfrac{m}{2^n}$.

5. No. Let $a = 32$, $b = 8$, and $c = 2$. Then
$$a \div (b \div c) = 32 \div 4 = 8$$
   but
$$(a \div b) \div c = 4 \div 2 = 2.$$

11. $\dfrac{a}{b} \times \dfrac{c}{d} = \dfrac{ac}{bd}$ Definition of multiplication for rationals.

    $= \dfrac{ca}{db}$ Commutative property for multiplication of natural numbers.

    $= \dfrac{c}{d} \times \dfrac{a}{b}$ Definition of multiplication for rationals.

13. $\left(\dfrac{a}{b}+\dfrac{c}{d}\right)+\dfrac{e}{f}=\dfrac{ad+bc}{bd}+\dfrac{e}{f}=\dfrac{(ad+bc)f+(bd)e}{(bd)f}$

$$=\dfrac{[(ad)f+(bc)f]+(bd)e}{b(df)}=\dfrac{a(df)+[b(cf)+b(de)]}{b(df)}$$

$$=\dfrac{a(df)+b(cf+de)}{b(df)}=\dfrac{a}{b}+\dfrac{cf+de}{df}$$

$$=\dfrac{a}{b}+\left(\dfrac{c}{d}+\dfrac{e}{f}\right)$$

Chapter 4, Section 2, page 74

1. Yes; Yes; Yes; No.
3. Part (a).
5. (a) No.   (b) No.
7. No. It is true for each rational number $x \neq 0$.
9. (a) No. (b) It is true provided B is between A and C. (c) Yes.
11. Since $y - x$ is the distance between the points, $\dfrac{y-x}{5}$ is one-fifth the distance. Hence,

$$x+\dfrac{y-x}{5}=\dfrac{5x+y-x}{5}=\dfrac{4x+y}{5}$$

is the coordinate of the point one-fifth the distance from point x to point y.

13. $\dfrac{a}{b}+\dfrac{x}{y}=\dfrac{c}{d}$. Multiply both sides by bd; thus, we obtain $ad+\dfrac{bdx}{y}=bc$ and $\dfrac{bdx}{y}=bc-ad$ is an integer.

15. If $a+c=b$, then $b-a-c=0$. In the last step, a mistake is made by dividing by zero.

Chapter 4, Section 3, page 80

1. (a) $9+6\sqrt{3}$. (b) 14. (c) $29+17\sqrt{3}$. (d) 52. (e) $\dfrac{19}{2}+\dfrac{11\sqrt{3}}{2}$.

3. No. For example, $\sqrt{2}+(-\sqrt{2})=0$.

5. No. If rational $+$ irrational $=$ rational, then rational $-$ rational $=$ irrational, but the set of rational numbers is closed with respect to subtraction.

7. Yes. $(a+b\sqrt{3})(c+d\sqrt{3})=(ac+bd)+(ad+bc)\sqrt{3}$.

9. Use same pattern of proof to prove $\sqrt{2}$ irrational.

Chapter 4, Section 4, page 85

1. 0.375   3. $0.45\overline{45}.\ .\ .$ 5. $0.\overline{857142}.\ .\ .$

7. $\frac{1}{8}$ 9. $\frac{41}{99}$ 11. $\frac{309}{550}$

13. (a) The sum of two terminating decimals must be a terminating decimal. The sum of two repeating decimals must be a repeating or terminating decimal. The sum of a repeating and terminating decimal must be repeating.

    (b) The sum of a nonrepeating decimal with either a terminating or repeating decimal is a nonrepeating decimal.

15. $abc.defgh_{\text{two}} = a(2^2) + b(2) + c + d\left(\frac{1}{2}\right) + e\left(\frac{1}{2^2}\right) + f\left(\frac{1}{2^3}\right) + g\left(\frac{1}{2^4}\right) + h\left(\frac{1}{2^5}\right)$ in base ten.

    Thus, $101.10111_{\text{two}} = 5 + \dfrac{1}{2} + \dfrac{1}{2^3} + \dfrac{1}{2^4} + \dfrac{1}{2^5}$ (base ten)

$$= 5 + \frac{16}{32} + \frac{8}{32} + \frac{2}{32} + \frac{1}{32}$$
$$= \frac{187}{32} = 5.84375.$$

17. No. If $1/p$ is a terminating decimal then $1/p = m/10^n$ for some integers m and n. Thus, $pm = 10^n$ and p is a factor of 10, a contradiction.

19. Let $x = 0.2121\overline{21}\ .\ .\ .$ (base 7)

    Then $\qquad\qquad (100_{\text{seven}})x = 21.21\overline{21}.\ .\ .$ (base 7)

    Subtract $\qquad\qquad\qquad x = \ \ 0.2121.\ .\ .$ (base 7)

    $$(66_{\text{seven}})x = 21_{\text{seven}}$$

    $$x = \frac{21_{\text{seven}}}{66_{\text{seven}}}.$$

    Since $\qquad\qquad 21_{\text{seven}} = 15_{\text{ten}}$ and $66_{\text{seven}} = 48_{\text{ten}},$

    $$\frac{21_{\text{seven}}}{66_{\text{seven}}} = \frac{15}{48} = \frac{5}{16}.$$

    Thus, $0.2121\overline{21}.\ .\ .$ (base 7) $= 0.3125$ (base 10).

Chapter 4, Section 5, page 91

1. $x = 6$ or $x = -1$.

3. $x = \dfrac{1 + \sqrt{5}}{2}$ or $x = \dfrac{1 - \sqrt{5}}{2}.$

5. $x = -1 + i\sqrt{3}$ or $x = -1 - i\sqrt{3}.$

7. $64 - 60 = 4;\ (-2 + \sqrt{3})^3 - 15(-2 + \sqrt{3}) = -8 + 12\sqrt{3} - 18 + 3\sqrt{3} + 30 - 15\sqrt{3} = 4.$ Similarly, $(-2 - \sqrt{3})^3 - 15(-2 - \sqrt{3}) = -8 - 12\sqrt{3} - 18 - 3\sqrt{3} + 30 + 15\sqrt{3} = 4.$

9. $a\left(x - \dfrac{b}{3x}\right)^3 + b\left(x - \dfrac{b}{3a}\right)^2 + c\left(x - \dfrac{b}{3a}\right) + d = ax^3 - bx^2 + \dfrac{b^2x}{3a} - \dfrac{b^3}{27a^2} +$

$bx^2 - \dfrac{2b^2x}{3a} + \dfrac{b^2}{9a^2} + cx - \dfrac{bc}{3a} + d = ax^3 + \dfrac{1}{3a}(3ac - b^2)x +$

$\dfrac{3b^2 - b^3 - 9abc + 27a^2d}{27a^2} = 0.$ Thus, $p = \dfrac{1}{3a^2}(3ac - b^2)$ and $q =$

$\dfrac{3b^2 - b^3 - 9abc + 27a^2d}{27a^3}.$

Chapter 5, Section 1, page 99   **CHAPTER 5**

1. (a) 50th term: $4 + (49)5 = 4 + 245 = 249.$
    (b) $S = {}^{50}\!/_2[8 + (49)5] = (25)(253) = 6325.$

3. 50th term: $3 + (49)(\tfrac{4}{3}) = (9 + 196)/3 = {}^{205}\!/_3.$
    $S = {}^{50}\!/_3[6 + (49)(\tfrac{4}{3})] = 25[(18 + 196)/3] = [(25)(214)]/3 = {}^{5350}\!/_3.$

5. (a) $6 + 19(\tfrac{2}{3}) = {}^{56}\!/_3.$ (b) ${}^{740}\!/_3 = 246\tfrac{2}{3}.$

7. $3 + 6 + 9 + \cdots + 90 = 3(1 + 2 + 3 + \cdots + 30) = \dfrac{3(30)(31)}{2} = 1{,}395.$

9. (a) $8\tfrac{1}{2}.$ (b) $3\tfrac{1}{2}.$ (c) 765.

11. (a) $\tfrac{4}{3}.$ (b) ${}^{14}\!/_3.$ (c) ${}^{110}\!/_3.$

13. (a) $-2 = 4 + 3d,\ d = -2.$ Thus, $u = 2.$ (b) $v = 0.$ (c) $-300.$

15. (a) $52 = 2 + 20d,\ d = {}^{5}\!/_2.$ (b) 567.

17. $S = {}^{15}\!/_2[16{,}600 + (14)500] = 177{,}000$ dollars.

19. (a) No. However, the *differences* in successive terms is an arithmetic
    sequence.
    (b) 21, 28, 36, and 45.
    (c) In the figure we see that the second number is $1 + 2$, the third is
    $1 + 2 + 3$, the fourth is $1 + 2 + 3 + 4$ etc.
    (d) $2^2,\ 3^2,\ 4^2,\ 5^2,$ etc.
    (e) Answer is $n^2.$
    Algebraic proof: $[(n - 1)n/2] + [n(n + 1)/2] = n^2.$
    Geometric proof: Notice, for example, that putting together the 4th and
    5th triangular configurations gives a parallelogram of five parallel lines
    with five dots in each; that is, 5^2 dots. A similar argument works for
    any two consecutive triangular numbers.

21. (a) Addition of the numbers verifies the equalities.
    (b) Group the first n terms and notice that n is a common factor.
    $n + 2n + 3n + \cdots + n^2 = n(1 + 2 + 3 + \cdots + n) = n\,\dfrac{n(n + 1)}{2}.$ Doing
    the same with the last $(n - 1)$ numbers, we notice that this sum is
    n times the sum of the first $(n - 1)$ integers; that is, the sum is
    $n\,\dfrac{(n - 1)n}{2}.$ Now, find the sum: $\dfrac{n^2(n - 1)}{2} + \dfrac{n^2(n + 1)}{2} = n^3.$

Chapter 5, Section 2, page 106

1. (a) $r = -1$; seventh term is 3.
   (b) $r = 3$; seventh term is 1458.
   (c) $r = -\frac{1}{2}$; seventh term is $\frac{1}{16}$.

3. (a) $r = \frac{1}{2}$; sixth term is $\frac{1}{48}$.
   (b) $r = -\frac{1}{4}$; sixth term is $-\frac{1}{128}$.
   (c) $3.6 \div 3 = \frac{36}{10} \times \frac{1}{3} = \frac{6}{5} = 1.2$; sixth term is 7.46496.

5. (a) $S = \dfrac{ar^n - a}{r - 1} = \dfrac{4(-\frac{1}{2})^{10} - 4}{-\frac{1}{2} - 1} = \dfrac{(\frac{1}{2})^8 - 4}{-\frac{3}{2}} = \dfrac{1023}{384}$.

   (b) $\dfrac{2}{x} = \dfrac{x}{9}$. $x^2 = 18$, $x = 3\sqrt{2}$.

   (c) $\dfrac{16}{x} = \dfrac{x}{y}$ and $\dfrac{x}{y} = \dfrac{y}{54}$. Thus, $x^2 = 16y$ and $y^2 = 54x$. Hence, $x = \dfrac{y^2}{54}$
   and $\left(\dfrac{y^2}{54}\right)^2 = 16y$.

   $y^3 = (54)^2(16) = (27 \times 2)^2(2^4) = 3^6 \times 2^6$. Thus, $y = 3^2 \times 2^2 = 36$. Then,
   $x = 24$ and $y = 36$.

7. (a) $\dfrac{x}{2} = \dfrac{7}{x}$; $x^2 = 14$, $x = \sqrt{14}$.

   (b) $x \div 3 = y \div x$ and $y \div x = \dfrac{8}{9} \div y$. Thus, $x^2 = 3y$ and $\dfrac{8x}{9} = y^2$. It

   follows that $\dfrac{x^4}{9} = y^2$ and $\dfrac{8x}{9} = \dfrac{x^4}{9}$. Since $x \neq 0$, $x^3 = 8$ and $x = 2$. Therefore, $y = \frac{4}{3}$.

9. Since $x = 2$, $r = \frac{2}{3}$. Thus, the sixth term is $3(\frac{2}{3})^5 = \frac{32}{81}$.

11. $\dfrac{x + 3}{x} = \dfrac{2x - 2}{x + 3}$; $x^2 + 6x + 9 = 2x^2 - 2x$; $x^2 - 8x - 9 = 0$; $(x + 1)(x - 9) = 0$; $x = -1$ or $x = 9$. The numbers are 9, 12, and 16. $r = \frac{4}{3}$.

13. (a) First year's interest is Pi and total is $P + Pi = P(1 + i)$.
   Second year's interest is $P(1 + i)i$ and total is $P(1 + i) + P(1 + i)i = P(1 + i)(1 + i) = P(1 + i)^2$.
   Third year's interest: $P(1 + i)^2 i$.
   nth year's interest: $P(1 + i)^{n-1}i$.
   (b) The total interest is the geometric series

$$Pi + P(1 + i)i + P(1 + i)^2 i + \cdots + P(1 + i)^{n-1}i$$

   where Pi is the first term and $(1 + i)$ is the ratio. Thus, the total interest is

$$\frac{Pi(1 + i)^n - Pi}{(1 + i) - 1} = P(1 + i)^n - P$$

   and the total amount of the investment is

$$P + [P(1 + i)^n - P] = P(1 + i)^n.$$

15. (a) $A = 1000[1 + (0.05/4)]^4 = 1000(1 + 0.0125)^4 = 1000(1.0125)^4$.
Using the table on page A-14, $A \approx 1000(1.05095) = \$1050.95$.
(b) 5.095 percent.

17. $2P = p[1 + (0.05/4)]^{4n}$, $(1 + 0.0125)^{4n} = 2$, $(1.0125)^{4n} = 2$. Using table on page A-15, $(1.0125)^{56} = 2.005^+$. Thus, $4n = 56$ and $n = 14$ years.

19. $P(1 + 0.05)^n = P[1 + (0.03/4)]^{4(10)}$, $(1.05)^n = (1.0075)^{40}$. Using table on page A-12, $(1.0075)^{40} \approx 1.34835$. Also $(1.05)^n \approx 1.34835$ for $n = 6^+$.

Chapter 5, Section 3, page 110

1. (a) $28 = 2^2 \times 7$. (b) $64 = 2^6$.
(c) $320 = 2^6 \times 5$. (d) $420 = 2^2 \times 3 \times 5 \times 7$.
(e) $426 = 2 \times 3 \times 71$. (f) $1,800 = 2^3 \times 3^2 \times 5^2$.

3. (a) 1, 2, 4, 7, 14, 28.
(b) 1, 2, 2^2, 2^3, 2^4, 2^5, 2^6, or 1, 2, 4, 8, 16, 32, 64.
(c) 1, 2, 4, 5, 8, 10, 16, 20, 32, 40, 64, 80, 160, 320.
(d) 1, 2, 3, 4, 5, 6, 7, 10, 12, 14, 15, 20, 21, 28, 30, 35, 42, 60, 70, 84, 105, 140, 210, 420.
(e) 1, 2, 4, 8, 16, 383, 766, 1532, 3064, 6128.
(f) 1, 2, 4, 13, 17, 26, 34, 52, 68, 221, 442, 884.

5. Yes. **7.** (a) Yes. (b) No. It is not possible for 149.

9. $13! + 2$, $13! + 3$, $13! + 3$, $13! + 4$, $13! + 5$, . . . , $13! + 13$.

11. (a) q = 2, 3, 5, 7, 13. *Note:* $2^{11} - 1 = 2,047$ is not a prime since $2,047 = 23 \times 89$.
(b) We conclude that $2^q - 1$ is composite. If $q = mn$ where $m \neq 1$ and $n \neq 1$, then $2^{mn} - 1 = (2^m)^n - 1^n$ has $2^m - 1$ as a factor. Notice if $m \neq 1$, then $2^m - 1 \neq 1$. We use the algebraic fact that $x^n - y^n$ has $x - y$ as a factor.

Chapter 5, Section 4, page 112

1. (a) 1, 2, 4, 5, 10, 20.
(b) 1, 3, 5, 9, 15, 45.
(c) 5.

3. (a) 1, 2, 3, 4, 5, 6, 8, 9, 10, 12, 15, 18, 20, 24, 30, 36, 40, 45, 60, 72, 90, 120, 180, 360.
(b) 1, 2, 3, 6, 9, 13, 18, 26, 39, 78, 117, 234.
(c) 18.

5. (a) $20 \times 45 = 900$. (b) $900 \div 5 = 180$. (c) Yes. (d) No.

7. (a) 84,240. (b) 4,680. (c) Yes. (d) No.

9. Let a and b be two positive integers with greatest common factor G and least common multiple M. Then $(a \times b) \div G = M$.

11. (a) Yes $n = 1$, for example. $1 + 1(2)(3)(4) = 25 = 5^2$.

(b) $n = 2$, $1 + (2)(3)(4)(5) = 11^2$.

$n = 3$, $1 + (3)(4)(5)(6) = 19^2$.

$n = 4$, $1 + (4)(5)(6)(7) = 29^2$.

$n = 5$, $1 + (5)(6)(7)(8) = 41^2$.

$n = 6$, $1 + (6)(7)(8)(9) = 55^2$.

(c) The expression is always a square for any positive integer.
(d) In (b) observe that for n the sum seems to be $[(n+1)^2 + n]^2$. It is easy to prove that this is true; that is, $1 + n(n+1)(n+2)(n+3)$ and $[(n+1)^2 + n]^2$ are both equal to

$$n^4 + 6n^3 + 11n^2 + 6n + 1.$$

13. (a) Yes. (b) No. Consider 14 and 15.
15. (a) $s(p) = 1 + p$.
(b) In general, no. However, if $p \neq q$, the answer is "Yes."

$$s(p) = 1 + p \quad \text{and} \quad s(q) = 1 + q.$$

The factors of pq are 1, p, q, and pq; thus,

$$s(pq) = 1 + p + q + pq.$$

Furthermore,

$$s(p)s(q) = (1+p)(1+q) = 1 + p + q + pq.$$

(c) No. Use $p = 3$ to obtain a counterexample.
17. $d(28) = 6$; $d(64) = 7$; $d(320) = 14$; $d(420) = 24$.
19. (a) $d(2) = 2$; $d(3) = 2$; $d(6) = 4$.
(b) $d(5) = 2$; $d(7) = 2$; $d(14) = 4$.
(c) $d(4) = 3$; $d(7) = 2$; $d(28) = 6$.
(d) $d(4) = 3$; $d(15) = 4$; $d(60) = 12$.
(e) $d(4) = 3$; $d(6) = 4$; $d(28) = 8$.
(f) $d(6) = 4$; $d(21) = 4$; $d(126) = 12$.
21. (a) No. See part (e) of Exercise 19.
(b) $d(m)d(n) = d(mn)$ if m and n are relatively prime (have no common factors except 1).
23. (a) The factors of p^q are 1, p, p^2, ..., p^q which is $(q+1)$ factors.
(b) Since p_1^q has $(q+1)$ factors and p_2^r has $(r+1)$ factors, the total number is $(q+1)(r+1)$.
(c) (i) $d(28) = 3 \times 2 = 6$, (ii) $d(64) = 7$, (iii) $d(320) = 7 \times 2 = 14$ (see Exercise 17), (iv) $d(420) = 3 \times 2 \times 2 \times 2 = 24$, (v) $d(426) = 8$, (vi) $d(1800) = 36$.
25. (a) 4. (b) 4. (c) 8.
27. (a) 18. (b) 24. (c) 312. (d) 80.

CHAP. 5 · SEC. 5

Chapter 5, Section 5, page 121

1. $1 + \frac{1}{2} + \frac{1}{3} + \frac{1}{6} = 2.$

3. Two. Proof: Using the formula for the sum of a geometric sequence,

$$1 + \frac{1}{2} + \frac{1}{2^2} + \cdots + \frac{1}{2^{p-1}} + \left(\frac{1}{2^p - 1}\right)\left(1 + \frac{1}{2} + \frac{1}{2^2} + \cdots + \frac{1}{2^{p-1}}\right)$$

$$= 2 - \left(\frac{1}{2}\right)^{p-1} + \left(\frac{1}{2^p - 1}\right)\left[2 - \left(\frac{1}{2}\right)^{p-1}\right]$$

$$= \frac{2^{p+1} - 2 - 2 + (1/2)^{p-1} + 2 - (1/2)^{p-1}}{2^p - 1} = 2$$

5. Factors of 1184: 1, 2, 4, 8, 16, 32, 37, 74, 148, 296, 592, 1184. Factors of 1210: 1, 2, 5, 10, 11, 22, 55, 110, 121, 242, 605, 1210. $s(p) = s(q) = p + q = 2{,}394.$

7. (a) No. The sum of an even and odd integer would be odd.
    (b) Every multiple of 6 can be expressed as the sum of three consecutive integers. This is not unique; notice that $18 = 7 + 6 + 5 = 6 + 5 + 4 + 3.$

9. (a) $1 + 2 + 3 + \cdots + n = \dfrac{n(n+1)}{2}.$

$$\frac{n(n+1)}{2} - \frac{m(m+1)}{2} = \frac{n^2 + n - m^2 - m}{2}$$

$$= \frac{n^2 - m^2 + n - m}{2}$$

$$= \frac{(n-m)(n+m)(n-m)}{2}$$

$$= \frac{(n-m)(n+m+1)}{2}$$

(b) If it were a power of 2 then $(n-m)(n+m+1)$ would be a power of 2. If $n - m = 2^p$ and $n + m + 1 = 2^q$ then $2n + 1 = 2^p + 2^q$, a contradiction.

11. Yes. $s(30{,}240) = 120{,}960 = 4(30{,}240).$

13. (a) (1) If m is even it has at least one factor of 2 so $p - 1 > 0$ and $p > 1$. If we remove all factors of 2 from m, then q is an odd integer. (2) $s(2^{p-1}q) = s(2^{p-1})s(q)$ since 2^{p-1} and q have only 1 as positive factor. (3) All of the factors of 2^{p-1} are $1, 2, 2^2, \ldots, 2^{p-1}$ and the sum of this geometric sequence $1 + 2 + 2^2 + \cdots + 2^{p-1}$ is $2^p - 1$. (4) It is given that $s(m) = 2m$ since m is perfect. (5) $2m = 2(2^{p-1}q) = 2^p q$. (6) 2^p is a factor of the product $(2^p - 1)s(q)$. Since 2^p is not a factor of $2^p - 1$, it is a factor of $s(q)$. (7) Definition of factor. (8) Substitute $2^p w$ for $s(q)$ in $2^p q = (2^p - 1)s(q)$ and cancel 2^p. (9) From $q = (2^p - 1)w$ we know w is a factor of q. Since $p > 1$, $2^p - 1 > 1$ and $q \neq w$.
    (b) Any even perfect number must be of the form $2^{p-1}(2^p - 1)$ where $2^p - 1$ is a prime.

Chapter 5, Section 6, page 126

1. One method (see text):

$$1 + (1+2) + (1+2+3) + (1+2+3+4) + (1+2+3+4+5)$$
$$+ \cdots + (1+2+3+ \cdots +30)$$

$$= \frac{1(2)}{2} + \frac{2(3)}{2} + \frac{3(4)}{2} + \frac{4(5)}{2} + \cdots + \frac{30(31)}{2}$$

$$= \frac{1}{2} \left[1(1+1) + 2(2+1) + 3(3+1) + 4(4+1) + \cdots + 30(30+1) \right]$$

$$= \frac{1}{2} \left[(1^2 + 2^2 + 3^2 + 4^2 + \cdots + 30^2) + (1+2+3+4+ \cdots +30) \right]$$

$$= \frac{1}{2} \left[\frac{30(31)(61)}{6} + \frac{30(31)}{2} \right] = \frac{1}{2} [9{,}455 + 465] = 4960.$$

3. $$\frac{1}{1 \cdot 2} + \frac{1}{2 \cdot 3} + \frac{1}{3 \cdot 4} + \cdots + \frac{1}{99 \cdot 100}$$

$$= 1 - \frac{1}{2} + \frac{1}{2} - \frac{1}{3} + \frac{1}{3} - \frac{1}{4} + \cdots + \frac{1}{99} - \frac{1}{100} = 1 - \frac{1}{100} = \frac{99}{100}.$$

5.
$$k = 10, \quad 10^4 - 9^4 = 4(10)^3 - 6(10)^2 + 4(10) - 1$$
$$k = 9, \quad 9^4 - 8^4 = 4(9)^3 \ - 6(9)^2 \ + 4(9) \ - 1$$
$$k = 8, \quad 8^4 - 7^4 = 4(8)^3 \ - 6(8)^2 \ + 4(8) \ - 1$$
$$k = 7, \quad 7^4 - 6^4 = 4(7)^3 \ - 6(7)^2 \ + 4(7) \ - 1$$
$$k = 6, \quad 6^4 - 5^4 = 4(6)^3 \ - 6(6)^2 \ + 4(6) \ - 1$$
$$k = 5, \quad 5^4 - 4^4 = 4(5)^3 \ - 6(5)^2 \ + 4(5) \ - 1$$
$$k = 4, \quad 4^4 - 3^4 = 4(4)^3 \ - 6(4)^2 \ + 4(4) \ - 1$$
$$k = 3, \quad 3^4 - 2^4 = 4(3)^3 \ - 6(3)^2 \ + 4(3) \ - 1$$
$$k = 2, \quad 2^4 - 1^4 = 4(2)^3 \ - 6(2)^2 \ + 4(2) \ - 1$$
$$k = 1, \quad 1^4 - 0^4 = 4(1)^3 \ - 6(1)^2 \ + 4(1) \ - 1$$

Sum: $\quad 10^4 - 0^4 = 4S - \dfrac{6(10)(11)(21)}{6} + \dfrac{4(10)(11)}{2} - 10.$

$$4S = 10{,}000 + (110)(21) - (20)(11) + 10.$$
$$4S = 12{,}100.$$
$$S = 3{,}025.$$

7. $k^5 - (k-1)^5 = 5k^4 - 10k^3 - 10k^2 - 5k + 1.$

Thus,
$$20^5 - 19^5 = 5(20)^4 - 10(20)^3 - 10(20)^2 - 5(20) + 1$$
$$19^5 - 18^5 = 5(19)^4 - 10(19)^3 - 10(19)^2 - 5(19) + 1$$
$$18^5 - 17^5 = 5(18)^4 - 10(18)^3 - 10(18)^2 - 5(18) + 1$$
$$\cdots \cdots \cdots \cdots \cdots \cdots \cdots \cdots \cdots \cdots \cdots \cdots \cdots$$
$$2^5 - \ 1^5 = 5(2)^4 \ - 10(2)^3 \ - 10(2)^2 \ - 5(2) \ + 1$$
$$1^5 - \ 0^5 = 5(1)^4 \ - 10(1)^3 \ - 10(1)^2 \ - 5(1) \ + 1$$

Sum: $\quad 20^5 = 5S - 10 \left[\dfrac{(20)(21)}{2} \right]^2 + \dfrac{10(20)(21)(41)}{6} - \dfrac{5(20)(21)}{2} + 20.$

$$5S = 3{,}200{,}000 + 10(210)^2 - 10(2870) + 5(210) - 20.$$
$$5S = 3{,}613{,}330.$$
$$S = 722{,}665.$$

9. Since the nth pentagonal number is the sum of an arithmetic sequence where $a = 1$ and the last term is $(3n - 2)$ where the number of terms is n, the nth pentagon number is

$$\frac{n}{2}[1 + (3n - 2)] = \frac{n(3n - 1)}{2}.$$

11. (a) Add rows:

$(1 + 2 + 3 + 4 + 5 + 6) + (2 + 4 + 6 + 8 + 10 + 12)$
$\qquad\qquad\qquad + \cdots + (6 + 12 + 18 + 24 + 30 + 36)$
$= (1 + 2 + 3 + 4 + 5 + 6) + 2(1 + 2 + 3 + 4 + 5 + 6)$
$\quad + 3(1 + 2 + 3 + 4 + 5 + 6) + \cdots + 6(1 + 2 + 3 + 4 + 5 + 6)$
$= (1 + 2 + 3 + 4 + 5 + 6)(1 + 2 + 3 + 4 + 5 + 6)$
$= (1 + 2 + 3 + 4 + 5 + 6)^2.$

Adding along the "paths,"

$1 + (2 + 4 + 2) + (3 + 6 + 9 + 6 + 3) + \cdots + (6 + 12 + \cdots + 12 + 6)$
$\qquad\qquad\qquad\qquad = 1^3 + 2^3 + 3^3 + 4^3 + 5^3 + 6^3.$

Hence,

$$1^3 + 2^3 + 3^3 + 4^3 + 5^3 + 6^3 = (1 + 2 + 3 + 4 + 5 + 6)^2.$$

(b) Argument in part (a) generalizes.

13. *Note:* $1 \cdot 2 \cdot 3 + 2 \cdot 3 \cdot 4 = \dfrac{1 \cdot 2 \cdot 3 \cdot 4 - 0 \cdot 1 \cdot 2 \cdot 3}{4} + \dfrac{2 \cdot 3 \cdot 4 \cdot 5 - 1 \cdot 2 \cdot 3 \cdot 4}{4}$

$= \dfrac{2 \cdot 3 \cdot 4 \cdot 5}{4}.$ In general, $1 \cdot 2 \cdot 3 + 2 \cdot 3 \cdot 4 + \cdots + 10 \cdot 11 \cdot 12 =$

$\dfrac{10 \cdot 11 \cdot 12 \cdot 13}{4} = 4{,}290.$

Chapter 6, Section 1, page 133

1. (a) It cannot be done. This will be proved in Section 2. (b) It cannot be done. This will be proved in Section 3.

3. It can be done. One way is as follows:

5. It can be done. One way is as follows:

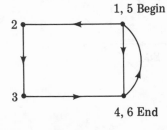

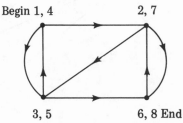

7. It can be done. One way is as follows:

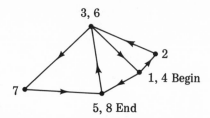

9. It cannot be done. This will be proved in Section 2.

11. It can be done. One way is as follows:

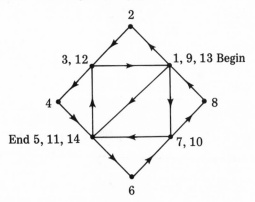

13. It can be done. One way is as follows:

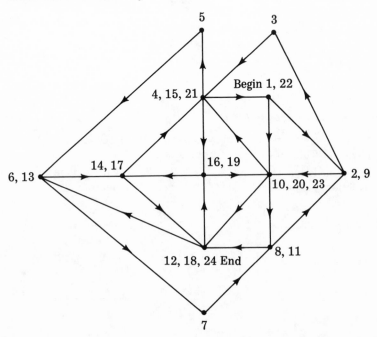

Chapter 6, Section 2, page 141

1. Yes.

3.

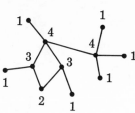 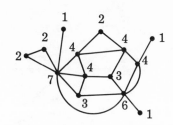

$$a_1 = 6 \quad a_2 = 1$$
$$a_3 = 2 \quad a_4 = 2$$
$$a_5 = 0 \quad a_6 = 0$$
$$A = 8 \text{ and } B = 22$$

(2)

$$a_1 = 3 \quad a_2 = 3$$
$$a_3 = 2 \quad a_4 = 4$$
$$a_5 = 0 \quad a_6 = 1 \quad a_7 = 1$$
$$A = 6 \text{ and } B = 44$$

(3)

5. (a) None. (b) None. (c) 28.

(d)

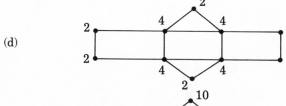

(e)

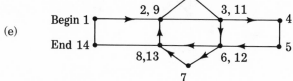

7. (a) Two. (b) Two. (c) 30.

(d)

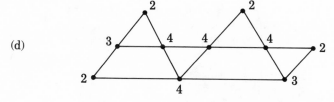

(e)

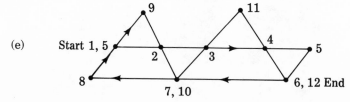

9. (a), (b), (e), and (f).

11. (a) Yes.

(b)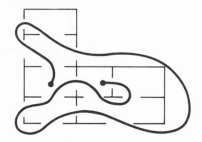

13. (a) Yes.

(b)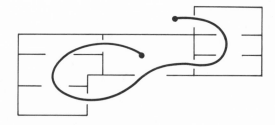

15. (a) Yes.

(b)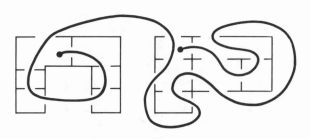

17. No. There would be four vertices of odd order.

19. No. There would be four vertices of odd order.

21. (a) It is best to consider one side of a rectangular sheet which is rolled into a cylinder and then "stretched" into a torus. Consider the following, which is one answer to this part. (Solid lines are boundaries of the map.)

(i)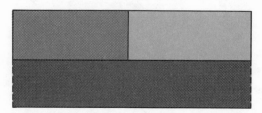

(ii) This is the cylinder obtained.

(iii) Now, bend into torus.

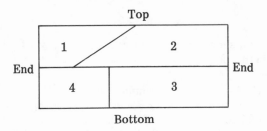

(b) For this and subsequent figures, notice that (2) borders on (1), (3) borders on (1) and (2), (4) borders on (1), (2), and (3), etc. Recall that top and bottom sides are joined and then the "ends."

(c)

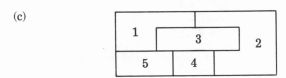

(d)

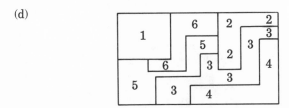

(e) *Note:* Dotted lines indicated connecting regions. Solid lines are boundaries.

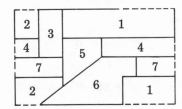

Chapter 6, Section 3, page 153

1. Case 2. $u = 4$, $v = 3$. $\dfrac{1}{4} + \dfrac{1}{3} = \dfrac{1}{2} + \dfrac{1}{E}$, $\dfrac{7}{12} - \dfrac{6}{12} = \dfrac{1}{E}$, $E = 12$, $F = \dfrac{24}{4} = 6$,

$V = \dfrac{24}{3} = 8$.

3. Case 4. $u = 5$, $v = 3$. $\dfrac{1}{5} + \dfrac{1}{3} = \dfrac{1}{2} + \dfrac{1}{E}$, $\dfrac{16}{30} - \dfrac{15}{30} = \dfrac{1}{E}$, $E = 30$, $F = $

$\dfrac{60}{5} = 12$, $V = \dfrac{60}{3} = 20$.

9. (b) A cube will show that four colors are necessary. It is an unsolved problem whether five colors are ever needed; it can be proved that five are sufficient.

11. (1) The polyhedron has a finite number of sides.

(2) Since each vertex is of order 3 and since each edge ends at two vertices. $3V$ is twice the number of edges.

(3) nF_n is the total number of edges on all faces with n sides. Since each edge borders on two faces, the sum is twice the number of edges.

(4) Solving (4) and substituting in:

$$V + F = E + 2$$
$$\tfrac{2}{3}E + F = E + 2$$
$$2E + 3F = 3E + 6$$
$$E + 6 = 3F.$$

(5) Multiply $E + 6 = 3F$ by 2 and substitute (3) for $2E$.

(6) Substitute for F.

(7) Collect F_3, F_4, F_5 terms on left from preceding equation and take other terms to right-hand side.

13. A cube.

15. A prism with triangular bases.

17. Since each face has 3 or more edges and since each edge borders on 2 faces, $3F \le 2E$. From Euler's Formula $E + 2 = V + F$, we obtain

$$3E + 6 = 3V + 3F.$$

Thus, $$3E + 6 \le 3V + 2E$$

and $$E + 6 \le 3V.$$

19. From $E + 6 \le 3V$ in Exercise 17, we conclude that

$$2E + 12 \le 6V.$$

Also, since $3F \le 2E$, we obtain

$$3F + 12 \le 2E + 12.$$

Thus, $$3F + 12 \le 6V.$$

21. From Exercise 19, $6V \ge 3F + 12$. Since a polyhedron must have at least four faces, $F \geq 4$, $3F \geq 12$ and $3F + 12 \geq 24$. Hence, $6V \geq 24$ and $V \geq 4$.

23. From Exercise 17, $2E \geq 3F$. Since each polyhedron must have at least 4 faces, $F \geq 4$, $3F \geq 12$ and $2E \geq 12$. Hence, $E \geq 6$.

25.

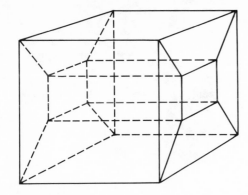

$V = 16$
$F = 16$
$E = 32$

27. Let V be the number of vertices, F be the number of faces, and E be the number of edges. Since each vertex is of order 3, it follows that (1) $3V = 2E$. Furthermore, (2) $F_3 + F_5 = F$ and (3) $3F_3 + 5F_5 = 2E$. Hence, $3V = 3F_3 + 5F_5$. Since $V + F - E = 2$, $6V + 6F - 6E = 12$. Substituting,

$$6F_3 + 10F_5 + 6F_3 + 6F_5 - 9F_3 - 15F_5 = 12, \quad \text{or} \quad 3F_3 + F_5 = 12.$$

Thus, (4) $F_5 = 12 - 3F_3$. If $F_3 = 1$, then $F_5 = 9$; if $F_3 = 2$, then $F_5 = 6$; and if $F_3 = 3$, then $F_5 = 3$. By assumption $F_3 \neq 0$ and from (4) we can conclude that $F_3 < 4$.

Chapter 7, Section 2, page 165

CHAPTER 7

1. (a) $7 \times 7 \times 7 = 343$.
(b) $P_3^7 = 7 \times 6 \times 5 = 210$.

3. $C_5^9 = 9!/5!4! = 126$.

5. $2 \times 4 = 8$.

7. $(n+1)! - n! = (n+1)(n!) - (n!) = (n!)(n+1-1) = n(n!)$.

9. (a) $P_4^6 = 6 \times 5 \times 4 \times 3 = 360$.
(b) $6 \times 6 \times 6 \times 6 = 1296$.
(c) First, the seven numbers 3656, 3661, 3662, 3663, 3664, 3665, and 3666 are greater than 3655. With each of 4, 5, and 6 as first digits, we can obtain $6 \times 6 \times 6$ different four-digit numbers using the given digits. Thus, $7 + 3(216) = 655$ is the total number.
(d) With each of 2, 4, or 6 as last digit, there are $5 \times 4 \times 3 = 60$ different arrangements for the first three digits. Thus, the total number is $3 \times 60 = 180$.

(e) There are 180 odd numbers where no digit is repeated. (The total of the answers in (d) and (e) is the answer to (a) as should be anticipated.)

11. (a) $2^5 = 32$.

(b) It is the total number of subsets of a set with five elements.

13. $C_1^5 + C_2^5 + C_3^5 + C_4^5 + C_5^5 = 5 + 10 + 10 + 5 + 1 = 31$.

15. $C_3^7 = \dfrac{7!}{3!4!} = 35$.

17. $C_2^4 = \dfrac{4!}{2!2!} = 6$ and $C_3^7 = \dfrac{7!}{3!4!} = 35$. The total number if different selections is $C_2^4 \times C_3^7 = 210$.

19. (a) even. (b) odd. (c) even. (d) even (e) odd. (f) even. (g) odd. (h) odd. (i) even.

21. (a) (iii) and (vi). (b) 15!/2.

Chapter 7, Section 3, page 177

1. (a) $P(E) = n(E)/n(S) = 2/36 = 1/18$.

(b) $P(E) = 1/18$. (c) $p(E) = 8/36 = 2/9$. (d) $P(E) = 5/18$.

3. (a) $n(S) = 2^6 = 64$. The number of ways exactly two heads can come up is $C_2^6 = 15$. Thus, $P(E) = 15/64$.

(b) $n(E) = C_3^6 = 20$ and $P(E) = 5/16$.

5. Since there are seven balls, the number of ways to pick two balls is $C_2^7 = 21$; thus, $n(S) = 21$. Since three balls are black, $n(E) = C_2^3 = 3$. Thus, $P(E) = 3/21 = 1/7$.

7. Let E be the event that five cards will be hearts. The number of five card hands from a deck with fifty-two cards is C_5^{52} and the number of five card heart hands is C_5^{13}. Thus, $P(E) = C_5^{13}/C_5^{52} = 0.00049519$.

9. (a) Since each selection of three numbers in the set has a different sum and since addition is commutative and associative, $n(S) = C_3^5 = 10$. The ways to get a number less than forty are three: $1 + 5 + 10 = 16$, $1 + 5 + 25 = 31$, and $1 + 10 + 25 = 36$. Thus, $P(E) = 3/10$.

(b) Since the tags with 5, 10, and 25 are the only ones to give a sum of forty, $P(E) = 1/10$.

(c) Using (a) and (b), we see that $P(E) = 1 - 4/10 = 3/5$. Notice that there are six ways to get sums over forty with three tags: $50 + 25 + 10$, $50 + 25 + 5$, $50 + 25 + 1$, $50 + 10 + 5$, $50 + 10 + 1$, and $50 + 5 + 1$.

11. To have change for a quarter if three coins are picked a nickel is needed. Thus, the probability is that of picking the nickel from the box. First, determine the probability that a nickel will not be selected. On the first draw, there are 4 ways to select a coin different from the nickel, on the second draw there would be 3, etc. Thus, the number of ways to avoid a nickel in three draws is $4 \times 3 \times 2 = 24$; thus, the probability of not selecting a nickel is $(4 \times 3 \times 2)/(5 \times 4 \times 3) = 2/5$. Thus, the probability is $3/5$ of getting change for a quarter. Another way to look at the problem is to observe that there are $C_3^5 = 10$ sets of three coins that can be selected; of these, $C_3^4 = 4$ collections would not contain a nickel. Thus, $4/10 = 2/5$ is the probability a nickel would not be selected.

13. (a) $1/4$ (b) $3/4$

15. Since 7 is the number of events in S, $C_2^7 = \dfrac{7!}{2!5!} = 21$ is the number of pairs that can be picked. $C_2^4 = \dfrac{4!}{2!2!} = 6$ is the number of even pairs and $C_2^3 = 3$ is the number of odd pairs. Thus, $\dfrac{6+3}{21} = \dfrac{3}{7}$ is the probability a pair has an even sum. Thus $1 - 3/7 = 4/7$ is the probability the sum is odd.

17. The numbers with 3 as factor are 3, 6, . . . , 99, a total of 33 numbers. The numbers with 5 as factor are 5, 10, . . . , 90, 95, a total of 19 numbers. The numbers with 7 as factor are 7, 14, . . . , 98, a total of 14 numbers. The sets of multiples of 3, 5, and 7 are not distinct, and such multiples as $3 \times 5 = 15$, $3 \times 7 = 21$, and $5 \times 7 = 35$ are in two sets. Since the number of elements "counted twice" is 12, the elements in {15, 30, 45, 60, 75, 90, 21, 42, 63, 84, 35, 70}, $33 + 19 + 14 - 12 = 54$ is the number of numbers with 3, 5, or 7 as factors. Hence, $54/99 = 6/11$ is the probability that one is picked.

19.

Outcome	Probability	Value
4	$3/36$	4
6	$5/36$	6
8	$5/36$	8
10	$3/36$	10

M.E. $= 3/36(4) + 5/36(6) + 5/36(8) + 3/36(10) = 112/36 = 28/9 < 3.25$.
House game.

Chapter 7, Section 4, page 182

1. 11, 12, 14, 15, 16, 16, 18, 19, 19, 19, 20, 20, 20, 20, 21, 22, 23, 23, 24, 25, 27, 27, 28, 28, 29, 29, 29, 30, 30, 31, 31, 33, 33, 34, 35, 35, 35, 35, 35, 36, 37, 37, 37, 39, 39, 40, 41, 43, 43, 43.

3.

Class	Frequency	Class	Frequency
41–43	4	23–25	4
38–40	3	20–22	6
35–37	9	17–19	4
32–34	3	14–16	4
29–31	7	11–13	2
26–28	4		

5.

Class	Frequency
40–44	5
35–39	11
30–34	7
25–29	8
20–24	9
15–19	7
10–14	3

7.

Class	Frequency	Class	Frequency
42–43	3	26–27	2
40–41	2	24–25	2
38–39	2	22–23	3
36–37	4	20–21	5
34–35	6	18–19	4
32–33	2	16–17	2
30–31	4	14–15	2
28–29	5	12–13	1
		10–11	1

9. (a) $2/25$, $3/50$, $9/50$, $3/50$, $7/50$, $2/25$, $2/25$, $3/25$, $2/25$, $2/25$, $1/25$. (b) One.

11. Twenty-five.

13.

Class	Frequency
700–799	25
600–699	145
500–599	301
400–499	199
300–399	22

Chapter 7, Section 5, page 186

1. $\sqrt{272.72} \approx 16.5$ **3.** $\sqrt{164.54} \approx 12.9$

5. Using $m = 26$,

$$v = \frac{4(3.5)^2 + 19(1.5)^2 + 8(0.5)^2 + 5(2.5)^2 + 3(4.5)^2 + (6.5)^2}{40} = 5.725.$$

Thus, $\sigma = \sqrt{5.725} \approx 2.4$.

7. $m = \dfrac{3(12) + 7(17) + 9(22) + 8(27) + 7(32) + 11(37) + 5(42)}{50} = 28.2.$

$$v = \frac{3(16.2)^2 + 7(11.2)^2 + 9(6.2)^2 + 8(1.2)^2 + 7(3.8)^2 + 11(8.8)^2 + 5(13.8)^2}{50}$$

$= 78.56.$ Thus, $\sigma = \sqrt{78.56} \approx 8.9$.

9. $m = 27.98$. Using $m = 28$, $v = 72.6$ and $\sigma = \sqrt{72.6} \approx 8.5$.

Chapter 8, Section 1, page 198

1. (a) Nine is not an even number and it is not a prime. (b) If I succeed, then I work hard. (c) If Smith wins the election, then he got the nomination. (d) If two triangles are similar then they are congruent. (This is false.) (e) If a person is nine feet tall, then he will get on the basketball team. (f) If Wintergreen carries Maine, then he will be elected and if he is elected, then he carries Maine.

3. (a)

p	q	not q	p implies (not q)
T	T	F	F
T	F	T	T
F	T	F	T
F	F	T	T

(b)

p	q	not q	p and (not q)
T	T	F	F
T	F	T	T
F	T	F	F
F	F	T	F

5. (a) No.

p	q	p implies q	q implies p
T	T	T	T
T	F	F	T
F	T	T	F
F	F	T	T

(b) No.

p	q	not p	not q	(not p) implies (not q)	p implies q
T	T	F	F	T	T
T	F	F	T	T	F
F	T	T	F	F	T
F	F	T	T	T	T

(c) Yes. See tables in parts (a) and (b).

7.

p	q	not p	not q	p or q	not (p or q)	(not p) and (not q)
T	T	F	F	T	F	F
T	F	F	T	T	F	F
F	T	T	F	T	F	F
F	F	T	T	F	T	T

9. (a)

p	q	r	p or q	(p or q) implies r
T	T	T	T	T
T	F	T	T	T
F	T	T	T	T
F	F	T	F	T
T	T	F	T	F
T	F	F	T	F
F	T	F	T	F
F	F	F	F	T

(b)

p	q	r	q implies r	p or (q implies r)
T	T	T	T	T
T	F	T	T	T
F	T	T	T	T
F	F	T	T	T
T	T	F	F	T
T	F	F	T	T
F	T	F	F	F
F	F	F	T	T

(c)

p	q	r	p implies r	q implies r	(p implies r) or (q implies r)
T	T	T	T	T	T
T	F	T	T	T	T
F	T	T	T	T	T
F	F	T	T	T	T
T	T	F	F	F	F
T	F	F	F	T	T
F	T	F	T	F	T
F	F	F	T	T	T

(d) None are equivalent.

(e) No.

(f) Yes, p is false. In fact, you can also conclude that q is true and r is false.

11. (a)

p	q	p or q	(p or q) implies p
T	T	T	T
T	F	T	T
F	T	T	F
F	F	F	T

This is not a tautology.

(b)

p	q	p or q	p implies (p or q)
T	T	T	T
T	F	T	T
F	T	T	T
F	F	F	T

This is a tautology.

(c)

p	q	not q	p and q	(p and q) or (not q)
T	T	F	T	T
T	F	T	F	T
F	T	F	F	F
F	F	T	F	T

This is not a tautology.

(d)

p	not p	p and (not p)
T	F	F
F	T	F

This is not a tautology.

(e) See part (d). *p* or (not *p*) is a tautology.

(f)

p	q	r	p or q	q or r	(p or q) and (q or r)
T	T	T	T	T	T
T	F	T	T	T	T
F	T	T	T	T	T
F	F	T	F	T	F
T	T	F	T	T	T
T	F	F	T	F	F
F	T	F	T	T	T
F	F	F	F	F	F

This is not a tautology.

(g)

p	q	not q	not q and p	p implies q	(p implies q) and (not q and p)
T	T	F	F	T	F
T	F	T	T	F	F
F	T	F	F	T	F
F	F	T	F	T	F

This is not a tautology.

Chapter 8, Section 2, page 207

1. $(p \lor q) \land (\sim r)$
3. $(\sim p \lor q) \land (\sim r)$
5. $\sim p \lor \sim q \lor \sim r$
7. $p \land q \land \sim r$
9. $p \land q \land \sim r$
11. (a) If x^2 is a positive integer, then x is a positive integer.
    (b) If x is not a positive integer, then x^2 is not a positive integer.
    (c) If x^2 is not a positive integer, then x is not a positive integer.
    (d) x is a positive integer and x^2 is not a positive integer.

13. (a)

p	q	$p \to q$	$q \to p$	$(p \to q) \lor (q \to p)$
T	T	T	T	T
T	F	F	T	T
F	T	T	F	T
F	F	T	T	T

Yes, the statement is a tautology.

(b)

p	q	$\sim p$	$\sim q$	$p \land q$	$\sim p \lor \sim q$	$(p \land q) \lor (\sim p \lor \sim q)$
T	T	F	F	T	F	T
T	F	F	T	F	T	T
F	T	T	F	F	T	T
F	F	T	T	F	T	T

Yes, the statement is a tautology.

15. (a) If x^2 is a positive real number or x^2 is zero, then x is a real number.
    (b) If x is not a real number, then x^2 is a nonpositive real number and x^2 is not zero.
    (c) If x^2 is a nonpositive real number and x^2 is not zero, then x is not a real number.
    (d) x is a real number and x^2 is a nonpositive real number and x^2 is not zero.

17. invalid. 19. valid. 21. invalid.
23. valid. 25. valid. 27. valid.

29. We need to show that the following is a valid argument by truth-table. *Note:* This should be ample evidence to show another approach is desirable.

Given: (i) $\sim q \lor p$
         (ii) $\sim [\sim p \to r]$
         (iii) $\sim r \to t$
         (iv) $\sim s \to (q \lor \sim t)$
Conclusion: s

31. valid. 33. valid. 35. valid.

Chapter 8, Section 3, page 216

1. None of them. **3.** P_3. **5.** P_1. **7.** P_2 and P_3.
9. Given an example of an infinite set with properties P_1, P_2, and P_3 which does not have the property expressed in Theorem 3. Let S be the set of positive integers and let $L = \{(a, b) | a \in S, b \in S, \text{ and } a < b\}$.

Chapter 8, Section 4, page 222

1. (a) $\{1, 2, 3, 4, 5, 6, 7, 8\} = A$.   (b) $\{1, 2, 4, 8\} = B$.
   (c) $\{1, 2, 3, 4, 5, 7, 8, 9, 11, 13\}$.   (d) $\{1\}$.
   (e) $\{1, 2, 3, 4, 5, 6, 7, 8, 9, 11, 13\}$.   (f) $\{1, 3, 5, 7\}$.
3. (a) $\{9, 10, 11, 12, 13, 14, 15\}$.
   (b) $\{3, 5, 6, 7, 9, 10, 11, 12, 13, 14, 15\}$.
   (c) $\{2, 4, 6, 8, 10, 12, 14, 15\}$.
   (d) $\{3, 5, 6, 7, 9, 10, 11, 12, 13, 14, 15\}$.
   (e) $\{3, 5, 6, 7, 9, 10, 11, 12, 13, 14, 15\}$.
   (f) $\{9, 10, 11, 12, 13, 14, 15\}$.
   (g) $\{9, 10, 11, 12, 13, 14, 15\}$.
   (h) $\{6, 10, 12, 14, 15\}$.
   (i) $\{6, 10, 12, 14, 15\}$.
5. (a) $A' \cap B$.
   (b) $A \cap (B \cup C)'$ or $A \cap B' \cap C'$.
   (c) $A \cap (B \cup C)$ or $(A \cap B) \cup (A \cap C)$.
   (d) $A \cap B' \cap C$.
7.
(a) 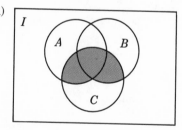   (b)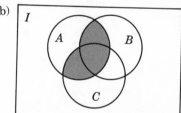

(c) 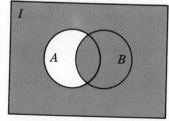   (d)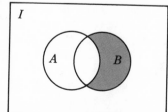

(e)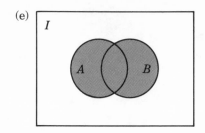

(f)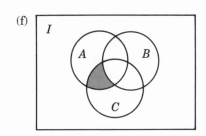

9. PART 2. Let $x \in [(A \cap B) \cup (A \cap C)]$. Then $x \in (A \cap B)$ or $x \in (A \cap C)$. In either case, $x \in A$. Also, $x \in B$ or $x \in C$; thus, $x \in (B \cup C)$. Consequently $x \in [A \cap (B \cup C)]$.

11.
$$n[R \cup (S \cup T)] = n(R) + n(S \cup T) - n[R \cap (S \cup T)]$$
$$= n(R) + n(S) + n(T) - n(S \cap T)$$
$$- n[(R \cap S) \cup (R \cap T)]$$
$$= n(R) + n(S) + n(T) - n(S \cap T)$$
$$- \{n(R \cap S) + n(R \cap T) - n[(R \cap S) \cap (R \cap T)]\}$$
$$= n(R) + n(S) + n(T) - n(S \cap T) \cap n(R \cap S)$$
$$- n(R \cap T) + n(R \cap S \cap T).$$

13. (a) 2. (b) 11. (c) 47. (d) 32.

15. Let P be the set of sane people; let L be the set that can do logic; let J be the set that are fit to serve on a jury; and let S be the set of your sons. From (i) $P \subseteq L$; from (ii) $P' \subseteq J'$, and from (iii) $S \subseteq L'$. From $P \subseteq L$ we conclude that $L' \subseteq P'$. Since $S \subseteq L'$, we have $S \subseteq P'$; and since $P' \subseteq J'$, we have $S \subseteq J'$. The last statement says that your sons are a subset of those not fit to serve on a jury.

17. Let G be the set of logic examples I work without grumbling; let U be the set of logic examples I can understand; let R be the set that are arranged in the order I'm used to; let S be this set of examples; let H be the set that give me a headache; and let E be the set of easy examples. From (i) $G \subseteq U$, from (ii) $S \subseteq R'$, from (iii) $E \subseteq H'$, from (iv) $R' \subseteq U'$, and from (v) $G' \subseteq H$. From $E \subseteq H'$ we have $H \subseteq E'$. Since $G' \subseteq H$, it follows that $G' \subseteq E'$. From $S \subseteq R'$ and $R' \subseteq U'$, we have $S \subseteq U'$. From $G \subseteq U$ we have $U' \subseteq G'$. From $S \subseteq U'$ and $U' \subseteq G'$ we have $S \subseteq G'$. Since $S \subseteq G'$ and $G' \subseteq E$, we conclude that $S \subseteq E'$.

19. Let B be the set of persons who appreciate Beethoven; let S be the set who keep silent while the *Moonlight Sonata* is being played; let G be the set of guinea pigs; and let M be the set of those who are ignorant of music. From (i) $B \subseteq S$, from (ii) $G \subseteq M$, and from (iii) $M \subseteq S'$. From $B \subseteq S$ we have that $S' \subseteq B'$. Since $M \subseteq S'$, we obtain $M \subseteq B'$. Since $G \subseteq M$, we conclude that $G \subseteq B'$.

21. Let D be the set of dated letters in this room; let P be the set written on blue paper; let B be the set written in black ink; let F be the set that are filed; let R be the set I can read; let S be those written on one sheet; let C be those that are crossed; let W be the set written to Brown; let

T be these that begin with "Dear Sir"; and let *V* be the set written in the third person. (*Deduce: W ⊆ R'.*) *Given statements:* (i) *D ⊆ P*, (ii) *B ⊆ V*, (iii) *R ⊆ F'*, (iv) *S ⊆ D*, (v) *C' ⊆ B*, (vi) *W ⊆ T*, (vii) *P ⊆ F*, (viii) *S' ⊆ C'*, and (ix) *T ⊆ V'*. Use the following steps.

(vi) *W ⊆ T*.	(ix) *T ⊆ V'*.	(ii) *V' ⊆ B'*.
(v) *B' ⊆ C*.	(viii) *C ⊆ S*.	(iv) *S ⊆ D*.
(i) *D ⊆ P*.	(vii) *P ⊆ F*.	(iii) *F ⊆ R'*.

Using the transitive property in the nine preceding steps, we conclude that *W ⊆ R'*.

Chapter 9, Section 1, page 232

1. 50   LET DIAM = 2∗RADIUS
   60   PRINT DIAM
3. 317
   317
5. (a) V+1 is not a location name.
   (b) INCHES must be omitted.
   (c) and (d) DIVIDE and BY are not command words.
   (e) The ")" is missing.
   (f) SET is not a command word.
   (g) 2∗R is not a location name.
7. 1.75
9. 100   PRINT "I THINK; THEREFORE I AM."
   200   END

Chapter 9, Section 2, page 235

1. (a) 10   LET N = 1973   (c) 10   LET N = 1
      20   PRINT N   20   PRINT N
      30   LET N = N+1   30   LET N = 2∗N
      40   GO TO 20   40   GO TO 20
      50   END   50   END

3. 10   LET P = 60
   20   LET Y = 0
   30   PRINT "THERE ARE", P, "PEOPLE/S.M. IN YEAR", Y
   40   LET P = 60∗1.02
   50   LET Y = Y+1
   60   GO TO 30
   70   END

7. In the first case "THE FORMULA IS SATISFIED" is printed. In the second "ERROR, THE FORMULA IS NOT SATISFIED".

9.
```
5    INPUT N
10   IF N < = 0 THEN 5
15   IF N > = 5 THEN 5
20   PRINT N
25   GO TO 5
30   END
```

Chapter 9, Section 3, page 242

1. Change Instruction 30 to
   LET S = S + I*I

3.
```
10    LET I = 0
20    INPUT N
30    LET I = I+1
40    IF I = 1 THEN 60
50    IF N < = M THEN 70
60    LET M = N
70    IF I < 30 THEN 20
80    PRINT M
1000  END
```

5. *Hint:* There is only one sequence of replies that will allow the computer opponent to draw.

7. The second player should pick up 1 if the first player picks up 3; 2 if 2; 3 if 1. (Why does this work?)
```
10    LET T = 13
20    PRINT "THERE ARE", T, "STICKS."
30    PRINT "HOW MANY DO YOU TAKE?"
40    INPUT N
50    LET R = 4−N
60    LET T = T−4
70    IF T < = 0 THEN 100
80    PRINT "I TAKE", R
90    GO TO 20
100   PRINT "THE GAME IS OVER.  YOU LOSE."
1000  END
```

CHAPTER 10 *Chapter 10, Section 1, page 252*

1. $a \equiv b$, mod m, implies that there is an integer x such that $mx = a - b$. Multiplying by c, $(mx)c = ac - bc$ and $m(xc) = ac - bc$. Hence, m is a factor of $ac - bc$ and $ac \equiv bc$, mod m.

3. *Hint:* Let $a = c$ and $b = d$.

5. $a \equiv 0$, mod m, if and only if $a - 0 = a$ has m as a factor by definition of congruence.

7. For any integer x, $x \equiv 0$, $x \equiv 1$, $x \equiv 2$, $x \equiv 3$, $x \equiv 4$, $x \equiv 5$, $x \equiv 6$, or $x \equiv 7$, mod 8. Thus, for any integer, $x^2 \equiv 0$, $x^2 \equiv 1$, $x^2 \equiv 4$, $x^2 \equiv 9$, $x^2 \equiv 16$, $x^2 \equiv 25$, $x^2 \equiv 36$, or $x^2 \equiv 49$, mod 8. Since $9 \equiv 1$, $16 \equiv 0$, $25 \equiv 1$, $36 \equiv 4$, and $49 \equiv 1$, mod 8, we see that the square of any integer is congruent to 0, 1, or 4, mod 8.

9. $1x \equiv 1$, mod 8, has 1 as a solution; $2x \equiv 1$, mod 8, has no solution; $3x \equiv 1$, mod 8, has 3 as solution; $4x \equiv 1$, mod 8, has no solution; $5x \equiv 1$, mod 8, has 5 as solution; $6x \equiv 1$, mod 8, has no solution; $7x \equiv 1$, mod 8, has 7 as solution.

11. (a) $5x + 3y \equiv 5$, mod 7   (multiply 2nd congruence by 3)
$$\underline{2x + 3y \equiv 2, \text{ mod } 7}$$
$$3x \equiv 3, \text{ mod } 7$$
$$x \equiv 1, \text{ mod } 7$$
$$y \equiv 0, \text{ mod } 7$$

(b) $5x + 2y \equiv 6$, mod 7   (multiply 1st congruence by 4)
$$\underline{5x + y \equiv 2, \text{ mod } 7}$$ (multiply 2nd congruence by 3)
$$y \equiv 4, \text{ mod } 7$$
Thus, $5x + 4 \equiv 2$, mod 7,
$$5x \equiv 5, \text{ mod } 7,$$
$$x \equiv 1, \text{ mod } 7$$

Chapter 10, Section 2, page 259

1. $\{7, 24, 25\}$.   **3.** $\{11, 60, 61\}$.   **5.** $\{5, 12, 13\}$.

7. $\{9, 40, 41\}$.   **9.** $u = 10$ and $v = 13$.

Chapter 10, Section 3, page 263

1. Let $S = \left\{ n \,\middle|\, 1 \cdot 2 + 2 \cdot 3 + \cdots + n(n+1) = \dfrac{n(n+1)(n+2)}{3} \right\}$.

PART 1. Since $1 \cdot 2 = \dfrac{1 \cdot 2 \cdot 3}{3}$, 1 is in S.

PART 2. Assume k is in S. Thus,

$$1 \cdot 2 + 2 \cdot 3 + \cdots + k(k+1) = \frac{k(k+1)(k+2)}{3} \quad \text{(true by assumption)}.$$

Adding $(k+1)(k+2)$ to both sides of the equality,

$$1 \cdot 2 + 2 \cdot 3 + \cdots + k(k+1) + (k+1)(k+2)$$

$$= \frac{k(k+1)(k+2)}{3} + (k+1)(k+2)$$

$$= \frac{k(k+1)(k+2) + 3(k+1)(k+2)}{3}$$

$$= \frac{(k+1)(k+2)(k+3)}{3}$$

Hence, $(k+1)$ is in S and $S = N$.

3. See Exercise 1 for pattern of proof and notice that

$$\begin{aligned}
k^2(2k^2 - 1) + (2k+1)^3 &= 2k^4 - k^2 + 8k^3 + 12k^2 + 6k + 1 \\
&= 2k^4 + 8k^3 + 11k^2 + 61 + 1 \\
&= 2k^4 + 8k^3 + 12k^2 + 8k + 2 - (k+1)^2 \\
&= 2(k^4 + 4k^3 + 6k^2 + 4k + 1) - (k+1)^2 \\
&= 2(k+1)^4 - (k+1)^2 \\
&= (k+1)^2[2(k+1)^2 - 1]
\end{aligned}$$

5. See Exercise 1 for pattern of proof and notice that

$$\begin{aligned}
(k+1)^5 - (k+1) &= k^5 + 5k^4 + 10k^3 + 10k^2 + 5k + 1 - k - 1 \\
&= k^5 - k + 5(k^4 + 2k^3 + 2k^2 + k)
\end{aligned}$$

7. See Exercise 1 for pattern of proof and notice that

$$\begin{aligned}
4^{k+2} + 5^{2k+1} &= 4^{k+2} + 4 \cdot 5^{2k-1} - 4 \cdot 5^{2k-1} + 5^{2k+1} \\
&= 4(4^{k+1} + 5^{2k-1}) + 5^{2k-1}(5^2 - 4) \\
&= 4(4^{k+1} + 5^{2k-1}) + 5^{2k-1}(21)
\end{aligned}$$

9. See Exercise 1 for pattern of proof and notice that

$$\frac{(k+1)^7}{7} + \frac{(k+1)^3}{3} + \frac{11(k+1)}{21} = \frac{k^7}{7} + k^6 + 3k^5 + 5k^4 + 5k^3$$

$$+ 3k^2 + k + \frac{1}{7} + \frac{k^3}{3} + k^2 + k + \frac{1}{3} + \frac{11k}{21} + \frac{11}{21}$$

$$= \left(\frac{k^7}{7} + \frac{k^3}{3} + \frac{11k}{21}\right) + (k^6 + 3k^5 + 5k^4 + 5k^3 + 4k^2 + 2k + 1)$$

11. If $S \neq N$ then $S' \neq \varnothing$. Let t be the least element in S'. Since 1 is in S, $t > 1$. Furthermore, for each $y < t$ where y is a positive integer, y is in S. By (b), we conclude that t is in S, a contradiction.

Chapter 10, Section 4, page 267

1. (a) $3{,}124 = 2 \times 2 \times 2 \times 17 \times 23$
   (b) $1{,}240 = 2 \times 2 \times 2 \times 5 \times 31$
   (c) $4{,}386 = 2 \times 3 \times 17 \times 43$

3. Yes.

5. $(5n-1)^2 = 25n^2 - 10n + 1 = 25n^2 - 10n + 5 - 4 = 5m - 4$
$(5n-2)^2 = 25n^2 - 20n + 4 = 25n^2 - 20n + 5 - 1 = 5m - 1$
$(5n-3)^2 = 25n^2 - 30n + 9 = 25n^2 - 30n + 10 - 1 = 5m - 1$
$(5n-4)^2 = 25n^2 - 40n + 16 = 25n^2 - 40n + 20 - 4 = 5m - 4$
$(5n)^2 = 25n^2 = 5m.$
S_2 and S_3 have no perfect squares.

7. (a) No. (b) No.

9. $(4k+1)(4m+1) = 16km + 4k + 4m + 1 = 4n + 1.$ Yes.

11. If $a \mid b$ and $a \mid c$, then there exist integers x and y such that $ax = b$ and $ay = c$. Thus, $ax - ay = b - c$ and $a(x - y) = b - c$. Since $x - y$ is an integer $a \mid (b - c)$.

13. If $a \mid b$ and $a \mid c$, there exist integers x and y such that $ax = b$ and $ay = c$. Thus, $(ax)(ay) = bc$ and $a(xay) = bc$. Since xay is an integer, $a \mid bc$.

15. If $a^2 \mid b^2$, then there exists an integer x such that $a^2 x = b^2$. Thus, $x = b^2/a^2 = (b/a)^2$ and b/a is the integer whose square is x.

17. No. One would not be expressible as the product of primes.

19. The set of integers are the union of four disjoint sets.

$S_1 = \{t \mid t = 4n\}$ $\qquad S_2 = \{t \mid t = 4n - 1\}$
$S_3 = \{t \mid t = 4n - 2\}$ $\qquad S_4 = \{t \mid t = 4n - 3\}$

Since $(4n)^2 = 16n^2 = 4(4n^2) \in S_1$
$\qquad (4n-1)^2 = 16n^2 - 8n + 1 = 16n^2 - 8n + 4 - 3$
$\qquad\qquad\qquad = [4(4n^2 - 2n + 1) - 3] \in S_4$
$\qquad (4n-2)^2 = 16n^2 - 16n + 4 = 4(4n^2 - 4n + 1) \in S_1$
and $\qquad (4n-3)^2 = 16n^2 - 24n + 9 = 16n^2 - 24n + 12 - 3$
$\qquad\qquad\qquad = [4(4n^2 - 6n + 3) - 3] \in S_3$

there are no perfect squares in S_2, the given sequence.

21. The T-composites are not closed with respect to subtraction or addition.

Chapter 10, Section 5, page 275

1.
```
              3
  6,096 ) 22,225
         18,288      1
          3,937 ) 6,096
                  3,937      1
                  2,159 ) 3,937
                          2,159      1
                          1,778 ) 2,159
                                  1,778      4
                                    381 ) 1,778
                                          1,524      1
                                            254 ) 381
                                                  254      2
                            g.c.f. =        127 ) 254
                                                  254
                                                    0
```

3.
$$1{,}712\overline{)4{,}815}\,^{3}$$
$$\underline{3{,}424}\quad^{1}$$
$$1{,}391\overline{)1{,}712}$$
$$\underline{1{,}391}\quad^{4}$$
$$321\overline{)1{,}391}$$
$$\underline{1{,}284}\quad^{3}$$
$$\text{g.c.f.} = 107\overline{)321}$$
$$\underline{321}$$
$$0$$

5.
$$17{,}186\overline{)33{,}711}\,^{1}$$
$$\underline{17{,}186}\quad^{1}$$
$$16{,}525\overline{)17{,}186}$$
$$\underline{16{,}525}\quad^{25}$$
$$\text{g.c.f.} = 661\overline{)16{,}525}$$
$$\underline{13{,}22}$$
$$3{,}305$$
$$\underline{3{,}305}$$
$$0$$

7.
$$168\overline{)889}\,^{5\,=\,q_1}$$
$$\underline{840}\quad^{3\,=\,q_2}$$
$$49\overline{)168}$$
$$\underline{147}\quad^{2\,=\,q_3}$$
$$21\overline{)49}$$
$$\underline{42}\quad^{3\,=\,q_4}$$
$$G = 7\overline{)21}$$
$$\underline{21}$$

$$u = 1 + q_2 q_3 = 7; \quad v = -q_1 - q_3 - q_1 q_2 q_3 = -38$$
$$7 = (889)(7) + (168)(-37)$$

9. Since 1 is the greatest common factor of a and b, there exists integers u and v such that $1 = au + bv$; thus, $c = acu + bcv$. Since $a|bc$ there is an integer x such that $ax = bc$. Substituting in the previous equation, $c = acu + axv$. Hence, $a(cu + xv) = c$. Since $(cu + xv)$ is an integer, $a|c$.

11. (a) The greatest common factor is the given number a. Since $a = (a)(2) + (a)(-1)$, let $u = 2$ and $v = -1$. (b) Yes.

Chapter 11, Section 2, page 283

1. Slope of line containing A and D: $\dfrac{e/2 - 0}{d/2 - a/2} = \dfrac{e}{d - a}$.

   Slope of line containing B and C: $\dfrac{(c + e)/2 - c/2}{(b + d)/2 - (a + b)/2} = \dfrac{e}{d - a}$.

3. $A(-3, -1)$, $B(2, 5)$, $C(5, \frac{5}{2})$. $|AB| = \sqrt{5^2 + 6^2} = \sqrt{61}$. $|BC| = \sqrt{3^3 + (\frac{5}{2})^2} = \sqrt{61}/2$. $|AC| = \sqrt{8^2 + (\frac{7}{2})^2} = \sqrt{305}/2$. $|AB|^2 + |BC|^2 = |AC|^2$.

5. $A(-4, 10)$, $B(18, 6)$, $C(2, -2)$. $|AB| = \sqrt{500}$. $|AC| = \sqrt{180}$. $|BC| = \sqrt{320}$. $|AC|^2 + |BC|^2 = |AB|^2$.

7. $A(2, 3)$, $B(6, 7)$, $C(3, 6)$. Yes. $|AC| = \sqrt{10} = |BC|$.

9. $|AB| = 2\sqrt{13}$, $|BC| = 3\sqrt{13}$, and $|AC| = 5\sqrt{13}$. A, B, and C are collinear with B between A and C.

11. $A(2, -1)$, $B(4, 5)$, $C(-1, -10)$. Yes. Slope of line containing A and B is 3 and slope of line containing B and C is 3. (One could use distances to prove the points collinear.)

13. (b) The midpoints of each diagonal is $\left(\dfrac{a + b}{2}, \dfrac{c}{2}\right)$.

15. See Chapter 4, Section 2, Exercise 10. Consider the line through the point parallel to the y axis. It divides the segment between a and c on the x axis in the same ratio. The x coordinate is $(a + 2c)/3$. Similarly, the y coordinate is $(b + 2d)/3$.

Chapter 11, Section 3, page 289

1. (a) Line with x intercept 6 and y intercept 8.
   (b) Line with x intercept 8 and y intercept -4.

3. $2x - 3y = 1$

5. $2x - 3y = -27$

7. $5x - 7y = 0$, or $y = (\frac{7}{5})x$

9. $(\frac{23}{22}, \frac{13}{11})$

11. $A(-4, 10)$, $B(18, 6)$, $C(2, -2)$. Slope of line containing B and C has slope $\frac{1}{2}$ and line containing A and C has slope -2.

13. $5x + 6y = 69$.   15. $12x + 5y = 99$.

17. (a) $\sqrt{(x + 2)^2 + (y - 7)^2} = \sqrt{(x - 1)^2 + (y - 4)^2}$

$$x^2 + 4x + 4 + y^2 - 14y + 49 = x^2 - 2x + 1 + y^2 - 8y + 16,$$

$$x - y = -6.$$

(b) Midpoint: $(-\frac{1}{2}, \frac{11}{2})$. Slope of line containing given points is 1. Slope of perpendicular line is -1. Thus, $x - y = -6$ is equation of perpendicular bisector.

19. $(3x + 5y - 11) + k(2x - 3y - 3) = 0$ is equation of a line through intersection of the given lines. For the line to contain $(1, 2)$, $(3 + 10 - 11) + k(2 - 6 - 3) = 0$, or $k = \frac{2}{7}$. Thus, $(3x + 5y - 11) + (\frac{2}{7})(2x - 3y - 3) = 0$, or $25x + 29y = 83$ is an equation of the line.

21. $(x - 3)^2 + (y + 4)^2 = 16$.

23. $(x + 3)^2 + (y - 7)^2 = 65$.

25. $x^2 + y^2 + 2x - 4y - 20 = 0$.

Chapter 11, Section 4, page 296

1. (a) Yes. (b) 7. (c) -8. (d) $\{1, 0, -1, 3\}$. (e) $\{3, 0, 7, -8\}$.

3. (a) Yes. (b) 2. (c) 2. (d) $\{-1, 3, 17\}$. (e) $\{2\}$.

5. (a) Yes. (b) No maximum. (c) 0. (d) All reals. (e) All nonnegative real numbers.

7. (a) Yes. (b) No maximum. (c) -8. (d) All reals. (e) All real numbers greater than or equal to -8.

9. (a) Yes. (b) 1. (c) -1. (d) All positive integers. (e) $\{1, -1\}$.

11. (a) Yes. (b) No maximum. (c) $-\frac{37}{4}$. (d) All reals. (e) $y \geq -\frac{37}{4}$.

13. (a) Yes. (b) No maximum. (c) $-\frac{109}{12}$. (d) All reals. (e) $y \geq -\frac{109}{12}$.

15. (a) Yes. (b) $-\frac{11}{4}$. (c) No minimum. (d) All reals. (e) $y \leq -\frac{11}{4}$.

17. Let x be one number. $p(x) = x(x + 20) = x^2 + 20x$ is a minimum where $x = 10$. Thus, both numbers are 10.

19. $p(x) = x - x^2$ has a maximum where $x = \frac{1}{2}$.

Chapter 11, Section 5, page 304

1.

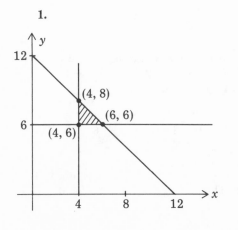

3.

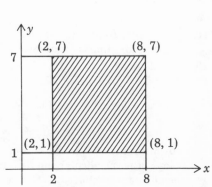

5.

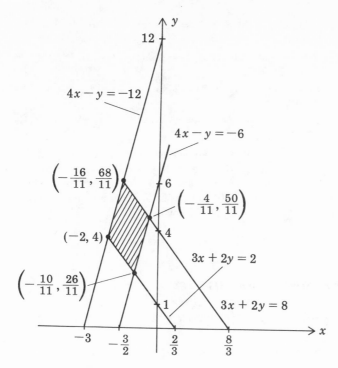

7.

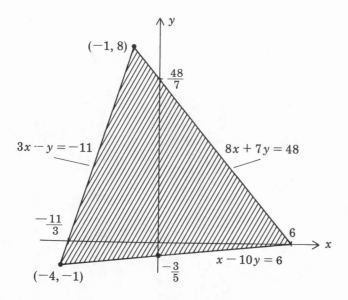

9. (a) $F(4, 8) = 44$. (b) $F(8, 7) = 52$. (c) $F(-16/11, 68/11) = 224/11$.
   (d) $F(-1, 8) = 29$.

11. (a) $G(6, 6) = -30$. (b) $G(8, 1) = 9$. (c) $G(-10/11, 26/11) = -202/11$.
   (d) $G(-4, -1) = -1$.

13. (a) $g(6, 6) = 42$. (b) $g(8, 7) = 54$. (c) $g(-16/11, 68/11) = 56/11$.
   (d) $g(6, 0) = 30$.

15. (a) $f(4, 8) = 56$. (b) $f(2, 7) = 55$. (c) $f(-16/11, 68/11) = 676/11$.
   (d) $f(-1, 8) = 76$.

17. Let x be the number produced of product A and y be the number produced of product B. $x \geq 400$, $y \geq 700$, and $8x + 5y \leq 8,000$. We want to maximize $p(x, y) = 40x + 60y$. The vertices of the convex polygonal domain are $(400, 700)$, $(562.5, 700)$, and $(400, 960)$. The maximum profit is $p(400, 960) = 73,600$.

Chapter 12, Section 1, page 315

1. (a) $\dfrac{x^2 - 4}{x - 2} = x + 2$ provided $x \neq 2$.

   (b) $f'(2) = \lim_{x \to 2} \dfrac{x^2 - 4}{x - 2} = \lim_{x \to 2} (x + 2) = 4$.

   (c) $2t$

3. (a) $\dfrac{1/x - 1/2}{x - 2} = -\dfrac{1}{2x}$

   (b) $f'(2) = \lim_{x \to 2} \left(-\dfrac{1}{2x}\right) = -\dfrac{1}{4}$

   (c) $-t^{-2}$

5. (a) $\dfrac{(2x + 1)/(5x + 3) - 5/13}{x - 2} = \dfrac{26x + 13 - 25x - 15}{13(x - 2)(5x + 3)} = \dfrac{1}{13(5x + 3)}$

   (b) $f'(2) = \lim_{x \to 2} \dfrac{1}{13(5x + 3)} = \dfrac{1}{169}$

   (c) $1/(5t + 3)^2$

7. (a) $\dfrac{x^{1/2} - 2^{1/2}}{x - 2} = \dfrac{\sqrt{x} - \sqrt{2}}{(\sqrt{x} - \sqrt{2})(\sqrt{x} + \sqrt{2})} = \dfrac{1}{\sqrt{x} + \sqrt{2}}$

   (b) $f'(2) = \lim_{x \to 2} \dfrac{1}{\sqrt{x} + \sqrt{2}} = \dfrac{1}{2\sqrt{2}}$

   (c) $1/2t^{-1/2}$

9. (a) $\dfrac{x^{1/3} - 2^{1/3}}{x - t} = \dfrac{x^{1/3} - 2^{1/3}}{(x^{1/3} - 2^{1/3})(x^{2/3} + x^{1/3}2^{1/3} + 2^{2/3})} = \dfrac{1}{x^{2/3} + x^{1/2}2^{1/3} + 2^{2/3}}$

   (b) $f'(2) = \lim_{x \to 2} \dfrac{1}{x^{2/3} + x^{1/3}2^{1/3} + 2^{2/3}} = \dfrac{1}{3(2^{2/3})}$

   (c) $1/3t^{-2/3}$

11. $v(x) = x(16 - 2x)(10 - 2x) = 160x - 52x^2 + 4x^3$

$v'(t) = \lim\limits_{x \to t} \dfrac{v(x) - v(t)}{x - t} = 12t^2 - 104t + 160$

$v'(t) = 0$ if and only if $3t^2 - 26t + 40 = 0$

Thus, $(3t - 20)(t - 2) = 0$ and $t = {}^{20}/_3$ or $t = 2$.

Obviously, ${}^{20}/_3$ is not in the domain of the volume function since $0 < x < 5$. Hence, 2 inch squares should be cut from the corners to maximize the volume.

13. $x \geq 0$, $y \geq 0$, and $x^2 + y = 18$; i.e., $y = 18 - x^2$. We want to maximize $xy = x(18 - x^2) = 18x - x^3$. If $f(x) = 18x - x^3$, then $f'(t) = 18 - 3t^2$. $f'(t) = 0$ if and only if $t = \sqrt{6}$ where $t \geq 0$. Thus, $\sqrt{6}$ and 12 are the two numbers that maximize the product. The maximum product is $12\sqrt{6}$.

Chapter 12, Section 2, page 321

1. $f'(x) = 15x^2 + 7$ **3.** $f'(x) = 15x^{14} - 18x^2$

5. $f'(x) = {}^4/_3 x^{1/3}$ **7.** $f'(x) = -{}^2/_3 x^{-5/3}$

9. $f'(x) = \dfrac{-28}{(2x - 6)^2}$ **11.** $f'(x) = \dfrac{-3x^2 - 2x + 12}{(x^2 + 4)^2}$

13. $f'(x) = {}^2/_3 (3x^5 - 4x)^{-1/3} (15x^4 - 4)$

15. $f'(x) = 4x(3x + 2)^{1/3} + (3x + 4)^{4/3} = (3x + 2)^{1/3}(7x + 4)$

17. $f'(x) = {}^1/_2 x^2 (x + 3)^{-1/2} + (x + 3)^{1/2}(2x) = \dfrac{5x^2 + 12}{2(x + 3)^{1/2}}$

19. $f'(x) = \dfrac{x + 2}{(2x + 5)^{3/2}}$

21. Use hint and the fact that the limit of the sum is the sum of the limits.

23. Use hint, part (a) and part (b).

25. Use hint and limit theorems. Notice that

$$\frac{h(x) - h(t)}{x - t} = \frac{g(t)}{g(x)g(t)} \cdot \frac{f(x) - f(t)}{x - t} - \frac{f(t)}{g(x)g(t)} \cdot \frac{g(x) - g(t)}{x - t}.$$

We need the fact that $\lim\limits_{x \to t} g(x) = g(t)$; this is true since the existence

of $\lim\limits_{x \to t} \dfrac{g(x) - g(t)}{x - t}$ implies $\lim\limits_{x \to t} g(x) = g(t)$.

Chapter 12, Section 3, page 330

1. $f'(x) = 3x^2 + 2x$. $f'(x) = 0$ where $x = 0$ or $x = -{}^2/_3$. $f(0) = 0$ is a relative minimum and $f(-{}^2/_3) = {}^4/_{27}$ is a relative maximum.

3. $g'(x) = 9x^2 + 9$. $g'(x) \neq 0$ for any real number x; thus, there are no relative maxima or minima.

5. $G'(x) = 3x^2 - 12x - 15$. $G'(x) = 0$ where $x = 5$ or $x = -1$. $G(5) = -100$ is a relative minimum and $G(-1) = 8$ is a relative maximum.

7. $p(x) = x + (2/x)$ is the function to minimize. $p'(x) = 1 - (2/x^2)$. $p'(x) = 0$ if and only if $1 = 2/x^2$, $x^2 = 2$; thus $x = \sqrt{2}$ where $x \geq 0$ is the only solution. $p(\sqrt{2}) = \sqrt{2} + (2/\sqrt{2}) = 2\sqrt{2}$ is the minimum value.

9. $v(x) = x(13 - 2x)(20 - 2x) = 260x - 66x^2 + 4x^3$ and $v'(x) = 12x^2 - 132x + 260$. $v'(x) = 0$ if and only if $3x^2 - 33x + 65 = 0$; $x = \dfrac{33 \pm \sqrt{1089 - 780}}{6} = \dfrac{33 \pm \sqrt{309}}{6}$; thus, $x = \dfrac{33 - \sqrt{309}}{6} \approx 2.57$ inches.

11. Let x be the width of the base; thus, length $= 3x$. Since it has a fixed volume, $V = 3x^2 h$ and $h = V/3x^2$. The total surface area is

$$2(\text{length} \times \text{width}) + 2(\text{length} \times \text{height}) + 2(\text{height} \times \text{width});$$

thus, $$T(x) = x(3x^2) + 2\left(3x \cdot \frac{V}{3x^2}\right) + 2\left(\frac{V}{3x^2} \cdot x\right)$$

$$= 6x^2 + \frac{2V}{x} + \frac{2V}{3x} = 6x^2 + \frac{8V}{3x}$$

Hence, $T'(x) = 12x - \dfrac{8V}{3x^2}$. $T'(x) = 0$ if and only if $12x = \dfrac{8V}{3x^2}$, $36x^3 = 8V$, $x = \dfrac{2V^{1/3}}{\sqrt[3]{36}}$.

13. Let x be the width for print on a page; thus, $50/x$ is the length for print. Now, the width of a page is $(x + 1)$ and the length of a page is $(50/x) + 2$. The area of a page for each x will be

$$A(x) = (x + 1)\left(\frac{50}{x} + 2\right) = 2x + \frac{50}{x} + 52$$

Hence, $A'(x) = 2 - (50/x^2)$ and $A'(x) = 0$ if and only if $2 = 50/x^2$, $x^2 = 25$, $x = 5$ or $x = -5$. Consequently, $x + 1 = 6$ should be the width of the page and $(50/x) + 2 = 12$ should be the length.

15. $V(t) = [x(t)]^3$. Thus, $V'(t) = 3[x(t)]^2 \cdot x'(t)$, and $200 = 3[10]^2 \cdot x'(t)$. Hence, $x'(t) = \frac{2}{3}$ ft per min.

17. $x^2 + r^2 = R^2$ and height of cone is $R + x = R + \sqrt{R^2 - r^2}$. Thus,

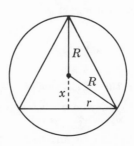

$$V(r) = \frac{\pi}{3}\, r^2\, (R + \sqrt{R^2 - r^2}\,)$$

$$= \frac{\pi}{3}\, (r^2 R + r^2 \sqrt{R^2 - r^2}\,)$$

$$V'(r) = \frac{\pi}{3}\, [2rR + r^2\, (R^2 - r^2)^{-1/2}(-r) + (R^2 - r^2)^{1/2}(2r)]$$

Letting $V'(r) = 0$ and assuming that $r \neq 0$,

$$2rR - \frac{r^3}{\sqrt{R^2 - r^2}} + 2r\sqrt{R^2 - r^2} = 0$$

$$2rR\sqrt{R^2 - r^2} - r^3 + 2rR^2 - 2r^3 = 0$$

$$2R\sqrt{R^2 - r^2} = 3r^2 - 2R^2$$

$$4R^2(R^2 - r^2) = 9r^4 - 12r^2 R^2 + 4R^4$$

$$9r^4 = 8r^2 R^2$$

$$9r^2 = 8R^2$$

$$r = \frac{2\sqrt{2}}{3} \cdot R$$

Height $= R + \sqrt{R^2 - \dfrac{8}{9}\,R^2} = \dfrac{4}{3}\,R.$

19. $h'(t) = {}^1\!/_{8}\pi$ ft/min

Chapter 12, Section 4, page 334

1. $\dfrac{x^3}{3} - \dfrac{5x^2}{2} + 3x + C$ **3.** $\dfrac{x^4}{4} - \dfrac{x^2}{2} + C$

5. $\dfrac{2}{5}\,x^{5/2} - \dfrac{7}{2}\,x^2 + C$ **7.** $\dfrac{x^3}{3} - 3x^2 - \dfrac{5}{x} + C$

9. $\dfrac{(x^2 + 1)^6}{6} + C$ **11.** $\dfrac{(3x^2 - 5)^{7/3}}{14} + C$

13. $2\sqrt{x^2 - 5x + 6} + C$

Chapter 13, Section 1, page 344

1. $L_2 = {}^{32}\!/_3(1 - {}^1\!/_2)(2 - {}^1\!/_2) + 4 = 12$

3. $L_8 = {}^{32}\!/_3({}^7\!/_8)({}^{15}\!/_8) + 4 = {}^{43}\!/_2$

5. $L_{50} = {}^{32}\!/_3({}^{49}\!/_{50})({}^{99}\!/_{50}) + 4 = {}^{15,436}\!/_{625} = 24.698$

7. $U_n = \dfrac{4}{n} \left[f(x_1) + f(x_2) + f(x_3) + \cdots + f(x_n) \right]$

$\qquad = \left(\dfrac{4}{n} \right)^3 \left[1^2 + 2^2 + 3^2 + \cdots + n^2 \right] + 4$

$\qquad = \dfrac{64}{n^3} \left(\dfrac{n(n+1)(2n+1)}{6} \right) + 4 = \dfrac{32}{3} \left(1 + \dfrac{1}{n} \right) \left(2 + \dfrac{1}{n} \right) + 4$

9. (a) $L_6 = 1^2 + 2^2 + 3^2 + 4^2 + 5^2 + 6^2 = 91$ square units

$\qquad$ (b) $U_6 = 2^2 + 3^2 + 4^2 + 5^2 + 6^2 + 7^2 = 139$ square units

$\qquad$ (c) 115 square units

11. (a) $x_k = 1 + k \left(\dfrac{6}{n} \right)$ and the width of each rectangle is $\dfrac{6}{n}$.

$L_n = \dfrac{6}{n} \left[1^2 + \left(1 + \dfrac{6}{n} \right)^2 + \left[1 + 2 \left(\dfrac{6}{n} \right) \right]^2 + \cdots + \left[1 + (n-1) \left(\dfrac{6}{n} \right) \right]^2 \right]$

$\qquad = \dfrac{6}{n} \left[n + 2 \left(\dfrac{6}{n} \right) (1 + 2 + \cdots + (n-1)) \right.$

$\qquad\qquad\qquad\qquad\qquad \left. + \dfrac{6^2}{n^2} (1^2 + 2^2 + \cdots + (n-1)^2) \right]$

$\qquad = 6 + \dfrac{72}{n^2} \left[\dfrac{n(n-1)}{2} \right] + \dfrac{216}{n^3} \left[\dfrac{n(n-1)(2n-1)}{6} \right]$

$\qquad = 6 + 36 \left(1 - \dfrac{1}{n} \right) + 36 \left(1 - \dfrac{1}{n} \right) \left(2 - \dfrac{1}{n} \right)$

$\qquad$ (b) $L_6 = 6 + 36(5/6) + 36(5/6)(11/6) = 91$

$\qquad\quad L_{12} = {}^{409}/_4$

15. (a) $F(x) = \dfrac{x^3}{3} + x$

$\qquad$ (b) $F(4) - F(0) = {}^{76}/_3 = 25^1/_3$ square units

17. (a) $L_6 = 1^3 + 2^3 + 3^3 + 4^3 + 5^3 + 6^3 = 441$ square units

$\qquad$ (b) $U_6 = 2^3 + 3^3 + 4^3 + 5^3 + 6^3 + 7^3 = 783$ square units

$\qquad$ (c) 612 square units

Chapter 13, Section 2, page 353

1. $\left(\dfrac{x^3}{3} - x^2 + 5x \right) \Big|_{-1}^{5} = 48$

3. $\left(\dfrac{x^4}{4} + \dfrac{1}{2x^2} \right) \Big|_{2}^{6} = 319^8/_9$

5. $2/21 (3x + 13)^{7/2} \Big|_{-3}^{4} = 2/21 (5^7 - 2^7)$

7. $\dfrac{1}{5} (x^2 + 2)^{5/2} \Big|_{-2}^{2} = 0$

9. $\dfrac{1}{20}\,(x^2+2)^{10}\,\Big|_0^1 = \dfrac{1}{20}\,(3^{10}-2^{10})$

11. $\displaystyle\int_1^5 (x+x^2)\,dx = \left(\dfrac{x^2}{2}+\dfrac{x^3}{3}\right)\Big|_1^5 = 53\frac{1}{3}$

13. $\displaystyle\int_0^2 (x^2+2x+3)\,dx = (\dfrac{x^3}{3}+x^2+3x)\,\Big|_0^2 = 12\frac{2}{3}$ square units

15. $\displaystyle\int_4^{16} x^{1/2}\,dx = \dfrac{2x^{3/2}}{3}\,\Big|_4^{16} = 112\frac{1}{3}$ square units

17. $\displaystyle\int_{-3}^3 [(18-x^2-x^2]\,dx = \int_{-3}^3 (18-2x^2)\,dx = 72$ square units

19. Area $= \displaystyle\int_{-5}^0 (x^3+x^2-20x)\,dx - \int_0^4 (x^3+x^2-20x)\,dx$

$= 210\frac{1}{12}$ square units

Chapter 13, Section 3, page 358

1. $V = \pi\displaystyle\int_2^6 x^4\,dx = \dfrac{\pi x^5}{5}\,\Big|_2^6 = 1{,}584\frac{4}{5}\pi$ cubic units

3. $V = \pi\displaystyle\int_1^8 x^3\,dx = \dfrac{\pi x^4}{4}\,\Big|_1^8 = 1{,}023\frac{3}{4}\,\pi$ cubic units

5. $V = \pi\displaystyle\int_0^1 (x-x^2)^2\,dx = \dfrac{\pi}{30}$ cubic units

7. $V = 2\pi\displaystyle\int_0^3 x(18-x)^2\,dx - 2\pi\int_0^3 x^3\,dx = \dfrac{207\pi}{2}$ cubic units

Chapter 14, Section 1, page 363

CHAPTER 14

1. $z+y=z+x$ Given.
$y+z=x+z$ Property 5.
$x+z=y+z$ Symmetric property of equality.
$x=y$ Theorem 1.

3. Assume 1 and 1* are multiplicative identities. By Property 8, $1^* \cdot 1 = 1^*$ and $1 \cdot 1^* = 1$. By Property 10, $1^* \cdot 1 = 1 \cdot 1^*$; thus, $1^* = 1$ by equality properties.

5. Assume $x+y=0$ and $x+z=0$. Thus, $x+y=x+z$ and $y=z$ by Exercise 1.

7. (a) Properties 5 and 3. (b) Property 6 and equality properties. (c) Property 11. (d) Property 8. (e) Properties 5 and 3.

9. $8 \cdot 0 = 6 \cdot 0$, for example, but $8 \neq 6$.

11. $(-x)[y + (-y)] = x \cdot 0$ and $(-x)(y) + (-x)(-y) = 0$. Now, $(-x)(y) = (y)(-x) = [-(yx)] = [-(xy)]$. Thus, $[-(xy)] + (-x)(-y) = 0$. Also, since $[-(xy)]$ is the additive inverse of (xy), $[-(xy)] + (xy) = 0$. Hence, $[-(xy)] + (-x)(-y) = [-(xy)] + xy$ and $(-x)(-y) = xy$.

13. $(xx^{-1})(yy^{-1}) = 1$. By associative and commutative properties of multiplication $(xy)(x^{-1}y^{-1}) = 1$. Since $(x^{-1}y^{-1})$ is the unique multiplicative inverse of xy, it follows that $(xy)^{-1} = x^{-1}y^{-1}$.

15. Let $x = b + (-a)$. Then $x + a = [b + (-a)] + a$, $x + a = b + [(-a) + a]$, $x + a = b + 0$, and $a + x = b$. Thus, $x = b - a$ by definition.

17. It is straightforward to show that the set is closed both with respect to addition and multiplication. Since the set is a subset of the set of real numbers, we have the associative and commutative properties of both addition and multiplication and we have the distributive property. The additive identity is $0 + 0\sqrt{3}$ and the multiplicative identity is $1 + 0\sqrt{3}$. The additive inverse of $r + s\sqrt{3}$ is $(-r) + (-s)\sqrt{3}$. The multiplicative inverse of $r + s\sqrt{3}$ is $u + v\sqrt{3}$ where $u = \dfrac{r}{r^2 - 3s^2}$ and $v = \dfrac{-s}{r^2 - 3s^2}$. Notice that if r and s are rational numbers then u and v are rational numbers provided $r^2 - 3s^2 \neq 0$. If r and s are not both zero then $r^2 - 3s^2 \neq 0$.

Chapter 14, Section 2, page 369

1. (a) Trichotomy property: If a and b are two points on the number line, a is to the left of b, a is the same point as b, or a is to the right of b. Transitive property: If a is to the left of b and b is to the left of c, then a is the left of c.

   (b) Since $a < b$, there is a positive number x such that $a + x = b$. Since $b < c$, there is a positive number y such that $b + y = c$. (The number represented by y is not necessarily different from the number represented by x, but since the numbers may be different it is necessary to use different letters.) Now

$$(a + x) + y = b + y \qquad \text{since } a + x = b$$
$$(a + x) + y = c \qquad \text{since } b + y = c$$
$$a + (x + y) = c \qquad \text{by the associative property}$$

   Since x and y are positive, the sum $(x + y)$ is positive. Hence, $a < c$ as a consequence of the definition of less-than.

3.
$a < b$	Given.
$a + (-c) < b + (-c)$	Theorem 4.
$a - c < b - c$	Exercise 15, Section 1.

5. $a < b$ Given.
    $(-c) > 0$ Theorem 5.
    $a(-c) < b(-c)$ Theorem 7.
    $-(ac) < -(bc)$ Exercise 10, Section 1.
        Equality and field properties
    $bc < ac$ Field properties.
    $ac > bc$ Definition of greater-than.

7. (1) Trichotomy property. (2) Field Property 8. (3) Theorem 8. (4) Property 8 and Exercise 9, Section 1. (5) Trichotomy property.

8. Proof by contradiction. If $a^{-1} = 0$ then $a \cdot a^{-1} = a \cdot 0$ and $1 = 0$, a contradiction of Property 8. If $a^{-1} < 0$, then since $a > 0$ it follows that $a \cdot a^{-1} < a \cdot 0$ from Theorem 7. Thus, $1 < 0$, a contradiction of Theorem 10.

9. See solution of Exercise 8.

11. With equality properties, the proof of Part (b) is completely analogous to Part (a). Part (c). Show $a + c < b + c$ and $b + c \le b + d$.

13. If $a > 0$, then $a^{-1} > 0$ by Theorem 11. Since $ab < 0$, $a^{-1}(ab) < a^{-1} \cdot 0$ by Theorem 7. Hence, b < 0 by field properties.

15. $x < -\frac{1}{2}$ or $x > \frac{5}{3}$

17. $x < -\frac{13}{3}$ or $x > \frac{2}{5}$

19. $-\frac{11}{2} < x \le \frac{14}{3}$

21. Since $i^2 = -1 < 0$ for the complex number i, the complex number system, though a field, cannot have the ordered field properties.

23. We previously exhibited that the system consisting of F with addition and multiplication has the field properties. Now, we need to check the order properties with respect to P_1.
    (a) Let $r + s\sqrt{3}$ and $u + v\sqrt{3}$ be elements in P_1. Thus, $r + s\sqrt{3} > 0$ and $u + v\sqrt{3} > 0$. Hence, $(r + s\sqrt{3}) + (u + v\sqrt{3}) = (r + u) + (s + v)\sqrt{3} > 0$. Since $r + u$ and $s + v$ are rational numbers, the sum is in P_1. Similarly, the product $(r + s\sqrt{3})(u + v\sqrt{3}) = (ru + 3sv) + (rv + su)\sqrt{3}$ is in P_1.
    (b) By definition $0 \notin P_1$.
    (c) Let $(x + y\sqrt{3})$ be in F and $\ne 0$. By the trichotomy property for reals, $x + y\sqrt{3} > 0$ or $x + y\sqrt{3} < 0$. If $x + y\sqrt{3} > 0$, it is in P_1 and its additive inverse is less than zero and not in P_1. Similarly, if $x + y\sqrt{3} < 0$ it is not in P_1; its additive inverse is greater than zero and is in P_1.

25. See Exercises 23 and 24.

Chapter 14, Section 3, page 372

1. (a) 2. (b) 60. (c) 273. (d) 9.
3. (a) $-\frac{3}{2}$. (b) 137. (c) 4. (d) 0.
5. 17.

7. (a) Yes.

(b) No. Assume there is a finite number of elements *in* S greater than $z - \epsilon$ for a given $\epsilon > 0$. Let t be the greatest. Now, $t \in S, z \notin S$ and $t < z$. Furthermore, $t < \dfrac{t+z}{2} < z$ and $\dfrac{t+z}{2}$ is an upper bound of S less than the least upper bound, a contradiction.

9. Prove by contradiction. The statement is for each $\epsilon > 0$, there exists $x \in S$ such that $x < w + \epsilon$. Assume there is an $\epsilon > 0$ such that for each $x \in S, x \geq w + \epsilon$. This states that $w + \epsilon$ is a lower bound of S. But $w + \epsilon > w$, a contradiction.

11. Let S have s as a lower bound. Then for each $x \in S, x \geq s$. Thus, $-x \leq -s$ for each $x \in S$ and $-s$ is an upper bound of T. Now, let $t = \text{lub } T$. Since for each $x \in S - x \leq t$, it follows that $x \geq -t$ and $-t$ is a lower bound of S. If $-t$ is not the greatest lower bound of S, there exists a lower bound w of S such that $-t < w \leq -x$ for each $x \in S$. Thus, $t > -w \geq -x$ for each $x \in S$ and $-w$ would be a least upper bound of T less than the least upper bound t.

13. The rational number system.

CHAPTER 15   *Chapter 15, Section 1, page 384*

1. (a) $(a + b\sqrt{2})(c + d\sqrt{2}) = ac + bc\sqrt{2} + ad\sqrt{2} + 2bd$
$$= (ac + 2bd) + (bc + ad)\sqrt{2}$$
$$= u + v\sqrt{2}$$

where u and v are rational numbers. (Closure)

(b) Since these are real numbers, we have the associative property.

(c) $1 + 0\sqrt{2} = 1$ is the identity.

(d) The inverse of $a + b\sqrt{2}$ is

$$\frac{1}{a + b\sqrt{2}} = \frac{a - b\sqrt{2}}{(a + b\sqrt{2})(a - b\sqrt{2})}$$

$$= \frac{a}{a^2 - 2b^2} + \frac{-b\sqrt{2}}{a^2 - 2b^2}$$

$$= s + t\sqrt{2}$$

where s and t are rational numbers. Since a and b are rational and not both zero, $a - b\sqrt{2}$ is irrational and not zero.

3. See Exercise 1.

5. (a) The group itself and the group consisting of only the identity element.

(b) $\{e\}; \{e, a\}; \{e, b\}; \{e, c\}; \{e, a, b, c\}$.
  $\{e\}; \{e, p, q\}; \{e, r\}; \{e, s\}; \{e, t\}; \{e, p, q, r, s, t\}$.

7. (b) $p * r = s$ and $s^{-1} = s$. Since $p^{-1} = q$ and $r^{-1} = r, p^{-1} * r^{-1} = q * r = t$.
No.

(c) Yes.

9. (a)

	e	a	b	c	d
e	e	a	b	c	d
a	a	b	c	d	e
b	b	c	d	e	a
c	c	d	e	a	b
d	d	e	a	b	c

(b) $e \leftrightarrow e$

$a \leftrightarrow p$

$b \leftrightarrow q$

$c \leftrightarrow r$

$d \leftrightarrow s$

11. (b) $r * (s * p) = r * r = e$, but $(r * s) * p = p * p = q$.
(c) No. (d) No.

13. (b) Yes.

15. It is a factor of the order of the group.

Index

A

Abelian, 380
Absolute maximum, 322
Absolute minimum, 322
Addition, 12, 362
Additive identity, 13, 362
Additive inverse, 72
Algebra, 3
Algebraic operations, 68
Amicable numbers, 121
Analysis, 3
Analytic geometry, 278–305
Antecedent, 193
Antiderivative, 332
Arc, 136
Arc end, 136
Archimedean property, 372
Area, 66, 67
Arithmetic, 2
Arithmetic mean, 183
Arithmetic sequence, 94–100
Associative property of addition, 13, 68, 362
Associative property of multiplication, 15, 68, 362
Associative property of set intersection, 10
Associative property of set union, 10
Axiomatic approach, 209
Axioms, 191, 210

B

Base eight, 28, 29, 35, 36
Base number, 19
Base twelve, 27, 28
Base two, 30, 31, 36, 37
BASIC language, 228–245
Binary operation, 12
Binary system, 30

Birthday problem, 174
Boole, George (1815–1864), 188
Bounded, 372

C

Cancellation property of addition, 363
Cantor, Georg (1845–1918), 40
Cardinal number, 8
Cartesian coordinate system, 279
Cartesian geometry, 278
Cartesian product, 160
Casting out nines, 56–60, 61 (Exercise 15)
Checks and pseudo-checks, 42–61
Class, 180
Class limits, 180
Closed (Closure), 362
Combination, 163
Command words, 213
Common difference, 96
Common ratio, 102
Commutative property of addition, 13, 68, 362
Commutative property of multiplication, 15, 68, 362
Commutative property of set intersection, 10
Commutative property of set union, 10
Complement of a set, 11, 218
Completeness property, 371
Complex number, 86–91
Composite number, 107
Computer program, 230
Conditional statement, 193
Congruent, mod m, 249
Conjunction, 193
Connected network, 136
Connectives, 192
Consequent, 193
Continuous path, 136

Contrapositive, 198
Converse, 199 (Exercise 5)
Convex polygonal set, 298
Convex polyhedron, 146
Coordinate, 65
Coordinate axes, 279
Counting number, 9
Cube, 151
Cycles, 382

D

Decimal fraction, 81
Decimal notation, 80–86
Decimal point, 82
Dedekind, Richard (1831–1916), 360
Denominator, 64
Derivative, 316
Descartes, René (1596–1650), 276
Difference, 13, 364 (Exercise 15)
Differential calculus, 308–335
Disjoint sets, 10
Disjunction, 194
Disk method, 354
Distance, 73
Distance formula, 280
Distributive property, 16, 68, 362
Divisibility tests, 45–53
Division, 16
  by zero, 17
Division algorithm, 25
Dodecahedron, 151
Domain of a function, 292

E

Element of a set, 169
Elliptic geometry, 212
Empty set, 10
Equality of sets, 9
Equation of a graph, 285
Equivalent postulates, 211
Equivalent statements, 194
Euclidean algorithm, 271
Euclid's fifth postulate, 211
Euler, Leonhard (1707–1783), 246
Euler's formula, 147
Euler's phi-function, 115 (Exercise 26)
Even integer, 45
Even permutation, 167 (Exercise 20)
Event, 169
Experiment, 169

F

Factor, 45
Fermat, Pierre (1601–1665), 92
Fermat's Last Theorem, 258
Field, 362
Fifteen puzzle, 167 (Exercise 21)
Finite network, 136
First mean value theorem for integrals, 348
First principle of mathematical induction, 263
Five room house problem, 130, 131, 134, 139
Four color problem, 141
Frequency distribution, 180
Frequency polygon, 180
Friendly numbers, 121
Function, 292
Fundamental theorem of algebra, 89
Fundamental theorem of arithmetic, 266
Fundamental theorem of calculus, 349

G

Galois, Evariste (1811–1832), 374
Gauss, Karl Friedrich (1777–1855), 1
Geometric sequence, 100–107
Geometry, 3
Goldbach's conjecture, 112
Graph, 284
Greater than, 73, 365
Greatest common factor, 271
Greatest lower bound, 372
Greatest number in a set, 371
Group, 376
Group table, 378

H

Halve-double-sum algorithm, 54, 55
Hexagonal numbers, 127
Hilbert, David (1862–1943), 6
Hindu–Arabic notation, 19
Histogram, 180
Hyperbolic geometry, 212

I

Icosahedron, 151
Identity, 376, 387

Implication, 196
Incomplete quotient, 23
Independent event, 168
Independent postulates, 216
Induction, 259
Inductive reasoning, 260
Inequalities, 73
Infinite decimal, 83
Infinite geometric series, 104
Input, 237
Integers, 70–74
Integral calculus, 338–359
Intersection of sets, 10
Inverse, 376
Inverse of an implication, 199 (Exercise 5)
Inversion, 166 (Exercise 18)
Irrational number, 78
Isomorphic, 71, 381

L

Least common multiple, 119 (Exercises 5–9)
Least number in a set, 370
Least upper bound, 371
Leibniz, Gottfried Wilhelm (1646–1716), 336
Less than, 73, 365
Lewis Carroll puzzles, 220–225
Linear programming, 297–305
Local maximum, 322
Local minimum, 322
Logic, 190–209
Logically equivalent, 211
Long division, 25
Loop, 235
Lower bound, 372
Lower sum, 345

M

Map coloring, 131, 132
Mathematical expectation, 176
Mathematical induction, 259–264
Maximum value, 293, 322
Median, 184
Mersenne prime, 119
Midpoint, 73, 280
Minimum value, 293, 322
Missing digit, 42, 43
Mode, 184
Modus ponens, 201

Modus tollens, 201
Moebius strip, 145 (Exercise 22)
Multiperfect numbers, 121 (Exercise 6)
Multiple, 45
Multiplication, 22
Multiplicative identity, 15, 362
Multiplicative inverse, 362

N

Natural number, 9
Negation, 193
Negative number, 70–73
Network, 134–145
Newton, Isaac (1642–1727), 306
Newton quotient, 316
Nim, 32, 33
Null set, 10
Number congruence, 248
Number line, 65
Number sense, 8
Number theory, 3
Numerals, 18
  base eight, 28, 29
  Hindu–Arabic, 19
  Roman, 18, 19
Numerator, 64

O

Octahedron, 151
Odd integer, 45
Odd permutation, 167 (Exercise 20)
Odds, 175
Ordered arrangement, 161
Ordered field, 365
Ordered pair, 160
Order of a vertex, 137
Ordinal number, 9
Origin, 65
Output, 237

P

Pascal, Blaise (1623–1662), 156
Pentagonal number, 126 (Exercise 8)
Perfect numbers, 115–122
Permutation, 161
Place-holder, 19
Playfair's axiom, 212
Poincaré, Henri (1854–1912), 128
Polygon, 145
Polyhedron, 145

Postulates, 191, 210
Prime number, 45, 107–111
Primitive pythagorean triple, 255
Probability, 170
Product, 14
Proof, 210
Proper subset, 11
Public utility problem, 132, 152
Pythagorean number triple, 255
Pythagorean theorem, 76

Q

Quotient, 16, 269, 364 (Exercise 16)

R

Range, 170
Range of a function, 292
Rational number, 64
Rational operations, 12
Rational point, 65
Real number, 76–80
Real number line, 78
Reflexive property, 249
Regular polyhedron, 145–155
Relation, 292
Relative frequency, 182 (Exercise 9)
Relatively prime, 113 (Exercise 13)
Remainder, 23, 269
Riemann integral, 345, 347
Roman numerals, 18, 19

S

Sample space, 169
Set, 8
Seven bridges of Königsberg, 140
Shell method, 356
Slope, 281
Slope-intercept form, 286
Square unit, 67
Squares, 58, 59
Standard deviation, 186
Statement, 191
Statistical probability, 177
Statistics, 178–187
Subset, 10
Sum, 12
    of an arithmetic sequence, 97
    of a geometric sequence, 102
Syllogism, 202

T

Tautology, 200 (Exercise 11)
Terminating decimal, 82
Tetrahedron, 150, 151
Theorem, 191, 210
Tic-tac-toe, 243
Topology, 130
Tower of Hanoi, 264 (Exercise 12)
Transcendental number, 78
Transfer, 239
Transitive property, 365
Traversible network, 136
Triangular numbers, 100 (Exercise 19),
    124–126
Trichotomy property, 365
Truth-table, 193
Truth-value, 192
Twin primes, 109, 110

U

Union of sets, 10
Unit length, 65
Universal set, 218
Universe of discourse, 218
Upper bound, 371
Upper sum, 346

V

Valid argument, 200–209
Variable on a set, 10
Variance, 185
Velocity, 314
Venn diagrams, 217–225
Vertex of a network, 136
Vest problem, 133
Void set, 10
Volume, 353–359
von Neumann, John (1903–1957), 226

W

Weierstrass, Karl (1815–1897), 62
Well-ordering property, 261
Whole numbers, 9

Z

Zero, 15, 19, 20